Molecular Spectra
and
Molecular Structure

I. DIATOMIC MOLECULES

PRENTICE-HALL PHYSICS SERIES

E. U. CONDON, PH.D., EDITOR

VECTOR AND TENSOR ANALYSIS, *by* A. P. Wills

A SURVEY COURSE IN PHYSICS, *by* Carl F. Eyring

ELEMENTS OF NUCLEAR PHYSICS, *by* Franco Rasetti

PRINCIPLES OF ELECTRIC AND MAGNETIC MEASURE-
MENTS, *by* P. Vigoureux *and* C. E. Webb

ATOMIC SPECTRA AND ATOMIC STRUCTURE, *by* Gerhard Herzberg

ELECTRICITY AND MAGNETISM, *by* A. W. Hirst

PROPERTIES OF MATTER, *by* F. C. Champion *and*
N. Davy

THERMODYNAMICS, *by* Enrico Fermi

COLLEGE PHYSICS, *by* Henry A. Perkins

PROCEDURES IN EXPERIMENTAL PHYSICS, *by* John
Strong, *in collaboration with* H. Victor Neher,
Albert E. Whitford, C. Hawley Cartwright, *and*
Roger Hayward

INTRODUCTORY QUANTUM MECHANICS, *by* Vladimir
Rojansky

FUNDAMENTAL PRINCIPLES OF PHYSICS, *by* Herman
G. Heil *and* Willard H. Bennett

THE STRUCTURE OF STEEL SIMPLY EXPLAINED, *by*
Eric N. Simons *and* Edwin Gregory

MOLECULAR SPECTRA AND MOLECULAR STRUCTURE,
I. DIATOMIC MOLECULES, *by* Gerhard Herzberg

Molecular Spectra
and
Molecular Structure

I. DIATOMIC MOLECULES

Gerhard Herzberg

Research Professor of Physics
University of Saskatchewan

TRANSLATED
WITH THE CO-OPERATION OF THE AUTHOR
BY

J. W. T. Spinks

Professor of Physical Chemistry
University of Saskatchewan

NEW YORK
PRENTICE-HALL, INC.
1939

AUTHOR AND TRANSLATOR
DEDICATE THIS BOOK
TO

DR. WALTER C. MURRAY

PRESIDENT EMERITUS
OF THE
UNIVERSITY OF SASKATCHEWAN

Preface

THE present volume is the first one of a comprehensive presentation of the field of molecular spectra and the conclusions that can be drawn from them about molecular structure. This first volume is limited to *diatomic molecules*. A second volume, dealing with polyatomic molecules, will follow as soon as possible.

I have endeavored to give a presentation which is readable by the beginner in the field and also will be useful to those who do or want to do research work in this field. In order to assist the former, I have frequently made use of small type for those sections that are not necessary for an understanding of the fundamentals. For the benefit of those working in the field, numerous references to original papers have been included.

A satisfactory presentation of molecular spectra and molecular structure is nowadays not possible without treating thoroughly, apart from the empirical results, the theoretical background also. Therefore I have included as much of the *theory* of molecular spectra as is possible without going into the more difficult mathematical details. A large number of diagrams, graphical representations of eigenfunctions and potential curves, as well as energy level diagrams, serve to illustrate and to explain the theory. On the other hand, I have added numerous carefully selected spectrograms of bands and band systems (some of which have been taken specially for this purpose) in order to give an accurate idea of the experimental material that forms the basis of the developments.

While of course most of the material presented is not new, it seems that the actual procedure followed in analyzing a band spectrum has not previously been given as specifically in a book of this kind. The same holds for the applications of band spectra to other parts of physics, to chemistry, and to astrophysics given in the last chapter. I hope that both these features will be found useful.

Naturally I have used the occasion of the English translation to improve upon the original German version. A number of additions have been made, and in certain places the discussion has been made to cover more recent developments. Table 36, which gives the molecular constants for the ground states of all diatomic molecules thus far investigated, has been brought up to date as of July, 1939.

Great care was taken to make this table as reliable and consistent as possible. Throughout the table as well as the text, the new values for the fundamental atomic constants have been employed. The very detailed subject index, which contains also all symbols, quantum numbers, and so forth, should be useful to both beginners and research workers in the field.

It is a great pleasure to acknowledge the help and co-operation I have received from a number of persons during the writing of the book. My sincere thanks are due to Professor J. W. T. Spinks (Saskatoon), who, as in the case of my previous book, *Atomic Spectra and Atomic Structure*, undertook the translation into English and also assisted with the proofreading and with the preparation of the index. I am deeply indebted to Professor R. N. H. Haslam (Saskatoon), who read the entire manuscript and the proof with the greatest care and made very numerous invaluable suggestions. I am also very grateful to my wife, who prepared almost all the figures and has helped considerably to improve the presentation. Finally, I should like to express my thanks to Professor R. S. Mulliken (Chicago) and Dr. H. Beutler (Chicago) for a number of suggestions, and to the former as well as to Dr. E. Bengtsson-Knave (Stockholm), Professor R. T. Birge (Berkeley), Dr. B. A. Brice (Washington), Professor W. G. Brown (Chicago), Professor F. A. Jenkins (Berkeley), Professor R. Mecke (Freiburg), Dr. R. W. B. Pearse (London), Professor F. Rasetti (Quebec), Lord Rayleigh (Chelmsford), and Professor R. W. Wood (Baltimore), for having assisted me materially by supplying valuable spectrograms for the illustrations (see the footnotes below the particular figures).

I am under great obligation to Professor E. U. Condon, editor of the Prentice-Hall Physics Series, and the staff of Prentice-Hall, Inc., for their sympathetic co-operation and for meeting all my wishes concerning the printing of the book.

G. H.

Contents

Illustrations

Tables

Molecular Spectra
and
Molecular Structure

I. DIATOMIC MOLECULES

Introduction

General remarks. In the course of the last two decades, very considerable progress has been made in the investigation and theoretical interpretation of molecular spectra. The study of molecular spectra has thereby become one of the most important, perhaps the most important, means for investigating molecular structure.

From the spectra the various discrete energy states of a molecule can be derived directly. From these again, we can draw accurate and reliable conclusions concerning the motion of the electrons (electronic structure) and the vibration and rotation of the nuclei in the molecule. The study of electronic motions has led to a deeper theoretical understanding of chemical valence. From the vibrational frequencies the forces between the atoms in the molecule, as well as the heats of dissociation of molecules, can be calculated with great accuracy. From the rotational frequencies we obtain accurate information about the geometrical arrangement of the nuclei in the molecule— in particular, extremely accurate values for the internuclear distances.

The knowledge of the different properties of the individual molecules so obtained allows us to understand many of the physical and chemical properties of the gases under consideration and, in fact, sometimes allows us to predict these properties—for example, the specific heat and magnetic susceptibility. Also, on the basis of this knowledge, chemical equilibria can be predicted theoretically with great certainty and chemical elementary processes can be elucidated.

A further important result of the investigation of spectra is that proof has been obtained of the existence of a large

1

number of molecules which were previously unknown in chemistry or were not thought capable of free existence. Among these are CH, OH, C_2, He_2, Na_2, CP, and many others. The structures of these molecules have also been determined.

The investigation of the spectra of diatomic molecules is also of great significance for the physics of atomic nuclei, since certain nuclear properties (spin and statistics) influence these spectra in a characteristic manner and can be determined from them, and since, furthermore, in some cases ιare isotopes may be detected by means of these spectra.

Finally, the investigation of molecular spectra has recently become very important in astrophysics. On the basis of spectra, not only can the presence of certain molecules on fixed stars, planets, and comets be detected but also definite conclusions can be drawn concerning the physical conditions on these heavenly bodies.

This volume deals with the spectra of *diatomic molecules* and the conclusions which can be drawn from them concerning the structure of these molecules. A second volume will deal with *polyatomic molecules*. Since a thorough treatment of molecular spectra presumes a certain knowledge of atomic spectra and atomic structure, a short survey of the fundamentals of atomic theory is given in the first chapter.

The experimental methods for the production and investigation of spectra will not be dealt with here. Reference should be made to Meissner (14),[1] Baly (3), Jenkins and White (7), Geiger-Scheel (1a), Wien-Harms (2a), Eucken-Wolf (6b), and Kayser-Konen (4).

The nomenclature of the various quantities concerning the molecule—energy levels, quantum numbers, and so on—was made subject to international regulation in 1930 [Mulliken (515)]. We shall use this *international nomenclature* throughout.

---

[1] The numbers in parentheses refer to the bibliography, p. 535.

Physical constants. The values of the most important physical constants used in the following are collected in Table 1 [see Birge (107)–(110)]. The value of Planck's

TABLE 1

PHYSICAL CONSTANTS

Electronic charge...............	e	$4.8029 \cdot 10^{-10}$ e.s.u.
Planck's constant................	h	$6.626 \cdot 10^{-27}$ erg sec.
Velocity of light.................	c	$2.99776 \cdot 10^{10}$ cm/sec.
Electronic mass (rest mass).......	m	$9.111 \cdot 10^{-28}$ gm
$\frac{1}{16}$ mass of the O^{16} atom..........	M_1	$1.6600 \cdot 10^{-24}$ gm
Number of molecules in a mol:		
Referred to Aston's atomic-weight scale ($O^{16} = 16$)......	$N_A = \dfrac{1}{M_1}$	$6.0240 \cdot 10^{23}$
Referred to the chemical atomic-weight scale.................	N_{ch}	$6.0224 \cdot 10^{23}$
Boltzmann's constant............	k	$1.3807 \cdot 10^{-16}$ erg/degree

quantum of action obtained from the limit of the continuous X-ray spectrum [DuMond and Bollmann (193)] is $h = 6.610 \cdot 10^{-27}$, a value in poor agreement with the value calculated from the Rydberg constant and given in the table. The reason for this discrepancy is not yet known. Following Birge (110), we have given preference to the value calculated from the Rydberg constant without thereby regarding the question as settled.[2]

Units and conversion factors. The *wave lengths*, λ, of the spectral lines in the infrared are measured in μ ($1 \mu = \frac{1}{1000}$ mm) and in the visible and ultraviolet spectral regions in Ångström units ($1 \text{ Å} = 10^{-7}$ mm $= 10^{-8}$ cm). In theoretical discussions, the reciprocal of the wave length, called the *wave number*, is much more important than the wave length itself: $\nu = 1/\lambda_{vac.}$ (λ measured in vacuum or

---

[2] Millikan (496) has recently given values for e, h, and N slightly different from those given in Table 1. The deviations are, however, within the limits of accuracy given by Millikan. Therefore a recalculation of the conversion factors and other numerical values given below does not appear to be necessary, particularly since Millikan, too, does not explain the above-mentioned discrepancy.

corrected to vacuum). Wave numbers are measured in
cm^{-1}. The *frequency* of light of wave number ν is $\nu' = c\nu$.

The frequency ν', and the wave number, ν, depend on the
energy, E, according to the fundamental Planck relation
$E = h\nu' = h\nu c$, where h is Planck's constant. We can
therefore take the *wave number as a measure of the energy,*
as is very frequently done in spectroscopy. Using the values
in Table 1, we find that 1 cm^{-1} corresponds to $1.9863 \cdot 10^{-16}$
erg/molecule. If we wish to refer the energy to 1 mol instead of to a single atom or molecule, we have to multiply
by the number of molecules N_{ch} in 1 mol. Therefore, 1
cm^{-1} corresponds to $11.962 \cdot 10^7$ ergs/mol (referred to the
chemical atomic-weight scale) or, converting to calories,
2.8581 15° C. cal./mol.

In addition, the *electron-volt* (*e-volt*) is used in measuring
energy in atomic and molecular physics. By V *e*-volts we
understand an energy equal to the kinetic energy of an
electron (or singly charged ion) that has been accelerated
through a potential of V volts. This energy is $eV/299.776$
ergs (the factor $1/299.776$ is introduced in converting to absolute units). Substituting the numerical value for e gives
1 *e*-volt equivalent to $1.6022 \cdot 10^{-12}$ erg/molecule, or 8066.0
cm^{-1}, or 23,053 cal./mol. These and some other derived
conversion factors for the energy units are collected in
Table 2.[3]

TABLE 2

CONVERSION FACTORS FOR ENERGY UNITS

Unit	cm^{-1}	erg/molecule	cal./mol chem.	electron-volts
1 cm^{-1}.........	1	$1.9863 \cdot 10^{-16}$	2.8581	$1.2398 \cdot 10^{-4}$
1 erg/molecule..	$5.0344 \cdot 10^{15}$	1	$1.4389 \cdot 10^{16}$	$6.2416 \cdot 10^{11}$
1 cal./mol chem..	0.34988	$6.9498 \cdot 10^{-17}$	1	$4.3378 \cdot 10^{-5}$
1 electron-volt...	8066.0	$1.6022 \cdot 10^{-12}$	23,053	1

[3] This table replaces the corresponding table in the author's *Atomic Spectra
and Atomic Structure* (Prentice-Hall, Inc., New York, 1937, in the following
referred to as A.A.), which was calculated with the old values for e, h, and N.

CHAPTER I

Résumé of the Elements of Atomic Structure [1]

1. BOHR THEORY

Stationary energy states. Niels Bohr was the first to suggest that an atom or molecule cannot exist in states having any arbitrary energy, but only in *certain discrete energy states* called *stationary states*. According to the Bohr theory, these stationary states are obtained when one selects, by means of certain *quantum conditions*, some of the states from the continuous range of classically possible states. For example, in the case of a single electron moving in the Coulomb field of an atomic nucleus, we obtain, classically, *elliptical orbits* of all possible half axes. According to the Bohr theory, only certain of these, with quite definite values of the half axes, are possible. For the possible orbits, the major half axis is proportional to the square of a whole number n, called the *principal quantum number*. For a given value of n, the minor axis is proportional to a second whole number l, the so-called *azimuthal quantum number*. While the principal quantum number can take any integral value greater than 0,

$$n = 1, 2, 3, \cdots, \qquad (\text{I}, 1)$$

the azimuthal quantum number l, for a given value of n, can take only the values

$$l = 0, 1, 2, \cdots, n - 1. \qquad (\text{I}, 2)$$

The energy E of the atom contains an arbitrary additive constant. If this constant is chosen so that $E = 0$ when

---

[1] A detailed presentation has been given in A.A. Some other presentations are listed in the bibliography at the end of the book [(8)–(13)].

the electron is completely separated from the nucleus and no relative kinetic energy is present, the following expression for the *energy* of the possible Bohr elliptical orbits in the H atom or hydrogen-like ions is obtained (neglecting a very small relativity correction):

$$E_n = -\frac{2\pi^2 \mu e^4}{h^2} \frac{Z^2}{n^2} = -\frac{R'Z^2}{n^2}. \tag{I, 3}$$

In this expression, Z is the atomic number (for hydrogen, equal to 1) and $\mu = mM/(m + M)$, where m is the electron mass and M is the nuclear mass. In this case the energy depends only on the principal quantum number n and is negative for all stationary states. The state with lowest energy is that with $n = 1$, corresponding to the innermost orbit. It is the ground state of the atom or ion. With increasing n, the energy increases and eventually approaches the limit $E = 0$.

In the more general case of the motion of a single electron about an atomic core which is not a point charge, the orbits are no longer simple ellipses but, to a first approximation, ellipses whose axes rotate uniformly (*rosette motion*). As before, they can be characterized by the two quantum numbers n and l. The energy is, to a first approximation,

$$E_{n,l} = -\frac{R'Z^2}{(n + a)^2}, \tag{I, 4}$$

where a, the so-called *Rydberg correction*, depends on the azimuthal quantum number l and approaches zero rapidly with increasing l. Z is in this case the charge on the core— that is, the nuclear charge (atomic number) minus the number of core electrons. In this general case the energy depends on n as well as l.

As an example, Fig. 1 gives a diagrammatic representation of the observed energy levels of the lithium atom, which has a single electron revolving about an atomic core consisting of the nucleus and two electrons. The energy levels are indicated by horizontal lines whose vertical height corresponds to the energy of the atom as given by the energy scales to the left and right. For each value of l there is a series of energy levels (drawn one under another) which correspond to the different values of n and approach one another as n increases, finally going to the limit $E = 0$. The energy level diagram of the H atom is quite similar, except that, according to (I, 3), all levels with the same n have the same height.

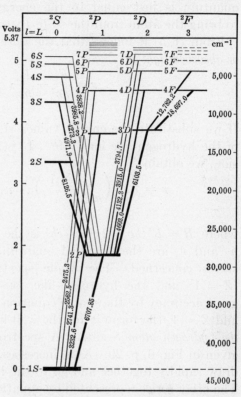

Radiation. According to Bohr, but in contradiction to classical electrodynamics, radiation does not take place while an electron moves in its orbit but only *when the electron goes from one quantum orbit of energy E_1 to another of energy E_2.* (This process is called a *quantum jump.*) The liberated energy $E_1 - E_2$ is emitted as a quantum of light or photon of energy $h\nu' = hc\nu$ ($\nu' =$ frequency, and $\nu =$ wave number of the light):

$$h\nu' = hc\nu = E_1 - E_2. \qquad (\text{I, 5})$$

Fig. 1. Energy Level Diagram of the Li Atom (after Grotrian). The wave lengths of the spectral lines are written on the sloping connecting lines, which represent the transitions (see below). The symbols S, P, $\cdots$ are explained on p. 24. The numbers before the symbols P, D, and F are the principal quantum numbers n of the outer electron, and those before S are smaller by 1.

This *Bohr frequency condition* holds for absorption as well as for emission. That is to say, a quantum of light is absorbed by an atom only when the energy of the light quantum is just equal to the energy which is necessary to bring the atom from the state E_2 to the state E_1.

From (I, 5) it follows that the *wave number of the emitted or absorbed light* is

$$\nu = \frac{E_1}{hc} - \frac{E_2}{hc}. \tag{I, 6}$$

If we substitute the energy values (I, 3) of the H atom or of the hydrogen-like ions (He^+, $Li^{++}, \cdots$) into this expression, we obtain

$$\nu = RZ^2 \left(\frac{1}{n_2{}^2} - \frac{1}{n_1{}^2} \right), \quad n_1 > n_2, \tag{I, 7}$$

where $R = R'/hc = 2\pi^2 \mu e^4/ch^3$ is the *Rydberg constant* and n_2 and n_1 are the principal quantum numbers of the two states concerned. The whole spectrum of the H atom ($Z = 1$) and the hydrogen-like ions is represented with great accuracy by the simple equation (I, 7). When $n_2 = 2$ and $Z = 1$, the formula for the well-known *Balmer series of the hydrogen atom* results. A spectrogram of this series is given in Fig. 6, p. 29. As n_1 increases, the lines of this series draw rapidly together and go to the limit $R/4$ for $n_1 \to \infty$. The other series represented by equation (I, 7) behave correspondingly.

In the more general case, using (I, 4), we obtain

$$\nu = RZ^2 \left[\frac{1}{(n_2 + a_2)^2} - \frac{1}{(n_1 + a_1)^2} \right], \tag{I, 8}$$

where the first and second terms now depend on l as well as n. A greater number of transitions therefore results. For fixed values of n_2, a_2, and a_1 we obtain a series of lines similar to the Balmer series illustrated in Fig. 6. Such series are sometimes called *Rydberg series*. In Fig. 1, in which the transitions are indicated by sloping lines joining the levels in question, a Rydberg series corresponds to sloping lines that lead from the levels of a series, having a definite value of l, to a fixed lower-lying level.

It can be seen from Fig. 1 that transitions do not take place between *any* two levels, but only such transitions are observed for which the quantum number l changes by unity. Such a limitation is called a *selection rule*. In the present case it is written

$$\Delta l = \pm 1. \qquad (I, 9)$$

Transitions for which l does not alter or alters by 2, 3, $\cdots$ units do not occur and are said to be *forbidden*. In the Bohr theory, this selection rule can be derived with the help of the so-called correspondence principle.

Terms. According to (I, 6), (I, 7), and (I, 8), the wave number ν of a spectral line can be represented as the difference between two quantities called, for short, *terms*. More precisely, the positive quantities RZ^2/n^2 or $RZ^2/(n + a)^2$ and similar, possibly more complicated, expressions are designated as terms. Terms are thus the negative energy values divided by hc. A series of terms of the form $RZ^2/(n + a)^2$ with $n = 1, 2, 3, \cdots$ is called a *Rydberg series of terms*.

The terms can be obtained empirically from the observed spectrum. The first term in (I, 8), for example, is always given by the wave number of the limit of the series of spectral lines in question, while, for the second term, a has to be chosen so that all the observed lines of the series are accurately represented.

Often, the word *term* is used synonymously with *energy state* or *quantum state*, and the expression *term value* is used synonymously with *energy value*. This practice is even more justifiable in molecular than in atomic spectroscopy, since here a zero of energy differing from that for atoms is used throughout—namely, the ground state of the molecule. Hence term value and energy value differ only by the factor $1/hc$ (without the minus sign). In the following we shall employ frequently this somewhat looser usage of the concept *term*.

Continuous spectra. According to the above, when the usual atomic energy scale is used, all stable discrete quantum states of an atom have negative energy. A positive value of E corresponds to an energy greater than that of a system consisting of an electron and an ion infinitely separated and at rest. That is to say, the two particles approach or separate from one another with a kinetic energy that is not zero even at infinity. The electron then moves on a *hyperbolic orbit*, through which it goes, of course, only once. Such *aperiodic motions are not quantized*. The kinetic energy of the two particles can take any value; that is to say, all positive values of E are possible. Hence, extending from the limit $E = 0$ of the series of discrete energy values of an atom, there is a *continuous region of possible energy values* (*continuous term spectrum*).

Corresponding to the continuous region of energy values, there is a *continuous* absorption or emission *spectrum*, which arises by the transition of an electron from a discrete state E_2 into the continuous region, or conversely. The continuous absorption spectrum therefore corresponds to the *removal of the electron* (photoeffect) with more or less kinetic energy; the continuous emission spectrum corresponds to the *capture of the electron*. The continuum begins at the limit of the line series having the same n_2 and extends toward shorter wave lengths. The *series limit*, which is at the same time the beginning of the continuum, corresponds to the removal or capture of the electron with zero velocity; that is to say, it gives directly the energy required to separate the electron from the atom (*ionization potential*) for the lower state of the line series.

One can say quite generally that continuous spectra of gases always correspond to such splitting or recombination processes, since of all forms of molecular energy only the kinetic energy of translation is unquantized.

2. WAVE MECHANICS (QUANTUM MECHANICS)

Fundamental equations. The essential point in the
Bohr theory, the idea of *discrete stationary states*, is retained
in wave mechanics, but the derivation of these stationary
states is altered.   Apart from that, the wave mechanical
energy values for non-hydrogen-like systems agree quantitatively with experiment, while the values calculated according to the Bohr theory do not.

Whereas the Bohr theory starts out with the classical
laws of motion, and subsequently, by means of certain
quantum conditions, selects as possible only a few of the
orbits so obtained, wave mechanics puts in the place of the
classical laws of motion another law, which is, however,
so constituted that for large masses it goes over asymptotically into the classical laws of motion.   Wave mechanics
can therefore claim to be more comprehensive than classical
mechanics, which fails for atomic dimensions.

According to the fundamental idea of De Broglie, *the
motion of any corpuscle of matter is associated with a wave
motion of wave length*

$$\lambda = \frac{h}{mv}, \tag{I, 10}$$

where m is the mass and v the velocity of the corpuscle.
This idea has been brilliantly confirmed by the discovery of
the *diffraction of corpuscular rays* (electrons as well as atoms).

When, therefore, we wish to investigate a motion in an
atom, we must investigate the wave motion associated with
it.   Let Ψ be the *wave function*, whose physical meaning
will be discussed later.   Since we are dealing with a wave
motion, Ψ must vary periodically with time at every point in
space.   We can therefore write

$$\Psi = \psi \sin 2\pi\nu't \quad \text{or} \quad \Psi = \psi \cos 2\pi\nu't,$$

or, combining both together,

$$\Psi = \psi e^{2\pi i\nu't}. \tag{I, 11}$$

Here ν' is the frequency of the vibrations, and ψ is the amplitude, which, in the case of the motion of a single mass point of mass m, depends only on the co-ordinates x, y, z.

For the amplitude ψ, Schrödinger put forward the equation

$$\frac{\partial^2 \psi}{\partial x^2} + \frac{\partial^2 \psi}{\partial y^2} + \frac{\partial^2 \psi}{\partial z^2} + \frac{8\pi^2 m}{h^2}(E - V)\psi = 0, \quad \text{(I, 12)}$$

where V is the potential energy and $E = h\nu'$ is the total energy. This *Schrödinger equation* replaces for atomic systems the fundamental equations of classical mechanics. To this we have to add the restriction that ψ is to be everywhere single-valued, finite, and continuous, and vanishes at infinity.

The mathematical investigation of equation (I, 12) shows that, under the restriction given, it is in general soluble only for quite definite values of E, the so-called *eigenvalues*. The discrete energy values of an atom which are experimentally observed in the spectrum appear, therefore, according to Schrödinger, as the eigenvalues of the wave equation of the system.

For the case of *several* (N) *particles*, (I, 12) must be replaced by the equation

$$\sum_k \frac{1}{m_k}\left(\frac{\partial^2 \psi}{\partial x_k^2} + \frac{\partial^2 \psi}{\partial y_k^2} + \frac{\partial^2 \psi}{\partial z_k^2}\right) + \frac{8\pi^2}{h^2}(E - V)\psi = 0, \quad \text{(I, 13)}$$

where ψ now depends on the $3N$ co-ordinates, x_k, y_k, z_k, and m_k is the mass of the kth particle.

If, in (I, 12), we substitute for V the potential energy $(-Ze^2/r)$ of an electron in the field of a nucleus with a charge Ze, the solution of the wave equation leads exactly to the energy values (I, 3) [see texts on wave mechanics (15)–(26a)]. On the other hand, when we are not dealing with the field of a point charge but that of an atomic core, energy values of the form (I, 4) result. At the same time it follows that, in both cases, all positive energy values are possible; that is to say, a continuous region $(E > 0)$ adjoins the series of discrete energy levels $(E < 0)$.

Even for systems with several electrons, the solution of the wave equation leads to energy values that are not only qualitatively but also quantitatively in agreement with the empirical values—for example, for He and Li$^+$, among others. This is in contrast to the Bohr theory, which leads here to values for the ionization potential and other term values that are entirely at variance with experiment.

Physical interpretation of the Ψ function. The complete solution of the Schrödinger equation [(I, 12) or (I, 13)] yields not only the eigenvalues—that is, the energy values . of the stationary states—but also the corresponding functions ψ (or $\Psi = \psi e^{2\pi i(E/h)t}$), the so-called *eigenfunctions*. For one and the same eigenvalue there may sometimes be several different eigenfunctions. This is called *degeneracy*. The interpretation of Ψ (and ψ), due to Born, is as follows: $\Psi\Psi^* d\tau = |\Psi|^2 d\tau = |\psi|^2 d\tau$ (where Ψ^* is the complex conjugate of Ψ) gives the *probability that the particle under consideration will be found in the volume element $d\tau$ at the position given by the co-ordinates.* Consequently $|\psi|^2$ is the *probability density*. Its dependence on the co-ordinates—that is, the *probability density distribution* for the electron or electrons in an atom—is the essential thing that wave mechanics has to tell us about the motions in an atom. (See A.A., Fig. 21, p. 44.) It tells us nothing, however, about the orbits of the electrons.

The electron may be observed at any point in space with a certain probability; it is, so to speak, smeared out over the whole of space. However, the ψ function decreases exponentially with increasing distance from the nucleus, so that the probability of finding the electron appreciably outside the region of the old Bohr orbits is extremely small.

On the other hand, in the states of positive energy, the eigenfunction is an outgoing or incoming spherical wave corresponding to the removal or capture of the electron. Here the decrease in $|\psi|^2$ is only inversely proportional to the square of the distance from the center and not exponential.

It can be shown [see, for example, (23)] that, for any particular system, the eigenfunctions corresponding to different eigenvalues of the wave equation have an important mathematical property: They are *orthogonal* to one another; that is,

$$\int \psi_n \psi_m{}^* \, d\tau = 0 \qquad \text{for } n \neq m,$$

where n and m represent the quantum numbers of two different states, and where the integration extends over the whole of space.

The Heisenberg uncertainty principle. The fact that, in wave mechanics, the orbits of the old Bohr theory have lost their meaning is closely connected with the Heisenberg uncertainty principle. According to it, the *position and momentum* (or velocity) *of a particle cannot be simultaneously measured with any desired accuracy.* Rather, if Δx is the uncertainty of the x co-ordinate and Δp_x is the uncertainty of the x component of the momentum $(m\Delta v_x)$, always

$$\Delta x \cdot \Delta p_x \geqq \frac{h}{2\pi}, \qquad (I, 14)$$

where h is Planck's constant.[2] Analogous relations hold for the other co-ordinates, and also, for example, for energy and time:

$$\Delta E \cdot \Delta t \geqq \frac{h}{2\pi}. \qquad (I, 15)$$

The uncertainty relations are a direct result of the wave properties of matter (see A.A., Chapter I).

Momentum and angular momentum. Even though in wave mechanics the orbits of the electron cannot be given—that is to say, the momentum is not defined for every point—yet a probability density distribution of the momentum can be given (see A.A., p. 47). Quite definite statements may be made regarding the *angular momentum* of an atom. For any mechanical system the angular

---

[2] Following Dirac, many theoretical physicists use the symbol $\hbar$ for $h/2\pi$.

momentum is given by $\Sigma m_i v_i \rho_i$, where ρ_i is the perpendicular distance of the momentum $m_i v_i$ of the ith particle from a fixed point, usually the center of gravity. In wave mechanics, as in classical mechanics, the angular momentum of an isolated system is constant.[3]   According to wave mechanics, it can take only discrete values as can the energy; in the case of one electron, it can have the values $\sqrt{l(l+1)}(h/2\pi)$, which is approximately $l(h/2\pi)$. The *azimuthal quantum number* l gives us therefore the *orbital angular momentum of the electron in units* $h/2\pi$. Consequently, the various term series of lithium, for example (see Fig. 1), differ in the angular momentum of the electron.

The fact that even in wave mechanics the angular momentum has a perfectly definite value shows that we can still speak of an electron revolving about an atomic nucleus, provided that we are quite clear that there is no point in speaking of definite orbits. Consequently, we can in many instances use the angular momentum in the same way as in the Bohr theory; for example, under certain conditions, angular momenta can be added vectorially (see section 3).

In the following discussion the angular momentum vectors will be indicated by heavy (boldface) type to distinguish them from the corresponding quantum numbers, printed in regular type. Thus l means an angular momentum vector of magnitude $\sqrt{l(l+1)}(h/2\pi) \approx l(h/2\pi)$.

It should be noticed that, in the continuous states of positive energy, the angular momentum l of the electron can also take only the discrete values given above.

Transition probabilities. The *eigenvalues* of the wave equation [(I, 12) or (I, 13)] give the energy values of the atomic system under consideration and thereby determine, according to the Bohr frequency condition (I, 5) (which holds unaltered in wave mechanics), the frequencies of all emitted spectral lines. The *eigenfunctions* of the wave

---

[3] For a closed system (on which no external forces act) the angular momentum is independent of the point of reference. As such, usually the center of mass is chosen.

equation serve to calculate not only the probability density distribution in individual quantum states (see above), but also the *probability of transitions* between these states under the influence of radiation or of collisions with other particles. Thus the intensities of the emitted or absorbed spectral lines are obtained. In particular, when the eigenfunctions are known, we can calculate whether or not two states can combine with one another; that is to say, we obtain the *selection rules*.

Wave mechanics shows that the probability of a transition between two states m and n is proportional to the square of the magnitude of certain vector quantities R^{nm} (the so-called *matrix elements*), whose components depend in the following manner on the eigenfunctions ψ_n and ψ_m of the two states:

$$R_x^{nm} = \int \psi_n \psi_m{}^* p_x d\tau, \quad R_y^{nm} = \int \psi_n \psi_m{}^* p_y d\tau,$$

$$R_z^{nm} = \int \psi_n \psi_m{}^* p_z d\tau, \tag{I, 16}$$

where p is some physical vector quantity which depends on the $3N$ co-ordinates of the N particles in the system. The integrals are taken over the whole space of the $3N$ co-ordinates. In the simplest and most common case, p is the dipole moment of the system; that is, $p_x = \Sigma e_i x_i$, $p_y = \Sigma e_i y_i$, and $p_z = \Sigma e_i z_i$, where e_i is the charge on the ith particle of the system. If we substitute this in (I, 16) we obtain the *matrix elements of the dipole moment* of the system:

$$R_x^{nm} = \int \psi_n \psi_m{}^* (\Sigma e_i x_i) d\tau, \quad R_y^{nm} = \int \psi_n \psi_m{}^* (\Sigma e_i y_i) d\tau,$$

$$R_z^{nm} = \int \psi_n \psi_m{}^* (\Sigma e_i z_i) d\tau. \tag{I, 17}$$

If the matrix element R^{nm} differs from zero for two states n and m, the two states combine with one another with a certain probability with emission or absorption of radiation;

if it is zero, the transition under consideration is forbidden as a dipole transition.

p may also be any one of a number of other quantities, as, for example, the quadrupole moment, the magnetic dipole moment, the polarizability, or the magnitude of the interaction with a colliding electron, atom, or ion. In every case we obtain from (I, 16) the transition probability due to the physical quantity in question.

A transition might be allowed according to (I, 16) as a *quadrupole transition*, for example, even though it is forbidden as a dipole transition. However, a detailed calculation shows that the absolute magnitude of the quadrupole transition probability for radiation of visible light is 10^{-8} times that of the dipole transition probability, and therefore transitions which can occur only as quadrupole transitions are extremely weak.

When we calculate the matrix elements (I, 17) for the case of one electron, we find that they all disappear with the exception of those for which the quantum number l for the two states differs by only 1; that is to say, we have the *selection rule*

$$\Delta l = \pm 1.$$

This is the same selection rule as that already given above in the Bohr theory (I, 9) and found to agree with experiment.

The intensity of a spectral line in absorption ($I_a{}^{nm}$) or emission ($I_e{}^{nm}$) is proportional to the transition probability and therefore to the square of the corresponding matrix element. For the ordinary case of dipole radiation, a more detailed calculation yields, apart from constant factors,

$$I_a{}^{nm} \sim \nu^{nm} \left| R^{nm} \right|^2, \quad I_e{}^{nm} \sim (\nu^{nm})^4 \left| R^{nm} \right|^2. \quad \text{(I, 18)}$$

If the probability of a transition from some excited state to any lower state differs from zero, it follows that the system will remain in the excited state only for a certain length of time (lifetime). The *mean life* of a state is inversely proportional to the sum of the probabilities of all possible transitions to lower states. If the transition from an excited to any lower state is forbidden as a dipole transition, the mean life is very much larger than otherwise. Such states are called *metastable*.

Space quantization. In a magnetic or electric field, a *precession of the angular momentum* of an atom takes place in consequence of the influence of the field on the atom. This precession is shown diagrammatically in Fig. 2 for the case of one electron. While classically the precession could take place at any angle to the field direction, according to quantum theory, only those angles are possible for which the components of the angular momentum in the direction of the field have the discrete values $m_l(h/2\pi)$, where

Fig. 2. Precession of the Angular Momentum l of an Electron in a Magnetic or an Electric Field F. The vector l describes a cone with the field direction as axis.

$$m_l = l, (l-1), (l-2), \cdots, -l. \quad (I, 19)$$

This *space quantization* is shown in Fig. 3 for $l = 3$. m_l is called the *magnetic quantum number* of the electron. It keeps its meaning for any field, however small—in the limiting case, for zero field.

For given n and l there is a different eigenfunction for each value of m_l. These eigenfunctions, in the absence of a field, would all belong to the same energy value. The $2l + 1$ different modes of motion corresponding to them are *degenerate* with respect to one another. One speaks of a $(2l + 1)$-*fold degeneracy*.

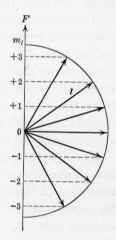

Fig. 3. Space Quantization of l in a Field F for $l = 3$. The figure also holds generally for other angular momentum vectors (see p. 23). Corresponding to the rigorous formula, the length of the vector l is drawn proportional to $\sqrt{l(l+1)}$, which is always greater than l. It should be noted that consequently l is always inclined to the field direction at an angle that is different from zero.

Electron spin.   Investigations of the multiplet structure of spectral lines (for example, the alkali doublets) and of the anomalous Zeeman effect have led, at first quite independently of quantum mechanics, to the assumption (Goudsmit and Uhlenbeck) that the electron has an *angular momentum of its own* (usually called "spin"). That is to say, the electron rotates about its own axis. The corresponding quantum number is $s = \frac{1}{2}$, and the angular momentum itself, *s*, has the magnitude $\sqrt{s(s+1)}\,(h/2\pi) = \frac{1}{2}\sqrt{3}\,(h/2\pi)$. The electron spin appears as a necessary result of Dirac's relativistic wave mechanics. [See texts on wave mechanics (15)–(26a).]

In a magnetic field, the spin of the electron can set itself only so that its component in the field direction has the value $m_s h/2\pi$, where m_s can be only $+\frac{1}{2}$ or $-\frac{1}{2}$.

3. ATOMS WITH SEVERAL ELECTRONS; VECTOR MODEL

Quantum numbers of the individual electrons.   To a first approximation, even when a number of electrons are present, we can ascribe to each individual electron the same quantum numbers as are ascribed to a single electron moving in the field of an atomic core. This is true because, to a first approximation, we can replace the action of the remaining electrons—on the one selected for consideration—by a mean centrally symmetric field. Thus, also, when several electrons are present in an atom, we have the following quantum numbers for each electron: n, the principal quantum number, which is a measure of the extent of the corresponding "electron cloud"; l, the azimuthal quantum number, which gives the orbital angular momentum of the electron; m_l, the magnetic quantum number, which gives the component of *l* in a given direction (for example, that of a magnetic field); and m_s, the spin quantum number, which gives the component of the spin *s* in a given direction.

In Table 3 the *possible states of an electron* are given up to $n = 4$, the restrictions for l, m_l, and m_s being taken into account. The value of m_s is indicated by an arrow directed

TABLE 3

POSSIBLE STATES OF AN ELECTRON IN AN ATOM

n	K 1	L 2				M 3									N 4															
l	0 s	0 s	1 p			0 s	1 p			2 d					0 s	1 p			2 d					3 f						
m_l	0	0	−1	0	+1	0	−1	0	+1	−2	−1	0	+1	+2	0	−1	0	+1	−2	−1	0	+1	+2	−3	−2	−1	0	+1	+2	+3
m_s	⇄	⇄	⇄	⇄	⇄	⇄	⇄	⇄	⇄	⇄	⇄	⇄	⇄	⇄	⇄	⇄	⇄	⇄	⇄	⇄	⇄	⇄	⇄	⇄	⇄	⇄	⇄	⇄	⇄	⇄

up $(+\frac{1}{2})$ or down $(-\frac{1}{2})$. Electron "orbits" with different n have widely differing energies. Such groups of orbits are called K, L, M, $\cdots$ *shells*, corresponding to the values of $n = 1, 2, 3, \cdots$. The energy difference between orbits with the same n but different l is much smaller. According as $l = 0, 1, 2, 3, \cdots$, the electrons are designated $s, p, d, f, \cdots$ *electrons* (see the table). The value of the principal quantum number is usually placed before the symbol for l so that one speaks, for example, of a $2p$ electron. In the absence of a magnetic field, states with the same n and l but with different m_l and m_s have the same energy—that is, are degenerate with one another.

The Pauli principle. In order to represent the observed spectra of the atoms, it is necessary to assume the following principle, which was first enunciated by Pauli: *In one and the same atom, no two electrons can have the same set of values for the four quantum numbers n, l, m_l, and m_s.* This principle does not result from the fundamentals of quantum mechanics but is an additional assumption.

It follows directly from Pauli's principle that, in each "cell" with a given n and l in the above scheme, there can be only as many electrons as there are arrows between the corresponding vertical lines. In the K shell ($n = 1$, $l = 0$), for example, there can be at the most two electrons, since a third electron would necessarily have exactly the same four quantum numbers as one of those already present, and that, according to the above principle, is forbidden. The K shell is thus *"closed"* with two electrons. Similarly, in the L shell, there can be only eight electrons, two of them in the $2s$ subgroup and six of them in the $2p$ subgroup. Other shells are analogous. (See also A.A., Chapter III.)

Quantum theoretical addition of angular momentum vectors. According to what has been said above, each electron in an atom has an orbital angular momentum l and a spin s. These individual angular momenta can be added in different ways to form a resultant. However, before we go into the particular case of the resultant angular momentum of an atom, let us briefly discuss quite generally the quantum theoretical addition of angular momentum vectors, since such additions are also of great importance for molecules.

Let A and B be two angular momentum vectors. According to quantum theory, their magnitudes are given by $\sqrt{A(A+1)}\,(h/2\pi)$ and $\sqrt{B(B+1)}\,(h/2\pi)$, respectively, or approximately by $A(h/2\pi)$ and $B(h/2\pi)$, where A and B are the quantum numbers belonging to the angular momenta and can be integral, 0, 1, 2, $\cdots$, or half integral, $\frac{1}{2}$, $\frac{3}{2}$, $\frac{5}{2}$, $\cdots$. The resultant C, of A and B, is obtained in the usual way from the parallelogram of vectors. However, we must remember that C is again quantized—that is to say, can take only the values $\sqrt{C(C+1)}\,(h/2\pi)$, or approximately $C(h/2\pi)$, where C is integral when A and B are both integral or both half integral, but is half integral when only A or only B is half integral. Therefore, in order to obtain the quantized values of C, we can add A and B only in certain directions relative to one another. The possible values of C are

$$C = (A+B),\ (A+B-1),\ (A+B-2),\ \cdots,\ |A-B|. \qquad (\text{I, 20})$$

Fig. 4 illustrates the *vector addition* for the case $A = 2$, $B = \frac{3}{2}$. For simplicity, the lengths of the vectors have been taken as proportional to the corresponding quantum numbers, which is, however, only approximately correct. We see that, to this approximation, the extreme C values, $(A+B)\,(h/2\pi)$ and $|A-B|\,(h/2\pi)$, agree with the maximum and minimum classical resultants, respectively. However, not all intermediate values (as on the classical theory) but only the above discrete values are possible. According to the exact formula for the magnitude of the vectors $[\sqrt{A(A+1)}(h/2\pi)$, and so forth], all the three vectors cannot point in exactly the same direction even in the case of the extreme values.

If a *coupling* exists between the vectors A and B, they *precess about the resultant C as axis*, the precession being the more rapid the stronger the coupling. The states with the different C values (I, 20) then have different energies. At the same time, A and B lose more and more their meaning as angular momenta (their direction being no longer constant). However, the quantum numbers A and B retain their significance for ascertaining the number of possible C values.

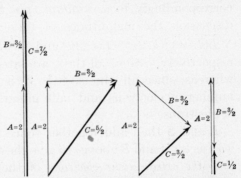

Fig. 4. **Quantum Theoretical Addition of Two Angular Momentum Vectors** A **and** B **to Form a Resultant** C **for the Case** $A = 2$, $B = \frac{3}{2}$. The figure gives all the possible mutual orientations for the example. The lengths of the vectors have been taken proportional to the quantum numbers, which is only approximately correct (see text).

If there are several angular momenta, it is best first to add the strongly coupled vectors to form partial resultants and then to add these more weakly coupled partial resultants to give a total resultant.

In a field, the angular momentum vector A is space quantized in such a way that its component in the field direction is $M_A \cdot (h/2\pi)$, where

$$M_A = A, (A - 1), (A - 2), \cdots, -A. \qquad \text{(I, 21)}$$

M_A is therefore integral or half integral according as A is integral or half integral. The space quantization corresponds exactly to that for l shown in Fig. 3. Accordingly, in a field, a state with angular momentum A has $(2A + 1)$ components of slightly different energy. In the absence of a field, there is a $(2A + 1)$-fold degeneracy.

Quantum numbers and angular momenta of the whole atom; term symbols. In general, in an atom containing several electrons, the orbital angular momenta l_1, l_2, l_3, $\cdots$ of the individual electrons may be regarded as strongly coupled among themselves, and the spins s_1, s_2, s_3, $\cdots$ among themselves. The l_i add together in the above-mentioned manner to give a resultant which is the *resultant orbital angular momentum* and is designated by L. The s_i add up correspondingly to a *resultant spin* S. From our previous discussion the magnitudes of these vectors are given by $\sqrt{L(L+1)}(h/2\pi) \approx L(h/2\pi)$ and $\sqrt{S(S+1)}(h/2\pi) \approx S(h/2\pi)$, respectively. Since all the l_i are integral, L is also integral, whereas, since all the $s_i = \frac{1}{2}$, S is integral for an even number of electrons and half integral for an odd number of electrons.

L and S then add together (once more in just the same way as for A and B above) to give the *total angular momentum J of the extranuclear electrons* of the atom, which has the magnitude $\sqrt{J(J+1)}(h/2\pi) \approx J(h/2\pi)$, where J is integral or half integral according as S is integral or half integral. According to (I, 20), the quantum number J is given by

$$J = (L+S), (L+S-1), (L+S-2), \cdots, |L-S|. \quad (I, 22)$$

Thus we have the following scheme:

$$\underbrace{l_1, l_2, l_3, \cdots}_{L} \qquad \underbrace{s_1, s_2, s_3, \cdots}_{S} \qquad (I, 23)$$
$$\underbrace{}_{J}$$

The *vector diagram* for a simple case with two electrons is given in Fig. 5. Apart from this coupling [Russell-Saunders or (L, S) coupling], there is also a so-called (j, j) coupling (see A.A., p. 174), which, however, is of no great importance for the following.

According as $L = 0, 1, 2, 3, \cdots$, the terms are called $S, P, D, F, \cdots$ terms, respectively (see the energy level diagram of Li in Fig. 1, in which $L = l$, the orbital angular momentum of the one outer electron).

Each of the possible L values can occur with each of the possible S values. Owing to the strong coupling between the l_i themselves and the s_i themselves, terms with different

L or different S have very different energies, while those terms that result from one and the same L and S have only slightly different energies. The latter form together a *multiplet term*, the number of whose components, according to (I, 22), is $(2S + 1)$ when $L > S$. $(2S + 1)$ is called the *multiplicity* and is added as an upper left index to the term symbol, thus: ^3P (triplet P), ^4D (quartet D), and so forth. In addition, the J value is added as a lower right index—for example, $^2P_{\frac{1}{2}}$, $^2P_{\frac{3}{2}}$. Thus the example in Fig. 5 represents a $^3G_4$ term. Sometimes the whole electron configuration (or the most important part of it) is added to the term symbol, so that we may have, for example, $1s^2 2s^2 2p^2\ ^3P_1$. In this, the exponents indicate the number of electrons in the "orbits" considered.

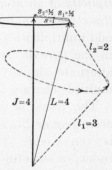

Fig. 5. Vector Diagram for the Case of Two Electrons with $l_1 = 3$, $l_2 = 2$, $L = 4$, $S = 1$, $J = 4$. The precessions are indicated by broken-line and solid-line ellipses. The "broken-line" precession takes place much faster than the "solid-line" precession.

As an example, let us consider an atom with an f-electron and a d-electron ($l_1 = 3$, $l_2 = 2$; see Fig. 5). According to (I, 20), L can take the values 1, 2, 3, 4, and 5, while S can take the values 0 and 1. We therefore obtain the terms P, D, F, G, and H, which can occur with $S = 0$—that is, as singlets—and with $S = 1$—that is, as triplets. We therefore have the terms $^1P_1$, $^1D_2$, $^1F_3$, $^1G_4$, $^1H_5$, $^3P_{0,1,2}$, $^3D_{1,2,3}$, $^3F_{2,3,4}$, $^3G_{3,4,5}$, and $^3H_{4,5,6}$.

When more than one electron is in one and the same "orbit" (same n and l)—that is, when there are *equivalent electrons*—the Pauli principle must be taken into consideration in deriving the possible terms. Its application leads, among other things, to the result that, when a shell contains the maximum number of electrons (*closed shell*), the resultant L and S values can be only zero. Thus, in the derivation of resultants, no account need be taken of closed shells.

A series of electron configurations differing only in the principal quantum number of one electron (for example, $1s^2 2s^2 np$) results in a *Rydberg series* of the corresponding terms (in the example, ^2P; see above).

From what has been said above, it follows that the *multiplicity* of an atomic term is *odd for an even number of electrons* and *even for an odd number of electrons*. Even and odd multiplicities therefore alternate for successive elements in the periodic system (*alternation of multiplicities*). They alternate similarly in the series of ions with single and multiple charges for a given element.

The terms of an atom are distinguished as *even* or *odd* according as Σl_i, summed over all the electrons of the atom, is even or odd. This is indicated by adding g or u as a lower index, or sometimes by adding an upper index o for the odd terms (for example, ^2P_u or $^2P^o$).

Influence of a magnetic or electric field. According to the above, when an atom with total angular momentum J is brought into a field, a *space quantization* takes place, so that the components of J in the field direction have the value $M_J(h/2\pi)$, where M_J can take the $2J + 1$ values given by (I, 21). In a magnetic field, states with different M_J have different energy (Zeeman effect), but, in an electric field, only those with different $|M_J|$ differ. (States which differ only in the sign of M_J have the same energy in an electric field.)

In a very strong field, a *Paschen-Back effect* takes place: L and S are *uncoupled* from each other by the field and are space quantized with respect to the field direction independently of each other, with components $M_L(h/2\pi)$ and $M_S(h/2\pi)$, respectively. For still stronger fields, the coupling between the various l_i and the various s_i can be broken so that an independent space quantization of all the individual vectors takes place.

Selection rules. A determination of the selection rules according to the method previously given (p. 16) leads to the following results. For dipole radiation there are two *rigorous* selection rules:

$$\Delta J = 0, \pm1, \textit{ with the restriction } J = 0 \nleftrightarrow J = 0 \qquad \text{(I, 24)}$$

($\nleftrightarrow$ means "does not combine with") and the Laporte rule,

even terms combine only with odd and odd terms combine only with even. (I, 25)

Furthermore, we obtain the following *approximate* selection rules. As long as the coupling between L and S is weak—that is to say, as long as the multiplet splitting is small (light elements)—the following holds to a good approximation:

$$\Delta L = 0, \pm1. \qquad \text{(I, 26)}$$

$$\Delta S = 0. \qquad \text{(I, 27)}$$

The latter rule is also known as the *prohibition of intercombinations*. It states that terms of different multiplicities cannot combine with one another.

If the coupling between the l_i is not too strong, only one electron alters its quantum numbers in a transition and for this electron the following rule holds:

$$\Delta l_i = \pm1. \qquad \text{(I, 28)}$$

Finally, in a magnetic or electric field the following selection rules hold for the magnetic quantum numbers:

For a weak field: $\Delta M_J = 0, \pm1$; with the restriction

$$M_J = 0 \nleftrightarrow M_J = 0 \textit{ for } \Delta J = 0. \qquad \text{(I, 29)}$$

For a strong field: $\Delta M_L = 0, \pm1$; $\Delta M_S = 0.$ (I, 30)

Nuclear spin. In order to explain the *hyperfine structure of atomic spectral lines* (see A.A., Chapter V) and the *intensity alternation in band spectra* (see Chapters III and V) it was found necessary to assume that the atomic nucleus, as well as the electron, possesses an intrinsic angular momentum (*nuclear spin*)—that is, rotates about its own axis. The magnitude of this angular momentum is

$$\sqrt{I(I+1)}(h/2\pi) \approx I(h/2\pi),$$

where I is the quantum number of the nuclear angular momentum. It has different values (including zero) for different nuclei.

According to the general rules for vector addition outlined above, the nuclear angular momentum I adds to the total angular momentum J of the extranuclear electrons to give a resultant F, the *total angular momentum of the atom, inclusive of nuclear spin.* The corresponding quantum number is given by

$$F = (J+I),\ (J+I-1),\ (J+I-2),\ \cdots,\ |J-I|. \quad (I, 31)$$

The different values of F correspond to somewhat different energies of the total system. However, the coupling between J and I is so weak that the energy differences are extremely small. This causes a minute splitting of the spectral lines (hyperfine structure) which can be detected only by spectral apparatus of the greatest resolving power.

CHAPTER II

Observed Molecular Spectra and Their Representation by Empirical Formulae

1. SPECTRA IN THE VISIBLE AND ULTRAVIOLET REGIONS

Coarse structure. If the spectra of various kinds of electric discharges, of flames, or of fluorescence are investigated, in addition to the characteristic line spectra (of which Fig. 6 gives a simple example), spectra of a quite different

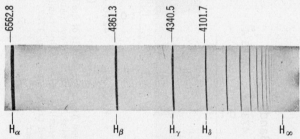

Fig. 6. Emission Spectrum of the Hydrogen Atom in the Visible and Near Ultraviolet Region [Balmer Series, after Herzberg (302)]. H_∞ gives the position of the series limit.

type are observed, particularly when molecular gases are used. With small dispersion, these consist not of single, sharp lines but of more or less broad wave-length regions (*bands*). We therefore speak of *band spectra*. In Figs. 7–11 some typical *emission* band spectra are reproduced. They should be compared with the typical line spectrum of the H atom in Fig. 6. In emission, bands and lines very often occur mixed together, as the figures show. In *absorption*, however, when light with a continuous spectrum (for example, the light of a filament lamp) is sent through a molecular gas, bands appear exclusively (see Figs. 13–16).

29

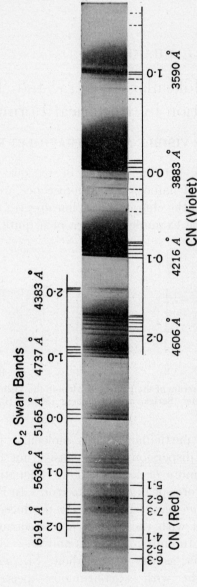

Fig. 7. Band Spectrum of the Carbon Arc in Air (Bands of the Molecules CN and C₂). The bands whose leading lines are connected to the same horizontal line belong to one band system. For the violet CN bands and the C₂ Swan bands the numbering and wave length of only the first band of each sequence (see p. 43) is indicated. The broken leading lines refer to the so-called tail bands (see p. 175). The longest-wave-length group of C₂ is strongly overlapped and is therefore not very clear.

30

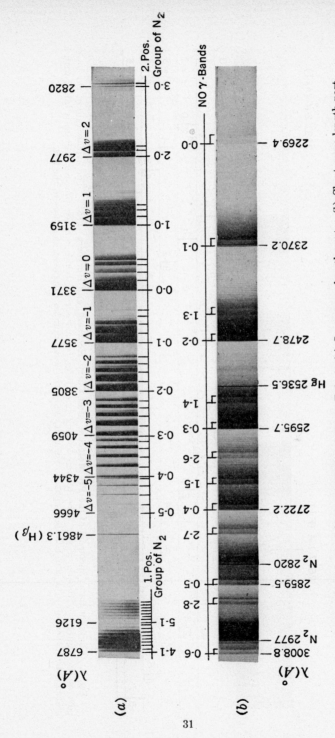

Fig. 8. Band Spectrum of an Air-Filled Geissler Tube. (a) Long-wave-length part. (b) Short-wave-length part. The latter is much more strongly exposed than the former.

31

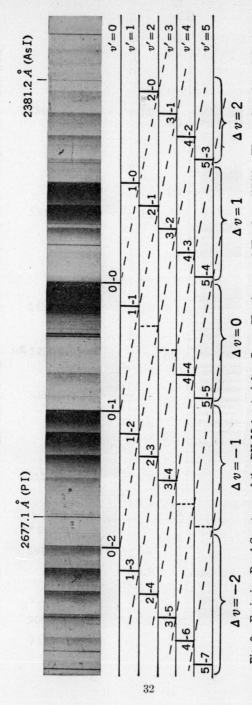

Fig. 9. Emission Band Spectrum of the PN Molecule [after Curry, Herzberg, and Herzberg (176)]. The explanation of the lower part of the figure is given on p. 37. The broken leading lines refer to unobserved bands. Since the spectrogram is taken with a grating, the dispersion in Å/mm is approximately constant, while the wave-number dispersion increases to the left.

As can be seen from the figures, the bands usually have a sharp edge, called a *band head* (or band edge), at one end, where the intensity falls suddenly to zero, while on the other side the intensity falls off more or less slowly. According as this gradual falling off in intensity takes place toward shorter or longer wave lengths, the bands are said to be *shaded* (degraded) to the violet or the red.

Apart from these kinds of bands, bands also occur, somewhat more rarely, in which the heads are not so clearly developed or not present at all. As an example of this, the bands of the Hg_2 molecule are given in Fig. 17. In rare cases—for example, for H_2 (see Fig. 12) and the alkali hydrides—no well-developed bands are observed but only an enormous number of lines, a so-called *many-line spectrum* that is scarcely to be distinguished in appearance from a complicated atomic spectrum.

Finally, more extended continuous regions, so-called *continuous spectra*, or, briefly, *continua*, also appear as molecular spectra. They are observed in absorption joining onto a series of bands—for example, for I_2 (Fig. 15) and other halogen molecules. However, they

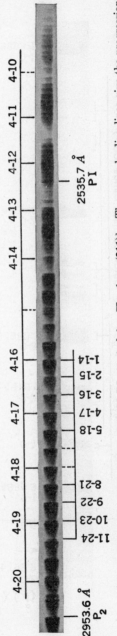

Fig. 10. Emission Band Spectrum of the P_2 Molecule [after Herzberg (311)]. The upper leading lines give the progression $v' = 4$, and the lower leading lines give the sequence $\Delta v = -13$ (see p. 43). Bands that are not observed because of low intensity or overlapping are indicated by broken leading lines. The band spectrum extends a considerable distance farther to both sides.

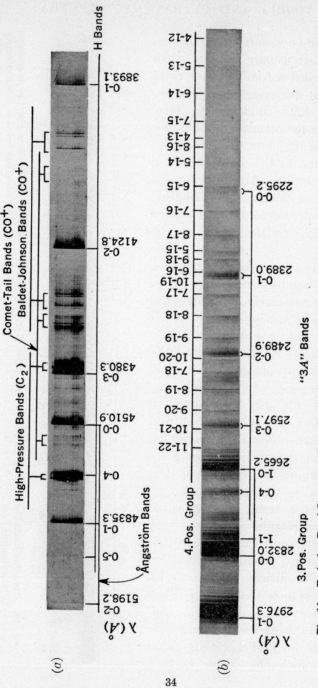

Fig. 11. Emission Band Spectrum of the CO Molecule. (a) Spectrum of an electrodeless discharge in CO at 1 mm pressure in the visible region. The bands indicated here as H bands are called *Herzberg bands* in the literature. (b) Ultraviolet part of the spectrum of an uncondensed discharge with electrodes in CO.

34

also appear without accompanying bands—for example, for the hydrogen halides. They are also observed in emission—for example, for H_2 (see Fig. 12).

A comparison of Figs. 7–17 with Fig. 6 shows that the regularity with which the bands are arranged is of quite a different kind from that of the lines in a line spectrum. Rydberg series occur only in a very few cases—for example, in the band spectrum of helium, which appears in a weakly condensed discharge through helium. The wave numbers ν of the band heads in such a series follow a Rydberg formula [see (I, 8)],

$$\nu = A \pm \frac{R}{(n+a)^2}, \quad (II, 1)$$

where A, R, and a are constants and n is a whole number. The formula shows that the separation between successive bands in such a series decreases very rapidly.

However, in by far the most cases, molecular spectra consist of series of bands whose separation alters but slowly. They are called *progressions*. In the absorption spectra of CO, I_2, and S_2 (Figs. 14–16), only one such pro-

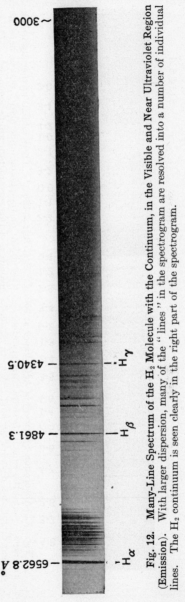

Fig. 12. Many-Line Spectrum of the H_2 Molecule with the Continuum, in the Visible and Near Ultraviolet Region (Emission). With larger dispersion, many of the "lines" in the spectrogram are resolved into a number of individual lines. The H_2 continuum is seen clearly in the right part of the spectrogram.

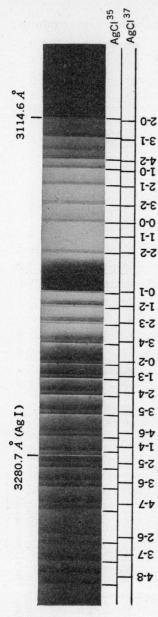

3280.7 Å (Ag I)

3114.6 Å

AgCl 35
AgCl 37

0-2 3-1 4-2 1-0 2-1 3-2 0-0 1-1 2-2 0-1 1-2 2-3 3-4 0-2 1-3 2-4 3-5 4-6 1-4 2-5 3-6 4-7 2-6 3-7 4-8

Fig. 13. Absorption Spectrum of AgCl Vapor at 900° C. [after Brice (125)].* These and all further absorption spectrograms (as also the emission spectra) are reproduced as they appear on the photographic plate; that is, here the bands appear bright on a dark background. A more detailed explanation of this spectrogram will be given on p. 177.

* The author is greatly indebted to Dr. B. R. Brice for this spectrogram.

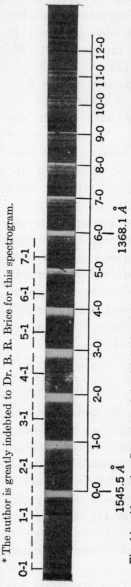

1545.5 Å

1368.1 Å

0-1 1-1 0-0 2-1 3-1 4-1 5-1 6-1 7-1 1-0 2-0 3-0 4-0 5-0 6-0 7-0 8-0 9-0 10-0 11-0 12-0

Fig. 14. Absorption Spectrum of the CO Molecule [4. Positive Group of CO; after Hopfield and Birge (332)].†
The main series of absorption bands is indicated below; a very weak series, originating from the first excited vibrational level of the ground state, is indicated above (see p. 169).

† The author is greatly indebted to Professor R. T. Birge for this spectrogram.

36

gression occurs for each. In the emission band spectrum of PN, shown in Fig. 9, a number of progressions are present and are indicated separately below the spectrogram.

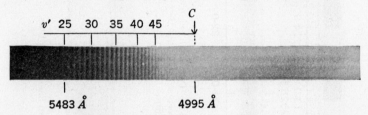

Fig. 15. Absorption Spectrum of I$_2$ Vapor. The arrow denoted by C indicates the position of the convergence limit of the bands, where a continuous absorption joins on.

The separations between successive bands in such a progression of the PN spectrum are approximately equal but decrease slowly toward longer wave lengths (to the left in the figure) if measured in cm^{-1}. On closer examination the following important regularity is found: When the series given in Fig. 9 are shifted relative to one another, so that the bands with the shortest wave length for each of the series coincide, then all the other bands corresponding to one another in the different series will also coincide. However, for an exact coincidence the diagram should be drawn to a wave-number scale, whereas the spectrogram has a linear wave-length scale.

Since the separation of the bands decreases only very slowly, the wave numbers of the bands in each progression can be represented approximately by a formula

$$\nu = \nu_{v'} - (a''v'' - b''v''^2), \tag{II, 2}$$

where $\nu_{v'}$, a'', and b'' are constants, $(b'' \ll a'')$, and v'' is a whole number which takes the values $0, 1, 2, \cdots$. If $b'' = 0$, (II, 2) would give a series of equidistant bands (separation $= a''$). A small value of b'' ($\ll a''$) different from zero gives the observed gradual decrease in the separation of the bands. We fix the constants in (II, 2) so that for the band of shortest

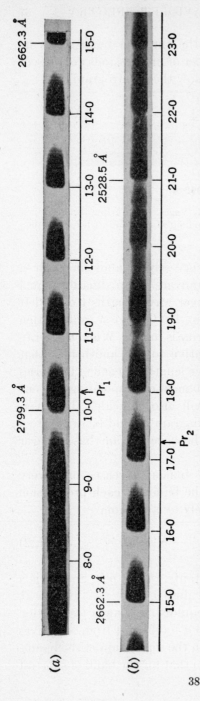

(a)

(b)

Fig. 16. Absorption Spectrum of S₂ Vapor [after Herzberg and Mundie (317)]. (a) and (b) Two much enlarged prints of two adjacent parts of the same original spectrogram. For the sake of clearness, the prints have been so made that they overlap slightly (15–0 band). The arrows denoted by Pr indicate the positions at which the bands become diffuse.

Fig. 17. Diffuse Emission Bands of Hg Vapor [after Rayleigh (581)].* The sharp lines are Hg lines.

* The author is greatly indebted to Lord Rayleigh for this spectrogram.

38

wave length $v'' = 0$—that is, $\nu = \nu_{v'}$.[1] For example, for the
second series in the PN spectrum (Fig. 9),

$$\nu = 40{,}786.8 - (1329.38\, v'' - 6.98\, v''^2). \qquad (II, 2a)$$

Table 4 shows the agreement between the observed wave
numbers and those obtained from this formula. The fact
already mentioned above that, by suitable shifting, all the
band series are made to
coincide very exactly means
that, in (II, 2), a'' and b''
have the same value for all
the progressions and only $\nu_{v'}$
is different.

It may happen that the
first band in a progres-
sion—that is, the one with
$v'' = 0$—is not observed.
In this case a shift of this
progression of bands relative to another one will
result in a coincidence only

TABLE 4

v''-PROGRESSION IN THE
PN SPECTRUM ($v' = 1$)

v''	$\nu_{\text{obs.}}$	$\nu_{\text{calc.}}$ according to (II, 2a)
0	40,786.2	40,786.8
1	39,467.2*	39,464.4
2	38,155.5	38,156.0
3	36,861.3	36,861.5

* This band is badly overlapped by
the 0–0 band 39,698.8 cm⁻¹ (see Fig. 9)
and therefore not as accurately measured as the others.

when the first *observed* band of the progression under consideration is correlated with the second (or even the third,
and so forth) band of the other progression. This is, for
example, the case for the fourth progression in Fig. 9.

Progressions such as those discussed here, for which the
band separations decrease toward *longer* wave lengths, are
called v''-*progressions*.

Taking the first band ($\nu_{v'}$) in each of the different progressions (whether observed or extrapolated), once more we
obtain a progression, but with other constants, and in particular in this progression the band separations decrease

---

[1] By a suitable choice of the constants in (II, 2) we could also represent the
observed bands using some other numbering (for example, $v'' = 10$ for the
first band). We have chosen here the numbering which appears to be the
simplest and which later proves to be of theoretical significance (see Chapter
IV).

toward *shorter* wave lengths. Accordingly, they can be represented by

$$\nu_{v'} = \nu_{oo} + (a'v' - b'v'^2), \qquad (\text{II, 3})$$

where v' takes the values 0, 1, 2, $\cdots$ and ν_{oo}, a', and b' are constants. In the case of the PN spectrum,

$$\nu_{v'} = 39{,}699.0 + (1094.80\,v' - 7.25\,v'^2). \qquad (\text{II, }3a)$$

Table 5 shows the agreement between the observed or extrapolated wave numbers with those calculated by this formula.

If we substitute $\nu_{v'}$ from (II, 3) into (II, 2), we obtain

$$\nu = \nu_{oo} + (a'v' - b'v'^2) - (a''v'' - b''v''^2); \qquad (\text{II, 4})$$

that is, in our example,

$$\nu = 39{,}699.0 + (1094.80\,v' - 7.25\,v'^2)$$
$$- (1329.38\,v'' - 6.98\,v''^2). \qquad (\text{II, 5})$$

This formula now represents all the bands. For $v' = 0$ and $v'' = 0$, we have $\nu = \nu_{oo}$, the wave number of the first band of the first series (see Fig. 9), the so-called 0–0 *band*, which is frequently, as in the present case, the most intense band in the system (see also Figs. 7 and 8). The totality of those bands of a molecule which can be represented by a formula of the type (II, 4), possibly with cubic or still higher terms in v' and v'', is called a *band system*. In many cases a number of such band systems are observed for the same molecule. In favorable cases, the different band systems of a molecule lie in different spectral regions, as, for

TABLE 5

v'-PROGRESSION IN THE
PN SPECTRUM ($v'' = 0$)

v'	$\nu_{obs.}$	$\nu_{calc.}$ according to (II, $3a$)
0	39,699.1	39,699.0
1	40,786.8	40,786.6
2	41,858.9	41,859.6
3	42,919.0	42,918.2
4	43,962.0	43,962.2
5	44,991.3	44,991.8
6	46,007.3	46,006.8
7	47,005.6	47,007.4
8	47,995.0	47,993.4
9	48,964.4	48,965.0

example, for N_2 (see Fig. 8). However, they often overlap one another, as, for example, for CO (see Fig. 11).

The wave numbers of the bands in a band system are commonly arranged in a so-called *Deslandres table* (or *scheme of band heads*) such that the bands of every v''-progression are put in a separate horizontal row. In so doing, the different horizontal rows are arranged in such a way that corresponding bands of different v''-progressions are vertically below one another.[2] As an example, the Deslandres table for the PN bands discussed above is given in Table 6. The wave-number differences for the bands in successive horizontal and vertical rows are added in smaller type. It will be noticed that these differences in a given horizontal row are *very nearly constant*, in agreement with what was said above—namely, that, after a suitable shift, one series comes into coincidence with the previous series.

Naturally, according to (II, 4), instead of considering the band system as consisting of a number of v''-progressions (II, 2), it can also be considered to be made up of v'-progressions

$$\nu = \nu_{v''} + (a'v' - b'v'^2), \qquad (II, 6)$$

where the $\nu_{v''}$ then form a v''-progression:

$$\nu_{v''} = \nu_{oo} - (a''v'' - b''v''^2). \qquad (II, 7)$$

It follows from this that the differences between corresponding bands in two vertical rows in the Deslandres scheme must also be constant, which Table 6 likewise shows. The progressions (II, 6) are indicated in Fig. 9 by the sloping broken lines.

In the spectrogram in Fig. 9 we notice that certain bands of different progressions form characteristic groups of bands lying relatively close together (indicated by braces). It is

---

[2] Sometimes, particularly in older papers, wave lengths are given instead of wave numbers; however, in this case, the differences are not constant (see below).

TABLE 6

DESLANDRES TABLE OF THE PN BANDS

(With horizontal and vertical differences)

v' \ v''	0		1		2		3		4		5		6		7		8		9		10
0	39,698.8	1322.3	38,376.5	1307.8	37,068.7																
	1087.4		1090.7		1086.8																
1	40,786.2	1319.0	39,467.2	1311.7	38,155.5	1294.2	36,861.3														
	1072.9		1069.0				1071.6														
2	41,859.1	1322.9	40,536.2				37,932.9	1280.4	36,652.5	1265.3	35,387.2										
			1061.2						1060.0		1059.2										
3			41,597.4	1309.1	40,288.3				37,712.5	1266.1	36,446.4	1252.4	35,194.0								
					1042.9				1043.9				1042.6								
4					41,331.2				38,756.4		*		36,236.6	1238.3	34,998.3						
															1029.4						
5							41,066.1				38,519.4				36,027.7	1225.5	34,802.2				
							1015.9														
6							42,082.0												34,607.1	1194.5	33,412.6
																					998.7
7									41,798.3												34,411.3
8											41,522.6										
9													41,239.4								

42

easily seen that in Deslandres' scheme (Table 6) the bands of such a group lie on a parallel to the diagonal from the upper left to the lower right corner. Because of this, they are sometimes called *diagonal groups*, but usually *sequences*. For the bands which lie on the diagonal itself, $v' = v''$. They include the 0–0 band and extend from it to longer wave lengths. For the other sequences, there is a constant positive or negative difference between v' and v''. That bands of such a sequence occur close together is observed in many emission band systems (see, for example, the C_2 and CN bands in Fig. 7). However, it is not a necessary property. In the N_2 spectrum in Fig. 8 they are not so clearly developed and in the P_2 band spectrum in Fig. 10 they are not conspicuous at all.

Fine structure. When spectrographs of greater resolving power are used, it is found that most of the bands (in emission or absorption) consist of a large number of individual lines, as is shown by Figs. 18–23. In general, the arrangement of the individual lines in a band is completely regular; however, the regularity is of a quite different kind from that, say, of the lines in a multiplet of an atomic spectrum. In the simplest case, which occurs fairly frequently, one finds a structure like that of the CN band shown in Fig. 18(*a*). This band consists of a simple series of lines which draw farther and farther apart from one another as the distance from the band head increases.

In Table 7, the wave numbers of the lines of the CN band are given, together with the differences and second differences of successive lines. As Deslandres first noticed (182), the *separation of successive lines increases very nearly linearly*, since the second difference is a constant within the accuracy of measurement. From this it follows that the lines can be represented by a formula of the type

$$\nu = c + dm + em^2, \tag{II, 8}$$

where c, d, and e are constants and m is a whole number which numbers the successive lines.

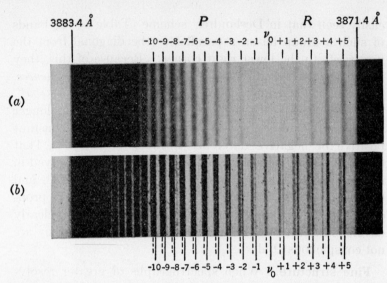

Fig. 18. Fine Structure of the CN Band 3883 Å (0–0 Band) at Low and High Temperature. The numbers given are the running numbers m (see Fig. 24). The broken leading lines refer to the returning limb of the P branch. The head of the 1–1 band may be seen to the right. The upper spectrogram (a) was made in the first order of a grating, and the lower (b) was made in the second order. In order to compensate for this the upper was enlarged twice as much as the lower. Because of this, the lines in the upper spectrogram appear broader than those in the lower.

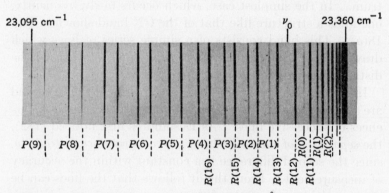

Fig. 19. Fine Structure of the CuH Band λ4280 Å.* The band extends much farther to the left than is shown in the spectrogram. However, it is then overlapped by another band. The numbers in parentheses after R and P are the J values (see p. 183 f.).

* The author is greatly indebted to Professor R. Mecke for this spectrogram.

TABLE 7

WAVE NUMBERS OF THE LINES OF THE CN BAND 3883.4 Å

[Calculated from the data of Uhler and Patterson (675)]

m	$\nu_{obs.}$ (cm^{-1})	$\Delta\nu$	$\Delta^2\nu$	$\nu_{calc.}$ according to (II, 8a)
−24	25,744.73			25,744.43
−23	45.34	0.61		45.11
−22	46.08	0.74	0.13	45.91
−21	46.99	0.91	0.17	46.85
−20	48.02	1.03	0.12	47.92
−19	49.19	1.17	0.14	49.14
−18	50.52	1.33	0.16	50.49
−17	51.98	1.46	0.13	51.98
−16	53.47	1.49	0.03	53.60
−15	55.39	1.92	0.43	55.35
−14	57.26	1.87	−0.05	57.25
−13	59.29	2.03	0.16	59.26
−12	61.47	2.18	0.15	61.42
−11	63.75	2.28	0.10	63.72
−10	66.16	2.41	0.13	66.14
− 9	68.72	2.56	0.15	68.71
− 8	71.35	2.63	0.07	71.41
− 7	74.23	2.88	0.25	74.24
− 6	77.19	2.96	0.08	77.21
− 5	80.32	3.13	0.17	80.32
− 4	83.53	3.21	0.08	83.55
− 3	86.90	3.37	0.16	86.93
− 2	90.41	3.51	0.14	90.44
− 1	94.03	3.62	0.11	94.07
0				97.85
+ 1	25,801.81			25,801.77
+ 2	05.80	3.99		05.81
+ 3	10.01	4.21	0.22	10.01
+ 4	14.23	4.22	0.01	14.32
+ 5	18.77	4.52	0.30	18.77
+ 6	(23.88)*			23.37
+ 7	28.06			28.09
+ 8	33.02	4.96		32.94
+ 9	37.97	4.95	−0.01	37.94
+10	43.13	5.16	0.21	43.07
+11	48.40	5.27	0.11	48.34
+12	53.77	5.37	0.10	53.74
+13	59.28	5.51	0.14	59.26
+14	64.90	5.62	0.11	64.93
+15	70.60	5.70	0.08	70.74
+16	76.69	6.09	0.39	76.68
+17	82.73	6.04	−0.05	82.75
+18	88.91	6.18	0.14	88.96
+19	95.22	6.31	0.13	95.30
+20	25,901.63	6.41	0.10	25,901.78
+21	08.26	6.63	0.22	08.40
+22	14.95	6.69	0.06	15.15
+23	21.86	6.91	0.22	22.03
+24	28.83	6.97	0.06	29.05

* This line is overlapped by another band head.

If we allow negative values of m as well as positive, by suitable choice of c and d, we can begin the counting ($m = 0$) at any line. Now it is seen that at one point in the series a line is missing (marked ν_0 in Fig. 18). We shall see later that it is useful to give to this missing line the value $m = 0$ (*zero*

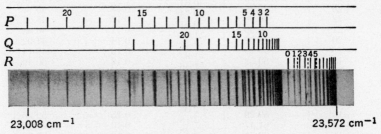

23,008 cm^{-1} 23,572 cm^{-1}

Fig. 20.   **Fine Structure of the AlH Band 4241 Å** [after Bengtsson-Knave (84)].*   The numbers are the J values (see p. 185).   The broken leading lines refer to the returning part of the R branch.

* The author is greatly indebted to Dr. E. Knave for this spectrogram.

line or *null line*)—that is, $c = \nu_0$. This place in the band is also called the *zero gap* (or null-line gap). In the example, using this kind of numbering (see the first column in Table 7), we obtain the formula

$$\nu = 25,797.85 + 3.848m + 0.0675m^2. \qquad \text{(II, 8a)}$$

The values of ν calculated according to this formula [3] are given in the last column in Table 7 and agree very well with the observed values.

    The series of lines corresponding to the positive values of m

---

[3] The coefficient e of m^2 in the formula is obtained from the mean value of the observed second differences $\Delta^2\nu$. It is easily seen that $\Delta^2\nu = 2e$ (see also p. 120). The coefficient d of the linear term is obtained, for example, by considering that the wave-number difference between lines with $m = +1$ and $m = -1$ is equal to $2d$. One must naturally allow for the fact that the wave numbers of both these lines include some error of observation. When, therefore, the ν values calculated with the coefficients thus obtained still show a systematic deviation from the observed values, we have to alter the coefficients by a small amount. It is most practical to obtain the calculated values $\nu_{\text{calc.}}$ by calculating the first differences $\Delta\nu$ from the constant second difference and by then adding or subtracting consecutively the first differences, starting with ν_0.

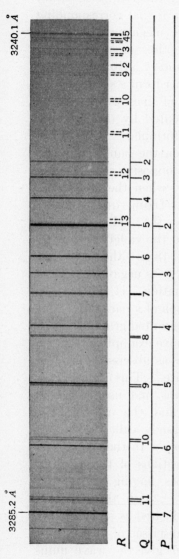

Fig. 21. Fine Structure of the NH Band 3240 Å [after Pearse (558)].* The broken leading lines refer to the returning part of the *R* branch. The numbers are *J* values (see p. 185). The band extends farther to the left but is then overlapped by the intense NH band at 3340 Å, a few lines of which are to be seen at the extreme left of the spectrogram.

* The author is greatly indebted to Dr. R. W. B. Pearse for this spectrogram.

Fig. 22. Fine Structure of the N_2 Band 3805 Å (0–2 Band of the 2. Positive Group). The short leading lines refer to the lines of the *P* branch, and the long ones refer to those of the *R* branch. The numbers are the *K* values (see p. 297 f.). The head of the 1–3 band appears at the extreme right.

47

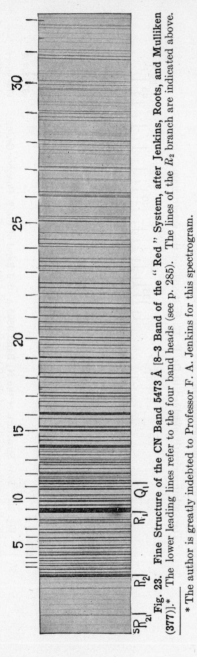

Fig. 23. Fine Structure of the CN Band 5473 Å [8–3 Band of the "Red" System, after Jenkins, Roots, and Mulliken (377)].* The lower leading lines refer to the four band heads (see p. 285). The lines of the R_2 branch are indicated above.

* The author is greatly indebted to Professor F. A. Jenkins for this spectrogram.

is called the *positive branch* or *R branch*; that corresponding to the negative values is called the *negative branch* or *P branch*. However, both together form a single simple series of lines which can be represented by one and the same formula.

When the band is shaded to the opposite side—that is to say, when the lines draw apart from one another toward the red instead of toward the violet, as they do in Fig. 18(a)—the constant e in (II, 8) is negative.

Equation (II, 8) is the equation of a parabola. This is represented graphically for the above example in Fig. 24, with ν as abscissa and m as ordinate. This representation was first used by Fortrat, and the parabola is accordingly called a *Fortrat parabola*. In the figure, the intersections of the horizontal lines, having $m = 0, \pm 1, \pm 2, \cdots$, with the parabola are indicated by small circles. The abscissae of these intersections give the wave numbers of the lines. It is seen very clearly from this method of representation how the *head of the band* is formed:

The nearer one comes to the vertex of the parabola, the more the lines crowd together.   The vertex itself corresponds to the head.   At the head there is by no means an infinite number of lines, as for the series limit in line spectra, but only a *finite* number.

Naturally, lines are also possible which correspond to the other limb of the parabola above the vertex (broken curve in

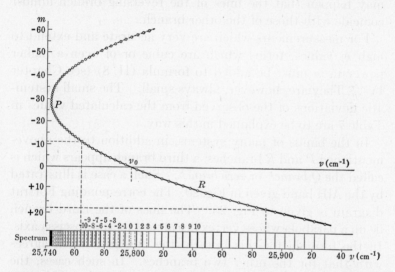

Fig. 24.   Fortrat Parabola of the CN Band 3883 Å (see Fig. 18). The schematic spectrum below is drawn to the same scale as the Fortrat parabola above. The relation between curve and spectrum is indicated by broken lines for two points ($m = -11$ and $m = +18$). No line is observed at $m = 0$ (dotted line).

Fig. 24).   Actually, the spectrogram, Fig. 18(b), for the same CN band as Fig. 18(a) (taken under conditions for which lines with higher m appear) shows such lines beyond the vertex (broken leading lines).   They may be represented by exactly the same formula as the other lines and correspond to the broken part of the Fortrat parabola in Fig. 24.   The branch that forms the head (in the present case, the P branch) *turns at the head* and can be followed back for a certain distance.   The CuH band shown in Fig. 19

gives a still better example of such a reversing (head-forming) branch, since this branch (in this case, the R branch) is resolved almost up to the head and the head lies nearer to the zero line. As Fig. 24 shows, the lines of the head-forming branch divide the spaces between the lines of the other branch in an approximately constant ratio whose value depends on the value of the constants d and e in (II, 8). It may happen that the lines of the reversing branch almost coincide with those of the other branch.

For measurements which are very accurate and extend to high m values, terms which are cubic or of even a higher power in m must be added to formula (II, 8) (see Chapter IV). They are, however, always small. The small systematic deviations of the observed from the calculated values in Table 7 are to be explained in this way.

In the bands of many systems, in addition to the above-mentioned P and R branches, a third branch appears which is called the Q *branch* or *zero branch*. Such a case is illustrated by the AlH band given in Fig. 20. The corresponding Fortrat diagram is given in Fig. 25. The lines of the third branch lie on a parabola whose vertex lies almost on the abscissa axis. In the formula for this branch, the quadratic term agrees with that for the other two branches. In such cases, the bands often have two heads each, as is the case for the AlH band.

Bands also occur with still more branches and correspondingly more heads. For example, in two CO^+ band systems, of which Fig. 11 shows some of the members, each band has four heads and the N_2 band in Fig. 22 has three (not very distinct) heads. Very often, in such cases, two or three branches lie very close together for high m values. Fig. 22 shows this for the N_2 band. On the other hand, there are also cases where lines of a branch which are single for low values of m split into two or three components for higher values of m. This is barely indicated in Fig. 18(b) for the lines of the reversing part of the P branch of the CN band but is more clearly to be seen in the NH band in Fig. 21. In spite of the more complicated appearance of these bands with more than three branches, in almost all cases the individual branches may be represented by simple formulae of the type of formula (II, 8).

All bands in one and the same system have the *same number of branches*. For different bands of a system, the constants d and e in (II, 8) differ only slightly from one

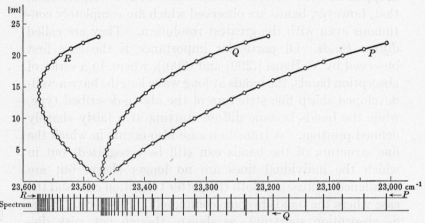

Fig. 25.   **Fortrat Diagram of the AlH Band Fig. 20.** In contrast to the foregoing figure, the Fortrat parabolae of all three branches are drawn *above* the ν axis ($|m|$ as ordinate). By reflection at the ν axis, the curve for the P branch would lie in the continuation of the R branch, as in Fig. 24. As an aid in picking out the branches in the schematic spectrogram below, the lines of the P and R branches have been extended above and those of the Q branch below, with the exception of the lines of the returning limb of the R branch.

another and alter regularly from band to band. Therefore, as a rule, the *bands in a system are all shaded in the same direction*.

It has been found that the *many-line spectra* mentioned briefly above arise from a superposition of bands of the type discussed above, for which, however, the line separation is so great that different bands overlap one another strongly and no definite heads appear.

The extensive *continuous* emission or absorption spectra mentioned on p. 33 show absolutely no fine structure even when spectral apparatus of the greatest resolution is used; they are true continuous spectra.

The bands with no pronounced heads mentioned above are sometimes found to have a fine structure quite similar to that of bands with heads. The only distinction lies then in the fact that e in (II, 8) is so small that the convergence of the lines is very slight and consequently the intensity has dropped to zero before the head is reached. Apart from that, however, bands are observed which are completely continuous even with the greatest resolution. They are called *diffuse bands*. Of particular importance is the case first observed by V. Henri [(299) and (300)], where, in a series of absorption bands, the bands at long wave lengths have a well-developed sharp fine structure of the above-described type, while the bands become diffuse starting at a fairly sharply defined position. A transition case also occurs in which the fine structure of the bands can still be recognized, but in which the individual lines are no longer sharp, but are broadened (diffuse). Both this latter transition case and the case where the bands become completely diffuse occur in the S_2 absorption spectrum, as shown, though not very distinctly, in Fig. 16 at the points marked Pr_1 and Pr_2, respectively.

Intensity distribution. In general, the intensity of the bands in a band system observed in *emission* decreases more or less regularly in all directions from the 0–0 band in the Deslandres table, though it may first go through one or two maxima. With increasing time of exposure, more and more bands of the system are obtained. However, it sometimes happens that, even with very much increased time of exposure, no bands appear above a definite v' (or v'') value; that is to say, only a certain number of horizontal (or vertical) rows appear in the Deslandres table. We then speak of a *breaking off* of the band system at a certain v' (or v'') value.

In *absorption* at sufficiently low temperatures (often room temperature is low enough), only one progression appears, that with $v'' = 0$ (the first vertical row in the scheme of band heads, Table 6). This is clearly shown by Figs. 14–16. All the other bands of the system in question which possibly appear in emission have extremely small intensities in absorption at low temperatures. In the absorption spectrum of CO, Fig. 14, one progression other than that with $v'' = 0$ can be seen to appear very weakly (broken leading lines). However, bands with $v'' \neq 0$ do appear fairly strongly in absorption at high temperatures (see Fig. 13).

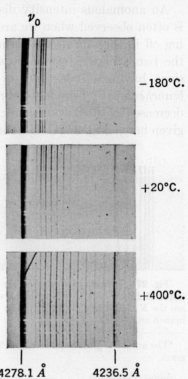

As an inspection of Figs. 18–23 shows, the *intensity distribution in the fine structure* of a band is normally such that the intensity in a branch first rises to a maximum and then gradually and regularly falls off. This is also shown by Fig. 26 for the λ4278 band of the so-called negative nitrogen group at three different temperatures. It can be seen how the intensity maximum shifts with increasing temperature (see

Fig. 26. Intensity Distribution in the Fine Structure of the N_2^+ Band λ4278.1 Å at −180° C., 20° C., and 400° C. (Electrodeless Discharge). The *P* branch is not completely resolved; however, the *R* branch is. In the reproduction, the weak lines lying between the strong lines (intensity alternation; see text) can be seen only in the neighborhood of the intensity maximum. The head of a further band of the system lies at 4236.5 Å.

Chapter IV, section 4). At the same time in this particular case a characteristic *alternation of intensities* can be seen—every alternate line is weak. This latter phenom-

enon, however, is found to occur only for molecules containing identical nuclei (homonuclear molecules).

An anomalous intensity distribution in the fine structure
is often observed when we are dealing with a case of breaking off in the vibrational structure.   One then finds that in
the bands of the last one, two, or more observed progressions having v' constant (or sometimes v'' constant) the
branches break off suddenly at a definite point or else a sudden
decrease in intensity occurs.   Two examples of this are
given here—Fig. 27 (CaH band) and Fig. 28 (AlH band).   A

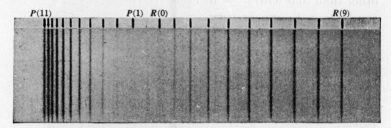

Fig. 27.   Breaking Off of the Fine Structure of the CaH Band λ3533.6 Å
[after Mulliken (509)].*   The numbers following the symbols for the branches
are the K values (see p. 271 f.).   The R branch breaks off at $K = 9$, the P
branch at $K = 11$.

*The author is greatly indebted to Professor R. S. Mulliken for this spectro-
gram.

breaking off occurs in each of the two or three branches,
respectively, which are present.

If a molecular gas is made to *fluoresce* by illuminating it with light of a definite wave length, say one of the
intense lines of a mercury lamp or cadmium lamp, it is found
that only a single progression with a definite v' appears in the
fluorescence spectrum, and not all the bands of the system,
as by excitation with white light.   By excitation with another
wave length, in general another series is obtained.   If the
fine structure of such fluorescence bands, excited by a single
line, is investigated, it is found that in general they consist of
only a few lines, as first found by Wood.   In the ideal case,
when the illuminating line covers only a single absorption

line, the "bands" consist either of only two lines, whose separation is approximately the same for the different bands,

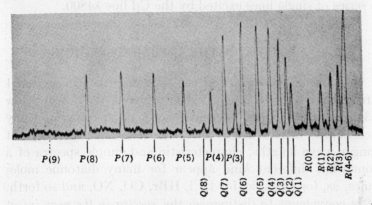

Fig. 28. Breaking Off in the Fine Structure of the AlH Band λ4354 Å [after Bengtsson-Knave and Rydberg (87)].* The numbers following the symbols for the branches are the J values (see p. 184). The P branch breaks off at $J = 8$, the Q branch at $J = 7$, and the R branch at $J = 6$.

_____

* The author is greatly indebted to Dr. E. Knave for this spectrogram.

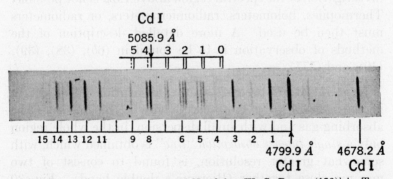

Fig. 29. Resonance Spectrum of Na₂ [after W. G. Brown (136)]. † Two resonance series are indicated above and below by the leading lines. The exciting lines are indicated by arrows. The broken leading lines refer to bands that are not observed, owing to low intensity or to overlapping.

† The author is greatly indebted to Professor W. G. Brown for this spectrogram.

or sometimes of only a single line. Such series of "bands" are called *resonance series*; a spectrum excited in the way described is called a *resonance spectrum*. Fig. 29 gives as an example the resonance spectrum of Na$_2$ excited by a Cd arc. There is a series of doublets excited by the Cd line λ5086 and a series of single lines excited by the Cd line λ4800.

2. SPECTRA IN THE INFRARED REGION

In a few cases, spectra of the type described in section 1 are observed also in the very near infrared, the region below 13,000 Å, which has recently become photographically accessible. Apart from that, however, particularly at longer wave lengths, characteristic and simple spectra of a somewhat different kind appear for many diatomic molecules, as, for example, for HCl, HBr, CO, NO, and so forth. It is convenient to distinguish the *spectra in the near infrared*, below about 20 μ, from the *spectra in the far infrared*, above this wave length. In both cases the observations are almost always made in absorption. Thus far a photographic investigation of the spectral region above 1.3 μ is not possible. Thermopiles, bolometers, radiomicrometers, or radiometers must then be used. A more detailed description of the methods of observation is to be found in (6*b*), (38), (39), (40), and (577).

Near infrared spectra. If the absorption spectrum in in the near infrared is observed with a thin layer of the absorbing gas and with small dispersion, in the whole region only a *single intense absorption "line"* is obtained which, with somewhat greater resolution, is found to consist of two maxima close together (Bjerrum's double band). Fig. 30 shows this for HCl, for which this band lies at 3.46 μ. For HF, HBr, HI, and CO the corresponding bands lie at 2.52 μ, 3.90 μ, 4.33 μ, and 4.66 μ, respectively. Such bands do *not* appear for the elementary molecules N$_2$, O$_2$, H$_2$, and so forth. For them there exists no absorption in the entire infrared region (possibly with the exception of the very near infrared, where in some cases bands of the type dealt with in section 1 appear).

If the absorption is observed with thicker layers, the intensity of absorption of the band naturally increases and in addition a *second band* of similar form appears quite weakly, with approximately half the wave length or double the frequency (wave number). If the thickness of the layer is still further increased, up to several meters at atmospheric pressure, a third and possibly even a fourth and a fifth band appear whose wave lengths are a third, a fourth, and a fifth, respectively, of that of the first band; that is to say, their frequencies are three, four, and five times as great. Fig. 31 gives schematically the complete infrared spectrum of HCl. In this figure the lengths of the vertical lines that represent the bands give an indication of the intensity of the bands.

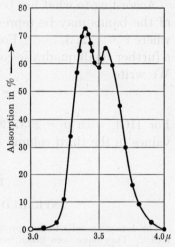

Fig. 30. **Fundamental Absorption Band of HCl in the Near Infrared [after Burmeister (148)].** With the dispersion used, the band has two maxima (Bjerrum double band). With larger dispersion, a further resolution is observed (Fig. 32).

However, the actual decrease

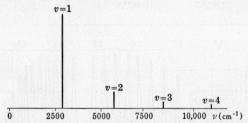

Fig. 31. **Coarse Structure of the Infrared Spectrum of HCl (Schematic).** The intensity actually falls off ten times faster than indicated by the height of the vertical lines; that is, compared to the first band, the second band from the left is ten times, the third band a hundred times, and the fourth a thousand times weaker than drawn.

in intensity is ten times as fast as is indicated in the drawing (that is to say, the second band is ten times, the third is one hundred times, and the fourth is one thousand times weaker than indicated in the diagram).

According to what has been said above, the wave numbers of the bands may be represented approximately by $\nu = a\nu$, where $\nu = 1, 2, 3, \cdots$. For a more accurate representation, a further small quadratic correction term in ν must be added. We write

$$\nu = a\nu - b\nu^2. \qquad (II, 9)$$

For HCl, with $a = 2937.30$ and $b = 51.65$, we obtain the values in the third column of Table 8, which are to be com-

TABLE 8

INFRARED BANDS OF HCl

The data given refer to the zero lines (see p. 118) of the bands of the isotope HCl[35]. They have been taken from Meyer and Levin (491), Herzberg and Spinks (318), and Cleaves and Edwards (158) (partly recalculated).

v	$\nu_{obs.}$	$\nu_{calc.}$	$\Delta G_{obs.}$	$\Delta^2 G_{obs.}$
0	(0)	0		
			2885.9	
1	2885.9	2885.7		103.8
			2782.1	
2	5668.0	5668.0		103.1
			2679.0	
3	8347.0	8347.1		103.3
			2575.7	
4	10,922.7	10,922.8		

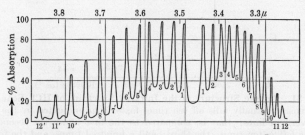

Fig. 32. Fine Structure of the Principal Absorption Band (Fundamental) of HCl in the Near Infrared [after Imes (354)]. The ordinates give the percentage absorption, calculated from the galvanometer deflections. The numbers by the individual lines are the m values. The P branch is to the left, and the R branch is to the right.

pared with the observed values (center of the bands) in the second column. It is seen that the representation of the observed wave numbers by (II, 9) is very good. According to Table 8 and formula (II, 9), the separation of successive bands (fourth column) decreases slowly.

Just as in the visible and ultraviolet spectral regions, by the use of spectroscopes of sufficiently great resolution the bands in the near infrared are resolved into a number of *individual lines* which are arranged in a particularly simple manner. Fig. 32 gives as an example the absorption curve of the principal band of HCl under large dispersion [Imes (354)]. Fig. 33 gives as a further example a spectrogram of the third band of HCl, which lies in the photographically accessible region. As one can see, the HCl band in Fig. 32 consists of a series of almost equidistant lines; however, a line is missing in the center of the band, as in the visible bands above. Going out from the gap (zero gap) there are two branches, which are again called the P branch (toward longer wave lengths) and R branch (toward shorter wave lengths). In Table 9 the measured wave numbers of the lines of the HCl band in

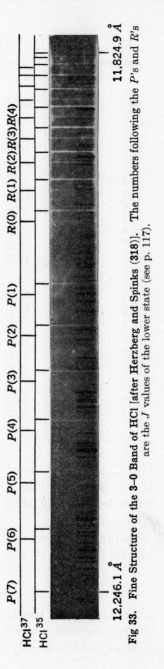

Fig 33. Fine Structure of the 3–0 Band of HCl [after Herzberg and Spinks (318)]. The numbers following the P's and R's are the J values of the lower state (see p. 117).

TABLE 9

FINE STRUCTURE LINES OF THE HCl BAND 3.46μ

The data of Meyer and Levin (491) for the isotope HCl[35] have been used.

m	$\nu_{obs.}(m)$	$\Delta\nu(m)$	$\Delta^2\nu(m)$	$\nu_{obs.} - \nu_{calc.}$ (II, 10)	$\nu_{obs.} - \nu_{calc.}$ (II, 11)
12	3085.62			−3.52	+0.31
		12.86			
11	72.76		−0.83	−2.78	+0.17
		13.69			
10	59.07		−0.50	−2.26	−0.04
		14.19			
9	44.88		−0.73	−1.64	−0.02
		14.92			
8	29.96		−0.75	−1.14	0
		15.67			
7	14.29		−0.84	−0.78	−0.02
		16.51			
6	2997.78		−0.37	−0.66	−0.18
		16.88			
5	80.90		−0.78	−0.36	−0.08
		17.66			
4	63.24		−0.77	−0.11	−0.03
		18.43			
3	44.89		−0.60	−0.09	−0.03
		19.03			
2	25.78		−0.50	−0.06	−0.04
		19.53			
1	06.25			+0.08	+0.08
0					
− 1	2865.09			+0.07	+0.07
		21.53			
− 2	43.56		−0.54	+0.03	+0.01
		22.07			
− 3	21.49		−0.64	+0.05	−0.01
		22.71			
− 4	2798.78		−0.28	+0.04	−0.10
		22.99			
− 5	75.79		−0.77	+0.36	+0.08
		23.76			
− 6	52.03		−0.52	+0.49	+0.03
		24.28			
− 7	27.75		−0.41	+0.75	−0.01
		24.69			
− 8	03.06		−0.64	+1.17	+0.03
		25.33			
− 9	2677.73		−0.43	+1.60	−0.02
		25.76			
−10	51.97		−0.47	+2.18	−0.04
		26.23			
−11	25.74		−0.51	+2.90	−0.05
		26.74			
−12	2599.00			+3.71	−1.12

Fig. 32, as well as their first and second differences, are given. It can be seen that the first differences alter relatively much less rapidly than for the violet CN band previously discussed.

As previously, we can represent the lines of the band very well by formula (II, 8),

$$\nu = c + dm + em^2,$$

where, however, the factor e of the quadratic term is, in comparison to d, smaller than for CN (m is again the running number, which is +1, +2, +3, ⋯ for the R branch and

−1, −2, −3, ⋯ for the P branch). The fifth column of
Table 9 gives the deviations between the observed values
and those calculated using

$$\nu = 2885.90 + 20.577m - 0.3034m^2. \qquad (II, 10)$$

The agreement for $|m| < 8$ is clearly very good. If we wish
to have a formula which also holds exactly for larger values
of m, we must, as above, add a cubic term, gm^3, to (II, 8).
The last column of the table gives the deviations from the
formula

$$\nu = 2885.90 + 20.577m - 0.3034m^2 - 0.00222m^3, \quad (II, 11)$$

which now represents all the lines
very well.[4]

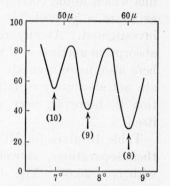

The third infrared band of HCl,
whose spectrogram is given in Fig.
33, consists of two overlapping
bands in consequence of the two
isotopic molecules HCl^{35} and
HCl^{37} [see Chapter III, section
2(g)]. Here the change in the
separation of successive lines is
considerably greater. However,
the lines of this band can also be
represented very accurately by a
quadratic formula (II, 8). Again
possibly a small cubic term has
to be added.

Far infrared spectra. In the
region above 30 μ, for each of the
hydrogen halides a *simple series
of absorption maxima* is observed.

Fig. 34. Part of the Ab-
sorption Spectrum of HCl in
the Far Infrared [after Czerny
(178)]. The ordinates give
the transmission of the gas.
Thus the minima correspond
to the absorption lines. The
numbers in parentheses are
the m values. The scale in
degrees (below) refers to the
spectrometer reading. The
wave-length scale is given
above.

In Fig. 34 some of these maxima are represented for the

---

[4] In calculating the value of $\nu_{calc.}$ according to (II, 11) or (II, 10), it is
usually more convenient to start out from the constant third or second difference (3g and 2e, respectively) and to calculate the values by successive
formation of the second and first differences, rather than to calculate each
term of the formula directly.

case of HCl, according to measurements by Czerny (178). The maxima, on a wave-number scale, are *very nearly equidistant* and can be represented fairly accurately by the formula

$$\nu = f_0 m, \tag{II, 12}$$

where f_0 is a constant characteristic of the particular gas and m is an integer. The wave numbers of the maxima are thus, to a good approximation, integral multiples of the constant f_0. In the example of HCl, the first observed maximum has $m = 4$ and the following maxima have $m = 6 \cdots 11$. Maxima which would correspond to smaller values of m (as well as to $m = 5$) probably occur but lie outside the region investigated. At any rate we can see that this series of absorption maxima is of remarkable simplicity. To be sure, here also, more accurate measurements show that the bands are not absolutely equidistant. The change in the separation is, however, very small compared to the separation itself.

Table 10 gives for HCl the observed wave numbers and their separations, as well as the wave numbers calculated with $f_0 = 20.68$. The slight systematic difference between observed and calculated values can be very well represented by a cubic term (a quadratic term is not present here), so that the accurate formula is

$$\nu = fm - gm^3, \tag{II, 13}$$

where g is very small compared to f. The last column in Table 10 contains the values calculated with $f = 20.79$ and $g = 0.0016$. It is seen that these calculated values agree with the observed values to within less than 0.1 cm^{-1}.

Up to the present time, such simple spectra in the far infrared have been observed only for the halogen hydrides. Theory shows (see Chapter III) that for other molecules, such as CO, for example, they would lie at considerably longer wave lengths, where the investigation would be very difficult and thus far has not been carried out.

TABLE 10

ABSORPTION SPECTRUM OF HCl IN THE FAR INFRARED

[After Czerny (178)]

m	$\nu_{obs.}$	$\Delta\nu_{obs.}$	$\nu_{calc.} = f_0 m$	$\nu_{calc.} = fm - gm^3$
1	......		20.68	20.79
2	......		41.36	41.57
3	......		62.04	62.33
4	83.03		82.72	83.06
5	......	(41.27)	103.40	103.75
6	124.30		124.08	124.39
7	145.03	20.73	144.76	144.98
8	165.51	20.48	165.44	165.50
9	185.86	20.35	186.12	185.94
10	206.38	20.52	206.80	206.30
11	226.50	20.12	227.48	226.55

3. RAMAN SPECTRA

Nature of the Raman effect. When a parallel beam of
light goes through a gas, a liquid, or a transparent solid body,
a small fraction of the light is *scattered* in all directions. The
light beam can therefore be seen from the side (Tyndall
effect). The intensity of the scattered light is inversely
proportional to the fourth power of the wave length; blue
light is much more strongly scattered than red.

If the incident light has a discrete line spectrum and the
spectrum of the scattered light is investigated, it is found
that the scattered light contains exactly the same frequencies
as the light producing it. This scattering is called *Rayleigh
scattering*. However, if, in taking the spectrogram of the
scattered light, the lines that are identical with those of the
light source are strongly overexposed, some weak *additional
lines* are found which do not appear in the spectrum of the
light source. This phenomenon was first noticed by Raman

and Krishnan and independently of them by Landsberg and Mandelstam, and is now commonly called the *Raman effect.*

A comparison of the wave numbers of these additional lines with those of the most intense lines of the incident light (or of the Rayleigh lines) shows that each one of the original lines is accompanied by one or more weak lines (*Raman spectrum*) such that the displacements (in cm^{-1}) of the *Raman lines* from the exciting lines are independent of the frequencies of the latter. If another light source with a different spectrum is used, other Raman lines are obtained for the same scattering substance. However, the displacements from the exciting lines are the same. For different scattering substances, the displacements have different magnitudes. Thus the *Raman displacements* are *characteristic of the scattering substance* under consideration. An explanation for this phenomenon will be given in Chapter III, section 1(d).

The following treats somewhat more fully the observed phenomena only for diatomic gases as scattering substances.

Large Raman displacements. When a spectrograph of small dispersion is used for the observations, for each of the

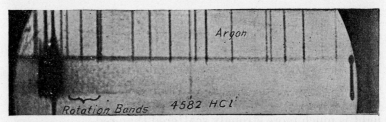

Fig. 35. Raman Spectrum of HCl [after Wood and Dieke (720)].* Above is an argon comparison spectrum. Below is the Hg spectrum scattered by HCl gas. The strongly overexposed line to the left is the Hg line 4358 Å, which gives rise to the weak Raman line 4582 Å, as well as to the weak Raman lines of small displacement (rotational band; see p. 95). To the extreme right is the Hg line 4916 Å.

* The author is greatly indebted to Professor R. W. Wood for this spectrogram.

diatomic gases only one relatively large Raman displacement is found; that is to say, for each exciting line only one Raman line is found and this is to the long-wave-length side. Fig.

35 gives a spectrogram for the case of HCl.   Table 11 gives
the observed Raman displacements for a number of diatomic
gases.   The third column contains the frequencies of the
main infrared bands of the gases under consideration.   It
is seen that, for a particular gas, the *Raman displacements*

TABLE 11

LARGE RAMAN DISPLACEMENTS AND INFRARED FREQUENCIES
OF DIATOMIC GASES

Gas	Raman Displacement $\Delta\nu$ (cm^{-1})	Infrared Frequency ν_0 (cm^{-1})	References
HCl	2886.0	2885.9	(720)
HBr	2558	2559.3	(611) (563)
HI	2233	2330.1	(611) (531)
NO	1877	1879 †	(101)
CO	2145	2144.0	(68) (643)
H$_2$	4160.2 *		(662)
N$_2$	2330.7		(578)
O$_2$	1554.7		(578)

* Refers to the transition $J = 0 \rightarrow J = 0$ (see p. 122).
† This figure is not very accurate.   It was taken from the absorption curve
of Snow, Rawlins, and Rideal (642), the numbering being shifted by one unit
against their selection.

*agree exactly with the frequencies of the main bands in the near
infrared*, insofar as both have been observed.   Therefore, in
these cases the Raman spectrum may be regarded as an
infrared spectrum shifted into the conveniently accessible
visible or ultraviolet region.   It should be noticed, however,
that Raman lines also appear for the elementary molecules
H$_2$, N$_2$, and O$_2$, for which no infrared spectrum occurs.

Small Raman displacements.   If the Raman spectra
are observed with larger dispersion, it is found that, apart
from the aforementioned lines, which now frequently appear
somewhat broadened—that is, more like a band—a *simple
series of equidistant lines* appears in the immediate neighborhood of each of the exciting lines and on both sides of them.
This can just be recognized for the case of HCl in Fig. 35,

for which these lines are rather widely spaced. Fig. 36
shows the similar Raman lines with greater dispersion for the

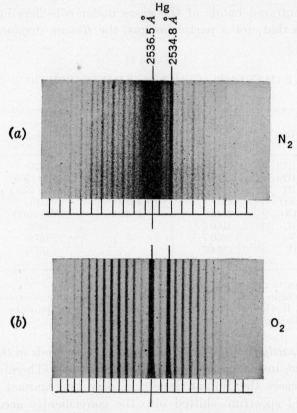

Fig. 36. Raman Spectrum of (a) N_2 **and** (b) O_2: **Small Raman Shifts,
Excited by the Hg Line 2536.5 Å** [after Rasetti (579)].* The exciting line
(longer leading line) is not so strongly overexposed in (b), since it has been
almost completely absorbed by Hg vapor before falling on the plate. The
relatively strong line to the right of the exciting line, which is superimposed
on a Raman line, is the Hg line 2534.8 Å. The dispersion of the enlarged
spectrogram is about 0.37 Å/mm.

* The author is greatly indebted to Professor F. Rasetti for this spectrogram.

cases of N_2 and O_2. The separation of these Raman lines
from the exciting line is only a small fraction of the separation of the Raman lines previously mentioned.

Table 12 gives the observed displacements from the exciting line for the case of HCl. It can be seen from the table that the separations of successive lines (column 3) are very nearly constant. To a good approximation, the line displacements on both sides of the exciting line may be represented by

$$\Delta\nu = \pm(\tfrac{3}{2}p + pm), \qquad (II, 14)$$

where p is the constant separation of successive lines and m takes the integral values given in the first column of Table 12.[5] The values calculated with $p = 41.64$ are shown in the last column of Table 12. The agreement is quite good. If there is a slight residual trend, it can be allowed for by a cubic term, quite analogous to that for the far infrared spectra (see p. 62).

TABLE 12

SMALL RAMAN DISPLACEMENTS
FOR HCl

[After Wood and Dieke (720)]

m	$\Delta\nu_{obs.}$	$\Delta(\Delta\nu)$	$\Delta\nu_{calc.}$
2	+143.8		145.7
3	+183.3	39.5	187.4
4	+232.2	38.9	229.0
1	−101.1		104.1
2	−142.7	41.6	145.7
3	−187.5	44.8	187.4
4	−229.4	41.9	229.0
5	−271.0	41.6	270.7
6	−312.9	41.9	312.3
7	−353.0	40.0	353.9

It is now very striking and noteworthy that the approximately constant *separation p of successive lines is very nearly twice as large as the separation of successive maxima in the far infrared spectrum.* For HCl, for example, $p = 41.64$, while f_0 was equal to 20.68 cm^{-1}. This strongly suggests that the small Raman displacements correspond to the far infrared spectra, just as the large Raman displacements correspond to the near infrared spectra.

[5] Naturally, one could also have chosen as the formula $\Delta\nu = \pm(\tfrac{1}{2}p + pm)$ or $\pm(\tfrac{5}{2}p + pm)$, with a corresponding alteration of the numbering. However, (II, 14) has the advantage that for N_2, for example (see Fig. 36), the first line on both sides of the exciting line has $m = 0$. For HCl, these lines are hidden by the overexposed exciting line. However, on the basis of the later theoretical discussion, there can be no doubt that they are also present for HCl.

The *intensity* of these Raman lines at first increases slightly on going out from the exciting line and then decreases again with increasing m. For N_2, in addition, there also appears a distinct *alternation of intensities*, as may be seen in Fig. 36. The lines are alternately strong and weak.

In one case, that of H_2, a fine structure is observed for the Raman bands of large displacement as well, which is of the same type as that for the small Raman displacements. However, we shall not go into that any further here (see Chapter III).

CHAPTER III

Rotation and Vibration of Diatomic Molecules; Interpretation of Infrared and Raman Spectra

1. INTERPRETATION OF THE PRINCIPAL FEATURES OF THE INFRARED AND RAMAN SPECTRA BY MEANS OF THE MODEL OF THE RIGID ROTATOR AND THE HARMONIC OSCILLATOR

When we compare the observed infrared molecular spectra (see Figs. 31–34) with an atomic spectrum such as that of the H atom (Fig. 6), we see at once that even qualitatively a fundamental difference exists. To be sure, we have in both cases series of lines or bands. However, while for atoms the line separation in a series decreases rapidly (Rydberg series), for infrared molecular spectra it is approximately constant. Therefore we cannot hope to be able to explain these infrared molecular spectra by the same model as for atomic spectra—namely, by the stationary states of an electron revolving about a core—but we must search for other models.

Actually, for a diatomic molecule, *two additional modes of motion*, which do not occur for atoms, are possible, and these have to be considered as possible causes of the quite different kind of spectra: First, the molecule can *rotate* as a whole about an axis passing through the center of gravity and perpendicular to the line joining the nuclei (internuclear axis), and, second, the atoms can *carry out vibrations* relative to each other. We have now to investigate what type of spectrum would be expected on the basis of the quantum theory for such a rotating or vibrating system and to compare it with the observed infrared spectrum in order to find out in what way this spectrum is produced. Conversely, this will help us to come to conclusions concerning the structure of molecules.

(a) Rigid Rotator

The molecule as a rigid rotator. We shall begin with the simplest possible model of a rotating molecule, the so-called dumbbell model (Fig. 37). We shall consider the two atoms of masses m_1 and m_2 to be point-like and fastened at a distance r apart to the ends of a weightless, rigid rod. In so doing, we neglect, on the one hand, the finite extent of the atoms and, on the other, the fact that in actuality the atoms are not rigidly bound to each other but that their distance can alter under the influence of their rotation. The neglect of the first factor is certainly well justified, since the mass of the atom is practically concentrated in the nucleus, which has a radius of only about 10^{-12} cm, while the internuclear distance in a molecule is of the order of magnitude of 10^{-8} cm (see below). The effect of the neglect of the second factor is in general also very small, as we shall see later.

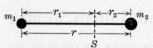

Fig. 37. Dumbbell Model of a Diatomic Molecule.

In *classical mechanics* the energy of rotation of a rigid body is given by

$$E = \tfrac{1}{2}Iw^2 = \frac{(Iw)^2}{2I} = \frac{P^2}{2I}. \qquad \text{(III, 1)}$$

Here w is the angular velocity of the rotation; that is,

$$w = 2\pi\nu_{\text{rot.}}, \qquad \text{(III, 2)}$$

where $\nu_{\text{rot.}}$ is the number of rotations per second (*rotational frequency*). Furthermore, I is the *moment of inertia* of the system about the axis of rotation ($I = \Sigma m_i r_i^2$), and $P = Iw$, the *angular momentum* of the system. Of course, for a system freely suspended in space, the axis of rotation passes through the center of gravity.

According to (III, 1), the rotational energy depends essentially on the moment of inertia. For the dumbbell model this is

$$I = m_1 r_1^2 + m_2 r_2^2,$$

where

$$r_1 = \frac{m_2}{m_1 + m_2} r \quad \text{and} \quad r_2 = \frac{m_1}{m_1 + m_2} r \quad \text{(III, 3)}$$

are the distances of the masses m_1 and m_2 from the center of gravity and r is the distance of the two mass points from each other (see Fig. 37). Substitution gives

$$I = \frac{m_1 m_2}{m_1 + m_2} r^2 ; \quad \text{(III, 4)}$$

that is, the moment of inertia is the same as that of a mass point of mass μ at a distance r from the axis, where

$$\mu = \frac{m_1 m_2}{m_1 + m_2} . \quad \text{(III, 5)}$$

μ is called the *reduced mass* of the molecule.

Thus, instead of considering the rotation of the dumbbell, we can equally well consider the rotation of a single mass point of mass μ at a fixed distance r from the rotational axis, a system that is called a *simple rigid rotator*.

Energy levels. In order to determine the possible energy states of such a rigid rotator according to the *quantum theory*, we have to solve the corresponding Schrödinger equation (I, 12). In this we have to put $m = \mu$ and $V = 0$—the latter since no potential energy is associated with the rotation so long as the rotator can be regarded as completely rigid. Thus we have the equation

$$\frac{\partial^2 \psi}{\partial x^2} + \frac{\partial^2 \psi}{\partial y^2} + \frac{\partial^2 \psi}{\partial z^2} + \frac{8\pi^2 \mu}{h^2} E\psi = 0. \quad \text{(III, 6)}$$

The solution of this equation is comparatively simple [see, for example, Sommerfeld (16)] but will not be carried out here. The result is that solutions ψ that are single-valued, finite, and continuous and disappear at infinity (see p. 12) occur only for certain values of E—namely, the eigenvalues

$$E = \frac{h^2 J(J + 1)}{8\pi^2 \mu r^2} = \frac{h^2 J(J + 1)}{8\pi^2 I} , \quad \text{(III, 7)}$$

where the *rotational quantum number* J can take the integral values 0, 1, 2, $\cdots$.   Thus we have a *series of discrete energy levels whose energy increases quadratically with increasing J* (Fig. 38).

If we compare formula (III, 7) with the classical formula (III, 1), we see that the classical *angular momentum* of the system in the quantum state J is

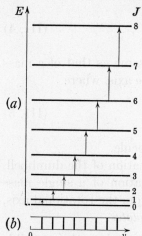

$$P = \frac{h}{2\pi} \sqrt{J(J+1)} \approx \frac{h}{2\pi}J. \quad \text{(III, 8)}$$

A more detailed calculation shows that this formula holds also in quantum mechanics for the angular momentum of the system.   Just as for the atom, the angular momentum can take only the discrete values (III, 8).   *The rotational quantum number J thus gives approximately the angular momentum in units $h/2\pi$.*   In the following we shall use the heavy-type quantum numbers as symbols for the corresponding angular momenta.   Thus $\mathbf{J}$ means an angular momentum vector of magnitude $\sqrt{J(J+1)}(h/2\pi) \approx J(h/2\pi)$.

Fig. 38. Energy Levels and Infrared Transitions of a Rigid Rotator. (*a*) The energy level diagram. (*b*) The resulting spectrum (schematic).

Since only certain discrete energy values and angular momenta of the rigid rotator are possible, it follows that *only certain rotational frequencies* are possible.   Since classically the angular momentum $P = Iw$, the angular velocity is [see (III, 8)]

$$w = \frac{h}{2\pi I} \sqrt{J(J+1)} \approx \frac{h}{2\pi I} J.$$

Therefore, according to (III, 2), the rotational frequency is

$$\nu_{\text{rot.}} = \frac{h}{4\pi^2 I} \sqrt{J(J+1)} \approx \frac{h}{4\pi^2 I} J. \quad \text{(III, 9)}$$

The rotational frequency thus increases approximately linearly with J.

It should be noticed that the frequency of rotation can be defined only with the help of the classical formula $P = I w$. In quantum mechanics it has, strictly speaking, no exactly definable meaning.

According to the old quantum theory, the angular momentum is exactly $J(h/2\pi)$, and therefore, according to (III, 1), the energy of the rotator

$$E = \frac{h^2}{8\pi^2 I} J^2. \qquad (III, 10)$$

As we shall see later, experiments have decided unambiguously in favor of the wave mechanical expression (III, 7).

Eigenfunctions. The eigenfunctions ψ_r of the rigid rotator are the so-called *surface harmonics*. They are exactly the same functions as those which give the direction dependency of the eigenfunctions of the hydrogen atom (see A.A., p. 39)—namely (apart from a constant factor),

$$\psi_r = P_J^{|M|} (\cos \theta) \, e^{iM\phi}, \qquad (III, 11)$$

where ϕ is the azimuth about a fixed axis (z axis) and θ is the angle with this axis. M is a second quantum number which takes the values

$$M = J, (J - 1), (J - 2), \cdots, -J. \qquad (III, 12)$$

It corresponds exactly to the magnetic quantum number M_J for atoms (see p. 26). $P_J^{|M|} (\cos \theta)$ is a function of the angle θ, the so-called *associated Legendre polynomial* [see, for example, Sommerfeld (16)]. The broken-line curves in Fig. 39 show the variation of the eigenfunctions (III, 11) in a plane ($\phi = 0$ and $\phi = 180°$, respectively) for $J = 0, 1, 2,$ and 3. The value of the function is plotted from the origin in every direction in the plane of the figure. The sign is indicated by a $+$ or $-$ in the corresponding loop.

The probability of finding the system oriented in the direction θ, ϕ is

$$\psi_r \psi_r^* = [P_J^{|M|} (\cos \theta)]^2. \qquad (III, 13)$$

Since $\psi_r \psi_r^*$ is independent of ϕ, the *probability distribution* is rotationally symmetric about the fixed axis. The dependence of

$\psi_r \psi_r{}^*$ on the angle θ is shown by the full curves in Fig. 39. It is seen that, for $J = 0$, all directions are equally probable, while, with increasing J, more and more preferred directions exist. For $|M| = J$, as J increases, the classical picture of a rotation

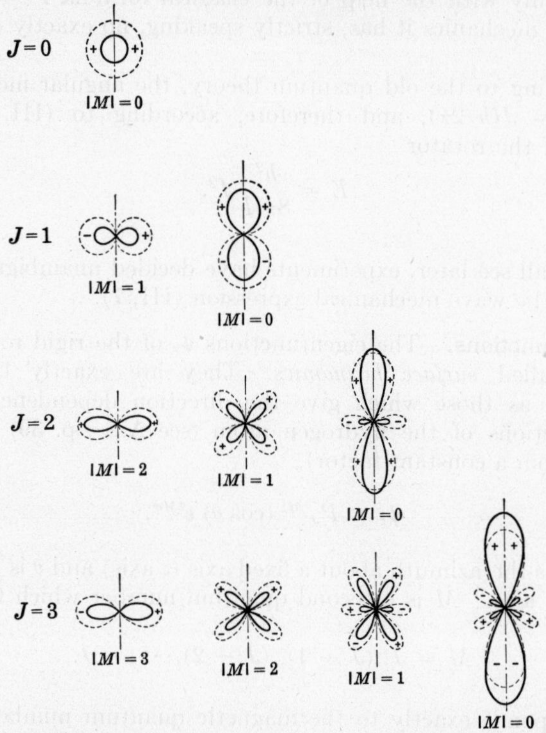

Fig. 39. **Eigenfunctions (Broken Curves) and Probability Distributions (Solid Curves) for the Rotator in the States $J = 0, 1, 2, 3$.** The value of the eigenfunction and the probability density distribution corresponding to a given orientation of the rotator is plotted in a polar diagram from the mid-point of each individual diagram in the direction under consideration. The figures represent plane sections through the spatial polar diagrams. All the figures are drawn to the same scale.

about the z axis is slowly approached; that is to say, the most probable values of θ lie in the neighborhood of $90°$.

Spectrum. According to classical electrodynamics, an intramolecular motion leads to radiation of light only if a *changing dipole moment* is associated with it. For a rigid rotator this can be caused by the rotating mass point possessing a charge or being associated with a *permanent dipole moment* that lies in the direction of the perpendicular from the mass point to the axis of rotation.   The latter alternative occurs in all molecules that consist of unlike atoms, since for them the centers of gravity of the positive and negative charges do not coincide, which gives rise to a permanent dipole moment.   During the rotation the component of the dipole in a fixed direction changes periodically with a frequency equal to the rotational frequency; that is to say, classically, the frequency $\nu_{rot.}$ should be radiated.   For molecules consisting of two like atoms, no dipole is present and therefore no radiation takes place.   Conversely, only if a permanent dipole moment is present can an infrared frequency be absorbed and thereby a rotation of the system be produced or a rotation already present be increased.   According to classical theory, the absorbed or emitted spectrum of the rotator is continuous, since $\nu_{rot.}$ can take any value.

According to *quantum theory*, emission takes place in a transition from a higher to a lower level, while absorption of a suitable light quantum produces a transition from a lower to a higher level.   The wave number of the emitted or absorbed line is, according to (I, 6),

$$\nu = \frac{E'}{hc} - \frac{E''}{hc} , \qquad (III, 14)$$

where E' and E'' are the rotational energies (III, 7) in the upper and lower states, respectively. [Throughout the following we shall indicate quantities associated with the upper state by a single prime mark (') and those associated with the lower state by two prime marks ('')]. $E/hc = F(J)$ is the *rotational term*[1] (units cm^{-1}), which, according to (III, 7), is given by

$$F(J) = \frac{h}{8\pi^2 cI} J(J + 1) = BJ(J + 1), \quad (III, 15)$$

---

[1] It should be observed that there is no minus sign in the definition for term values, in contrast to what is usual for atoms (see p. 9).

where the constant

$$B = \frac{h}{8\pi^2 cI} \qquad \text{(III, 16)}$$

is called the *rotational constant*. Apart from a factor, it is the reciprocal moment of inertia.

We can now rewrite (III, 14) in the following way:

$$\nu = F(J') - F(J'') = BJ'(J' + 1) - BJ''(J'' + 1). \quad \text{(III, 17)}$$

In order to calculate the frequency that is actually emitted or absorbed, it is necessary to know the *selection rule for the quantum number J*. According to Chapter I, p. 16, the selection rule is obtained by investigating the integrals (I, 16), in which p is now the dipole moment and the eigen-functions of the rotator are substituted for ψ. Since the components of p are, in this case, simply proportional to the corresponding co-ordinates of the rotator, we can see immediately that the integrals (I, 16) will disappear except when the dipole moment differs from zero; that is to say, emission or absorption will take place only when the dipole moment is not zero, in agreement with the results of classical theory. Apart from that, a more detailed calculation [see Sommerfeld (16)] shows that, if the integrals are not to vanish, we must have

$$J' = J'' \pm 1; \; \textit{that is,} \; \Delta J = J' - J'' = \pm 1. \quad \text{(III, 18)}$$

Thus the quantum number J can "jump" only by one unit.

For our choice of notation we have here $J' > J''$ (since J' refers to the upper state), and therefore only $\Delta J = +1$ comes into consideration. Consequently we obtain for the emitted or absorbed lines of the rotator

$$\nu = F(J'' + 1) - F(J'') = B(J'' + 1)(J'' + 2)$$

$$- BJ''(J'' + 1) = 2B(J'' + 1),$$

where J'' can take all integral values 0, 1, 2, $\cdots$. In the future, for simplicity we shall write J for J'' when only the J value of the lower state occurs, so that

$$\nu = 2B(J + 1); \qquad J = 0, 1, 2, \cdots. \qquad \text{(III, 19)}$$

Thus the spectrum of the simple rigid rotator consists of a series of equidistant lines. The first of these $(J = 0)$ lies at $2B$ and the separation of successive lines is also $2B$. The corresponding transitions are indicated in Fig. 38, and the spectrum is drawn schematically below. The comparison of this theoretical spectrum with experiment will be dealt with in subsection (c).

According to (III, 9) and (III, 16), the *rotational frequency* is

$$\nu_{\text{rot.}} = c\,2B\sqrt{J(J + 1)} \approx c\,2BJ; \qquad \text{(III, 20)}$$

that is, the rotational frequency in any given state of the rotator is approximately equal to the frequency of the line that has this state as upper state.

When the formula (III, 10) of the *old quantum theory* is used in place of the wave mechanical expression (III, 7) for the energy of the rotator, the wave numbers of the absorbed spectral lines are easily found to be

$$\nu = 2BJ + B. \qquad \text{(III, 21)}$$

According to this, the first line would lie at $\nu = B$ and not at $\nu = 2B$. The line separation, however, is the same as in wave mechanics.

(b) Harmonic Oscillator

The molecule as a harmonic oscillator. The simplest possible assumption that we can make about the vibration of a molecule is that we are dealing with a *harmonic* (sine form) vibration of two point-like atoms relative to one another. Such a motion of the two atoms can easily be reduced to the harmonic vibration of a single mass point about an equilibrium position—that is, to the model of the *harmonic oscillator*.

In classical mechanics a harmonic oscillator can be defined as a mass point of mass m which is acted upon by a force F proportional to the distance x from the equilibrium position and directed toward the equilibrium position. Therefore

$$F = - kx = m \frac{d^2x}{dt^2}. \qquad \text{(III, 22)}$$

The proportionality factor k is called the *force constant*. The well-known solution of this differential equation is

$$x = x_0 \sin(2\pi\nu_{\text{osc.}}t + \phi), \qquad \text{(III, 23)}$$

where the vibrational frequency

$$\nu_{\text{osc.}} = \frac{1}{2\pi}\sqrt{\frac{k}{m}}, \qquad \text{(III, 24)}$$

as may be immediately verified by substitution into (III, 22), and where x_0 is the amplitude of the vibration and ϕ is a phase constant dependent on the initial conditions.

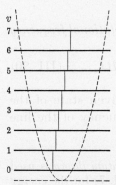

Fig. 40. Potential Curve, Energy Levels, and Infrared Transitions of the Harmonic Oscillator. The short vertical lines representing the transitions are spread apart from one another in a horizontal direction for the sake of clarity only. The abscissa for the broken curve is the displacement from the equilibrium position (minimum).

Since the force is always the negative derivative of the potential energy V, it follows from $F = -kx$ that, for the harmonic oscillator,

$$V = \tfrac{1}{2}kx^2 = 2\pi^2 m\nu_{\text{osc.}}^2 \, x^2. \qquad \text{(III, 25)}$$

We can therefore also define a harmonic oscillator as a system whose potential energy is proportional to the square of the distance from its equilibrium position; that is to say, the *potential energy curve is a parabola* (broken curve in Fig. 40).

The restoring force exerted by the two atoms of a molecule on one another when they are displaced from their equilibrium position is, at least approximately, proportional to the displacement. If we assume that this relation holds exactly, it follows immediately that the atoms in the molecule will execute harmonic vibrations when they are left to themselves after being displaced from their equilibrium positions.   For the first atom, of mass m_1 (according to Newton's law: mass $\times$ acceleration = force),

$$m_1 \frac{d^2 r_1}{dt^2} = - k(r - r_e),$$

and, correspondingly for the second atom, of mass m_2,

$$m_2 \frac{d^2 r_2}{dt^2} = - k(r - r_e).$$

Here r_1 and r_2 are the distances of the two atoms from the center of gravity (see Fig. 37), r is the momentary distance of the two atoms from each other, and r_e is the equilibrium distance.   By substitution of (III, 3) we obtain from both equations

$$\frac{m_2 m_1}{m_1 + m_2} \frac{d^2 r}{dt^2} = - k(r - r_e),$$

or, when the reduced mass μ is introduced according to (III, 5) and r, under the differential sign, is replaced by $(r - r_e)$ (which is allowed, since r_e is constant),

$$\mu \frac{d^2 (r - r_e)}{dt^2} = - k(r - r_e). \qquad \text{(III, 26)}$$

This equation is identical with the general equation (III, 22) for the harmonic oscillator, except that x is replaced by $(r - r_e)$, the displacement from the equilibrium position. Thus we have reduced the vibrations of the two atoms of a molecule to the vibration of a single mass point of mass μ, whose amplitude equals the amplitude of the change of nuclear distance in the molecule.

From (III, 26) in combination with (III, 24) it follows immediately that the classical *vibrational frequency* of the molecule is

$$\nu_{\text{osc.}} = \frac{1}{2\pi} \sqrt{\frac{k}{\mu}}. \qquad \text{(III, 27)}$$

Whereas, for the rotator, classically all rotational frequencies can occur, here even on the classical theory only one vibrational frequency is possible whose magnitude depends on the two atomic masses and the force constant. However, classically the amplitude, and therefore the energy, of this vibration can assume any desired value.

Energy levels. Also in the quantum mechanical treatment the vibrations of a diatomic molecule can be reduced to the vibrations of a harmonic oscillator of mass μ [see, for example, Kronig (31)]. We now define the harmonic oscillator by its potential energy (III, 25), and substitute this in the Schrödinger equation (I, 12). We then obtain

$$\frac{\partial^2 \psi}{\partial x^2} + \frac{8\pi^2 \mu}{h^2} (E - \tfrac{1}{2}kx^2)\psi = 0. \qquad (III, 28)$$

The mathematical discussion of this equation [see Sommerfeld (16)] shows that solutions that are single-valued, finite, and continuous and vanish at infinity do not exist for all values of E but only for the E values

$$E(v) = \frac{h}{2\pi} \sqrt{\frac{k}{\mu}} (v + \tfrac{1}{2}) = h\nu_{\text{osc.}}(v + \tfrac{1}{2}), \qquad (III, 29)$$

where the *vibrational quantum number* v can take only integral values, 0, 1, 2, $\cdots$. The values (III, 29) are the only *energy values* allowed by quantum theory *for the harmonic oscillator* and therefore also for the harmonically vibrating molecule. They are *half-integral multiples* of $h\nu_{\text{osc.}}$, where $\nu_{\text{osc.}}$ is the vibration frequency of the oscillator calculated from (III, 27) (that is, classically). Sometimes we also speak of half-integral vibrational quanta. The energy level diagram of the harmonic oscillator is represented in Fig. 40. From what has been said, it consists of a series of *equidistant levels*.

It should be particularly noted that (in contrast to the rotator) the state of lowest energy, $v = 0$, does not have $E = 0$ but $E(0) = \tfrac{1}{2}h\nu_{\text{osc.}}$. Thus, even in the lowest vibrational state, vibrational energy is present which is called *zero-point energy*. In spite of this *zero-point vibration* the state $v = 0$ is sometimes called, for the sake of brevity, the *vibrationless state*.

According to the old quantum theory, the energy of the harmonic oscillator was found to be $h\nu_{osc.}v$ (*integral* vibrational quanta). Thus, apart from the constant zero-point energy, the energy levels according to quantum mechanics are the same as on the old quantum theory.

If we transform energy values to *term values* (by dividing by hc), we obtain for the vibrational terms

$$G(v) = \frac{E(v)}{hc} = \frac{\nu_{osc.}}{c}(v + \tfrac{1}{2}). \qquad \text{(III, 30)}$$

In band spectroscopy, $\nu_{osc.}/c$ is generally designated by ω; that is,

$$G(v) = \omega(v + \tfrac{1}{2}). \qquad \text{(III, 31)}$$

ω is the vibrational frequency measured in cm^{-1}. The actual number of vibrations per second is c times as great.

Eigenfunctions. Without going into the details of the calculation, we give as broken curves in Fig. 41 the *vibrational eigenfunctions* ψ_v resulting from (III, 28) for $v = 0$, $1, 2, 3, 4$, and 10. The full curves are the resulting *probability density distributions* $\psi_v\psi_v{}^* = |\psi_v|^2$. The amplitude of the corresponding classical vibrational motion is obtained from the intersection of the potential energy curve (broken curve in Fig. 40) with the corresponding energy level, since classically the turning points are the positions at which the total energy is entirely potential energy. These classical turning points are indicated in Fig. 41 by vertical lines on the abscissa axis. It can be seen that the wave mechanical probability density distribution is essentially different from zero just in the classical vibrational region, but that the probability density is also appreciable somewhat outside this region, although it falls off exponentially there. While classically the oscillator stays for the greater part of the time at the turning points, wave mechanically, for $v \neq 0$, there is a broad maximum of the probability distribution in the neighborhood of each of the classical turning points but lying somewhat more toward the middle. Apart from that, according to wave mechanics, for $v > 1$, between the two outermost maxima there are other maxima for which there is no classical analogue.

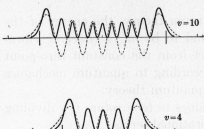

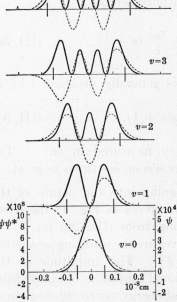

The curve of the probability density distribution for the lowest vibrational state is particularly important. Here the difference between the classical motion and the wave mechanical probability density is the greatest; instead of the two turning points there is now only a maximum in the middle. Of course, classically, the lowest state of the oscillator is that for which the system is at rest at the minimum of the potential curve (Fig. 40). According to quantum theory, such a state would contradict the Heisenberg uncertainty relation, since the position *and* velocity would then be exactly defined.

Fig. 41. **Eigenfunctions** (**Broken Curves**) **and Probability Density Distributions** (**Solid Curves**) **of the Harmonic Oscillator for** $v = 0, 1, 2, 3, 4,$ **and 10.** The abscissae give the displacement from the equilibrium position in 10^{-8} cm. The scales for abscissae and ordinates are the same for all the figures. However, they are given explicitly only for the lowest figure ($v = 0$). The functions are plotted for $\mu_A = 10$ and $\omega = 1000$. For other values they are obtained simply by altering the scale (see text).

The curves in Fig. 41 are drawn for the case $\mu_A = 10$, $\omega = 1000$ cm^{-1} ($\mu_A = $ reduced mass in atomic-weight units).   Corresponding curves for other cases may be obtained by changing the scale on the abscissa axis in inverse proportion to $\sqrt{\mu_A \omega}$.

According to what has been said, *we cannot in wave mechanics speak of a proper vibrational motion with a definite frequency*, $\nu_{\text{osc.}}$, any more than we can speak of electron orbits for atoms. Only the probability distribution of position (and momentum; see below) can be given. In quantum mechanics, $\nu_{\text{osc.}}$ has only a formal meaning— namely, that of the constant $(1/2\pi)\sqrt{k/\mu}$. When we speak of the vibrational frequency in the following, we shall always mean this constant, which gives the frequency that the system would have for classical motion (however, see below).

The vibrational quantum number v gives the number of nodes of the corresponding eigenfunction (that is, the number of times ψ_v goes through zero), as can be seen from Fig. 41.

The *mathematical form of the eigenfunctions* is

$$\psi_v = N_v e^{-\frac{\alpha}{2}x^2} H_v(\sqrt{\alpha}x). \tag{III, 32}$$

In this, N_v is a normalization constant, $\alpha = (2\pi\mu\nu_{\text{osc.}}/h$, and $H_v(\sqrt{\alpha}x)$ is a so-called Hermite polynomial of the vth degree [see Sommerfeld (16)]. Consequently, the probability distribution for the state $v = 0$ [since $H_0(\sqrt{\alpha}x) = 1$] is given by

$$\psi_0{}^2 = N_0{}^2 e^{-\alpha x^2} \tag{III, 33}$$

—that is, by a simple Gauss error function.

In Fig. 42 the *probability distribution for the momentum* (that is, also for the velocity) is plotted for the state $v = 0$, as obtained from wave mechanics. Since, as this curve shows, the velocity in this lowest state is not always zero (other than in the classical theory), the energy is also not zero, and hence the zero-point energy results. The two curves for the probability distributions of position and momentum for $v = 0$ give the minimum uncertainty of the position and momentum (or velocity) that is compatible with the Heisenberg uncertainty principle.

As for $v = 0$, the momentum distribution curves for $v > 0$ have the same form as the corresponding positional probability distribution curves, except that the meaning of the ordinates and abscissae is altered [see Elsasser (205)]. It is therefore unnecessary to reproduce them here again.

Classically, the time it takes the oscillator to go from one turning point to the other is half the period—that is, $1/2\nu_{osc.}$. In quantum mechanics neither the turning points nor the velocities are sharply defined. But we can see from the range of velocities in Fig. 42 (or in corresponding diagrams for $v \neq 0$) that the

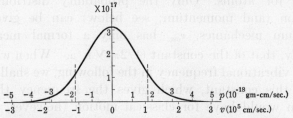

Fig. 42. **Probability Distribution of the Momentum (Velocity) in the State $v = 0$ of the Harmonic Oscillator.** The upper abscissae scale gives the momentum, the lower the velocity. The ordinate scale gives the probability of the momentum (per unit momentum). The broken vertical lines give the maximum classical momentum (velocity)—that is, when the oscillator is passing through the equilibrium position. The curve is plotted for $\omega = 1000$ cm^{-1} and $\mu_A = 10$.

average time for the oscillator to cover an appreciable fraction of the possible range of x values is of the order $1/2\nu_{osc.}$. Thus we may consider $\nu_{osc.}$ in quantum theory as a sort of *average vibration frequency*.

Spectrum. If the molecule in its equilibrium position has a *dipole moment*, as is always the case for molecules consisting of unlike atoms, this dipole moment will in general change if the nuclear distance changes. More precisely, the dipole moment will change, to a first approximation, linearly with the change in nuclear distance $(r - r_e)$. That is to say, the dipole moment changes with a frequency equal to the frequency of the mechanical vibration. On the basis of *classical* electrodynamics, this would lead to a radiation of the frequency $\nu_{osc.}$. Conversely, the oscillator could be set in vibration by absorption of the frequency $\nu_{osc.}$.

Quantum theoretically, emission of radiation takes place as a result of a transition of the oscillator from a higher to a lower state, and absorption takes place by the converse process. The wave number of the emitted or absorbed light is given by

$$\nu = G(v') - G(v'').   \text{(III, 34)}$$

However, as for the rigid rotator, transitions between any two levels are not possible but only those for which $\int p\psi_{v'}(x)\psi_{v''}{}^*(x)dx$ does not vanish (see p. 16). In this expression, as before, x is the displacement of the oscillator from the equilibrium position—that is, $r - r_e$ for the molecule—$\psi_{v'}$ and $\psi_{v''}$ are the eigenfunctions of the upper and lower states, and p is the dipole moment, which alters linearly with x. Therefore the integral becomes, apart from a constant factor, $\int x\psi_{v'}(x)\psi_{v''}{}^*(x)dx$. A more detailed calculation shows [see Sommerfeld (16)] that this integral differs from zero only if v' and v'' differ by unity; that is to say, *the selection rule for the vibrational quantum number for the harmonic oscillator* is

$$\Delta v = \pm 1.   \text{(III, 35)}$$

Using (III, 31), we obtain

$$\nu = G(v + 1) - G(v) = \omega;   \text{(III, 36)}$$

that is, quantum theoretically as well as classically, the *frequency of the radiated light is equal to the frequency of the oscillator* $(\nu_{osc.} = c \cdot \omega)$. This is true no matter what the v value of the initial state may be. The allowed transitions are indicated by vertical lines in Fig. 40. It is seen from this figure that they all give rise to the same frequency.

In anticipation it should perhaps be remarked here that, as soon as the system is no longer exactly a harmonic oscillator, transitions can also appear with $\Delta v > 1$, even though very weakly, whereas for the rotator the selection rule (III, 18) holds strictly, even if the system deviates from the model of the rigid rotator.

For a *molecule with like atoms* (N_2, O_2, $\cdots$), the dipole moment p is always zero, and therefore no transitions between the different vibrational levels occur; there is *no infrared emission or absorption.*[2]

(c) Comparison with the Observed Infrared Spectrum

If we compare the theoretical results so far obtained for the spectra of the rigid rotator and harmonic oscillator with the observed absorption spectra of the halogen hydrides, for example (see Figs. 31 and 34), we are led to the following interpretation: Since the spectrum in the far infrared consists of a series of nearly equidistant lines, it results from the rotation of the molecule about an axis through the center of gravity and perpendicular to the line joining the nuclei, the molecule behaving approximately like a rigid rotator (rotation spectrum). On the other hand, the spectrum in the near infrared, since it consists essentially of a single very intense line, results from the vibration of the molecule, the molecule behaving approximately like a harmonic oscillator (vibration spectrum). The weak occurrence of bands with nearly two and three times the frequency would then be connected with the deviations from the harmonic oscillator.

This interpretation of the infrared spectra has been confirmed by a large amount of experimental material. For the moment we shall verify it for only one simple example.

For HCl, the separation of the lines in the far infrared is 20.68 cm^{-1} [the empirical constant f_0 in (II, 12) (see Fig. 34)]. If this spectrum is a rotation spectrum, the number 20.68 cm^{-1} must be equal to $2B$; that is, $B = 10.34$ cm^{-1} (see III, 19). From this it follows, according to (III, 16), that the moment of inertia of HCl is $I = 2.71 \cdot 10^{-40}$ gm cm^2 and from this, using $\mu = 1.63 \cdot 10^{-24}$ gm, that the nuclear distance $r = 1.29 \cdot 10^{-8}$ cm. This value is just of the order of magnitude that one would expect on the basis of values of atomic and molecular radii obtained from gas viscosity and crystal structure measurements. We can therefore take it

---

[2] This holds only for dipole radiation. By quadrupole radiation, a transition probability can be produced, but it is extremely small [see Herzberg (315) and James and Coolidge (362); see also p. 305].

as proved that the *far infrared spectrum is a rotation spectrum*. From the value obtained for the rotational constant B, the frequencies of rotation in the quantum states $J = 1, 2, 3,$ and 4 are, according to (III, 20), 8.7, 15.2, 21.5, and 27.8 · 10^{11} sec^{-1}. The periods of rotation are the reciprocals of these values—that is, 1.15, 0.66, 0.46, and 0.36 · 10^{-12} sec., respectively.

In the near infrared spectrum, HCl has a single intense band at 2885.9 cm^{-1} (see p. 56 f.). If we are dealing here with a vibration spectrum, according to (III, 36) we have $\omega = 2885.9$. This means that the vibrational frequency is $\nu_{osc.} = \omega c = 8.65 \cdot 10^{13}$ sec^{-1}., which is about one hundred times greater than the rotational frequency. The period of vibration is $1.17 \cdot 10^{-14}$ sec. From $\nu_{osc.}$ and (III, 27), the force constant $k = 4.806 \cdot 10^5$ dynes/cm. If we use (III, 25) to calculate the energy required to increase the nuclear separation by 1 Å, we obtain the value $\sim$14 volts, which is of the order of magnitude of the energy set free in chemical reactions. Therefore it is quite possible to interpret the *near infrared spectrum as a vibration spectrum*.

In explaining the infrared absorption spectrum we might also have tried to explain the far infrared spectrum as a vibration spectrum and the near infrared spectrum as a rotation spectrum. Apart from the difficulty of explaining the structure of the spectrum on this assumption, we would have obtained nuclear distances ten times smaller than the known values for atomic and molecular radii (see above) and a force constant incompatible with the observed strength of chemical binding.

The above considerations have also been applied to the infrared spectra of other molecules, and lead to similar results. Also the discussion of Raman spectra (see below) confirms the explanation of the far and near infrared spectra as rotation spectra and vibration spectra, respectively.

Conversely, if we accept this explanation as correct, we can determine the *position of rotational and vibrational levels* with great accuracy from the observed infrared spectrum of a molecule. From the former we obtain the *moment of inertia*, the *nuclear distance*, and the *rotational frequency* of the molecule, and from the latter we obtain the *vibrational frequency* and the *force constant*. This determination of nuclear distances of molecules is of particular importance, since they can be obtained more accurately from molecular spectra than by any other method.

To be sure, rotation spectra have been measured for only a very few molecules. However, we shall describe later other methods which allow us to obtain rotational levels (and thereby the nuclear distance) from spectra in the near infrared and in the visible and ultraviolet regions.

(d) The Raman Spectrum of the Rigid Rotator and of the Harmonic Oscillator

As we have seen (p. 63 f.), the Raman effect consists of a frequency shift of the light scattered by gases (or by liquids or solids), the amount of the shift being characteristic of the substance considered.

Classical theory of light scattering and of the Raman effect. If an atom or molecule is brought into an electric field F, an electric dipole moment P is induced in the system; the center of gravity of the positive charges is moved a small distance in one direction, and that of the negative charges is moved in the opposite direction. The resulting dipole moment is proportional to the field; that is,

$$P = \alpha F, \tag{III, 37}$$

where α is called the *polarizability*.

In general, the magnitude of the induced dipole moment depends on the orientation of the system to the field. For a diatomic molecule, for example, a field lying along the internuclear axis obviously induces a dipole moment of different magnitude from that induced by a field at right angles to the axis. If we choose the system of co-ordinates so that the z axis lies in the symmetry axis of the molecule, from symmetry grounds

$$P_x = \alpha_{xx} F_x, \qquad P_y = \alpha_{yy} F_y, \qquad P_z = \alpha_{zz} F_z; \tag{III, 38}$$

that is, if the direction of the field lies in one of the axial directions, the dipole moment produced will also lie in the direction of this axis.   For a diatomic molecule, $\alpha_{xx} = \alpha_{yy}$, since the x direction is in no way distinguished from the y direction.   If F does not lie in one of the axial directions, the direction of P does not, in general, coincide with that of F.   In every case, however, the magnitude of P is proportional to the magnitude of F [see equation (III, 37)]. A more detailed calculation shows that the proportionality factor α plotted in the various directions from the origin gives an ellipsoid, the so-called *polarizability ellipsoid*.   For diatomic molecules this is an ellipsoid of rotation, with the line joining the nuclei as axis.

If a light wave of frequency ν' falls on an atom or molecule, there is a varying electric field

$$F = F_0 \sin 2\pi\nu't, \tag{III, 39}$$

where t is the time.   This field produces a varying dipole moment, which itself causes an emission of light of the same frequency as the incident light.   This is the so-called *Rayleigh scattering*, which is responsible for the phenomena of dispersion and of the Tyndall effect.   For visible and ultraviolet incident light, essentially only the electrons move under the influence of the alternating electric field and produce the dipole moment, since the nuclei cannot follow the rapid oscillations.

If the nuclear distance alters, obviously the polarizability must also alter, even though but slightly.   Furthermore, from what has been said above, the polarizability depends on the orientation of the molecule to the field.   Thus the *vibration as well as the rotation of the molecule is associated with a change in polarizability*—that is, with a change in the amplitude of the induced dipole moment. For the vibration, to a first good approximation, we can put

$$\alpha = \alpha_{0v} + \alpha_{1v} \sin 2\pi\nu_{\mathrm{osc.}}t, \tag{III, 40}$$

where α_{0v} is the polarizability in the equilibrium position and α_{1v} is the amplitude of the change in polarizability during the vibration ($\alpha_{1v} \ll \alpha_{0v}$).   Correspondingly, for the rotation

$$\alpha = \alpha_{0r} + \alpha_{1r} \sin 2\pi 2\nu_{\mathrm{rot.}}t, \tag{III, 41}$$

where α_{0r} is an average polarizability and α_{1r} is the amplitude of the change in polarizability for rotation about the rotational axis considered.   The frequency with which the polarizability alters during the rotation is twice as large as the rotational frequency [factor 2 in front of $\nu_{\mathrm{rot.}}$ in (III, 41)], since the polarizability is the same in opposite directions.

Now, according to (III, 37), (III, 39), and (III, 40), the *induced dipole moment for vibration* is

$$P_v = \alpha_{0v} F_0 \sin 2\pi \nu' t + \alpha_{1v} F_0 \sin 2\pi \nu' t \sin 2\pi \nu_{\mathrm{osc.}} t, \qquad \text{(III, 42)}$$

and *for rotation* [according to (III, 37), (III, 39), and (III, 41)]

$$P_r = \alpha_{0r} F_0 \sin 2\pi \nu' t + \alpha_{1r} F_0 \sin 2\pi \nu' t \sin 2\pi 2\nu_{\mathrm{rot.}} t. \qquad \text{(III, 43)}$$

From this, using well-known trigonometrical formulae, we obtain

$$P_v = \alpha_{0v} F_0 \sin 2\pi \nu' t$$
$$+ \tfrac{1}{2}\alpha_{1v} F_0 [\cos 2\pi(\nu' - \nu_{\mathrm{osc.}})t - \cos 2\pi(\nu' + \nu_{\mathrm{osc.}})t] \qquad \text{(III, 44)}$$

and

$$P_r = \alpha_{0r} F_0 \sin 2\pi \nu' t$$
$$+ \tfrac{1}{2}\alpha_{1r} F_0 [\cos 2\pi(\nu' - 2\nu_{\mathrm{rot.}})t - \cos 2\pi(\nu' + 2\nu_{\mathrm{rot.}})t]. \qquad \text{(III, 45)}$$

Thus, when we take account of the small alteration of α for a vibration or rotation of the molecule, the induced dipole moment changes not only with the frequency ν' of the incident light, but also with the frequencies $\nu' - \nu_{\mathrm{osc.}}$ and $\nu' + \nu_{\mathrm{osc.}}$ or with the frequencies $\nu' - 2\nu_{\mathrm{rot.}}$ and $\nu' + 2\nu_{\mathrm{rot.}}$. So, according to classical theory, in the spectrum of the scattered light we have to expect a *displaced line* on both sides of the undisplaced line—in the case of an oscillator, at a distance $\nu_{\mathrm{osc.}}$, and, in the case of a rotator, at a distance $2\nu_{\mathrm{rot.}}$. However, while $\nu_{\mathrm{osc.}}$ has a fixed value, classically, $\nu_{\mathrm{rot.}}$ can take any value. Therefore in the case of a rotator we should expect a *continuous* spectrum on either side of the undisplaced line. The intensities of the displaced lines (squares of the amplitudes), according to (III, 44) and (III, 45), are appreciably smaller than those of the undisplaced lines. They should be the same for the components displaced toward longer and shorter wave lengths. In the case of vibration, they should also depend on the amplitude of the vibrations.

Thus, qualitatively, even classical considerations lead to the Raman effect—displaced frequencies in the spectrum of the scattered light. However, quantitatively there is no agreement. Empirically, there is no continuous Raman spectrum present for diatomic molecules, and, apart from that, in general only the long-wave components are found for the larger displacements (vibrational effect) but not the corresponding short-wave components, which, according to (III, 44), would be expected to have the same intensity.

Quantum theory of the Raman effect. The quantum theoretical explanation of the Raman effect is as follows: When the incident light quantum $h\nu'$ collides with a molecule, it can either be scattered elastically, in which case its energy, and thereby its frequency, remains unaltered (Rayleigh scattering), or it can be scattered inelastically, in which case it either gives up part of its energy to the scattering system or takes energy from it. Naturally, the light quantum can give to or take from the system only amounts of energy that are equal to the energy differences between the stationary states of the system. Let $\Delta E = E' - E''$ be such an energy difference. Then if the system is initially in the state E'', it may be brought to the state E' by the scattering of a light quantum, the energy ΔE being taken from the light quantum. Thus, after the scattering, the energy of the light quantum is only $h\nu' - \Delta E$. If, on the contrary, the system was initially in the state E' and is transferred to E'' by scattering, the energy of the light quantum after the scattering is equal to $h\nu' + \Delta E$. The frequency of the scattered light quantum is equal to the energy divided by h; that is, the frequencies $\nu' - (\Delta E/h)$ and $\nu' + (\Delta E/h)$ appear in the scattered light as well as the undisplaced frequency ν'. In some cases ΔE may take a number of different values. If everything is measured in wave numbers, the *Raman shifts give directly the energy differences of the system in cm^{-1}*. The Raman lines displaced toward longer wave lengths are also called *Stokes lines* and those displaced towards shorter wave lengths are called *anti-Stokes lines*.[3]

In Fig. 43, the relationships for light scattering are shown in an energy level diagram. The levels indicated by broken lines do not correspond to any possible energy states of the

---

[3] This nomenclature has the following origin: Stokes' law says that the frequency of fluorescent light is always smaller or at most equal to that of the exciting light. Stokes lines in fluorescence are thus such as correspond to Stokes' law, and anti-Stokes lines are such as contradict it. This nomenclature has also been adopted for the Raman effect, in spite of its difference from fluorescence (see p. 92).

system but only give the energy of the light quantum above the initial state.

The elementary process underlying the Raman effect is clearly to be distinguished from the process of *fluorescence*. For the latter, the incident light quantum is completely absorbed and the system is transferred to an excited state from which it can go to various lower states only after a certain time (mean life). The result of both phenomena is, it is true, essentially the same: A light quantum of a frequency different from that of the incident quantum is produced, and the molecule is brought to a higher or lower level. But the essential difference is that the Raman effect can take place for any frequency of the incident light (it is a light-scattering phenomenon), whereas fluorescence can occur only for the absorption frequencies. In consequence of this also, the structure of the Raman spectrum is quite different from that of the fluorescence spectrum.

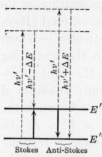

Stokes   Anti-Stokes

Fig. 43. Quantum Theory of the Raman Effect. The heavy arrows give the transitions actually taking place in the system considered.

In the more detailed theoretical treatment of the Raman effect, the wave mechanical analogue of the varying dipole moment produced by the incident radiation has to be formed (see Chapter I, p. 16 f.); that is,

$$(\boldsymbol{P}_x)_{nm} = F_x \int \alpha_{xx} \psi_n \psi_m{}^* d\tau, \quad (\boldsymbol{P}_y)_{nm} = F_y \int \alpha_{yy} \psi_n \psi_m{}^* d\tau,$$

$$(\boldsymbol{P}_z)_{nm} = F_z \int \alpha_{zz} \psi_n \psi_m{}^* d\tau.$$

(III, 46)

Here n and m are the quantum numbers of two different states of the system with eigenfunctions ψ_n and ψ_m. All the matrix elements (III, 46) taken together for all possible combinations of n and m represent the *scattering moment* [compare the classical expression (III, 38)]. If, for a given pair of values n and m, at least one of the quantities (III, 46) is different from zero, it means that a *transition* from n to m can take place under the influence of the incident light with a simultaneous change in the energy of the scattered light quantum.   For $n = m$, the undisplaced frequency is obtained (Rayleigh scattering).

If the polarizability α of a system (such as an oscillator or rotator) is constant (independent of vibration or rotation), it can be put in front of the integral sign in (III, 46).   Owing to the orthogonality of the eigenfunctions (see p. 14), the integrals are then all equal to zero, except for $m = n$; that is, when α is constant, only Rayleigh scattering and no Raman effect appears, in agreement with the results of classical theory.   A transition from one state to another, and thereby a *Raman shift, can occur only when the polarizability alters during the process under consideration* (that is, during the vibration or the rotation).

Vibrational Raman spectrum.   For the harmonic oscillator, the same *selection rule* results for the Raman effect as for the infrared spectrum; namely,

$$\Delta v = \pm 1. \tag{III, 47}$$

A transition can take place only to the adjacent vibrational state.   Thus the Raman spectrum consists of one Stokes and one anti-Stokes line, which are shifted by an amount

$$|\Delta \nu| = G(v + 1) - G(v) = \omega \tag{III, 48}$$

to either side of the original line.   However, at ordinary temperatures most of the molecules are in the lowest state ($v = 0$) and only an extremely small fraction are in the state with $v = 1$ (see p. 129).   As a result of this, the *intensity of the Stokes Raman line*, which corresponds to the transition $0 \rightarrow 1$, *is very much greater than that of the anti-Stokes line*, $1 \rightarrow 0$.   This agrees entirely with observation if the Raman lines of large displacement (see Fig. 35) are explained as vibrational Raman lines.   In all cases thus far investigated, the corresponding line displaced toward shorter wave lengths is so weak that it has not been observed.

We have seen before that the intense bands in the near infrared result from the transition $v = 0 \rightarrow v = 1$—that is to say, the same transition that takes place in the vibrational Raman effect.   This is the explanation of the observed agreement between the magnitudes of the large Raman displacements and the frequencies of the intense near infrared bands (see Table 11, p. 65.)

It is particularly important that the appearance of the Raman effect, vibrational as well as rotational, is quite *independent of the presence of a permanent dipole moment.* Thus the Raman effect can also appear for molecules that have no infrared spectrum.

For the oscillator, the motion depends on only one co-ordinate, which we shall call q. According to our previous discussion, the polarizability likewise depends on this co-ordinate. To a first approximation this dependence is linear, so that we can write

$$\alpha = \alpha^0 + \alpha^1 q. \qquad \text{(III, 49)}$$

[This expression obviously transforms into (III, 40) with α^0 instead of α_{0v} when we introduce the classical expression for q—namely, $q = q_0 \sin 2\pi\nu_{\text{osc.}}t$]. If we substitute (III, 49) in (III, 46), replacing at the same time n and m by v' and v'', we get

$$(P_x)_{v'v''} = F_x\alpha^0{}_{xx} \int \psi_{v'}(q)\psi_{v''}{}^*(q)dq$$
$$+ F_x\alpha^1{}_{xx} \int q\psi_{v'}(q)\psi_{v''}{}^*(q)dq. \qquad \text{(III, 50)}$$

Because of the orthogonality of the eigenfunctions, the first integral is zero except when $v' = v''$; that is, it gives the undisplaced frequency [corresponding to the first term in (III, 44)]. The second term contains the same integral as appears for the infrared spectrum of the oscillator (see p. 85, where x is used in place of q). It is different from zero only when $\Delta v = \pm 1$. This gives the displaced lines. Equation (III, 50) at the same time shows very clearly that displaced frequencies appear only when α^1 differs from zero—that is, *when the polarizability changes during the vibration.* The greater α^1 is—that is, the more sensitive the polarizability is to changes in nuclear distance—the greater is the intensity of the Raman lines.

Rotational Raman spectrum. Whereas for an oscillator the same selection rule holds in the Raman effect as in the infrared spectrum, for the rotator a different *selection rule* is obtained—namely,

$$\Delta J = 0, \pm 2. \qquad \text{(III, 51)}$$

As for the vibrational Raman spectrum, the appearance of the rotational Raman spectrum is not bound up with the presence of a permanent dipole moment.

When, as is usually the case, molecules with different J values are present, the rotational Raman spectrum consists of a *number* of lines.[4] $\Delta J = 0$ gives the undisplaced line. For the actual transitions of the simple rotator ΔJ can only be positive, since it is defined as $J' - J''$, where J' refers to the upper and J'' to the lower state.   Thus only $\Delta J = +2$ need be considered. Yet we obtain *two* series of lines, since the lower as well as the upper state may be the initial state in the scattering process. The first case (transition $J \rightarrow J+2$) results in a shift to longer wave lengths (Stokes lines), and the second case (transition $J + 2 \rightarrow J$) results in a shift to shorter wave lengths (anti-Stokes lines).   These transitions are indicated in the upper part of Fig. 44. Using (III, 15), we obtain for the magnitude of the frequency shift

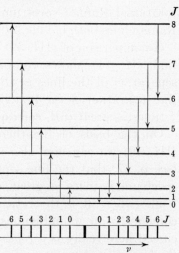

Fig. 44. Explanation of the Rotational Raman Spectrum.   In the schematic spectrogram below, the heavy line in the middle gives the position of the undisplaced line. To the left are the Stokes Raman lines, and to the right are the anti-Stokes lines.   The numbers added to the Raman lines are the J values of the lower state.

$$|\Delta\nu| = F(J+2) - F(J) = B(J+2)(J+3) - BJ(J+1)$$
$$= 4BJ + 6B = 4B(J + \tfrac{3}{2}). \quad \text{(III, 52)}$$

The Raman spectrum to be expected is drawn schematically at the bottom of Fig. 44.   According to (III, 52), we have *a*

---

[4] For the vibrational Raman spectrum, only one Stokes and one anti-Stokes line would result, even if molecules with different v values were present, since the vibrational levels of the harmonic oscillator are equidistant [see (III, 48)].

series of equidistant Raman lines on either side of the undis-placed line, as is actually observed (see Figs. 35 and 36). We can therefore identify the small Raman displacements as the rotational Raman spectrum. The two series of rotational Raman lines both having $\Delta J = +2$ are also called *S branches.*[5]

A comparison of (III, 52) with the earlier empirical equation (II, 14) shows complete agreement. The constant separation of the lines is $4B$ (equal to the previous p), and the separation of the first line from the undisplaced line is $\frac{3}{2}$ times as great ($6B$, corresponding to $\frac{3}{2}p$).

On the basis of the theoretical formulae (III, 52) and (III, 19) we can now also understand the empirical result (see p. 67) that the line separation in cm^{-1} in the Raman spectrum is twice as great as that in the far infrared spectrum (where it is theoretically $2B$). This empirical fact is conversely an unambiguous proof that the spectrum discussed here really is a *rotational Raman spectrum,* and that the far infrared spectrum is a rotation spectrum.

The experimentally observed *intensities* also agree with those theoretically expected. Owing to the smallness of the rotational energy, a number of rotational states are excited at room temperature because of the thermal motion [see section 2(e)]. As a result, Stokes as well as anti-Stokes lines are present in about equal intensity—in contrast to the vibrational Raman spectrum. The alternation of intensities observed in the rotational Raman spectrum for symmetrical molecules must be left for later discussion [see Fig. 36 and section 2(f)].

In the wave mechanical as well as in the classical treatment, the occurrence of the rotational Raman spectrum depends on the change in the component of the polarizability in a fixed direction, produced by the rotation of the molecule. That ± 2 appears here

---

[5] According to the international nomenclature [Mulliken (515)], the symbols S, R, Q, P, and O are used for branches with $\Delta J = +2$, $+1$, 0, -1, and -2, respectively, where $\Delta J = J' - J''$ is the difference between the J value in the upper and the lower state. But, in the case of the rotational Raman spectrum, some authors use S branch for the anti-Stokes and O branch for the Stokes Raman lines, in spite of the fact that $\Delta J = +2$ for both.

in the selection rule for J in the place of ± 1 in the infrared spectrum has exactly the same reason as the appearance of $2\nu_{rot.}$ instead of $\nu_{rot.}$ in the classical treatment (see p. 89).   For a more detailed theoretical treatment see Placzek (562) and Teller (664).

General remarks.   From the foregoing we see that we can obtain the same information from the Raman spectrum as from the infrared spectrum—namely, the magnitude of the vibrational quanta (that is, the constant ω) and the magnitude of the rotational quanta (that is, the constant B). From these, as previously discussed, we can derive, on the one hand, the vibrational frequencies and force constants and, on the other, moments of inertia, internuclear distances, and rotational frequencies.   The observed agreement between the values obtained from Raman and infrared spectra is a further strong argument that the *explanation of these spectra by the models of the rotator and oscillator is a good approximation.*

Even for the symmetrical molecules, which have no infrared spectrum (see p. 85), the rotational and vibrational constants can be derived with the aid of the Raman spectrum.   However, their determination from electronic band spectra (see Chapter IV) is experimentally simpler.

2.   INTERPRETATION OF THE FINER DETAILS OF INFRARED AND RAMAN SPECTRA

The models of the rigid rotator and the harmonic oscillator explain the main characteristics of the infrared and Raman spectra.   However, we have to make a number of refinements in these models if we wish to explain the finer details of these spectra.

(a) The Anharmonic Oscillator

The molecule as anharmonic oscillator.   According to equation (III, 25), a harmonic oscillator is characterized by a parabolic potential curve (broken-line curve in Fig. 45). This means that the restoring force, and with it the poten-

tial energy, increases steadily with increasing distance from
the equilibrium position.   It is, however, clear that in an
actual molecule, when the atoms are at a great distance from
one another, the attractive force is zero and, correspondingly,
the potential energy has a constant value.   Therefore the
potential curve of the molecule has the form of the full curve in
Fig. 45, which, with increasing nuclear distance r, approaches
(asymptotically) a constant value.   The minimum of the

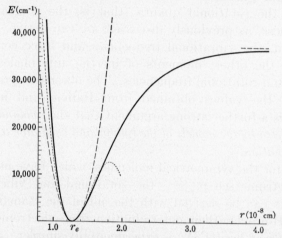

Fig. 45. Potential Curve of the Molecule (Anharmonic Oscillator). The
full curve is drawn for the ground state of HCl. The broken-line and the
dotted curves are the ordinary and the cubic parabola, respectively, that form
the best approximation to the full curve at the minimum.

curve corresponds to the *equilibrium position*. In the neighborhood of this, the curve can be represented approximately
by a parabola (broken-line curve), and therefore the model
of the harmonic oscillator reproduces the main characteristics of the vibration spectrum quite well.

The potential energy of the molecule can be represented
to a better approximation than by (III, 25), which is valid
for the harmonic oscillator, by the expression

$$V = f(r - r_e)^2 - g(r - r_e)^3 \qquad (III, 53)$$

[possibly with still further terms of higher powers in $(r - r_e)$].
Of the two constants f and g occurring in this expression, g is

$\ll f$. To be sure, even this function (dotted curve in Fig. 45) does not represent the whole of the potential energy curve, but at any rate does give a much better approximation for not too great $(r - r_e)$.

A mass point that moves under the influence of a potential of the type of the full or dotted curve in Fig. 45 is called an *anharmonic oscillator*.

Classical motion. Classically, the motion of the anharmonic oscillator is no longer given by (III, 23) (pure sine form). It can, however, be represented as a *superposition of fundamental and overtone vibrations* (Fourier series),

$$x = x_{01} \sin 2\pi\nu_{\text{osc.}}t + x_{02} \sin 2\pi2\nu_{\text{osc.}}t + x_{03} \sin 2\pi3\nu_{\text{osc.}}t + \cdots, \tag{III, 54}$$

where, when $g \ll f$ in (III, 53), $x_{02} \ll x_{01}$, and $x_{03} \ll x_{02}$. The vibrational frequency $\nu_{\text{osc.}}$ now depends on the amplitude $x_{\text{max.}}$ and decreases with increasing amplitude (as is the case, for example, for the vibrations of a pendulum with large amplitude).

Just as for the harmonic oscillator (see p. 79), we reduce the motion of the two nuclei in the molecule to the anharmonic motion [represented by (III, 54)] of a single mass point, with which is associated a dipole moment varying with the same frequency as does the position of the mass point. Thus, according to (III, 54), the classical infrared spectrum of the molecule should consist of the fundamental vibration $\nu_{\text{osc.}}$, the first overtone $2\nu_{\text{osc.}}$ (also called *second harmonic*), the second overtone $3\nu_{\text{osc.}}$ (also called *third harmonic*), and so forth, the amplitudes (intensities) of the overtones being small compared to that of the fundamental vibration.

Qualitatively, this agrees with the observed spectrum (see p. 57), since actually in addition to the intense fundamental vibration, further very weak bands at about twice and three times its frequency are present. More accurate measurements show, however (see p. 58), that the frequencies of the "overtones" are not exactly twice or three times the frequency of the fundamental, as would be expected from the classical calculation. This difference is explained by the quantum theoretical treatment.

Energy levels. If (III, 53) is substituted as potential energy in the wave equation (I, 12), it is found that for small anharmonicity of the oscillator ($g \ll f$) the eigenvalues of the wave equation—that is, the *energy values of the anharmonic oscillator*—are given by

$$E_v = hc\omega_e(v + \tfrac{1}{2}) - hc\omega_e x_e(v + \tfrac{1}{2})^2$$
$$+ hc\omega_e y_e(v + \tfrac{1}{2})^3 + \cdots, \tag{III, 55}$$

or correspondingly the *term values* are given by

$$G(v) = \omega_e(v + \tfrac{1}{2}) - \omega_e x_e(v + \tfrac{1}{2})^2 + \omega_e y_e(v + \tfrac{1}{2})^3 + \cdots. \tag{III, 56}$$

Here, the constant $\omega_e x_e \ll \omega_e$ and $\omega_e y_e \ll \omega_e x_e$. For the given choice of signs, when g is positive in (III, 53), $\omega_e x_e$ is positive. This is practically always the case. $\omega_e y_e$ is very often negligibly small. It can be positive or negative. The reason for writing the coefficients of the quadratic and cubic terms $\omega_e x_e$ and $\omega_e y_e$, respectively, is that some of the earlier authors wrote (III, 56) thus:

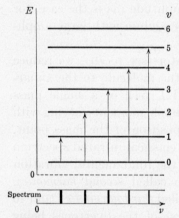

$$G(v) = \omega_e[(v + \tfrac{1}{2}) - x_e(v + \tfrac{1}{2})^2 + y_e(v + \tfrac{1}{2})^3 + \cdots].$$

Fig. 46. Energy Levels and Infrared Transitions for the Anharmonic Oscillator. The absorption spectrum is given schematically below.

Formula (III, 56) shows that the energy levels of the anharmonic oscillator are not equidistant like those of the harmonic oscillator, but that their separation decreases slowly with increasing v. This is shown in Fig. 46, where the decrease is faster than corresponds to most observed cases.

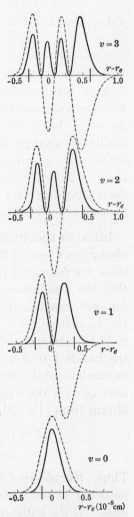

Just as for the harmonic oscillator, a *zero-point energy* is present. Namely, for $v = 0$

$$G(0) = \tfrac{1}{2}\omega_e - \tfrac{1}{4}\omega_e x_e \\ + \tfrac{1}{8}\omega_e y_e + \cdots. \qquad \text{(III, 57)}$$

If the energy levels are referred to this lowest level as zero, we obtain

$$G_0(v) = \omega_0 v - \omega_0 x_0 v^2 \\ + \omega_0 y_0 v^3 + \cdots, \qquad \text{(III, 58)}$$

where

$$\omega_0 = \omega_e - \omega_e x_e + \tfrac{3}{4}\omega_e y_e + \cdots,$$
$$\omega_0 x_0 = \omega_e x_e - \tfrac{3}{2}\omega_e y_e + \cdots, \qquad \text{(III, 59)}$$
$$\omega_0 y_0 = \omega_e y_e + \cdots.$$

Eigenfunctions and selection rules.
In Fig. 47 the *eigenfunctions* (broken curves) and the *probability density distributions* (solid curves) for the levels $v = 0, 1, 2,$ and 3 of a strongly anharmonic oscillator are illustrated. It can be seen that the functions are very similar to those of the harmonic oscillator (Fig. 41) except that they are not quite symmetrical. The somewhat greater height of the right-hand maxima corresponds to the fact that classically the molecule stays for a longer time on the shallow right-hand side of the potential curve (Fig. 45) than on the steeper left-hand side. The difference between the eigenfunctions of the harmonic and the anharmonic oscillator is still smaller for smaller

Fig. 47. Eigenfunctions (Broken Curves) and Probability Density Distributions (Solid Curves) of an Anharmonic Oscillator for $v = 0, 1, 2, 3$. The curves hold for the first excited triplet state of H_2 (see p. 364 f.) and are taken from Coolidge, James, and Present (162).

anharmonicities, such as are usually observed in actual cases. For approximations to the eigenfunctions of the anharmonic oscillator see Morse (504), Dunham (194a), Hutchisson (349a), Bewersdorff (99), and Norling (536).

As a result of the similarity of the eigenfunctions, the *selection rule* for the transitions of a harmonic oscillator, $\Delta v = \pm 1$, holds at least approximately for the anharmonic oscillator, giving the most intense transitions. But now, as shown by a more detailed calculation, transitions with $\Delta v = \pm 2, \pm 3$ can also appear, even though with rapidly decreasing intensity. This holds for the infrared spectrum as well as for the Raman effect.

Infrared spectrum. The transitions that are possible *in absorption* when all the molecules are in the lowest vibrational state are indicated in Fig. 46. It can be seen immediately that the transitions with $\Delta v = 2, 3, \cdots$ have approximately, but not exactly, double, three times, $\cdots$ the frequency of the transition $\Delta v = 1$, in agreement with observation (see p. 57 f.). In spite of this deviation from the classical result, the bands 1–0, 2–0, 3–0, $\cdots$ are still frequently referred to as fundamental, first overtone (or second harmonic), second overtone (or third harmonic), and so forth. As formula, we obtain from (III, 56–58)

$$\nu_{\text{abs.}} = G(v') - G(0) = G_0(v')$$
$$= \omega_0 v' - \omega_0 x_0 v'^2 + \omega_0 y_0 v'^3 + \cdots. \tag{III, 60}$$

Thus, *the observed absorption frequencies give directly the positions of the vibrational levels above the lowest vibrational state.* If the cubic term is neglected, (III, 60) agrees exactly with the empirical formula (II, 9), which represents the observed bands with great accuracy.

The separation between successive absorption bands (in cm^{-1}), which is equal to the separation between successive levels, is given by (again neglecting cubic terms)

$$\Delta G_{v+\frac{1}{2}} = G(v+1) - G(v) = G_0(v+1) - G_0(v)$$
$$= \omega_e - 2\omega_e x_e - 2\omega_e x_e v = \omega_0 - \omega_0 x_0 - 2\omega_0 x_0 v. \tag{III, 61}$$

These first differences are given in Table 8, p. 58, for the case of HCl. They decrease linearly, as they should according to (III, 61). The second difference,

$$\Delta^2 G = 2\omega_0 x_0 = 2\omega_e x_e, \qquad (III, 62)$$

is constant. It gives directly the constant $\omega_e x_e = \omega_0 x_0$, which is a measure of the *anharmonicity* of the oscillator— that is, of the asymmetry of the potential curve. In the case of HCl, from Table 8 we obtain $\omega_0 x_0 = 51.65$ cm^{-1}. The values of ω_0 and ω_e are then obtained according to (III, 61) or (III, 60)—for example, from the frequency of the first band (1–0), since we have

$$\nu(1\text{–}0) = \Delta G_{\frac{1}{2}} = \omega_e - 2\omega_e x_e = \omega_0 - \omega_0 x_0. \quad (III, 63)$$

Using the figures in Table 8 for HCl, we obtain $\omega_e = 2988.95$ and $\omega_0 = 2937.30$ cm^{-1}.[6] *Thus we can determine the vibrational constants ω_e and $\omega_e x_e$ (or ω_0 and $\omega_0 x_0$) from the observed position of the infrared absorption bands of a diatomic molecule.* (If the second difference is not constant, $\omega_e y_e$ can also be determined.)

The fact that the observed bands are so well represented by the theoretical formula (III, 60) and that, in addition, the intensities agree very well with those theoretically expected (very rapid decrease in the series of bands; see Fig. 31)[6a] is a further indication of the correctness of our interpretation of the near infrared spectra of diatomic molecules as vibration spectra.

Raman spectrum. Since the selection rules for the Raman spectrum of an anharmonic oscillator are the same as those for the infrared spectrum, the Raman displacements may be represented by the same formula (III, 60). As in the infrared, the transition $0 \rightarrow 1$ would be expected to be by

---

[6] ω_0 and $\omega_0 x_0$ correspond to the constants a and b in (II, 9) (see p. 58). The most practical way of determining the constants is to use the coefficients in the " best " empirical formula for the bands.

[6a] For a more detailed discussion of the intensities of infrared vibration bands see Matheson (482a), Scholz (625a), Bartholomé (80a), Mulliken (519a), and Rosenthal (601).

far the most intense; actually, no overtones have yet been observed for any diatomic molecule, since the Raman spectra are very weak. *Thus the observed Raman shifts give $\Delta G_{\frac{1}{2}}$, the first vibrational quantum*, which is somewhat smaller than ω_e (or ω_0) [see (III, 63)]. So long as no overtones are observed, the vibrational constants ω_e and $\omega_e x_e$ (or ω_0 and $\omega_0 x_0$) cannot be derived from the Raman spectrum.

Vibrational frequency and force constant. For the harmonic oscillator the separation of successive vibrational levels is equal to the classical vibration frequency (all in cm^{-1} units). It may be shown that this also holds for the anharmonic oscillator. To the decrease of the classical vibrational frequency with increasing amplitude of vibration (see p. 99) there corresponds a decrease of the vibrational quanta with increasing vibrational quantum number—that is, with increasing vibrational energy. The exact expression for the *vibrational frequency* $\nu_{osc.}(v)$ that the oscillator would have, according to classical theory, in the state v turns out to be

$$\nu_{osc.}(v) = c\Delta G_v. \qquad (III, 64)$$

Because of this relation, the vibrational quanta are sometimes also called vibrational frequencies. [It should be noted that (III, 64) contains ΔG_v and not $\Delta G_{v+\frac{1}{2}}$.]

From (III, 64) and (III, 61) it follows that

$$\begin{aligned} \nu_{osc.}(v) &= c[(\omega_e - 2\omega_e x_e) - 2\omega_e x_e(v - \tfrac{1}{2})] \\ &= c[(\omega_e - \omega_e x_e) - 2\omega_e x_e v]. \end{aligned} \qquad (III, 65)$$

From this it is seen that for the unrealizable state with $v = -\frac{1}{2}$, for which the vibrational energy (III, 55) is zero,

$$\nu_{osc.}(-\tfrac{1}{2}) = c\omega_e. \qquad (III, 66)$$

Thus ω_e gives the vibrational frequency that the anharmonic oscillator would have classically for an infinitesimal amplitude. The anharmonicity makes itself perceptible even for the lowest vibrational state in that the corresponding classical vibrational frequency is somewhat smaller than ω_e; namely,

$$\nu_{\text{osc.}}(0) = c(\omega_e - \omega_e x_e) = c\omega_0. \qquad \text{(III, 67)}$$

According to (III, 27), the vibrational frequency ω_e for infinitely small amplitudes yields the *force constant of the anharmonic oscillator for infinitely small displacements*; namely,

$$k_e = 4\pi^2 \mu c^2 \omega_e{}^2 = 5.8894 \cdot 10^{-2} \mu_A \omega_e{}^2 \text{ dyne/cm}, \qquad \text{(III, 68)}$$

where μ_A is the reduced mass in atomic-weight units (Aston scale) ($\mu_A = \mu \cdot N$; N = Avogadro number). For HCl, for example, from $\omega_e = 2988.95$ cm^{-1}, it follows that $k_e = 5.1556 \cdot 10^5$ dynes/cm, which deviates somewhat from the k value previously derived from $\Delta G_{\frac{1}{2}}$ (see p. 87). The value of k_e also determines the parabola which fits the actual potential curve best in the neighborhood of the minimum [that is, the quantity f in (III, 53); $f = \frac{1}{2}k_e$].

Continuous term spectrum and dissociation. When an anharmonic oscillator with a potential curve of the type drawn in Fig. 45 receives more energy than corresponds to the horizontal asymptote, the mass point is completely removed from its equilibrium position and does not return to it. This is perhaps most clearly seen if we think of a strip of metal bent into the shape of the potential curve; a ball placed to the left above the level of the asymptote and then released will roll out over the right side when there is no frictional loss. This motion of the mass point corresponds, in the molecule, to the atoms flying completely away from each other ($r \to \infty$); that is, a *dissociation of the molecule* results. If the energy of the system just corresponds to the asymptote, the atoms at a great distance from each other will have zero velocity. With increasing energy above that of the asymptote, the atoms at a great distance apart have increasing relative kinetic energy. This kinetic energy is *not quantized.* Therefore, above the asymptote a *continuous* *term spectrum,* corresponding to dissociation, joins onto the discrete vibrational term series. This is quite similar to the continuum that adjoins the atomic term series and corresponds to ionization. In both cases the continuous term spectrum also results from the rigorous quantum mechanical derivation (not given here). As an example, the potential

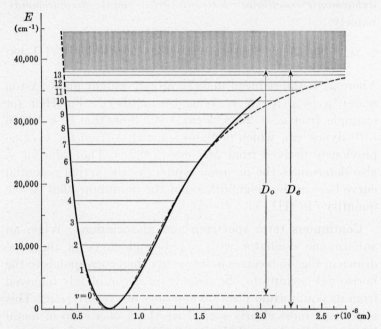

Fig. 48. **Potential Curve of the H_2 Ground State with Vibrational Levels and Continuous Term Spectrum.** The full curve is drawn according to Rydberg's data (610). The broken curve is a Morse curve. Above $v = 14$, there is a continuous term spectrum, corresponding to dissociation and indicated by vertical hatching.

curve is drawn in Fig. 48 for the special case of H_2, in its electronic ground state together with the series of observed discrete vibrational levels and the adjoining continuum.

The height of the asymptote (that is, the beginning of the continuum) above the lowest vibrational level gives the work that must be done in order to dissociate the molecule—the so-called *heat of dissociation.* It is designated D_0. It may be immediately seen from Fig. 48 that D_0 is equal to the *sum of all the vibrational quanta*:

$$D_0 = \sum_v \Delta G_{v+\frac{1}{2}}. \qquad \text{(III, 69)}$$

The energy difference, D_e, between the minimum and the asymptote is a little greater than D_0—namely, by an amount equal to the zero-point energy:

$$D_e = D_0 + G(0) = D_0 + \tfrac{1}{2}\omega_e - \tfrac{1}{4}\omega_e x_e + \tfrac{1}{8}\omega_e y_e + \cdots. \qquad \text{(III, 70)}$$

Since no discrete vibrational levels lie above the asymptote, D_e must be the maximum value of $G(v)$; that is,

$$D_e = G_{\max.}(v). \qquad \text{(III, 71)}$$

Therefore, at the limit, $\Delta G = 0$; the vibrational frequency correspondingly becomes zero [according to (III, 64)], and the period of vibration becomes infinitely great. This is to be expected, since the process of dissociation is, of course, aperiodic.

When the quadratic expression $\omega_0 v - \omega_0 x_0 v^2$ represents all the vibrational levels correctly, or, in other words, when ΔG is a linear function of v [see (III, 61)], ΔG_v becomes zero for

$$v_D = \frac{\omega_0}{2\omega_0 x_0}. \qquad \text{(III, 72)}$$

The next smaller integral value of v thus corresponds to the last discrete vibrational level before dissociation. Thus there is only a finite number of vibrational levels present, in contrast to the case of ionization, where there is an infinite number of discrete levels lying below the limit. The *heat of dissociation* D_0 (or D_e) is given in this case by

$$D_0 = \omega_0 v_D - \omega_0 x_0 v_D{}^2 = \frac{\omega_0{}^2}{4\omega_0 x_0} \left(\text{or } D_e = \frac{\omega_e{}^2}{4\omega_e x_e} \right). \qquad \text{(III, 73)}$$

However, in most cases ΔG is not simply a linear function of v. For the ground state of hydrogen, for example, the

ΔG curve is found to be that given in Fig. 49. Here also only a finite number of vibrational levels is present.[6b] The *heat of dissociation* in this case can be derived only by means of formula (III, 69) or (III, 71). It is seen immediately that the sum of the vibrational quanta (III, 69) is given very closely by the *area under the ΔG curve*. For a linear ΔG curve this relation holds exactly and, as can easily be seen, leads also to equation (III, 73).

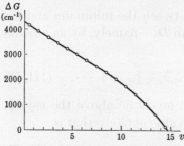

Fig. 49. ΔG Curve for the Ground State of the H_2 Molecule [after Data Given by Beutler (91)]. The observed $\Delta G_{v+\frac{1}{2}}$ values are plotted with the abscissae $v + \frac{1}{2}$.

The foregoing considerations regarding the limit of the vibrational terms are of no importance for infrared spectra, since the intensity in a series of bands falls off so rapidly that high v values can never be observed in practice. However, these considerations will prove to be very important in electronic band spectra and in the band-spectroscopic determination of heats of dissociation (Chapter VII).

Mathematical representation of the potential curves. As we have already mentioned, equation (III, 53) only represents the potential energy at not too great a distance from the equilibrium position. A mathematical expression for the potential energy which actually represents a variation of the kind shown in Figs. 45 and 48, even for large values of r, has been proposed by Morse (504). It is

$$U(r - r_e) = D_e(1 - e^{-\beta(r-r_e)})^2. \qquad (III, 74)$$

In this expression, D_e is the above-defined heat of dissociation, referred to the minimum, and β is a constant whose value will be derived. It can be seen that the *Morse function* gives a curve of the form of Fig. 45, since, for $r \to \infty$, U approaches D_e; for

---

[6b] An infinite number of vibrational levels below the limit is present for molecular states derived from ions [see Chapter VI, section 4(b)]—that is, when the potential energy for larger r values is the same as for an electron and an atomic ion.

$r = r_e$, U is a minimum—namely, $U = 0$. On the other hand, for $r = 0$, U does not approach ∞, as it must do for a correct potential energy function. However, the part of the curve in the neighborhood of $r = 0$ is of no practical importance.

Morse has shown that when (III, 74) is substituted in the wave equation (I, 12), the equation can be solved rigorously. The term values are found to be

$$G(v) = \beta \sqrt{\frac{D_e h}{2\pi^2 c \mu}} \, (v + \tfrac{1}{2}) - \frac{h\beta^2}{c 8\pi^2 \mu} \, (v + \tfrac{1}{2})^2 \qquad \text{(III, 75)}$$

without any higher powers of $(v + \tfrac{1}{2})$. According to (III, 56), the factor of $(v + \tfrac{1}{2})$ is ω_e. Therefore

$$\beta = \sqrt{\frac{2\pi^2 c \mu}{D_e h}} \, \omega_e = 1.2176 \cdot 10^7 \, \omega_e \sqrt{\frac{\mu_A}{D_e}} , \qquad \text{(III, 76)}$$

where μ_A is the reduced mass in atomic-weight units and D_e is in cm^{-1} units. The same formula results from the factor of $(v + \tfrac{1}{2})^2$ in (III, 75) when (III, 73) is substituted.

The Morse function (III, 74) is frequently used for the representation of potential curves, since it is very convenient. In cases in which the vibrational levels cannot be represented by a two-constant formula, it is best to take the empirical D_e and ω_e in order to calculate β from (III, 76). However, the factor of $(v + \tfrac{1}{2})^2$ in (III, 75) will then not agree with the observed $\omega_e x_e$.

Poeschl and Teller (568) have shown that for a given observed set of vibrational levels the Morse function is not the only possible potential function that will lead to these vibrational levels, even if the levels can be represented by a two-constant formula. In order to avoid uncertainty in the choice of the potential function, data on the rotational constants of the molecule must be used. Lotmar (469) has given a function which makes use of the dependence of the rotational constants on the vibrational quantum number (see below). [See also Kronig (32).]

Klein (404) and Rydberg [(608) and (609)] have given a method for constructing the potential curve point for point from the observed vibrational and rotational levels without using an analytical expression for the potential function. The exact curves obtained in this way are generally very closely approximated by the Morse curve (which is much simpler to calculate), so that the latter is usually satisfactory. The potential curve for the ground state of H_2 in Fig. 48 (full curve) has been derived by the Klein-Rydberg method. The corresponding Morse function is given as a broken-line curve [see also Hylleraas (351)]. Quite recently

Coolidge, James, and Vernon (162a) have given a very thorough discussion of the accuracy of the various methods of determining potential energy curves and have also generalized the Morse function so as to give a very accurate representation of the true potential function on the basis of spectroscopic data.

(b) The Nonrigid Rotator

Energy levels. Thus far we have used the models of the rigid rotator and the harmonic (or anharmonic) oscillator independently of each other. However, it is quite obvious that the molecule cannot be a strictly *rigid* rotator when it is also able to carry out vibrations in the direction of the line joining the two nuclei. Therefore a better model for representing the rotations of the molecule is given by the nonrigid rotator—that is, a rotating system consisting of two mass points which are not connected by a massless rigid bar but by a massless *spring*. As a result of the action of centrifugal force, the *internuclear distance*, and thereby the *moment of inertia* of such a system, *becomes greater with increasing rotation.* The expression (III, 15) for the rotational energy of a rigid rotator must therefore be so altered that the rotational constant itself, $B = h/8\pi^2cI$, depends on the rotational energy (that is, on the rotational quantum number), decreasing with increasing J. The more detailed quantum mechanical calculation shows that, to a first good approximation, the *rotational terms of the nonrigid rotator* are given by

$$F(J) = \frac{E_r}{hc} = B\,[1 - uJ(J+1)]J(J+1). \quad \text{(III, 77)}$$

That is to say, $B[1 - uJ(J+1)]$ appears in the place of B in (III, 15), where B is given by (III, 16) and u is very small compared to 1. Equation (III, 77) is usually written

$$F(J) = BJ(J+1) - DJ^2(J+1)^2. \quad \text{(III, 78)}$$

In this equation[7] D is very much smaller than B. In higher

---

[7] This D, of course, has nothing to do with the heat of dissociation D. Some authors use a positive sign in (III, 78) instead of the negative one used here. In that case D is of course negative.

approximation, further terms with higher powers of $J(J + 1)$ have to be added [see Jevons (34)].

In order to illustrate the effect of D, the rotational levels of a nonrigid rotator have been drawn in Fig. 50 (full lines) with an exaggerated value of D and are compared with the levels of the rigid rotator (broken lines). It can be seen that the effect of D is appreciable mainly for the higher rotational levels. However, in most cases occurring in practice it is considerably smaller than has been represented in Fig. 50.

The rotational constant D depends on the vibration frequency ω of the molecule, since the smaller ω is, the flatter will be the potential curve [according to (III, 25)] in the neighborhood of the minimum and therefore the greater will be the influence of centrifugal force—that is, the greater D will be. Theory shows that D is given by

$$D = \frac{4B^3}{\omega^2} \qquad \text{(III, 79)}$$

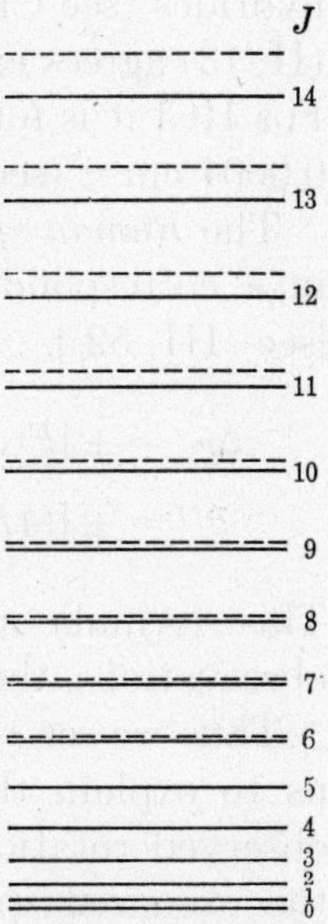

Fig. 50. Energy Levels of the Nonrigid Rotator. For comparison, the energy levels of the corresponding rigid rotator are indicated by broken lines (for $J < 6$, they cannot be drawn separately). The influence of the nonrigidity is considerably smaller in most practical cases.

if, for the vibrations, the model of the harmonic oscillator is used. As we have seen above, ω is always very much greater than B and therefore, according to (III, 79), D will be *very much smaller than B*.

Spectrum. The formula (III, 8) for the angular momentum and with it the *selection rule* (III, 18) for the rotational quantum number J are not altered when we go over from a rigid to a nonrigid rotator. However, as a result of changing the formula for the energy to (III, 78), the wave numbers of the lines in the *infrared rotation spectrum* are now given by

$$\nu = F(J + 1) - F(J) = 2B(J + 1) - 4D(J + 1)^3. \qquad \text{(III, 80)}$$

That is to say, the lines are no longer exactly equidistant, as for a rigid rotator, but draw somewhat closer together with increasing J. However, this effect is very small, since $D \ll B$. Nevertheless, it has actually been found for the halogen hydrides (see Chapter II, p. 61 f.). The empirical formula (II, 13) agrees exactly with the theoretical formula (III, 80). For HCl it is found in this way that $B = 10.395$ and $D = 0.0004$ cm^{-1} (see p. 62).

The *Raman spectrum* of the nonrigid rotator also deviates in a corresponding manner from that of the rigid rotator [see (III, 52)]. We have

$$|\Delta\nu| = \pm [F(J + 2) - F(J)]$$
$$= \pm [(4B - 6D)(J + \tfrac{3}{2}) - 8D(J + \tfrac{3}{2})^3].$$

This formula shows that here also, in agreement with observations, there is a slight deviation from equidistance.

Thus we see that the model of the nonrigid rotator allows us to explain the observed far infrared spectrum and the observed rotational Raman spectrum in all details. From the observed spectrum we obtain not only the rotational constant B and with it the moment of inertia and internuclear distance in the molecule, but also the rotational constant D, which gives a measure of the *influence of centrifugal force*.

If the *vibrational frequency* ω is not known from the vibrational spectrum (or electronic band spectrum; see Chapter IV), an approximate value for it can be calculated from D by using (III, 79). Of course, this value will not be very accurate, since D, being a correction term, cannot be determined very accurately. For HCl, for example, using the above B and D values, we obtain $\omega = 3350$ cm^{-1}, whereas the vibration spectrum yields $\omega_e = 2988.95$ cm^{-1}. The fact that in this case ω as determined from the rotational constants comes out to the right order of magnitude shows clearly that it actually is one and the same system that is carrying out the rotations as well as the vibrations.

Owing to the smallness of the rotational constant D (in practically all cases, $D < 10^{-4}B$), we may in future considerations often neglect the departure of the molecule from the model of a rigid rotator. The deviations from the model of the harmonic oscillator are, on the contrary, by no means negligible.

(c) The Vibrating Rotator

So far we have regarded the rotation and the vibration of the molecule quite separately. However, it seems natural to assume that rotation and vibration can take place simultaneously, and, in fact, the observed fine structure of the rotation bands suggests very strongly that such a *simultaneous rotation and vibration* is possible. For this reason, we shall now consider a model in which simultaneous rotation and vibration take place—the *vibrating rotator*.

Energy levels. If we could neglect the interaction of vibration and rotation, the energy of the vibrating rotator would be given simply by the sum of the vibrational energy of the anharmonic oscillator (III, 56) and the rotational energy of the nonrigid rotator (III, 78). Therefore a series of rotational levels of the type of Fig. 50 would exist for each of the vibrational levels of Fig. 46. However, in a more accurate treatment we must take into consideration the fact that during the vibration the nuclear distance and thereby the moment of inertia and the rotational constant B are changing.

Since the period of vibration is very small compared to the period of rotation (see p. 87), it seems plausible to use a *mean B value* for the rotational constant in the vibrational state considered; namely,

$$B_v = \frac{h}{8\pi^2 c\mu}\left[\overline{\frac{1}{r^2}}\right], \qquad \text{(III, 81)}$$

where $[\overline{1/r^2}]$ is the mean value of $1/r^2$ during the vibration. This assumption is justified by a rigorous calculation. It is to be expected that B_v will be somewhat smaller than the

constant B_e, which corresponds to the equilibrium separation r_e, since with increasing vibration, because of the anharmonicity, the mean nuclear separation will be greater.   The
value of B_e is given by

$$B_e = \frac{h}{8\pi^2 c\mu r_e{}^2} = \frac{h}{8\pi^2 cI_e} = \frac{27.994 \cdot 10^{-40}}{I_e}. \quad \text{(III, 82)}$$

The quantum mechanical calculation [see, for example,
Weizel (33)] shows that, to a first (usually satisfactory)
approximation, the *rotational constant B_v in the vibrational
state v* is given by

$$B_v = B_e - \alpha_e(v + \tfrac{1}{2}) + \cdots. \quad \text{(III, 83)}$$

Here α_e is a constant which is small compared to B_e, since
the alteration of the internuclear distance by the vibration
is small compared to the internuclear distance itself. Empirically it has been found (Birge) that fairly generally

$$\frac{\alpha_e}{B_e} \approx 1.4 \frac{\omega_e x_e}{\omega_e}. \quad \text{(III, 84)}$$

In a similar manner, a mean rotational constant D_v,
representing the influence of centrifugal force, must be used
for the vibrational state v, where, analogous to B_v,

$$D_v = D_e + \beta_e(v + \tfrac{1}{2}). \quad \text{(III, 85)}$$

Here β_e is small compared to

$$D_e = \frac{4B_e{}^3}{\omega_e{}^2}, \quad \text{(III, 86)}$$

which refers to the completely vibrationless state [see
(III, 79)].

We obtain, accordingly, for the *rotational terms in a given
vibrational state*

$$F_v(J) = B_v J(J + 1) - D_v J^2(J + 1)^2, \quad \text{(III, 87)}$$

where the second term, with D_v, is very small compared to
the first and can often be neglected.

Some authors prefer to use, instead of equation (III, 87), the equation

$$F_v(J) = B_v(J + \tfrac{1}{2})^2 - D_v(J + \tfrac{1}{2})^4,$$

which differs from (III, 87) only by a small additive constant and by a very slight alteration in the meaning of B_v (the new B_v being the old $B_v - \tfrac{1}{2}D_v$). For the interpretation of the spectra this difference is quite unimportant, but it has to be kept in mind in comparing term values taken from different papers.

By taking into consideration the interaction of vibration and rotation, in the way described above, we obtain for the *term values of a vibrating rotator*

$$T = G(v) + F_v(J) = \omega_e(v + \tfrac{1}{2}) - \omega_e x_e(v + \tfrac{1}{2})^2 + \cdots$$
$$+ B_v J(J + 1) - D_v J^2 (J + 1)^2 + \cdots. \qquad \text{(III, 88)}$$

The corresponding *energy level diagram* is given in Fig. 51. In this figure, for clarity of representation only, the individual rotational levels are represented by shorter horizontal lines than the "pure" vibrational levels $(J = 0)$.

For the *lowest vibrational state* $(v = 0)$, the rotational constant B_0 has to be used in (III, 88). According to (III, 83), B_0 is somewhat smaller than the constant B_e, which corresponds to the unrealizable complete-ly vibrationless state. It should be remarked here that the rotational con-stant B obtained from the pure rotation spectrum (in

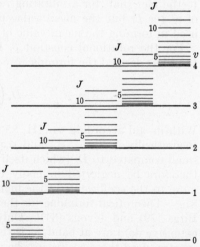

Fig. 51.   Energy Levels of the Vibrat-ing Rotator.   For each of the first five vibrational levels, a number of rotational levels are drawn (short horizontal lines).

the infrared or the Raman effect) is, of course, B_0. Corre-spondingly, the r value obtained (p. 86) is not r_e, corre-sponding to the minimum of the potential curve, but r_0, a mean value for the lowest vibrational state. r_0 is somewhat, though only very slightly, greater than r_e.

If the potential curve is known in a particular case, the averaging in (III, 81) can be carried out and α_e can then be calculated theoretically. The result of such a calculation is [see Teller (664)]

$$\alpha_e = 24 \frac{B_e{}^3 r_e{}^3 g}{\omega_e{}^3} - 6 \frac{B_e{}^2}{\omega_e}, \qquad \text{(III, 89)}$$

where g is the coefficient of the cubic term in the potential function (III, 53) (measured in cm^{-1})—that is, the term which brings about the asymmetry of the potential curve. If α_e is observed, the coefficient g can conversely be derived from (III, 89).

In practically all cases, the first term in (III, 89) outweighs the second, so that α is almost always positive. However, it can be seen from (III, 89) that even for a completely symmetrical curve (parabola) the constant α is not (as might perhaps have been expected) equal to zero, but has a negative value. This is related to the fact that, for a vibrating rotator, it is not the mean value of r^2 (or I) but the mean value of $1/r^2$ (or $1/I$) that has to be used in forming the mean value of B [see formula (III, 81)].

For the rotational constant β_e in (III, 85) Birge [see Jevons (34)] has derived the formula

$$\beta = -\frac{\alpha^2}{6\omega_e} + D_e \left(\frac{8\omega_e x_e}{\omega_e} - \frac{5\alpha}{B_e} \right).$$

With its aid according to (III, 85 and 86), D_v can be worked out theoretically if B_e, α_e, ω_e, and $\omega_e x_e$ are known. However, β_e is small compared to D_e (which itself is a small correction) and may therefore be neglected in many cases. The same applies even more to the coefficients of the higher powers of $J(J + 1)$ in (III, 87). Theoretical formulae for these coefficients may be found in Birge (29) and Jevons (34). Only if exceptionally accurate and extensive data are at hand, as is the case for a few electronic band spectra, need these coefficients be taken into account.

Furthermore, the calculation of the *finer interaction of vibration and rotation* [Dunham (194)] leads to the result that the constant B_e occurring in (III, 88) [by substituting (III, 83)] is not exactly $h/8\pi^2 c I_e$ [see (III, 82)] but deviates from this by a small amount. Similarly, ω_e in (III, 88) is not exactly the vibrational frequency for infinitesimal amplitudes (divided by c). However, these deviations are less than $\frac{1}{1000}$ of the actual values even for H_2

and the hydrides, where conditions are most unfavorable, and are much smaller for all other molecules. Extensive examples for the application of Dunham's formulae are given by Crawford and Jorgensen (173) and Dieke and Lewis (188).

Infrared spectrum. It may be shown [see Weizel (33)] that the *eigenfunctions of the vibrating rotator* are, to a first approximation, simply products of the corresponding vibrational and rotational eigenfunctions:

$$\psi = \psi_v(r - r_e)\psi_r(\theta, \phi). \tag{III, 90}$$

It follows from this that, for the vibrating rotator, both the selection rule previously given for the rotator and that for the oscillator hold. That is to say, v can alter by any integral amount, although $\Delta v = \pm 1$ gives by far the most intense transitions, and J can alter only by unity [see (III, 18)].

If we now consider a particular vibrational transition from v' to v'', we can write, according to (III, 88), for the *wave numbers of the resulting lines* (neglecting the rotational constant D)

$$\nu = \nu_0 + B_v'J'(J' + 1) - B_v''J''(J'' + 1),$$

where $\nu_0 = G(v') - G(v'')$ is the frequency of the pure vibrational transition without taking account of rotation ($J' = J'' = 0$). With $\Delta J = +1$ and $\Delta J = -1$, respectively, we obtain

$$\nu = \nu_0 + 2B_v' + (3B_v' - B_v'')J + (B_v' - B_v'')J^2;$$
$$J = 0, 1, \cdots (R \text{ branch}); \tag{III, 91}$$

$$\nu = \nu_0 \qquad - (B_v' + B_v'')J + (B_v' - B_v'')J^2;$$
$$J = 1, 2, \cdots (P \text{ branch}). \tag{III, 92}$$

Here, as usual (see p. 77), J'' has been replaced by J. Since J can take a whole series of values (see p. 131), two series of lines, which are called the R *and* P *branches*, respectively, are represented by these two formulae. The corresponding transitions are indicated in the energy level diagram, Fig. 52, while the spectrum resulting from them is represented schematically below. It can be seen that there is qualitatively complete agreement with the empirical fine structure of infrared bands (see p. 59 f.).

From Fig. 52 it is clear that for the R branch the smallest J value is 0, while for the P branch the smallest J value is 1.

If we neglect, for the moment, the interaction between rotation and vibration, we have $B_v' = B_v'' = B$ and formulae (III, 91) and (III, 92) simplify to

$$\nu_R = \nu_0 + 2B + 2BJ, \qquad \nu_P = \nu_0 - 2BJ; \quad \text{(III, 93)}$$

that is, we have two series of equidistant lines, the one, ν_R, going from ν_0 toward shorter wave lengths and the other, ν_P, going toward longer wave lengths. Owing to the above restriction for the J values, there is no line at ν_0; that is, we have a *zero gap*. The spectrum calculated according to (III, 93) is also shown in the lower part (*b*) of Fig. 52. It agrees qualitatively very well with the observed spectrum (Fig. 32, p. 58). The observed slight convergence of the lines is to be traced back to the *influence of the interaction of rotation and vibration*. In consequence of this interaction, B_v' differs from B_v'', giving rise to the quadratic terms in (III, 91) and (III, 92). This has the effect that, when $B_v' < B_v''$, the lines in the R branch draw closer together and those in the P branch draw farther apart [see Fig. 52(*a*)].

As may easily be verified, the two branches (III, 91) and (III, 92) can also be represented by a single formula—namely,

$$\nu = \nu_0 + (B_v' + B_v'')m + (B_v' - B_v'')m^2, \quad \text{(III, 94)}$$

where m is an integral running number which takes the values $1, 2, \cdots$ for the R branch (that is, $m = J + 1$) and the values $-1, -2, \cdots$ for the P branch (that is, $m = -J$). Thus we can also say that we have *a single series of lines for which a line is missing at $m = 0$*. The missing line is also called the *zero line* (*null line*). It would correspond to the forbidden transition between the two rotationless states $J = 0$ (see Fig. 52). ν_0 is also called the *band origin*.

Formula (III, 94) has exactly the same form as the empirical formula (II, 8). We conclude from this that the *molecule* actually is to be regarded as a *vibrating rotator* and that the spectra in the near infrared are *rotation-vibration spectra* and further that a band represents all the possible rotational transitions for a particular vibrational transition.[8]

Since α_e in (III, 83) is small, the difference between B_v' and B_v'' is, in general, small and the formulae (III, 93) give a fairly good representation of the observed spectra, particularly in the neighborhood of the zero gap. The separation of successive lines in the neighborhood of the zero gap gives an approximate value

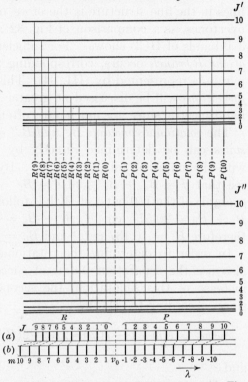

Fig. 52. **Energy Level Diagram for the Fine Structure of a Rotation-Vibration Band.** In general, the separation of the two vibrational levels is considerably larger compared to the spacing of the rotational levels than shown in the figure. In order to indicate this the vertical lines representing the transitions are partially broken. The schematic spectrograms (a) and (b) give the resulting spectrum with and without allowance for the interaction between rotation and vibration. In these spectrograms, unlike most of the others, short wave lengths are at the left.

---

[8] It should be remarked here that also with the old quantum theory expression BJ^2 for the rotational energy a formula of the form (II, 8) is obtained, but no missing line results, in disagreement with experiment.

for $2B$. The greater Δv is, the greater is the difference between B_v' and B_v'' [see (III, 83)]. The convergence of the lines in the fine structure is therefore more rapid for higher overtones, as a comparison of Fig. 32 and Fig. 33 (1–0 and 3–0 bands of HCl) shows. For sufficiently high J, a *reversal of the R branch* occurs, corresponding to the vertex of the parabola represented by (III, 94). This reversal (*band-head formation*) will be discussed at greater length for electronic band spectra, since it is much more often observed there.

The *rotational constants B_v' and B_v'' of the upper and lower states* can be determined directly by comparing (III, 94) with the empirical formula (II, 8). By this comparison we see that $d = B_v' + B_v''$ and $e = B_v' - B_v''$. Thus, in the example of the 1–0 band of HCl, it follows from (II, 10) that $B_1 + B_0 = 20.577$ cm^{-1}, $B_1 - B_0 = -0.3034$ cm^{-1}, and therefore $B_1 = 10.137$ cm^{-1} and $B_0 = 10.440$ cm^{-1}.

In order to determine the rotational constants we may also use the separation $\Delta \nu(m)$ of successive lines and the increase of this separation, the second difference $\Delta^2 \nu(m)$, since, according to (III, 94),

$$\Delta \nu(m) = \nu(m+1) - \nu(m) = 2B_v' + 2(B_v' - B_v'')m, \quad \text{(III, 95)}$$

and

$$\Delta^2 \nu(m) = \Delta \nu(m+1) - \Delta \nu(m) = 2(B_v' - B_v''). \quad \text{(III, 96)}$$

Thus the second difference is constant, in agreement with the empirical findings already mentioned in Chapter II. Its mean value gives a fairly accurate value for $2(B_v' - B_v'')$. A further equation for the constants B_v' and B_v'' is obtained from the first differences; for example, the intersection of the straight line representing (III, 95) with the axis $m = 0$ gives the value $2B_v'$. Other more accurate methods for the determination of B values will be discussed later (Chapter IV, p. 191 f.).

The B values for HCl, obtained from the 1–0, 2–0, and 3–0 bands, are summarized in Table 13. The difference between successive values is very nearly constant, as is to be expected from (III, 83). The mean value of this difference is the constant α_e, which is a measure of the interaction between vibration and rotation. Finally, the rotational constant B_e for the completely vibrationless state is obtained by adding $\frac{1}{2}\alpha_e$ to B_0.[9] For HCl, α_e is found to be 0.3019 cm^{-1} and B_e is found to be 10.5909 cm^{-1}; from this, according to (III, 82), we obtain for the nuclear

TABLE 13

ROTATIONAL CONSTANTS OF HCl IN THE DIFFERENT VIBRATIONAL STATES OF THE ELECTRONIC GROUND STATE

The B values for $v = 1$ and 2 have been recalculated from the data of Meyer and Levin (491).

v	B_v	ΔB_v
0	10.4400	
		0.3034
1	10.1366	
		0.3037
2	9.8329	
		0.2986
3	9.5343	

distance in the equilibrium position $r_e = 1.2747$ Å, while $r_0 = 1.2839$ Å.

It can be seen from Table 9 that there is a small but systematic trend in the second differences of the lines. This comes from the *influence of the rotational constant D*. When we take D into account in (III, 88), we obtain, in place of (III, 94),

$$\nu = \nu_0 + (B_v{}' + B_v{}'')m + (B_v{}' - B_v{}'' - D_v{}' + D_v{}'')m^2 \\ - 2(D_v{}' + D_v{}'')m^3 - (D_v{}' - D_v{}'')m^4. \quad \text{(III, 97)}$$

Since $D_v{}'$ is very nearly equal to $D_v{}''$ (see p. 114), the cubic term suffices in most cases for a complete representation of the two branches of a rotation-vibration band even for very accurate measurements [see the empirical formula (II, 11)]. It is obvious that conversely the rotational constant D can be derived from a determination of the cubic and possibly the fourth-power term in the empirical formula (see also Chapter IV, p. 198 f.). It is to be noted that taking account of the rotational constant D does not alter the earlier conclusion that both branches can be represented by a single formula.

---

[9] For an accurate evaluation of α_e and B_e it is necessary to calculate the B_v values according to (III, 83) with preliminary B_e and α_e values (obtained as described above) and then, when necessary, to alter α_e and B_e so that the deviation, B_v (observed) − B_v (calculated), is as small as possible. This can be done graphically or by the method of least squares.

Raman spectrum. For Raman transitions we must take account of the selection rule $\Delta J = 0, \pm 2$ (see p. 94). Accordingly, the *Raman vibration bands* consist of *three branches*, of which two, those with $\Delta J = \pm 2$, are similar to those of the infrared rotation-vibration bands, except that the line separation is twice as great. They are called S and O branches.[10] The third branch ($\Delta J = 0$) is called the *zero* or Q *branch*. For this branch

$$\Delta\nu = \Delta\nu_0 + F'(J) - F''(J)$$
$$= \Delta\nu_0 + (B_v' - B_v'')J + (B_v' - B_v'')J^2. \tag{III, 98}$$

Since the difference between B_v' and B_v'' is very small for the vibrational transition $0 \rightarrow 1$ (the only one so far observed in the Raman effect), practically all the lines of the Q branch fall very close to one another and are in general not resolved. Thus in the Raman effect we would expect one intense "line" at the position $\Delta\nu_0$ ($= \Delta G_{\frac{1}{2}}$), the line possibly being somewhat broadened towards shorter wave lengths (smaller $\Delta\nu$). This corresponds exactly to observations, as we have seen in Chapter II, p. 64 f. The two other branches (S and O) are very much weaker, since for them the individual lines do not superimpose. Thus far they have been observed only for hydrogen [by Rasetti (578)]. We shall therefore refrain from reproducing the formulae for these branches. For hydrogen, the Q branch is resolved into individual lines. In all other cases, including polyatomic molecules, the *Raman lines of large displacement represent the unresolved Q branches of the Raman rotation-vibration bands.*

(d) The Symmetrical Top

The molecule as a symmetrical top. Thus far in our considerations we have taken as a model for the rotations of the molecule a simple rotator, with the tacit assumption that the moment of inertia about the line joining the nuclei

---

[10] In contrast to the case of the rotational Raman spectrum (see p. 96), here $\Delta J = -2$ is also possible, giving rise to the O branch.

is zero. In actuality, however, there are a number of electrons revolving about the two nuclei, and, as a result, the *moment of inertia about the line joining the nuclei is not exactly zero*—it is only very small, owing to the smallness of the mass of the electron. Thus a better model for the diatomic molecule than the simple rotator would be a system somewhat like a dumbbell carrying a flywheel on its axis. Such a system is an example of the more general case of a *symmetrical top*, which is defined as a system having the moments of inertia about three mutually perpendicular axes passing through the center of gravity (the *principal axes*) all different from zero, but having two of the moments of inertia equal. The latter condition is obviously fulfilled for diatomic molecules, since the moments of inertia I_B about all the axes at right angles to the line joining the nuclei and passing through the center of gravity are equal to one another. The moment of inertia I_A about the line joining the nuclei is very much smaller than I_B. In spite of this, the corresponding *angular momenta* are of the same order of magnitude, since the electrons rotate much more rapidly than the heavy nuclei.

Angular momenta. According to classical mechanics, the total angular momentum of such a symmetric top need no longer be always perpendicular to the figure axis (internuclear axis), as is the case for the simple rotator, since a rotation about the figure axis can now take place in addition to the rotation about an axis perpendicular to it. The two corresponding angular momenta are added together to give the *total angular momentum* P. Only the total angular momentum is constant in magnitude as well as direction. However, its *component in the direction of the figure axis* (that is, the angular momentum about the figure axis) is *constant in magnitude* but not in direction. In fact, the figure axis rotates at a constant angle about P with a frequency $(1/2\pi)(P/I_B)$, which corresponds to the rotational frequency of the simple rotator (see p. 70). This motion of the figure axis is called *nutation*.[11] The constant component of the total angular momentum in the direction of the figure axis in the present case is due to the *revolution of the electrons*.

According to quantum theory, the component of the total angular momentum in the direction of the figure axis (that is, the electronic angular momentum), if we neglect electron spin (see Chapter V), can be only an integral multiple of $h/2\pi$. Therefore, designating this angular momentum by Λ, we have

$$|\Lambda| = \Lambda \frac{h}{2\pi}, \qquad (III, 99)$$

where Λ is the *quantum number of the angular momentum of the electrons about the internuclear axis*. As before, in quantum theory, the *total angular momentum*, designated by J, can take only the values

$$|J| = \sqrt{J(J+1)} \frac{h}{2\pi} \approx J \frac{h}{2\pi}. \qquad (III, 100)$$

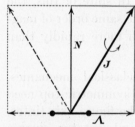

Fig. 53. Vector Diagram for the Symmetrical Top. The curved arrow indicates the rotation of the whole diagram about J. The dotted part of the figure gives the vector diagram when the sense of the direction of Λ is reversed.

Fig. 53 gives the corresponding vector diagram. In it N is the angular momentum, at right angles to the axis, that represents essentially the *rotation of the nuclei alone*.[12] Since Λ and J have integral values, N obviously cannot have integral values. Its magnitude is fixed by the values of Λ and J. It should be noted that J is no longer perpendicular to the axis except when $\Lambda = 0$. The whole system rotates about J with a frequency that is the same as that of the simple rotator with the same I_B and the same J [formula (III, 20)].

---

[11] Frequently it is referred to as *precession*, contrary to the usage in the theory of gyroscopic motion. Precession is the motion of an angular momentum vector under the action of a force (see below).

[12] This vector, of course, has nothing to do with the nuclear spin (see Chapter I).

If the sense of the rotation of the electrons about the internuclear axis is reversed, Λ has the opposite direction and the vector diagram drawn in broken lines in Fig. 53 is obtained. For the same N, the same J value is obtained, or, in other words, *for each value of J there are two modes of motion of the system* corresponding to the two directions of Λ.

Energy levels. According to quantum mechanical calculations [see, for example, Weizel (33)], the *terms* for the symmetrical top are given by

$$F(J) = BJ(J + 1) + (A - B)\Lambda^2, \qquad \text{(III, 101)}$$

where

$$B = \frac{h}{8\pi^2 c I_B}, \quad A = \frac{h}{8\pi^2 c I_A}. \qquad \text{(III, 102)}$$

$I_B = \mu r^2$ is the "ordinary" moment of inertia of the molecule about an axis perpendicular to the internuclear axis, as used previously, and I_A is the moment of inertia of the electrons about the internuclear axis. Owing to the smallness of I_A, A is very much larger than B. For a given electronic state, Λ is constant and has in general only a small (integral) value (see Chapter V). As a result, *the rotational levels of the symmetrical top are the same as those of the simple rotator apart from a shift of magnitude* $(A - B)\Lambda^2$, which is constant for a given electronic state. However, the *smallest value of J that can occur is now equal to Λ*, since J is the vector sum of Λ and N (Fig. 53). Thus we have only the J values

$$J = \Lambda, \Lambda + 1, \Lambda + 2, \Lambda + 3, \cdots. \qquad \text{(III, 103)}$$

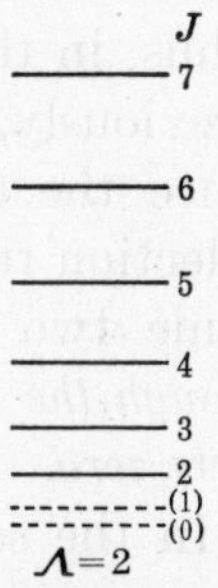

This is represented for $\Lambda = 2$ in Fig. 54, in which the rotational levels that do not occur $(J < \Lambda)$ are indicated by broken lines.

The sense of direction of Λ does not enter equation (III, 101); that is to say, the two states represented by the full-line and broken-line vector diagrams (Fig. 53) have exactly

Fig. 54. Energy Level Diagram of a Symmetrical Top with $\Lambda = 2$. The dotted levels do not occur.

the same energy (are *degenerate* with respect to each other). Each of the levels in Fig. 54 consists in actuality of *two levels which coincide with each other*.

In (III, 101), the influence of the interaction of vibration and rotation may again be taken into account by putting B_v in the place of B, and the influence of centrifugal force may be taken into account by subtracting $D_v J^2 (J + 1)^2$.

Infrared spectrum.   The derivation of the *selection rules* according to the methods previously indicated leads to different results according as $\Lambda = 0$ or $\Lambda \neq 0$ [see, for example, Weizel (33)].   For the present discussion we assume that Λ does not alter in the transition; that is, we exclude electronic transitions, which will be dealt with in the following chapter. Then,

$$\text{for } \Lambda = 0, \qquad \Delta J = \pm 1, \qquad \text{(III, 104)}$$

and

$$\text{for } \Lambda \neq 0, \qquad \Delta J = 0, \pm 1. \qquad \text{(III, 105)}$$

Thus, in the first case ($\Lambda = 0$), everything is just as it was previously, when we were considering the simple rotator, since the term $(A - B)\Lambda^2$ in (III, 101) disappears and the selection rule is the same as before.   We obtain exactly the same two branches, and thus we can treat this case *as though the moment of inertia about the line joining the nuclei were zero*.

In the second case ($\Lambda \neq 0$), the energy relations are the same, except for a constant shift.   However, in addition to the transitions with $\Delta J = \pm 1$, there also appear transitions with $\Delta J = 0$—that is, a series of lines given by

$$\nu = \nu_0 + F'(J) - F''(J) \qquad \text{(III, 106)}$$

and called a *Q branch*.   Substitution of (III, 101), with B_v instead of B, gives

$$\nu = \nu_0 + (B_v'' - B_v')\Lambda^2 + (B_v' - B_v'')J + (B_v' - B_v'')J^2. \quad \text{(III, 107)}$$

All the lines of this branch fall very near to the position ν_0, since B_v' is very nearly equal to B_v'' in infrared spectra.

Thus a relatively intense *"line"* would be expected at the position where, for $\Lambda = 0$, the zero gap appears. Further, owing to the restriction of the J values by (III, 103), one or more of the lines at the beginning of the P and the R branches must be missing (for further details see pp. 186, 282, 293, and 299).

A comparison of the observed infrared spectra with the theoretical spectrum of the symmetrical top shows that in practically all cases there is complete agreement with the first case, $\Lambda = 0$. That is to say, the model of the ordinary simple rotator reproduces these spectra in all details. From this we can conclude conversely that, for the molecules for which such simple infrared spectra are observed, $\Lambda = 0$ in the electronic ground state; that is, the motion of the electrons is such that *no angular momentum about the internuclear axis* results.

So far, in only one case—namely, that of NO—has a Q branch actually been observed in the infrared spectrum [Snow, Rawlins, and Rideal (642)]. In this case, therefore, we must conclude that there is an angular momentum of the electrons about the internuclear axis ($\Lambda \neq 0$), a conclusion that is confirmed by the investigation of the electronic band spectra of this molecule.

Raman spectrum.   The selection rules for the Raman spectrum of the symmetric top are found to be the following [see Placzek (562)]:

$$\text{for } \Lambda = 0: \quad \Delta J = 0, \ \pm 2,$$

$$\text{for } \Lambda \neq 0: \quad \Delta J = 0, \ \pm 1, \ \pm 2.$$

Thus again in the first case ($\Lambda = 0$) everything is the same as for the simple rotator (or vibrating rotator). The Raman spectrum consists of S, O, and Q branches. However, in the second case ($\Lambda \neq 0$), in addition, an R branch ($\Delta J = +1$) and a P branch ($\Delta J = -1$) appear. In the case of the rotational Raman spectrum, where only positive values of ΔJ are possible [see section 1(d) of this chapter], we expect, therefore, in addition to the Stokes and anti-Stokes S branches ($\Delta J = +2$), a Stokes and an anti-Stokes R branch ($\Delta J = +1$). These R branches have half the spacing of the S branches (that is, $2B$ compared to $4B$).

Every alternate line of the R branches coincides with a line of the S branches. Thus far such a case has not been observed for diatomic molecules. According to the infrared spectrum (see above), NO has $\Lambda \neq 0$ in its ground state, but, as shown by the electronic band spectrum, the latter is a doublet state. This leads to the consequence (as can easily be shown) that alternate lines of the R branches do not coincide with those of the S branches, giving a closer spacing of the lines in the Raman spectrum, which consequently has not yet been completely resolved.

(e) Thermal Distribution of the Quantum States; Intensities in Rotation-Vibration Spectra

The intensity of a spectral line depends not only on the transition probability and the frequency ν but also on the number of molecules in the initial state. Thus for a theoretical estimation of intensities, a knowledge of the number of molecules in the initial state is necessary, in addition to a knowledge of selection rules and transition probabilities. In the following we shall consider only the case of *thermal equilibrium*. The distribution of the molecules over the different quantum states in this case is of interest not only for the calculation of intensities but also for many other questions.

Vibration. According to the *Boltzmann energy distribution law*, the number of molecules dN_E that have a classical vibrational energy between E and $E + dE$ is proportional to $e^{-(E/kT)} dE$, where k is the gas constant per molecule and T is the absolute temperature. The function $e^{-(E/kT)} (= e^{-(E/0.6951T)}$, when E is expressed in cm^{-1}) is represented graphically in Fig. 55 for $T = 300°$ K. (room temperature). Classically, there is no restriction for the E values, and therefore, according to Fig. 55, at $300°$ K. most molecules are vibrating, even though with small amplitude.

In quantum theory, in contradistinction, only the discrete values (III, 58) are possible for the vibrational energy. The number of molecules in each of the vibrational states is again proportional to $e^{-(E/kT)} = e^{-[G_0(v)hc/kT]} = e^{-[G_0(v)/0.6951T]}$. The zero-point energy can be left out, since to add this to the exponent would mean only adding a factor that is constant for all the vibrational levels (including the zero level).

The ordinates corresponding to the discrete values of the vibrational energy are indicated by broken lines in Fig. 55 for the case of $I_2[G_0(v) = 213.67v - 0.592v^2]$. It is seen from this figure that the number of molecules in the higher vibrational states falls off very rapidly. The falling off will be even more pronounced for molecules such as H_2, N_2, O_2, and so forth, which have larger vibrational quanta (see abscissa scale in Fig. 55). In order to give some idea of the

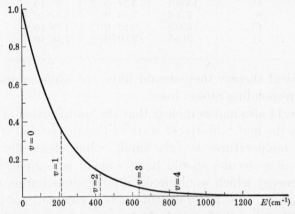

Fig. 55. **Boltzmann Factor and Thermal Distribution of the Vibrational States.** The curve gives the function $e^{-E/kT}$ for $T = 300°$ K. with E in cm^{-1}. The broken-line ordinates correspond to the vibrational states of the I_2 molecule.

quantitative relationships, the factor $e^{-(\Delta G_{\frac{1}{2}}hc/kT)}$—that is, the ratio of the number of molecules in the first to that in the zeroth vibrational state—is given in Table 14 for a number of gases for 300° K. and 1000° K. It is seen that this fraction is very small for gases such as HCl, CO, and N_2 even at 1000° K. Accordingly practically all the transitions observed in absorption in the infrared have $v = 0$ in the initial state. This is also the reason that anti-Stokes lines (for which the initial state has $v = 1$) are not observed in the Raman effect of diatomic molecules (see p. 93), while, according

TABLE 14

RATIO OF THE NUMBER OF MOLECULES IN THE FIRST TO
THAT IN THE ZEROTH VIBRATIONAL STATE
FOR 300° K. AND 1000° K.

Gas	$\Delta G_{\frac{1}{2}}(cm^{-1})$	$e^{-(\Delta G_{\frac{1}{2}} hc/kT)}$	
		For 300° K.	For 1000° K.
H_2	4160.2	$2.16 \cdot 10^{-9}$	$2.51 \cdot 10^{-3}$
HCl	2885.9	$9.77 \cdot 10^{-7}$	$1.57 \cdot 10^{-2}$
N_2	2330.7	$1.40 \cdot 10^{-5}$	$3.50 \cdot 10^{-2}$
CO	2144.0	$3.43 \cdot 10^{-5}$	$4.58 \cdot 10^{-2}$
O_2	1556.4	$5.74 \cdot 10^{-4}$	$1.07 \cdot 10^{-1}$
S_2	721.6	$3.14 \cdot 10^{-2}$	$3.54 \cdot 10^{-1}$
Cl_2	556.9	$6.92 \cdot 10^{-2}$	$4.49 \cdot 10^{-1}$
I_2	213.1	$3.60 \cdot 10^{-1}$	$7.36 \cdot 10^{-1}$

to classical theory, they should have the same intensity as
the corresponding Stokes lines.

Table 14 also makes it clear that the contribution of molecules in the first vibrational state to the *heat content of a gas*
at low temperatures is very small, while classically practically all molecules should have a small amount of vibrational energy which would make a large contribution to the
heat content. The latter conclusion is in complete contradiction to experiment. It is only for heavy molecules, such as I_2,
that there is an appreciable fraction of the molecules in the
first vibrational state at room temperature.

The quantities $e^{-[G_0(v)hc/kT]}$ give the relative numbers of molecules
in the different vibrational states referred to the number of
molecules in the lowest vibrational state. If we wish to refer
to the *total number of molecules*, we have to consider that the
latter is proportional to $1 + e^{-[G_0(1)hc/kT]} + e^{-[G_0(2)hc/kT]} + \cdots$ [the
so-called *state sum* (or *partition function*)] with the same factor of
proportionality as before. Therefore the number of molecules in
the state v is

$$N_v = N \frac{e^{-[G_0(v)hc/kT]}}{1 + e^{-[G_0(1)hc/kT]} + e^{-[G_0(2)hc/kT]} + \cdots}, \quad (III, 108)$$

where N is the total number of molecules. Successive terms in
the denominator decrease very rapidly. If the second term is

small compared to 1, for most practical purposes the number of molecules, N_v, can be put equal to $Ne^{-[G_0(v)hc/kT]}$. Thus those figures in Table 14 that are much smaller than 1 give directly the fraction of the molecules in the first vibrational state.

Rotation. The thermal distribution for the rotational states (other than for the vibrational states) is not given simply by the Boltzmann factor $e^{-(E/kT)}$; we have to allow for the fact that, according to the quantum theory, each state of an atomic system with total angular momentum J consists of $2J + 1$ levels which coincide in the absence of an external field; that is, the state is $(2J + 1)$-fold degenerate (see p. 23). The frequency of its occurrence (its *statistical weight*) is therefore $(2J + 1)$ times that of a state with $J = 0$.

The *number of molecules N_J in the rotational state J of the lowest vibrational state* at the temperature T is thus proportional to

$$(2J + 1)e^{-[F(J)hc/kT]}. \tag{III, 109}$$

For most practical cases ($\Lambda = 0$, rigid rotator)

$$N_J \propto (2J + 1)e^{-[BJ(J+1)hc/kT]}. \tag{III, 110}$$

This function is represented in Fig. 56 for $B = 10.44$ cm^{-1} (that is, for HCl) and $T = 300°$ K. Since the factor $2J + 1$ increases linearly with J, the number of molecules in the different rotational states does not from the beginning decrease with the rotational quantum number but first goes through a *maximum*. It is easily seen that this maximum lies at

$$J_{\text{max.}} = \sqrt{\frac{kT}{2Bhc}} - \frac{1}{2} = 0.5895 \sqrt{\frac{T}{B}} - \frac{1}{2} \tag{III, 111}$$

—that is, at a value of J that increases with decreasing B and increasing T. It should be noted that the number of molecules in the lowest rotational state, $J = 0$, is not zero.

For the *higher vibrational states* we have

$$N_J \propto (2J + 1)e^{-[(G+F)hc/kT]}$$

instead of (III, 109). However, the factor $e^{-(Ghc/kT)}$ can be separated off; that is, the distribution over the rotational states is the same, but the absolute frequency of occurrence of all the states is considerably smaller than for the lowest vibrational state, corresponding to the factor $e^{-(Ghc/kT)}$.

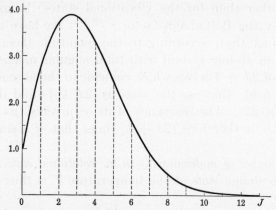

Fig. 56. Thermal Distribution of the Rotational States for $T = 300°$ K. and $B = 10.44$ cm^{-1} (That Is, for HCl in the Ground State). The curve represents the function $(2J + 1)e^{BJ(J+1)hc/kT}$ as a function of J. The broken-line ordinates give the relative frequency of occurrence of the corresponding rotational states.

Just as for the vibration, the actual number of molecules in the rotational states is obtained by multiplying by N and dividing by the state sum; that is,

$$N_J = N \frac{(2J + 1)e^{-[BJ(J+1)hc/kT]}}{1 + 3e^{-(2Bhc/kT)} + 5e^{-(6Bhc/kT)} + \cdots} \cdot \quad \text{(III, 112)}$$

For sufficiently large T, the sum in the denominator can be replaced by an integral—namely,

$$\int_0^\infty (2J + 1)e^{-[hcBJ(J+1)/kT]} \, dJ = \frac{kT}{hcB}$$

—so that we have

$$N_J = N \frac{hcB}{kT} (2J+1)e^{-[BJ(J+1)hc/kT]}. \quad \text{(III, 113)}$$

The *variation of the intensity of the lines* in a rotation-vibration band or in a pure rotation spectrum is given essentially by the thermal distribution of the rotational states;

that is, to a first approximation, the intensity is proportional to the expression (III, 110). However, it must be remembered that the intensity of a spectral line depends on the statistical weights of *both* the states concerned (as for atomic spectra). Accordingly, a more detailed calculation shows that the intensity depends on $(J' + J'' + 1)$ instead of $(2J + 1)$ in (III, 110); that is, it depends on the mean value of $(2J + 1)$ for the upper and lower states. In addition, the J value of the initial state must be used in the exponential term—that is, in absorption J'', in emission J'. Therefore, the intensities of the lines of rotation or rotation-vibration bands *in absorption* are given by

$$I_{\text{abs.}} = C(J' + J'' + 1)e^{-[B''J''(J''+1)hc/kT]} \quad \text{(III, 114)}$$

and *in emission* by

$$I_{\text{em.}} = C(J' + J'' + 1)e^{-[B'J'(J'+1)hc/kT]}. \quad \text{(III, 115)}$$

According to (I, 18), the factor C in (III, 114) and (III, 115) contains ν and ν^4, respectively, which are very nearly constant for a given rotation-vibration band, although they vary greatly for the pure rotation spectrum.

The theoretical intensity distribution for the rotation-vibration spectrum of HCl in absorption at 100° K., 300° K., and 1000° K. is represented in Fig. 57(a). The abscissae give the position of the lines, assuming that $B' = B''$; the ordinates are proportional to the intensities. It should be noted that for not too high temperature, when practically all molecules have $v = 0$, the total intensity of an absorption band is independent of the temperature. Therefore the factor C in (III, 114) has to be chosen differently for different temperatures in such a way that the total intensity of the band is unaltered. It can be seen from Fig. 57(a) that with increasing temperature the band extends farther; the intensity maxima of the two branches move outward and at the same time become flatter. A comparison of the curve for 300° K. with the observed spectrum (Fig. 32 or

33) shows that the agreement between theory and experiment is very good.

Fig. 57(*b*) illustrates the same relations for the case of a molecule with $B = 2$ cm^{-1}. The maxima lie here at greater J values, but in spite of this the separation of the maxima in cm^{-1} is less than for HCl with $B = 10.44$ cm^{-1}. By means

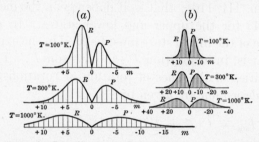

Fig. 57. Intensity Distribution in Rotation-Vibration Bands in Absorption at 100° K., 300° K., and 1000° K. (*a*) For $B = 10.44$ cm^{-1} (HCl). (*b*) For $B = 2$ cm^{-1}. The wave-length scale of the abscissae, which is not explicitly given, is the same for all the diagrams. The lines are drawn with the separation that they would have if the constant B were the same in the upper and lower states. *m* is the running number of the lines (see p. 118). Note that the longer wave lengths are to the right in this figure.

of (III, 111), the separation of the maxima for an unresolved band can be used to give a rough estimation of B when the temperature is known.

Similar curves hold for the pure rotation spectrum in the far infrared, and also for the Raman spectra. For the intensity distribution in the Q branch, if one is present, see p. 227.

(f) Symmetry Properties of the Rotational States

Positive and negative rotational levels. A more detailed investigation of the eigenfunctions of the rotator ψ_r (see p. 73 f.) shows that they have the following symmetry properties. *When reflected at the origin of co-ordinates, ψ_r remains unaltered for even values of J but changes to $-\psi_r$ for odd values of J.* By reflection of an eigenfunction at the origin (or inversion) we mean replacement of the co-ordinates x, y, z by $-x, -y, -z$. For a rigid rotator, the eigenfunctions depend only on the direction (r is constant), and therefore reflection at the origin means simply a reversal of direction.

The correctness of the above rule is easily verified from the rotational eigenfunctions reproduced in Fig. 39 (broken curves); in two opposing directions, the magnitude of the eigenfunction (given by the distance of the curve from the origin) is the same. However, the sign is the same only for even J values; for odd J values it is opposite.

The *total eigenfunction* of a molecule, allowing for the motion of the electrons, is, to a first approximation, a product of the electronic, vibrational, and rotational eigenfunctions (see p. 160) (quite similar to the eigenfunction of the vibrating rotator, which is a product of the eigenfunctions of the oscillator and the rotator [see (III, 90)]):

$$\psi = \psi_e \psi_v \psi_r. \qquad \text{(III, 116)}$$

A rotational level is now called *positive or negative according as the total eigenfunction remains unaltered or changes sign by reflection at the origin.* The vibrational eigenfunction, ψ_v, always remains unaltered by reflection at the origin, since it depends only on the internuclear distance (which has no sign). Thus, when the electronic eigenfunction, ψ_e, remains unaltered by reflection at the origin or when the electronic motion is altogether neglected and only the simple rotator or vibrating rotator is considered, *the rotational levels are positive or negative according as J is even or odd.* This is illustrated in Fig. 58(a). However, when the electronic motion is taken into account, it may happen, as will be further discussed in Chapter V, that ψ_e changes sign by reflection at the origin and that, as a result, the total eigenfunction (III, 116) remains unaltered for odd J and changes

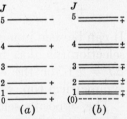

Fig. 58. Symmetry Properties of the Levels (a) of the Rotator and (b) of the Symmetrical Top. For the symmetrical top, $\Lambda = 1$ is assumed. The dotted level with $J = 0$ therefore does not occur.

sign for even J. The $+$ and $-$ have then to be exchanged in Fig. 58(a).

According to our previous discussion, a twofold degeneracy exists when $\Lambda \neq 0$ for the electronic motion (symmetrical top; see p. 125 f.) and to this corresponds, as a more detailed investigation shows, the fact that there is then for each value of J *a positive as well as a negative level.* The energy level diagram for $\Lambda = 1$ is drawn in Fig. 58(b) with the designation $+$ and $-$ added. In this figure the levels that are degenerate with respect to each other have been drawn separated. Actually, a splitting of the degenerate levels of the type indicated in the figure does appear when one takes account of the interaction of electronic motion and rotation (see Chapter V).

An important *selection rule* for transitions with radiation can easily be derived for positive and negative levels (see below). It is as follows: *Positive levels combine only with negative, and vice versa.* Transitions between two positive terms and two negative terms are forbidden. This selection rule can also be written symbolically:

$$+ \rightarrow -, \quad - \rightarrow +, \quad + \nrightarrow +, \quad - \nrightarrow -. \quad \text{(III, 117)}$$

It can be seen immediately from Fig. 58(a) and (b) that this selection rule does not contradict the previous selection rule $\Delta J = \pm 1$ for the simple rotator, or $\Delta J = 0, \pm 1$ for the symmetrical top, with $\Lambda \neq 0$.

The opposite selection rule holds for transitions taking place in the *Raman effect*; namely, positive terms combine only with positive and negative only with negative.

$$+ \rightarrow +, \quad - \rightarrow -, \quad + \nrightarrow -, \quad - \nrightarrow +. \quad \text{(III, 118)}$$

This rule also does not contradict the previous selection rule $\Delta J = 0, \pm 2$, which applies for the Raman effect.

The selection rules for dipole radiation are obtained by calculating $\int x\psi'\psi''^* d\tau, \int y\psi'\psi''^* d\tau$, and $\int z\psi'\psi''^* d\tau$ (see p. 16). If both the combining levels (with eigenfunctions ψ' and ψ'', respectively) are positive or if both are negative, the integrand will change sign for a reflection at the origin; that is, the integral will also change sign. Since, however, the value of a definite integral is independent of any transformation of co-ordinates, it follows that the above integrals are zero; that is, such transitions are forbidden. If, on the other hand, a transition between a positive and a negative term is considered, the integrand remains unchanged for a reflection at the origin and consequently the value of the integral may well be different from zero; that is, transitions between a positive and a negative level are allowed. This selection rule is completely analogous to the Laporte rule for atoms (see A.A., p. 154).

In the Raman effect, the transition probability depends on $\int \alpha_{xx} \psi' \psi'' d\tau$, and so forth, where α_{xx} is the polarizability (see p. 92), which has the same value for two opposite directions. Consequently, in this case the integrand remains unchanged for a reflection at the origin if ψ' and ψ'' have the same symmetry— that is, are both positive or both negative. Thus the selection rule (III, 118) is obtained. The same rule also holds for quadrupole and magnetic dipole radiation (see p. 303).

Symmetric and antisymmetric rotational levels for homonuclear molecules. According to quantum mechanics [see, for example, Kronig (31)], when two identical nuclei are present in a molecule—that is, if we have a homonuclear molecule ($H_2{}^1$, $C_2{}^{12}$, $O_2{}^{16}$, and so forth)—*for an exchange of the nuclei the total eigenfunction either remains unaltered or only changes its sign* (see p. 261). According as the former or the latter is the case, the state under consideration is said to be *symmetric* or *antisymmetric in the nuclei.* Exchange of the nuclei means that the co-ordinates of nucleus 1 (x_1, y_1, z_1) are exchanged with those of nucleus 2 (x_2, y_2, z_2) in the eigenfunction, which is, of course, a function of the co-ordinates of both nuclei as well as of the co-ordinates of the electrons.

$$[\psi(x_1, y_1, z_1, x_2, y_2, z_2, \cdots) \rightarrow \psi(x_2, y_2, z_2, x_1, y_1, z_1, \cdots)].$$

It will be shown later (see p. 261) that in a given electronic state of a molecule (in our present considerations we are always dealing with the electronic ground state) *either the positive rotational levels are symmetric and the negative are antisymmetric throughout, or, conversely, the positive are antisymmetric and the negative are symmetric.* We shall limit ourselves in this chapter to the consideration of the case $\Lambda = 0$, since it is practically the only one occurring in rotation and rotation-vibration spectra. (For other cases, see Chapter V.) For this case, according to the above, either the even-numbered levels are symmetric and the odd are antisymmetric, or vice versa, as shown in Fig. 59.

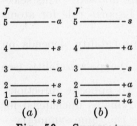

Fig. 59. Symmetry Properties of the Rotational Levels for Identical Nuclei for $\Lambda = 0$. In (a) the positive terms are symmetric (s) and the negative antisymmetric (a); in (b) the reverse is the case.

Provided we disregard nuclear spin (see below), there is an *absolutely strict prohibition of intercombinations* between the symmetric and antisymmetric states.

$$antisym. \leftrightarrow\!\!\!\!/ \ sym. \qquad \text{(III, 119)}$$

This prohibition holds *not only for transitions with radiation but also for transitions brought about in any other way* (collisions, Raman effect, and so forth).

On the basis of this selection rule we can immediately understand (without considering the vanishing dipole moment; see above) why homonuclear molecules do not have an ordinary rotation spectrum or rotation-vibration spectrum. The reason is that any two terms for which the selection rule $\Delta J = \pm 1$ is fulfilled have opposite symmetry in the nuclei (see Fig. 59). In the Raman effect, on the contrary, transitions do take place for homonuclear molecules, since, for these transitions, $\Delta J = 0, \pm 2$; that is, the symmetry does not change.[13]

---

[13] Similarly, transitions between the rotational and vibrational levels of the ground state of homonuclear molecules may take place by quadrupole radiation, since, for quadrupole transitions, $\Delta J = 0, \pm 2$ is possible [in addition to $\Delta J = \pm 1$, which here is forbidden by (III, 119)]. Thus infrared rotation-vibration spectra of homonuclear molecules may yet occur, but they are only about 10^{-9} times as intense as ordinary dipole rotation-vibration spectra and thus far have not been observed (see also p. 305).

The selection rule (III, 119) can easily be proved. According to (I, 17), the probability of transitions occurring by way of dipole radiation depends on $\int \psi_n \psi_m{}^*(\Sigma e_i x_i)d\tau$ (and similarly for y and z), where e_i is the charge and x_i the x co-ordinate of the ith particle. If ψ_n is the eigenfunction of a symmetric state and ψ_m that of an antisymmetric state, the integrand, and with it the integral, alters its sign by exchange of the nuclei, since $\Sigma e_i x_i$ does not alter by an exchange of the identical nuclei. Since the value of the integral cannot depend on the mode of designating the nuclei, it follows that the integral is zero—that is, that the transition is forbidden. The same result is obtained for any other radiation (quadrupole radiation, magnetic dipole radiation, and so forth), since the expression that then appears in the place of $\Sigma e_i x_i$ is also symmetric in the two nuclei. This holds even for transitions brought about by collisions, since the interaction between the molecule and any other particle is necessarily symmetric in the two nuclei. Thus, the selection rule (III, 119) holds absolutely rigorously.

On the basis of the selection rule (III, 119), if all the molecules of one kind (for example, all the O_2 molecules) were in symmetric states at the beginning of time (or all in antisymmetric states), they would still be in the same kind of state. That is, it would be as if the antisymmetric (or symmetric) states had never existed. For $\Lambda = 0$, they are either all the even-numbered or all the odd-numbered rotational levels (see Fig. 59). If this were the case, *every second line should be missing* in the rotation Raman bands (and also in the electronic bands; see Chapter V). This is actually observed in the Raman spectrum of O_2, as well as in the electronic band spectra of O_2 and of some other molecules —namely, C_2, He_2, S_2, and Se_2.

It might at first be thought difficult to decide whether every second line were missing or whether the rotational lines could be represented, by a suitable choice of the rotational constant B, without the assumption of missing lines. In order to see that an unambiguous decision is always possible, let us consider Fig. 60, in which a rotational Raman spectrum is once more schematically represented, the Raman lines with even-numbered lower levels (and therefore also even-numbered upper levels) being indicated by broken lines. If no line is missing, according to (III, 52) the separation between the first line of the long-wave-length branch and the first line of the short-wave-length branch is $12B$, while the separation of successive lines in both branches is $4B$. If the even-numbered rotational levels are missing, all the lines with even-numbered J (broken lines in Fig. 60) must be missing. As a result, the separation of the first line of the long-wave-length branch from that of the short-wave-

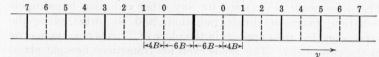

Fig. 60. **Rotational Raman Spectrum of a Molecule with Identical Nuclei (Schematic).** The lines corresponding to the even rotational levels are drawn broken. The heavy line in the center gives the undisplaced exciting line.

length branch would be $2(6 + 4)B = 20B$, while the line separation would be $8B$. If the odd-numbered lines were missing, the separation of the first line of the long-wave-length branch from the first line of the short-wave-length branch would be $12B$, while the line separation would be again $8B$. Thus the separation of the first long-wave-length from the first short-wave-length Raman line is to the separations of successive lines in the ratios $6 : 2$, $5 : 2$, and $3 : 2$, respectively, in the three cases. Therefore, even without any knowledge of the constant B it is possible to decide unambiguously with which case we are dealing. A measurement of the spectrogram for O_2 [Fig. 36(b)] shows that the above-mentioned ratio is $5 : 2$. It follows that the even-numbered levels are missing. They are, in the case of O_2, the antisymmetric levels, as in Fig. 59(b) (see also Chapter V, p. 276).

Influence of nuclear spin. Apart from homonuclear molecules with bands in which every second line is missing, others are known for which the intensity of every second line is only decreased. Such an *alternation of intensities* may be seen very well, for example, in the Raman spectrum of N_2 in Fig. 36(a). It is also found for H_2, Li_2, and many other molecules in their electronic band spectra.   The explanation for this phenomenon was first given by Hund (346).[14]   It depends on the fact that the nuclei in the molecules whose bands show only an alternation of intensities and no alternate missing lines possess an intrinsic nuclear angular momentum I (*nuclear spin*) different from zero (see Chapter I, p. 27). A theoretical investigation shows that *in the presence of nuclear spin the selection rule sym. $\leftrightarrow$ antisym. no longer holds absolutely*, although it is still very strict.   As a result, both term systems, the symmetric and the antisymmetric, can appear, although with different frequencies of occurrence. This difference from the case of nuclei with zero spin is intimately connected with the fact that an exchange of nuclei when a nuclear spin is present does not necessarily lead to a completely identical state, since the nuclei may still differ by the orientation of their spins.

The spin vectors I of the two nuclei form a resultant T, the *total nuclear spin of the molecule*.[15]   In the simplest case, when $I = \frac{1}{2}$, T is either 1 (parallel nuclear spins, $\uparrow\uparrow$) or 0 (antiparallel nuclear spins, $\uparrow\downarrow$).   It now appears (see below) that either all the symmetric rotational levels must have a total spin $T = 0$ and all the antisymmetric must have a total spin $T = 1$, or vice versa.

In a magnetic field, T can take only the directions for which the component in the field direction is $M_T(h/2\pi)$, where

$$M_T = T, (T-1), (T-2), \cdots, -T.   \quad \text{(III, 120)}$$

For $T = 1$, there are three possible orientations; for $T = 0$ there is only one.   That is, states with $T = 1$ have three

---

[14] R. Mecke (486) was the first to recognize that intensity alternation and alternate missing lines are characteristic of molecules with like nuclei.

[15] Because of the smallness of their magnetic moments, the two nuclear spins in the molecule may be uncoupled even by a very weak external or internal field.   However, this does not change the division of molecular states into symmetric and antisymmetric ones, nor does it change the statistical weights.

times the statistical weight of those with $T = 0$. From this it follows, according to the above, that *for $I = \frac{1}{2}$ the antisymmetric rotational states occur three times as frequently as the symmetric, or vice versa*; that is, the total statistical weights are $3 \times (2J + 1)$ and $1 \times (2J + 1)$, respectively [see section 2(e) of this chapter].[16] Since, according to (III, 119), the symmetric levels always combine with the symmetric and the antisymmetric always combine with the antisymmetric, and, since the symmetric and antisymmetric levels alternate (see Fig. 59), we would expect an intensity alternation 1 : 3 to appear in the Raman bands [and similarly in the electronic bands; see Chapter IV, section 4(b) and Chapter V, section 3(b)]. This is actually observed for H_2, the odd lines being strong and the even lines being weak. Conversely, from the occurrence and magnitude of the intensity alternation we may conclude that the H nucleus (the proton) has a spin of magnitude $I = \frac{1}{2}$. Theory shows (see Chapter VI) that the electronic eigenfunction of the ground state of H_2 is symmetric; that is, the even-numbered rotational levels are symmetric, and the odd are antisymmetric [compare Fig. 59(a)]. Thus, since the odd lines are strong, the antisymmetric levels have the greater statistical weight—that is, have parallel nuclear spins. Fig. 61(a) shows the symmetry, the nuclear spin orientation, and the statistical weight for the rotational levels of H_2 in the ground state.

If the nuclear spin $I = 1$, there are, according to the principles of quantum theoretical vector addition (see Chapter I, p. 21 f.), three possible values for the resultant nuclear spin of the molecule—namely, $T = 2$, 1, and 0. According to (III, 120), the statistical weights of these three states are 5, 3, and 1. A more detailed theoretical investigation now shows that either the symmetric rotational states

---

[16] Correspondingly, instead of the one curve in Fig. 56, we obtain *two* curves with the ratio 1 : 3 of the ordinates, one curve for the even and the other for the odd levels. Similar considerations apply to cases with other I values (see below).

can occur with even-numbered T values only and the anti-symmetric rotational states with odd T values, or vice versa. From this it follows that the symmetric rotational levels have a statistical weight of $(5 + 1) = 6$ and the anti-symmetric 3, or vice versa; that is, the total statistical weights are $6 \times (2J + 1)$ and $3 \times (2J + 1)$, respectively. In other words, we expect an *intensity alternation in the ratio* $1 : 2$ *in the bands of molecules having like nuclei whose spin* $I = 1$. Actually, just this value is obtained experimentally for N_2 [see Fig. 36(a)] and also for heavy hydrogen, D_2, which differs thereby from ordinary hydrogen (see above). Thus, conversely, we can conclude that the N and the D nuclei have a spin $I = 1$. In the ground state of N_2, as well as D_2, it is found that the symmetrical (even-numbered) levels have the greater statistical weight (different from the case of H_2). The relationships for this case are represented

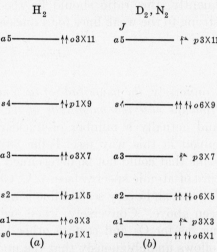

Fig. 61. Symmetry, Nuclear Spin Orientation, and Statistical Weight of the First Rotational Levels of H_2, D_2, and N_2 in the Ground State. The energy scale is different for H_2, D_2, and N_2. The length of the arrows representing the nuclear spin is no measure of the magnitude of the nuclear spin. The latter is, to the left, $\frac{1}{2}h/2\pi$, and to the right, $1h/2\pi$. The statistical weights are written as products of the parts due to nuclear spin and to J.

in Fig. 61(b). It should be noted that for D_2 and N_2, in contrast to H_2, the "intense" and "weak" levels are not differentiated by the parallel or antiparallel orientation of the nuclear spins, but by the fact that for the weak levels the nuclear spins are at 60° to each other, so that their resultant $T = 1$, while for the strong levels the nuclear spins may be parallel as well as antiparallel.

In the *general case*, the resultant nuclear spin can take the values $T = 2I$, $(2I - 1)$, $\cdots$, 0, of which the even numbers belong to the symmetric rotational levels and the odd to the antisymmetric, or vice versa. If the statistical weights $2T + 1$ for the even T values are added together by themselves and those of the odd T values by themselves, it is found that the sums are in the ratio $I + 1 : I$. Consequently, this ratio should be the *intensity ratio* R of the strong to the weak lines for a nuclear spin I.

$$R = \frac{I + 1}{I}. \qquad (\text{III, 121})$$

Conversely, *the magnitude of the nuclear spin may be deduced from the observed magnitude of the alternation of intensities*, and actually a number of nuclear spins have been determined in this way (see Table 38), including in particular some that could not be determined from the hyperfine structure of atomic spectra (see A.A., Chapter V). When $I = 0$, $R = \infty$ and every second line is missing, as we have already seen above. Conversely, when every alternate line is missing, as for O_2 and certain other homonuclear molecules, it follows unambiguously that the nuclear spin $I = 0$.

Influence of nuclear statistics. Let us imagine a box containing a gas consisting, for example, of He nuclei (for which band spectra show that $I = 0$). Then wave mechanics may be used to investigate the motion of the nuclei in this system. A theoretical investigation shows that the eigenfunction of the whole system either remains unaltered or changes sign by exchange of any two nuclei—that is, is symmetric or antisymmetric. As above, the strict selection rule, sym. ↔ antisym., holds. If all the He nuclei in the box are once in one of the symmetric states, they will remain permanently in the symmetric states. Under these circumstances, a particular statistics holds for them—the *Bose-Einstein statistics*, or, shortly, Bose statistics—which deviates in a characteristic manner from the classical Maxwell-Boltzmann statistics (different type of velocity distribution). If, on the contrary, the He nuclei are all initially in antisymmetric states, they must always remain in antisymmetric states. In that case, yet another statistics would hold for them—the *Fermi-Dirac statistics*, or, shortly, Fermi statistics[17] (with a velocity distribution different from that of Bose statistics and that of classical statistics).

The symmetry character, "symmetric or antisymmetric with respect to an exchange of any two nuclei," is not altered even when the He nuclei, each with two electrons, form He atoms and perhaps, in pairs, form He_2 molecules. The He nuclei that follow the Bose statistics in the free state would give rise to the above-mentioned symmetric molecular states, and the He nuclei following Fermi statistics in the free state would give rise to the antisymmetric molecular states.

Now it would appear to be extremely peculiar if a gas—for example, consisting of He nuclei—consisted of two modifications which could not, under any circumstances, be converted into one another and which followed quite different statistics. Actually, the band spectrum of He_2 (see above) shows that the antisymmetric levels do not occur at all; that means that only those He nuclei occur in nature that follow Bose statistics and none that follow Fermi statistics,[18] or, in other words, *the He nuclei always follow the Bose statistics*. This has to be considered as a characteristic and important property of He nuclei.

Investigations of band spectra have shown the same to be true for all the nuclei thus far investigated having a nuclear spin $I = 0$ (see Table 38). Thus we can regard the following of Bose statistics as a characteristic property of nuclei with a spin $I = 0$.

According to what has been said, it is to be expected that also *atomic nuclei with a spin $I \neq 0$* would follow either the one statistics or the other but not both. The question is then how to explain the fact that, for homonuclear molecules with $I \neq 0$, *both* term systems actually appear, the symmetric and the antisymmetric, only an alternation of intensities and no suppression of every second line being observed in their band spectra. In order to understand this fact, we have to consider that the complete prohibition of intercombinations holds only between states whose *total* eigenfunctions have different symmetries and that whether the nuclei follow Bose or Fermi statistics depends on this total

---

[17] The differences between the three statistics first become appreciable at extremely low temperatures. The fact that a gas then no longer follows the classical statistics is called *gas degeneracy*.

[18] It should be remarked that initially the conclusion about the statistics of the He nucleus from band spectra was not quite unambiguous. By altering the explanation of the electronic structure of the He_2 molecule, Fermi-Dirac statistics would have been obtained for the He nucleus. However, experiments on the scattering of α particles in He have shown conclusively that the Bose-Einstein statistics holds for the He nucleus.

eigenfunction. If the nuclei have a spin $I \neq 0$, the total eigen-function depends also on the orientation of these spins. To zero approximation, which is here a very good approximation, the new total eigenfunction ψ' is the product of the old function ψ, which we may call the *co-ordinate function*,[19] and the so-called *nuclear spin function* β, which depends on the orientations of the spins:

$$\psi' = \psi \cdot \beta. \qquad (III, 122)$$

A closer consideration, similar to that for electron spin (see A.A., p. 124), shows that the nuclear spin function β is symmetric in the nuclei for $T = 2I, (2I - 2), (2I - 4), \cdots, 0$, while it is anti-symmetric for the intermediate values. Thus, by a suitable choice of β (and therewith T), the total function ψ' can be made sym-metric for a symmetric as well as an antisymmetric ψ or can be made antisymmetric for a correspondingly different choice of β and T. This means that *for nuclei following Bose statistics as well as those following Fermi statistics, if $I \neq 0$, all the rotational levels* (even as well as odd) *can appear*—however, only with certain total nuclear spin values. These relationships are collected in Table 15.

TABLE 15

SYMMETRY OF THE EIGENFUNCTIONS FOR $I \neq 0$

Co-ordinate Function ψ	Nuclear Spin Function β	Nuclear Spin T	Total Function ψ'	For Bose Statistics of the Nuclei	For Fermi Statistics of the Nuclei
sym.	sym.	$2I, 2I-2, \cdots$	sym.	occurs	——
	antisym.	$2I-1, 2I-3, \cdots$	antisym.	——	occurs
antisym.	sym.	$2I, 2I-2, \cdots$	antisym.	——	occurs
	antisym.	$2I-1, 2I-3, \cdots$	sym.	occurs	——

We can see from this table that for Bose statistics the states with symmetric co-ordinate functions have the greater statistical weight, while for Fermi statistics the states with antisymmetric co-ordinate functions have the greater statistical weight. For brevity we shall call the states with symmetric co-ordinate functions *symmetric states* and those with antisymmetric co-ordinate functions *anti-symmetric states*.

For H_2, with nuclear spin $I = \frac{1}{2}$ (see above), the antisymmetric

---

[19] It includes *electron* spin.

levels (which in the ground state are the odd-numbered ones) have the greater statistical weight [see Fig. 61(*a*)]. It follows that the H *nuclei* (protons) *follow Fermi statistics.* On the other hand, the spectrum shows that for D_2 the symmetric (even-numbered) levels have the greater statistical weight [see Fig. 61(*b*)]. Therefore, *Bose statistics apply to the* D *nuclei* (deuterons). The same follows for the N nucleus from the Raman spectrum of N_2 [see Fig. 36(*a*)]. The importance of these results for the theory of nuclear structure will be discussed briefly in Chapter VIII.

The transition probability between two states with different symmetries of the total eigenfunctions ψ' is exactly zero (see above). This also holds, however, *for the co-ordinate function as well,* as long as the resolution (III, 122) is possible, since then, for example, for dipole radiation (see p. 139),

$$\int \psi_n'\psi_m'^*(\Sigma e_i x_i)d\tau' = \int \psi_n\psi_m^*(\Sigma e_i x_i)d\tau \int \beta_n\beta_m^*d\sigma, \quad \text{(III, 123)}$$

where $d\tau'$, $d\tau$, and $d\sigma$ are the volume elements of the whole configuration space, of the co-ordinate space alone, and of the nuclear spin space alone, respectively. But $\int \psi_n\psi_m^*(\Sigma e_i x_i)d\tau$, and thereby, according to (III, 123), the total transition probability, vanishes if the two co-ordinate functions ψ_n and ψ_m have opposite symmetries. The same holds for transitions brought about in other ways. Thus, in this approximation, transitions between symmetric and antisymmetric states do not occur even if the nuclear spin is different from zero. However, if the interaction of the nuclear spin with the rest of the molecule is taken into account, the resolution (III, 122) of the total eigenfunction, and therefore also the resolution (III, 123) of the matrix elements, is *no longer rigorously possible.* Consequently, even if $\int \psi_n\psi_m^*(\Sigma e_i x_i)d\tau$ is zero, the total transition probability, $\int \psi_n'\psi_m'^*(\Sigma e_i x_i)d\tau'$, may be different from zero— though only very slightly. There is thus a small probability for transitions between symmetric and antisymmetric states if $I \neq 0$; that is, for example, *transitions from the even-numbered levels to the odd-numbered levels of* H_2, D_2, N_2, $\cdots$, *could take place by collisions* (see Fig. 61). However, owing to the smallness of the magnetic moment associated with the nuclear spin, the interaction with the rest of the molecule is very small indeed, and, as a result, the *transition probability between symmetric and antisymmetric states is* *extremely small.* It is so small that its reciprocal, the mean life, is of the order of years.

The coupling between nuclear spin and the remaining angular momenta of the molecule should lead to a *hyperfine structure,* as for atoms. Such a hyperfine structure has not yet been observed with certainty. [See, however, (343a), (286a), and (505a).] It should, of course, appear for molecules with unlike nuclei as well as with like nuclei.

Ortho and para modifications. As we have stated above, *when the nuclear spin I* $\neq$ 0, the prohibition of transitions between symmetric and antisymmetric states (III, 119) does not hold absolutely rigorously, but, owing to the smallness of the coupling between nuclear spin and the rest of the molecule, it still holds sufficiently strictly that it takes many months, if not years, before, in gaseous hydrogen, for example, a molecule goes from an even-numbered to an odd-numbered rotational level. As a result, as first pointed out by Dennison (181), gases such as H_2, D_2, N_2, and so forth, may be regarded as a *mixture of two modifications*—a *symmetrical* with only even-numbered rotational levels and an *antisymmetrical* with only odd-numbered rotational levels. In the case of H_2, the one modification has antiparallel nuclear spins and the other has parallel nuclear spins [see Fig. 61(*a*)].

Actually, in the case of hydrogen, it is possible to obtain these two modifications separately. When the gas is cooled to a very low temperature (temperature of liquid H_2), without taking into consideration the prohibition sym. $\leftrightarrow$ antisym., one would expect practically all the molecules to go over to the lowest rotational level, $J = 0$, whereas, considering the selection rule, only those molecules that were originally in the higher even-numbered rotational levels go to the lowest even-numbered state, $J = 0$, while all the molecules originally in the higher odd-numbered rotational levels go to the lowest odd-numbered state, $J = 1$ [see Fig. 61(*a*)]. This means that the distribution of rotational levels does not correspond to thermal equilibrium. However, when the gas is kept for a sufficiently long time (many weeks or months) at the low temperature, even the molecules that were at first in the state $J = 1$ will eventually go into the state $J = 0$ belonging to the symmetric system; that is, thermal equilibrium should eventually be obtained. If the gas is now allowed to warm up again to normal temperatures, the molecules at first can go only from $J = 0$ to the higher *even-numbered* (symmetric) levels, and not to the odd-numbered (antisymmetric) levels (owing to the prohibition sym. ↔ antisym.). This means that for some time *only the one modification should be present.*

Bonhoeffer and Harteck (118) and, almost simultaneously, Eucken and Hiller (206) were the first to carry out experiments which strikingly confirmed the above theoretical conclusions, which are based on the application of wave mechanics to the molecule. The former authors made the important discovery that the addition of active charcoal to the hydrogen at the low temperature greatly accelerates the production of thermal equilibrium, so that it was no longer necessary to keep the hydrogen at the low temperature for weeks or months. That actually only the one modification was present after the temperature was raised again was shown in the first place by observations of the heat conductivity and heat capacity, which for the separated modification differ by a predictable amount from those of the mixture; and, in the second place, by investigation of the spectrum, which for the gas prepared in the above-mentioned manner does not contain the lines that are strongest in the spectrum of the mixture (absence of every alternate line, just as for $I = 0$). Thus, after such a conversion, all the molecules are in the even-numbered rotational levels, while, in normal hydrogen, three fourths of the molecules are in the odd levels.

The transformation back to the ordinary mixture has been investigated under various conditions (particularly at high temperature and by admixture of paramagnetic gases) but will not be discussed here. Detailed reviews of this field have been given by L. Farkas (214) and A. Farkas (48).

The modification with the *greater* statistical weight is usually called the *ortho modification* and that with the *smaller* weight the *para modification*. We differentiate correspondingly between *ortho* H_2 and *para* H_2, *ortho* D_2 and *para* D_2, *ortho* N_2 and *para* N_2, and so forth. Thus far, apart from H_2, the separation has been effected only for D_2 [A. and L. Farkas and P. Harteck (211) and K. Clusius and F. Bartholomé (159)]. For N_2, owing to the smallness of the rotational quanta, a temperature of less than 1° K. would be necessary for a noticeable enrichment of one modification. It should be noted that, while the even-numbered levels constitute the para modification of H_2, the odd-numbered levels constitute the para modification of N_2 and D_2. The designation o (ortho) and p (para) is added to the rotational levels in Fig. 61.

Isotopic molecules. When the nuclei are not exactly alike (heteronuclear molecules), the cause for the division of the rotational states into symmetric and antisymmetric ones disappears, since by exchange of the nuclei the molecule goes over into a configuration that is different from the original one. This applies even to isotopic molecules of homonuclear molecules such as $O^{16}O^{18}$, $Cl^{35}Cl^{37}$, or $N^{14}N^{15}$. As a result, there should be *no alternation of intensities* or *no missing of every alternate line* in these isotopic molecules. This is actually found to be the case (in electronic band spectra), and this observation must be regarded as a particularly impressive confirmation of quantum mechanical predictions; for example, in the bands of the $O^{16}O^{18}$ molecule, all the lines appear, whereas every second line is missing for $O^{16}O^{16}$; similarly, there is no alternation of intensities in the HD bands. Correspondingly, experiment shows that there are *not two modifications of* HD, as for H_2 or D_2 [(211) and (159)]. An HD molecule can go over without restriction from an even-numbered level to an odd-numbered level—for example, by collision.

(g) Isotope Effect

Vibration. The vibrational frequency $\nu_{\text{osc.}}$ of a molecule depends on the reduced mass μ, according to the relation $\nu_{\text{osc.}} = (1/2\pi)\sqrt{k/\mu}$ (see p. 78) if we assume harmonic vibrations. The *force constant* k, since it is determined by the electronic motion only, must be *exactly the same for isotopic molecules*—that is, molecules that differ only by the mass of one or both of the nuclei but not by their atomic number and therefore not by their electron configurations (for example, HCl^{35}, HCl^{37}; $B^{10}O$, $B^{11}O$).

However, since μ is different, it follows that the *vibrational frequencies* must be *different*. The heavier molecule must have the smaller vibrational frequency. This is easily visualized when we remember that the smaller a mass hanging on a spring is, the greater is its vibrational frequency.

Fig. 62. **Vibrational Levels of Two Isotopic Molecules (Schematic).** To the left for the lighter isotope, to the right for the heavier isotope; $\rho = 0.95$.

If we designate quantities referring to the heavier isotopic molecule by an upper index i and leave those referring to the lighter isotope without an index, we have, assuming harmonic vibrations,

$$\frac{\nu_{\text{osc.}}^{i}}{\nu_{\text{osc.}}} = \sqrt{\frac{\mu}{\mu^{i}}} = \rho. \qquad \text{(III, 124)}$$

Accordingly, ρ is a number that is somewhat less than 1. By substituting (III, 124) in (III, 31), the *vibrational levels of the two isotopic molecules* are found to be given by

$$G = \omega(v + \tfrac{1}{2}), \ G^{i} = \omega^{i}(v + \tfrac{1}{2}) = \rho\omega(v + \tfrac{1}{2}). \quad \text{(III, 125)}$$

For the general case of an anharmonic oscillator, a more detailed calculation shows that

$$
\begin{aligned}
G &= \omega_e(v + \tfrac{1}{2}) - \omega_e x_e(v + \tfrac{1}{2})^2 + \cdots, \\
G^{i} &= \rho\omega_e(v + \tfrac{1}{2}) - \rho^2\omega_e x_e(v + \tfrac{1}{2})^2 + \cdots.
\end{aligned}
\qquad \text{(III, 126)}
$$

Fig. 62 shows the relative positions of the vibrational levels of two isotopic molecules on the basis of these formulae. The separation of corresponding levels increases with increasing v. The levels of the lighter isotope always lie higher than those of the heavier.

This isotope effect, expected according to theory, was first noticed in the rotation-vibration spectrum of HCl by Loomis (456a) and independently by Kratzer (420b). On the basis of Fig. 62, since Cl has two isotopes of masses 35 and 37, instead of every single band we should expect two bands, one corresponding to HCl^{35} and the other to HCl^{37}. The band belonging to HCl^{37} should be shifted by a small amount toward longer wave lengths with respect to the band belonging to HCl^{35}. Actually, with sufficient resolution, the rotation-vibration bands of HCl show a *doubling of all the lines*; every line has a companion of smaller intensity at a constant separation to the long-wavelength side, as is shown for the 3–0 band in Fig. 33.[20] In Table 16 the measured shifts (mean for all the lines) for the three bands 1–0, 2–0, and 3–0 are compared with the theoretical shifts calculated on the basis of (III, 126). It can be seen that the agreement is very good.

TABLE 16

OBSERVED AND CALCULATED VIBRATIONAL ISOTOPE DISPLACEMENTS FOR THE INFRARED HCl BANDS

[According to the data of Meyer and Levin (491) and Herzberg and Spinks (318)]

Band	$\Delta\nu_{obs.}$	$\Delta\nu_{calc.}$
1–0	2.01	2.105
2–0	4.00	4.053
3–0	5.834	5.845
4–0		7.481

According to (III, 60), (III, 59), and (III, 126), the frequencies of the absorption bands are given by

$$\nu = (\omega_e - \omega_e x_e)v - \omega_e x_e v^2,$$
$$\nu^i = (\rho\omega_e - \rho^2\omega_e x_e)v - \rho^2\omega_e x_e v^2,$$

$$(III, 127)$$

[20] In the absorption curve of the 1–0 band given in Fig. 32 the dispersion is too small for a resolution of the doublets, particularly since the separation is only about a third of that in the 3–0 band (Fig. 33).

where terms higher than the quadratic in v have been neglected. The *isotope shift* is thus

$$\Delta\nu = \nu - \nu^i = \omega_e(1-\rho)v - \omega_e x_e(1-\rho^2)v - \omega_e x_e(1-\rho^2)v^2$$

$$= (1-\rho)\{[\omega_e - \omega_e x_e(1+\rho)]v - \omega_e x_e(1+\rho)v^2\}.$$

As long as ρ is only slightly different from 1, we can also write [according to (III, 61)]

$$\Delta\nu = (1-\rho)v\Delta G_{v+\frac{1}{2}}. \tag{III, 128}$$

Shortly after the discovery of heavy hydrogen by Urey, Brickwedde, and Murphy (676), the infrared spectrum of the isotopic molecule H^2Cl^{35} (and H^2Cl^{37}), present in minute concentration in ordinary HCl, was investigated by Hardy, Barker, and Dennison (280). In this case ρ^2 is nearly $\frac{1}{2}$, and, as a result, the isotope shift between H^1Cl^{35} and H^2Cl^{35} (or between H^1Cl^{37} and H^2Cl^{37}) is so great that the bands lie in quite different spectral regions. While the fundamental band of ordinary HCl lies at 3.46 μ, that of H^2Cl lies at 4.78 μ. It was found that the shift corresponds exactly to the above formula (III, 126).

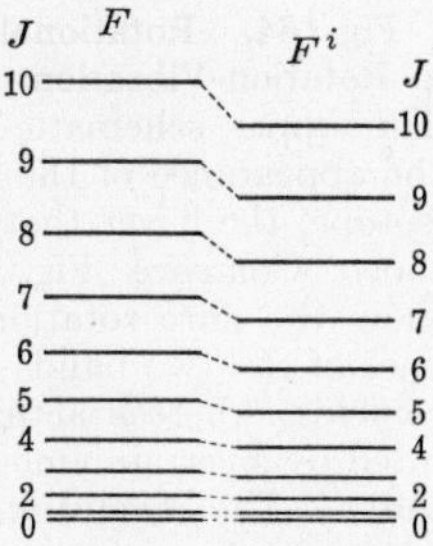

Fig. 63. Rotational Levels of Two Isotopic Molecules. To the left for the lighter isotope, to the right for the heavier isotope; $\rho = 0.95$. The lowest levels, $J = 0$, are drawn at the same height, which is actually not the case, owing to the vibrational effect which is always present.

Rotation. Like the force constants, the *nuclear distances of isotopic molecules* are *exactly equal*, owing to the practically complete equality of the electronic motions. However, since μ is different, the *rotational terms* for two isotopic molecules will be *different* [see (III, 7)]. Since $B^i = \mu^i r^2$, we have, if we introduce ρ from (III, 124),

$$F = BJ(J+1),\ F^i = B^iJ(J+1) = \rho^2 BJ(J+1). \tag{III, 129}$$

The rotational levels of two isotopic molecules are shown to scale in Fig. 63.

The rotational effect is, of course, added to the vibrational effect, and, as a result, the lines of a rotation-vibration band of an isotopic molecule do not have exactly the same separations as the lines of the corresponding band of the "normal" molecule; or, in other words, the isotope shift for corresponding lines of the two bands is not exactly the same but shows a small trend. This is shown schematically in Fig. 64, where the zero lines of the two bands are drawn one above the other, whereas actually they are separated by the vibrational isotope shift. The rotational effect is observed, for example, for the 3–0 band of HCl (318).

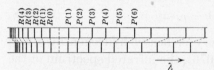

Fig. 64. Rotational Isotope Effect in a Rotation-Vibration Band (Schematic). The upper schematic spectrogram gives the appearance of the band of the lighter isotope, the lower that of the heavier isotope. Compare Fig. 52. In order to show the pure rotational effect, the zero lines of the two bands have been made to coincide, whereas actually they are separated by a certain amount (the vibrational shift). The magnitude of the rotational isotope effect is usually considerably smaller than that drawn.

Since the rotational term F is generally small compared to the vibrational term G, the rotational isotope effect is, in general, small compared to the vibrational isotope effect. In the 3–0 band of HCl, the rotational effect for the observed lines is < 0.2 cm^{-1}, while the vibrational shift amounts to 5.8 cm^{-1}.

The relation (III, 129) has to be somewhat altered for the *vibrating rotator*. A more detailed calculation shows that the rotational constants $B_e{}^i$, $\alpha_e{}^i$, and D^i of the isotopic molecule are given by

$$B_e{}^i = \rho^2 B_e; \quad \alpha_e{}^i = \rho^3 \alpha_e; \quad D^i = \rho^4 D. \qquad \text{(III, 130)}$$

From this it follows that for the rotational part of the isotope effect [according to (III, 83) and (III, 87)]

$$\Delta \nu_r = \nu_r - \nu_r{}^i = (1 - \rho^2) [B_e' J'(J' + 1) - B_e'' J''(J'' + 1)]$$

$$- (1 - \rho^3)[\alpha_e'(v' + \tfrac{1}{2})J'(J'+1) - \alpha_e''(v'' + \tfrac{1}{2})J''(J''+1)]$$

$$- (1 - \rho^4)[D' J'^2(J'+1)^2 - D'' J''^2(J''+1)^2]. \qquad \text{(III, 131)}$$

Here, ν_r ($= F' - F''$) is the rotational part of the wave number of a line. For the rotation-vibration spectrum, $B_e' = B_e''$, $\alpha_e' = \alpha_e''$, and $D' \approx D''$. The second and third terms in (III, 131) are, in general, very small compared to the first. We can therefore put, to a first, fairly good, approximation,

$$\Delta\nu_r = (1 - \rho^2)\nu_r. \qquad \text{(III, 132)}$$

In this formula, the second and third terms in (III, 131) are at least partly taken care of. The *rotational isotope shift* is thus, to a good approximation, *proportional to the distance from the zero line* (see Fig. 64).

An accurate measurement of the isotope effect can be used to obtain a precise value for the *ratio of the masses* of the two kinds of isotopic atoms concerned (from $\rho = \sqrt{\mu/\mu^i}$). Under favorable conditions, the accuracy of the ratio of the masses so obtained is comparable with the accuracy of mass-spectrographic values. Apart from that, the study of the isotope effect in electronic band spectra (see Chapter IV) has led to the discovery of new isotopes and to an unambiguous confirmation of the quantum mechanical formula for the energy of the oscillator.

CHAPTER IV

General Discussion of Electronic States and Electronic Transitions

The band spectra observed in the visible and ultraviolet regions of the spectrum (see Chapter II) obviously cannot be interpreted as simple rotation or rotation-vibration spectra, since their structure is generally more complicated than would be expected according to the theory of such spectra (Chapter III). Also, the frequency in the visible and ultraviolet regions is much too great for a rotational or vibrational frequency. However, it appears highly plausible to explain these visible and ultraviolet band spectra as due to *electronic transitions in molecules (as electronic band spectra)*, corresponding to the explanation of the visible and ultraviolet line spectra as due to electronic transitions in atoms (Chapter I). In this chapter we shall see that this interpretation is, in fact, the correct one.

1. ELECTRONIC ENERGY AND TOTAL ENERGY

The atomic nuclei in a molecule are held together by the electrons, since, according to the Coulomb law, the nuclei alone repel each other. Just as for atoms, we shall expect different electronic states of the molecule, depending on the "orbits" in which the electrons are. The details about these electronic motions will be taken up in the two following chapters. However, we shall say here that the different kinds of electronic states that have to be distinguished are designated by Σ, Π, Δ, $\cdots$, corresponding to the symbols S, P, D, $\cdots$ for atoms. The energy differences between different electronic states are of the same order as for atoms (1 to 20 volts).

156

Electronic energy and potential curves; stable and unstable molecular states. For a given electronic state, the electronic energy depends on the internuclear distance r. Owing to the smallness of the mass of the electron as compared to the mass of the nucleus, the electrons move much more rapidly than the nuclei. During the motion of the latter, the electronic energy at any moment takes up the value corresponding to their momentary position. Thus, the electronic energy added to the energy of the Coulomb repul-

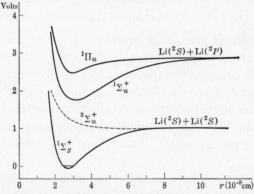

Fig. 65. Potential Curves of the Different Electronic States of the Li$_2$ Molecule [after Mulliken (514)]. The repulsive state with the broken potential curve is not directly observed.

sion of the nuclei gives the *potential energy* under whose influence the nuclei carry out their vibrations. Only if this potential energy, in its dependence on the internuclear distance, has a *minimum* is a *stable* state of the molecule possible. If there is no minimum, it means that the two atoms repel each other and that a stable molecule will not be formed in the electronic state under consideration.

The dependence of the electronic energy on the nuclear separation is different for each electronic state. This becomes quite clear if we consider, say, the case of a molecule with only two electrons—for example, H$_2$. Obviously, the attraction between the two atoms is quite different when one of the electrons moves at a great distance from the nuclei (large principal quantum number) from what it is when both electrons are very near the nuclei. *Each electronic state is thus characterized by a definite potential curve* that either may have a more or less deep minimum (curve of attraction, stable molecular state) or may have no minimum (curve of repulsion, unstable molecular state).

The potential curves of the Li_2 molecule, as derived from the analysis of band spectra, are represented in Fig. 65 and serve to illustrate the above. (For the nomenclature, see Chapters V and VI.) The curve designated by $^3\Sigma_u{}^+$ has no minimum; this electronic state is therefore unstable.

Resolution of the total energy. In the discussion of electronic transitions in diatomic molecules it is both useful and general practice to take *the energy of the minimum of the potential curve, E_e, as the electronic energy of a state.* The minimum of the lowest electronic state (the electronic ground state) of the molecule is almost always chosen as the zero point of the energy scale. This choice is different from that for atoms.

In each stable electronic state, the molecule can carry out vibrations about the equilibrium position—that is, can have a certain vibrational energy E_v—and can also rotate—that is, have a certain rotational energy E_r. Thus, to a very good approximation, the *total energy E* of the molecule is the sum of three component parts,

$$E = E_e + E_v + E_r, \tag{IV, 1}$$

or, when we write the equation in wave-number units (term values),

$$T = T_e + G + F. \tag{IV, 2}$$

For the vibrations and rotations of the molecule in the different electronic states, we use the model of the *vibrating rotator* (Chapter III) and put

$$G = \omega_e(v + \tfrac{1}{2}) - \omega_e x_e(v + \tfrac{1}{2})^2 + \omega_e y_e(v + \tfrac{1}{2})^3 + \cdots, \tag{IV, 3}$$

and

$$F = B_v J(J + 1) - D_v J^2(J + 1)^2 + \cdots. \tag{IV, 4}$$

According to what has been said in the preceding chapter, F is small compared to G. In general, we can neglect the second term in the expression for F. The constants occurring in G and F are of course of different magnitude for the different electronic states of a molecule.

By introducing in F the quantity B_v, which depends on v according to (III, 83), we have essentially taken into account the interaction between vibration and rotation. Similarly, if ω_e and $\omega_e x_e$ are so chosen that they correspond to the potential curve, we have taken into account the interaction between vibration and electronic motion, since the potential curve is a curve of the electronic energy. For the present we have neglected the interaction between electronic motion and the rotation of the molecule. This subject will be discussed in greater detail in the

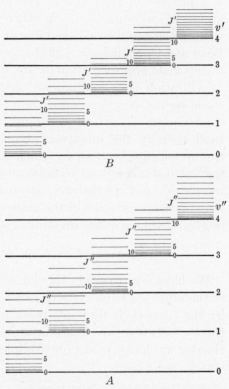

Fig. 66.   **Vibrational and Rotational States of Two Electronic States A and B of a Molecule (Schematic).** Only the first few rotational and vibrational levels are drawn in each case.

next chapter. It will appear that, in general, this interaction gives only a small correction.

As an illustration, two different electronic states with their vibrational and rotational levels are represented graphically in Fig. 66.

Total eigenfunction. In quantum mechanics the following theorem holds generally: The energy of an atomic system can be resolved into a sum of independent parts only if co-ordinates can be introduced such that the eigenfunction is a product of functions of the individual co-ordinates or groups of co-ordinates, or, in other words, if the wave equation of the problem is separable in these co-ordinates. As Born and Oppenheimer (122) have shown, this is the case to a very good approximation for the diatomic molecule as long as vibration and rotation are not too strong. *The total eigenfunction may be resolved into a product of an electronic eigenfunction ψ_e,* which depends only on the co-ordinates (and thereby the quantum numbers) of the electrons, *a vibrational eigenfunction ψ_v,* which depends only on the internuclear distance r (and thereby on the vibrational quantum number v), *and a rotational eigenfunction ψ_r,* which depends only on the orientation of the molecule in space (and thereby on the rotational quantum number J):

$$\psi = \psi_e \cdot \psi_v \cdot \psi_r. \qquad (IV, 5)$$

We have now to study the question whether the structure of the observed band systems (see Chapter II) is reproduced by the transitions that are possible, according to quantum theory, between two electronic states, as in Fig. 66. In this chapter we shall consider only simple electronic states (singlet states; see Chapter V).

2. VIBRATIONAL STRUCTURE OF ELECTRONIC TRANSITIONS

General formulae. Using the Bohr frequency condition (I, 6) and the equation (IV, 2), we find that the *wave numbers of the spectral lines* emitted or absorbed by a molecule are given by

$$\nu = T' - T'' = (T_e' - T_e'') + (G' - G'') + (F' - F''), \quad (IV, 6)$$

where the single-primed letters refer to the upper state and the double-primed letters refer to the lower state. Equation

(IV, 6) states that the emitted or absorbed frequency may be regarded as the sum of three constituent parts (which need not all be positive):

$$\nu = \nu_e + \nu_v + \nu_r. \qquad (IV, 7)$$

For a given electronic transition, $\nu_e = T_e' - T_e''$ is a constant. According to (IV, 6), the variable part, $\nu_v + \nu_r$, has a form similar to that for the rotation-vibration spectrum. The essential difference from the former is that G' and G'' now belong to *different* vibrational term series with different ω_e and $\omega_e x_e$, and that G' may now also be smaller than G''. Similarly, F' and F'' belong to two quite different rotational term series with different B_e and α_e.

Since F is, in general, small compared to G (see above), we may for the time being neglect $\nu_r (= F' - F'')$ in order to get a general picture. Expressed in another way, consideration of transitions between the rotationless states, $F' = F'' = 0$, gives us a survey of the *coarse structure*—also called the *vibrational structure*, since only ν_v is variable.

Using (IV, 3) and (IV, 6), we obtain as formula for the vibrational structure to be expected (transitions between rotationless states)

$$\nu = \nu_e + \omega_e'(v' + \tfrac{1}{2}) - \omega_e' x_e'(v' + \tfrac{1}{2})^2 + \omega_e' y_e'(v' + \tfrac{1}{2})^3 + \cdots$$
$$- [\omega_e''(v'' + \tfrac{1}{2}) - \omega_e'' x_e''(v'' + \tfrac{1}{2})^2 + \omega_e'' y_e''(v'' + \tfrac{1}{2})^3 + \cdots]. \qquad (IV, 8)$$

This equation represents *all possible transitions between the different vibrational levels of the two participating electronic states* (see Fig. 66). An investigation of the selection rules [see section 4(a) of this chapter] shows that for electronic transitions there is no strict selection rule for the vibrational quantum number v. In principle, each vibrational state of the upper electronic state can combine with each vibrational state of the lower electronic state. Thus, in accordance with (IV, 8), we can expect a large number of "lines."

For brevity, some authors use u as a shorthand symbol for

$v + \frac{1}{2}$ in formula (IV, 8). This formula may also be written in the following simpler way:

$$\nu = \nu_{00} + \omega_0'v' - \omega_0'x_0'v'^2 + \omega_0'y_0'v'^3 + \cdots$$
$$- (\omega_0''v'' - \omega_0''x_0''v''^2 + \omega_0''y_0''v''^3 + \cdots). \tag{IV, 9}$$

ν_{00} is the term independent of v' and v'' in (IV, 8); that is, it is the frequency of the transition $v' = 0 \rightarrow v'' = 0$ (0–0 band). By comparison of (IV, 8) and (IV, 9) it is seen that

$$\nu_{00} = \nu_e + (\tfrac{1}{2}\omega_e' - \tfrac{1}{4}\omega_e'x_e' + \tfrac{1}{8}\omega_e'y_e' + \cdots)$$
$$- (\tfrac{1}{2}\omega_e'' - \tfrac{1}{4}\omega_e''x_e'' + \tfrac{1}{8}\omega_e''y_e'' + \cdots), \tag{IV, 10}$$

while ω_0, ω_0x_0, and ω_0y_0 are given by (III, 59), p. 101. The factor $\omega_e y_e = \omega_0 y_0$ is generally very small and can often be neglected. If this is done, we see that the theoretical equation (IV, 9) agrees completely with the empirical equation (II, 4) for the bands of a band system. As a matter of fact, as we have seen in Chapter II, cubic terms have to be added to equation (II, 4) in certain cases, corresponding to the cubic terms in (IV, 9).

We therefore come to the conclusion that a *band system* of the type described in Chapter II represents the *totality of the transitions between two different electronic states of a molecule* (that is, corresponds to a single line or a single multiplet of an atomic spectrum). According to (II, 4) and (IV, 9), the empirical constants a' and a'' are to be identified with the vibrational frequencies ω_0' and ω_0'', and the empirical constants b' and b'' with the anharmonicities $\omega_0'x_0'$ and $\omega_0''x_0''$, from which ω_e and $\omega_e x_e$ can immediately be derived by use of (III, 59). The running numbers at first introduced empirically in the progressions are the vibrational quantum numbers in the upper and lower electronic states. Thus, on the basis of the analysis of the coarse structure of a band system in the visible or ultraviolet region of the spectrum, we can calculate the *position of the vibrational levels*, the *vibrational frequencies*, and the *anharmonicities*, as well as the *force constants* of the molecule in the two participating electronic states. Finally, from the empirical constant ν_{00}

(that is, the wave number of the 0–0 band) and relation
(IV, 10) we obtain ν_e, the difference in electronic energy of
the two states. This ν_e is also called the *origin of the band
system*.

The fact that not simply single lines appear, at the wave
numbers given by (IV, 8), but whole *bands*, is due to the
rotation, as we shall show in greater detail in the following
section. Formulae (IV, 8) and (IV, 9) refer to the so-called
origins (*zero lines*) of the bands ($J' = 0 \to J'' = 0$). In contrast to this, the empirical formulae for the coarse structure
of the bands usually refer to the *band heads*. Small differences between the theoretical and empirical relationships are
thereby introduced. These differences will also be discussed
in the following section.

Examples; graphical representation. All the different
bands in one and the same horizontal row in the Deslandres
table for PN (Table 6) have the same v'—that is, the
same upper vibrational state—while the lower vibrational
state v'' is different. These v''-*progressions* extend from the

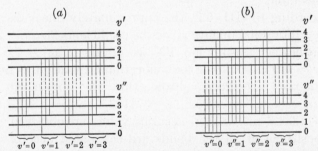

**Fig. 67. Vibrational Transitions Between Two Different Electronic
States.** (a) v''-progressions. (b) v'-progressions. The individual progressions
are indicated by braces. In each case, only the first five members are drawn.

first band ($v'' = 0$) toward longer wave lengths. Such progressions are represented graphically in the energy level
diagram Fig. 67(a).

However, a band system might equally well be regarded as
a series of progressions with constant v''—that is, the same
lower state v'' and variable v' (vertical rows in the Deslandres

table).   These v'-*progressions* extend from the first band, $v' = 0$, toward shorter wave lengths.   They are represented graphically in the energy level diagram Fig. 67(b).

A comparison of the two diagrams in Fig. 67 with the Deslandres table shows that the constant separation of the two first v''-progressions (with $v' = 0$ and 1) gives the first vibrational quantum, $\Delta G_{\frac{1}{2}}'$, of the upper state, the constant separation of the next two v''-progressions ($v' = 1$ and 2) gives the second vibrational quantum, $\Delta G_{\frac{3}{2}}'$, of the upper state, and so on.   In the example of PN (Table 6) the $\Delta G'$ values thus obtained are 1088.3, 1071.3, 1060.1, 1043.2 cm^{-1}, and so forth.   Similarly, the separation of the first two v'-progressions gives the first vibrational quantum, $\Delta G_{\frac{1}{2}}''$ of the lower state, and similarly the higher vibrational quanta are obtained.   In the case of PN the $\Delta G''$ values are 1321.5, 1309.5, 1294.2, 1280.4 cm^{-1}, and so forth.   According to what has been said, the equality of the separations of corresponding members of two progressions is an unambiguous check for the correctness of the arrangement of bands in the Deslandres table.

According to (III, 62), the approximately linear decrease of the vibrational quanta gives the coefficients $2\omega_0 x_0 = 2\omega_e x_e$ (if we neglect $\omega_0 y_0$).   For PN we obtain $\omega_0' x_0' = 7.5$ and $\omega_0'' x_0'' = 6.9$ cm^{-1}.   The first vibrational quantum is $\Delta G_{\frac{1}{2}} = \omega_0 - \omega_0 x_0 = \omega_e - 2\omega_e x_e$.   From this we obtain, in the present case, $\omega_0' = 1095.8$, $\omega_e' = 1103.3$, $\omega_0'' = 1327.4$, and $\omega_e'' = 1334.3$ cm^{-1}.   More accurate values are obtained when the positions of all the bands are calculated according to (IV, 9), the above preliminary values being used for the constants, and compared with the observed.   A possible systematic trend in the differences between observed and calculated values can then be corrected by a small alteration of the constants.   In the case of PN, the final formula, (II, 5), was obtained in this way.   The vibrational constants derived from this equation are given in Table 17, together with the force constants calculated from them [see formula (III, 68)].

TABLE 17

VIBRATIONAL CONSTANTS AND FORCE CONSTANTS IN THE
UPPER AND LOWER STATES OF THE PN BANDS AND
THE FOURTH POSITIVE GROUP OF CO

		PN	CO
Lower state	ω_e''	1336.36 cm^{-1}	2169.32 cm^{-1}
	ω_0''	1329.38	2156.05
	$\omega_e'' x_e''$	6.98	13.278
	k_e''	$1.0146 \cdot 10^6$ dynes/cm	$1.9008 \cdot 10^6$ dynes/cm
Upper state	ν_e	39,816.2 cm^{-1}	65,074.3 cm^{-1}
	ν_{00}	39,699.0	64,746.5
	ω_e'	1102.05	1515.61
	ω_0'	1094.80	1498.36
	$\omega_e' x_e'$	7.25	17.2505
	k_e'	$0.6900 \cdot 10^6$ dynes/cm	$0.9278 \cdot 10^6$ dynes/cm

The lower state is the ground state of the respective molecules.

The data for PN have been derived from band-head measurements; hence the true values are very slightly different from those given.

As a second example, we shall consider the so-called fourth positive group of CO, which forms a very extensive system of bands between 1300 and 2700 Å [see the spectrogram, Fig. 11(b), for part of the system] and often appears as an impurity in the spectra of discharges. The Deslandres table for these bands is given in Table 18. However, the band origins (corresponding to the transition $J' = 0 \rightarrow J'' = 0$; see p. 163) are given here and not the band heads, as for PN in Table 6. In order to save space, the values of the wave-number differences between neighboring bands have been omitted. However, it can easily be seen that the differences between any two horizontal or any two vertical rows really are constant within the accuracy of the measurements (2 to 3 cm^{-1}). In the manner described above, the following formula is obtained [Read (582)]:

$$\nu = 64{,}746.5 + (1498.36v' - 17.2505v'^2)$$
$$- (2156.05v'' - 13.2600v''^2 + 0.012v''^3). \tag{IV, 11}$$

DESLANDRES TABLE (SCHEME OF ORIGINS)

The data are taken from Birge (103), Estey (208), Headrick and Fox (283),
culated from the band heads, Schmid and Gerö's (621) rotational constants
accurate than the others. Apart from those given, the bands 9–22,

v' \ v''	0	1	2	3	4	5	6	7	8	9	10
0	(64,703)	62,601.8	60,484.7	58,393.2	56,329.4	54,291.8	(52,266)				
1	66,231.3	64,087.6	....	59,881.6	57,818.3	55,780.6	53,768.5	51,782.4	49,823.4	(47,887)	
2	67,674.8	65,533.1	63,416.1	61,325.2	....	57,224.2	55,212.9	53,227.7	51,268.2	49,334.5	47,427.3
3	69,087.8	66,944.3	64,828.1	....	60,674.5	58,636.3	....	54,640.3	52,680.6	50,747.2	48,839.7
4	70,469.5	68,323.4	(66,199)	64,116.5	62,055.3	(59,990)	58,002.9	(56,017)	(54,041)	52,125.2	50,218.2
5	71,807.2	69,666.1	(67,550)	65,458.2	....	61,356.6	(59,342)	57,360.0	55,400.9	(53,457)	51,560.0
6	(73,093)	70,973.2	68,855.9	(66,754)	(64,714)	62,665.1	....	58,667.1	....	54,774.5	(52,866)
7	....	72,248.3	70,131.1	....	(65,971)	....	(61,908)	....	....	....	(54,142)
8	....	(73,453)	71,370.8	(69,260)	(67,198)	(65,174)	....	....	....	....	
9	....	....	72,576.9	(70,466)	....	(66,360)	....	....			
10	....	....	73,750.0	(71,644)	....	....	....				
11	....	....	(74,902)	(72,791)	(70,717)	....	....				
12	....	....	....	(73,873)	(71,824)	....	(67,773)	(65,765)	....		
13	....	....	....	....	(72,893)	(70,848)	(68,846)	....			
14	....	....	....	....	....	....	....	(67,884)			

The vibrational constants derived from this are also given in
Table 17. For PN as well as CO the lower state is the ground
state (see also the energy level diagram of CO in Fig. 174,
p. 481).

It is particularly noteworthy that the first vibrational
quantum of CO in the lower state—obtained from Table 18
as the difference between the first two vertical rows, namely,
2143.2 cm^{-1}—agrees, within the accuracy of measurement,
with the first vibrational quantum obtained from the infrared spectrum and the Raman spectrum (see p. 103 f. and
Table 11). The same holds also for the second vibrational
quantum, which may be derived from the first overtone in
the infrared spectrum. This agreement shows that the lower
state of the ultraviolet bands actually is the ground state of
the molecule (which also follows from the fact that the bands
appear in absorption; see Fig. 14) and is, apart from that, a
very valuable support for the correctness of the interpretation of electronic band spectra in general.

Absorption. As we have already emphasized in Chapter II, when a band system is observed in absorption, in

18

OF THE FOURTH POSITIVE GROUP OF CO

Read (582), and Gerö (250). Where necessary, the origins have been cal-
being used (see p. 187). The figures in parentheses are considerably less
11–22, 12–22, 11–23, 12–23, 14–23, and 13–24 have been measured.

11	12	13	14	15	16	17	18	19	20	21
(45,529)										
46,959.2	45,101.9	(43,249)								
48,335.4	46,480.7	44,649.9	(42,845)	....	....	(37,567)	(35,866)			
49,678.2	47,821.9	45,992.8	44,187.4	42,408.2	40,655.3	....	(37,228)			
....	49,130.0	47,300.3	45,496.1	43,716.6	(41,962)	(40,234)	....	(36,842)		
....	....	....	46,770.2	44,990.5	43,238.1	41,509.0	(39,817)	....	(36,469)	
			....	(46,214)	44,476.5	42,748.6	41,045.5	39,367.7		
				....	(45,657)	43,953.9	42,251.3	40,574.0	38,920.2	(37,278)
						(43,403)	41,744.6	40,092.2	38,464.0	
							....	....	41,229.0	(39,580)
								(43,986)		
										(41,766)

general *only a single v′-progression* appears—namely, that
with $v'' = 0$. This is particularly striking for the CO band
system just mentioned, which in emission consists of the
numerous bands given in Table 18, whereas in absorption
only the bands in the first vertical row of this table appear
with appreciable intensity. The spectrogram in Fig. 14
shows this for just the CO system considered here. It is seen
from this spectrogram that in absorption, except for a few
extremely weak bands, only a single series of strong bands
appears whose separations decrease slowly toward shorter
wave lengths. This experimental result may now be readily
understood.

At room temperature practically all the molecules are in
the lowest vibrational state of the electronic ground state
(see Table 14, p. 130), and only an extremely small fraction
are in higher vibrational states. As a result, in absorption
we have practically only transitions from the lowest vibrational state to the different vibrational states of the upper
electronic state (see Fig. 68), so that we obtain only a single
progression of bands (Fig. 68, full lines in lower part). The

separations of the bands give directly the *vibrational quanta
of the upper state.* According to (IV, 9), with $v'' = 0$, the
formula for this band series is

$$\nu = \nu_{00} + \omega_0'v' - \omega_0'x_0'v'^2 + \cdots. \qquad \text{(IV, 12)}$$

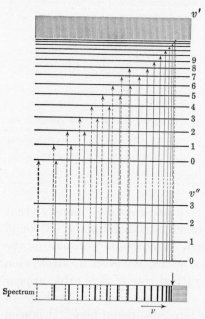

According to what has
been said in Chapter III,
with increasing v' the vibrational quanta approach
the value zero, and then a
continuous term spectrum
joins onto the series of
discrete vibrational levels.
Corresponding to this, we
have to expect a *continuous
absorption spectrum* joining onto the series of discrete absorption bands at
the point where the separation of the bands becomes
zero (the *convergence limit*).
This continuous absorp-
tion spectrum corresponds
to the dissociation of the
molecule. It is also indicated in Fig. 68. A con-
tinuum of this nature has
actually been observed in
a number of cases, such
as I_2, for which it is shown
in Fig. 15, p. 37. In other

**Fig. 68. Energy Level Diagram for an
Absorption Band Series with Convergence and Continuum (Schematic).** The
transitions starting from $v'' = 1$ at
higher temperature are indicated by
broken lines. The resulting spectrum
is drawn below. The vertical arrow in
the schematic spectrogram gives the
position of the point of convergence.

cases, such as, for example, CO (Fig. 14), it is not observed,
since the intensity of the bands has dropped to zero long
before the continuum is reached. In yet other cases, as,
for example, F_2, only a continuum appears. These continua will be dealt with in detail in Chapter VII.

If the vibrational quanta in the ground state are small (as, for example, for the I_2 molecule) or generally when the temperature is high, the number of molecules in the first or even higher vibrational states of the ground state is no longer negligibly small (see Table 14, p. 130). As a result, the progression $v'' = 1$ (and even higher progressions) appears in absorption in addition to the progression $v'' = 0$, although with smaller intensity. The separations of the bands in these progressions are exactly the same as in the progression $v'' = 0$ (see Chapter II, section 1). For an analytical representation the general formula (IV, 9) has to be used. The progression $v'' = 1$ is indicated by broken lines in Fig. 68. Such bands can also be observed in absorption at room temperature for molecules with large vibrational quanta if sufficiently thick absorbing layers or sufficiently high pressures are used. Some bands with $v'' = 1$ are just detectable in the CO absorption spectrum shown in Fig. 14.

It is obvious that a band system can be observed in absorption only when its lower electronic state is the *electronic ground state* of the molecule. Many emission band systems have an excited electronic state of the molecule as the lower state. They are therefore not observed in absorption.

Excitation of single progressions in emission. If a molecular gas is irradiated with light having the wave length of a single absorption band, the absorbing molecules will be brought into the upper state of this particular absorption band only. The excited molecules can then go over to the different vibrational states of the ground state with emission of radiation. We should thus expect, in *fluorescence*, a progression $v' = $ constant, which extends from the wave length of the exciting light toward *longer* wave lengths with *decreasing* band separation. This is in exact agreement with the observations of *resonance fluorescence* (see Chapter II). Fig. 69(a) shows by an energy level diagram how such a *resonance series* originates. It can be seen that the separations of the fluorescence bands are equal to the vibrational quanta in the ground state.

When the absorption band leading to the excitation of the fluorescence is a band with $v'' \neq 0$, as is possible for heavy molecules having small vibrational quanta (for example, I_2, Na_2, and so forth; see above), as before, transitions from the upper state, v', to all the vibrational states of the lower state are possible. However, it can be seen immediately from Fig. 69(b) that the fluorescence bands for which v'' is smaller than that for the exciting band lie on the *short*-wave-length side of the exciting band. These are called *anti-Stokes members* of the resonance series.

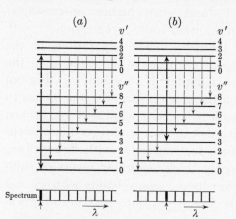

Fig. 69. Energy Level Diagram for Resonance Series (a) Without and (b) with anti-Stokes Members. The line exciting the fluorescence is indicated in the energy level diagram by a double arrow, and in the spectrum below by a small arrow.

In the fluorescence spectrum of Na_2, which was given earlier as an example (Fig. 29), a resonance series with anti-Stokes lines (upper leading lines) is present, as well as one without (lower leading lines).

In principle it is possible for the resonance series to be observed up to the point of convergence, where $\Delta G'' = 0$. At this point, then, a continuous spectrum extending to *longer* wave lengths should join on (somewhat similar to the continuum going from the point of convergence of absorption bands to *shorter* wave lengths). Actually, such a case of a continuous emission spectrum with preceding band series has not been observed, though one without the bands is known (see Chapter VII).

A selective excitation of a single v''-progression can appear in emission not only in fluorescence but under some circum-

stances also in electrical discharges, and may be due either to
an *instability of higher vibrational states* or to *resonance in collisions of the second kind* (see A.A., p. 231).　As an example
of the first case, we cite the H bands of CO, for which
only the v''-progression with $v' = 0$ appears, as Fig. 11(a),
p. 34, clearly shows.　The second case occurs, for example,
for H_2, when it is electrically excited in the presence of a
large excess of argon.　Then, in the
vacuum ultraviolet, instead of an extensive and complicated band system
(many-line spectrum) corresponding
to the transition from the first excited
electronic state B of H_2 to the ground
state (see Fig. 142, p. 364), essentially only one simple series of bands
appears, which converges toward
longer wave lengths and whose upper
state has $v' = 3$ (the so-called Lyman
bands).　It is found that the excitation energy of this upper state is very
nearly equal to the excitation energy
of the metastable ^3P state of argon.
By collision of these metastable A
atoms (which are fairly abundant in
a discharge) with normal H_2 molecules, according to the principle of
resonance in collisions of the second
kind, the $v = 3$ level of the B state of
H_2 is preferentially excited [see, for
example, Beutler (89)].　The separations of the Lyman bands
give directly the vibrational quanta for the ground state of
the H_2 molecule [Witmer (718)].

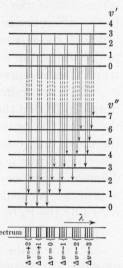

Fig. 70.　Energy Level
Diagram Representing the
Sequences in the Band
System of PN (see Fig. 9).
The individual sequences
are indicated by braces in
the schematic spectrogram
below.

Sequences (diagonal groups).　As we have already seen
in Chapter II, if the constants a' and a'' in (II, 4) are not
very different—that is, if the vibrational quanta in the
upper and lower states have similar magnitudes—the bands

that form the diagonal in the Deslandres table (from the upper left to the lower right) or those that lie on parallels to it occur together in the spectrum in characteristic groups (*sequences*, or *diagonal groups*) having $\Delta v = v' - v'' = $ constant. That this is so can be seen clearly from Fig. 70, in which the vibrational transitions for the PN molecule are once more represented. This time the figure is so drawn that the separation of the vertical transition arrows is proportional to the difference in length of the arrows—that is, is proportional to the separation of the bands in question. Thus the projection of the arrows on a horizontal line gives the spectrum. This is represented in the lower part of the figure. The sequences are indicated by braces. It is immediately clear from Fig. 70 that the bands of a sequence draw closer together the closer the agreement between the vibrational quanta in the upper and lower states. On the other hand, for a large difference in the ΔG values of the upper and lower state, the different sequences overlap one another and thus do not appear as particularly pronounced groups. This is illustrated by the P_2 bands in Fig. 10.

The *formula for the sequences* is easily obtained by putting $v' = v'' + \Delta v$ in the general formula (IV, 9) and regarding Δv as constant. Neglecting the cubic terms, we obtain

$$\nu = \nu_{00} + \omega_0'\Delta v - \omega_0'x_0'(\Delta v)^2 - (\omega_0'' - \omega_0' + 2\omega_0'x_0'\Delta v)v''$$
$$- (\omega_0'x_0' - \omega_0''x_0'')v''^2. \tag{IV, 13}$$

In this formula the quantum number v'' takes the values 0, 1, 2, $\cdots$ for the sequences with $\Delta v \geqq 0$ (diagonal in the Deslandres table and parallels below it), whereas it can take the values $|\Delta v|$, $|\Delta v| + 1$, $\cdots$ for the sequences with $\Delta v < 0$ (parallels to diagonal above it).

It can be seen from (IV, 13) that the bands in a sequence, as well as those in a progression, follow a quadratic formula except when $\omega_0'x_0'$ happens to be equal to $\omega_0''x_0''$. As long as the linear term is not too small, the sequences extend from an initial band (with the lowest v'') to longer or shorter wave lengths, according as $\omega_0'' >$ or $< (\omega_0' - 2\omega_0'x_0'\Delta v)$. In the example of the PN bands dealt with above (Figs. 70 and 9), the sequences extend toward longer wave lengths, the bands in them being approximately equidistant, since $\omega_0'x_0'$ is not very different from $\omega_0''x_0''$. Since, in general, the individual bands are shaded to the red or the violet according as $\omega_0'' >$ or $< \omega_0'$ (see p. 190), a sequence generally begins with a band head and the shading of the individual bands is in the direction toward which the sequences extend, as is the case for PN (Fig. 9).

If in (IV, 13) the term linear in v'' is small and has the opposite sign to the quadratic term, a *reversal* can take place in the succession of the bands in a sequence. This is best seen from the graphical representation in Fig. 71, in which, similar to a Fortrat diagram of an individual band (see p. 48), v'' is plotted as ordinate and ν

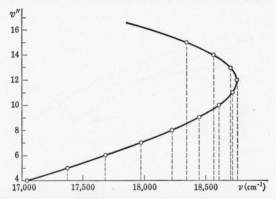

Fig. 71. Graphical Representation of the Sequence $\Delta v = -4$ of the N_2^+ Bands [after Herzberg (303)]. The abscissae of the small circles give the positions of the bands in the spectrum.

as abscissa for the sequence $\Delta v = -4$ of the N_2^+ bands. If no terms higher than the quadratic occur in (IV, 13), the curve is a parabola. The projections onto the abscissa axis of the points of the parabola, corresponding to the different values of v'', give the position of the bands in the sequence. It can be seen that with increasing v'' the bands draw together, eventually coming quite close to one another, and then draw apart again in the opposite direction. The turning point may be called a *head of heads*, since it forms a head in a series of band heads.

The value of v'' at which the *turning point* lies is obtained from (IV, 13) by putting $\dfrac{d\nu}{dv''} = 0$. We find

$$v_t'' = \frac{\omega_0' - 2\omega_0'x_0'\Delta v - \omega_0''}{2(\omega_0'x_0' - \omega_0''x_0'')}, \qquad \text{(IV, 14)}$$

where the whole number nearest to v_t'' gives the v'' value of the turning point.

If higher powers of v' and v'' have to be taken into consideration, the analytical expression for the turning point becomes much more complicated. In this case, a *graphical procedure for determining the turning point* is much simpler [see Herzberg (303)] and, in addition, makes even clearer the formation of the head of heads. The turning point evidently occurs when, for two successive bands of the diagonal, or a parallel to it, the vertical difference in the Deslandres table is equal to the horizontal difference. Therefore, if we plot the $\Delta G'$ values and $\Delta G''$ values against v in the same diagram (solid curves in Fig. 72, which refers to N_2^+), the inter-

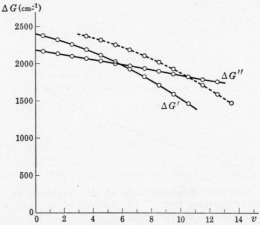

Fig. 72. ΔG Curves for N_2^+ in the Upper and Lower State of the Violet Bands. The broken-line curve is the ΔG curve shifted by 3 units to the right.

section of the two curves gives the v value of the turning point for the sequence $\Delta v = 0$ (in the example, at $v = 6$). The turning points in the remaining sequences ($\Delta v = $ constant) are obtained, as may easily be seen, by shifting the $\Delta G'$ curve by an amount $|\Delta v|$ to the left or the right according as Δv is positive or negative, and determining the intersection with the undisplaced $\Delta G''$ curve. In Fig. 72 the broken-line curve is the $\Delta G'$ curve displaced three units. Its intersection with $\Delta G''$ gives the turning point in the sequence $\Delta v = -3$, which lies at $v'' = 10$. From this mode of presentation we can see very clearly how the turning point shifts in the different sequences.

Since the intensity of the bands in a sequence always decreases with increasing v'' (possibly after passing first through an intensity maximum), the head of heads mentioned above can be observed only in very special cases, where the ΔG curves of the two participating electronic states intersect at fairly low v values.   This is the case for CN [Jenkins (366)], N_2^+ [Herzberg (303)], and some other band systems.   To be sure, for CN the turning point itself is not actually observed.   However, bands are observed which lie on the returning limb of the parabola in Fig. 71 beyond the first band of the sequence considered.   These bands are generally shaded in a direction opposite to that of the bands at the beginning of the sequence (see further discussion in section 3).   They are called *tail bands*.

Vibrational analysis.   When the sequences in a band system are well developed, the vibrational analysis is very simple.   Starting from longer wave lengths, the separations of the sequences (that is, of their first bands) at first gradually increase up to a certain point, at which they change suddenly and then slowly decrease from the new value (see Fig. 70).   This results from the fact that the first bands of the long-wave-length sequences have $v' = 0$, while the first bands of the short-wave-length sequences have $v'' = 0$.   The sequence for which the sudden change in the separations occurs is the main sequence with $\Delta v = 0$.   In this way the correct arrangement of the bands in a Deslandres table is immediately obtained, and the vibrational quanta in the upper and lower states can be determined in the manner already described.

If the sequences are not well developed, as, for example, in the above-mentioned CO spectrum (p. 166 f.) and the P_2 spectrum (Fig. 10), we have to try to find series of approximately equidistant bands whose separations decrease slowly either toward long wave lengths (v''-progressions) or toward short wave lengths (v'-progressions).   Whether the progressions found are genuine may be unambiguously tested by the fact that the separation of corresponding members of two v''-progressions (or two v'-progressions) must be exactly constant.[1]   Conversely, we may also adopt the procedure of looking for pairs of bands with equal separations.   When a series of such pairs has been found, all having the same separation, they must represent either two v''- or two v'-progressions.   If we have once found two such progressions, it is relatively easy to make further progress, since we need only to draw one of the progressions on a strip of paper and to shift it relative to

---

[1] It should be noticed that corresponding bands of two *sequences* do *not* have a constant separation.

the band system drawn on another strip of paper until a coincidence with another progression is obtained. In this way the whole Deslandres table, and from it the vibrational constants, can be obtained.

It may also happen, particularly if ω' is very close to ω'', that only one sequence is observed—namely, the principal sequence ($\Delta v = 0$). In such a case, the determination of the vibrational constants is naturally not possible, since for this purpose at least two sequences must be observed. On the other hand, when a single *progression* is observed, the vibrational constants of at least one of the states can be determined.

Isotope effect. Formulae (IV, 8 and 9) are of course completely equivalent for the representation of a band system. However, in using (IV, 9), we have to be quite clear that $\omega_0 v - \omega_0 x_0 v^2 + \cdots$ represents the position of the vibrational levels above the state with $v = 0$ and not above the minimum of the potential curve. But, if we wish to compare the band systems of two isotopic molecules, it is the *absolute positions of the vibrational levels* of the two electronic states that matter—that is, their distances from the *minimum* of the corresponding potential curves. It is therefore necessary, in this case, to use formula (IV, 8) with its *half-integral* vibrational quanta (that is, with $v + \frac{1}{2}$ instead of v). Conversely, as we shall see in the following, the necessity of assuming half-integral vibrational quanta was first shown by the investigation of the isotope effect in electronic band spectra, and thereby the correctness of the quantum mechanical formula for the energy levels of an oscillator and the existence of zero-point energy (vibration) was demonstrated [Mulliken (508) and Jenkins and Laszlo (372)].

It is to be expected that the electronic energy and with it the potential curve for each electronic state of two isotopic molecules such as $B^{10}O$ and $B^{11}O$ would be practically identical, since the number of electrons and the field in which they move is exactly the same. Any electronic isotope shift would be expected to be of the same order as the isotope shift for atoms, which in general is very small (see A.A., Chapter V). The energy (ν_e) of the pure electron jump for a given band system of the two isotopic molecules is therefore the same to a very good approximation. Thus, according to (III, 126), neglecting terms higher than the quadratic, we have the formulae for the band systems of the two molecules,

$$\nu = \nu_e + \omega_e'(v' + \tfrac{1}{2}) - \omega_e'x_c'(v' + \tfrac{1}{2})^2$$
$$- [\omega_e''(v'' + \tfrac{1}{2}) - \omega_e''x_e''(v'' + \tfrac{1}{2})^2],$$

$$\text{(IV, 15)}$$

$$\nu^i = \nu_e + \rho\omega_e'(v' + \tfrac{1}{2}) - \rho^2\omega_e'x_e'(v' + \tfrac{1}{2})^2$$
$$- [\rho\omega_e''(v'' + \tfrac{1}{2}) - \rho^2\omega_e''x_e''(v'' + \tfrac{1}{2})^2].$$

These two equations can be written in the approximate form

$$\nu = \nu_e + \nu_v, \quad \nu^i = \nu_e + \rho\nu_v,$$

if ρ^2 in the term with $(v + \tfrac{1}{2})^2$ is replaced by ρ. This does not introduce any great error, since this term is, in any event, small compared to the term linear in $(v + \tfrac{1}{2})$ and, in addition, ρ is usually quite close to unity. We can see, therefore, that the *band system of the heavier isotopic molecule is contracted compared to that of the lighter, approximately by a constant factor* $\rho = \sqrt{\mu/\mu^i}$, which is less than 1.

As an illustration, Fig. 13, p. 36, shows a spectrogram of the AgCl absorption bands after Brice (125). The bands belonging to the more abundant isotope $AgCl^{35}$ are clearly separated from those belonging to the less abundant isotope $AgCl^{37}$. It can be seen further that the isotopic displacement increases more or less linearly with increasing distance from the 0–0 band. To the right of the 0–0 band, the weaker $AgCl^{37}$ bands are overlapped by the stronger $AgCl^{35}$ bands and therefore cannot be seen separately in the reproduction. Fig. 13 shows that, although in general the factor ρ is nearly 1, the isotopic displacement can become comparable to the separation of successive bands for bands with large ν_v values. On photographs with greater dispersion, each of the AgCl bands is once more split into two components as a result of the isotopy of Ag. For the two Ag isotopes, Ag^{107} and Ag^{109},

ρ is much nearer to 1 than for the Cl isotopes, giving a much smaller splitting.

It is of particular importance that the *isotopic displacement* given by (IV, 15) is *not zero for the* 0–0 *band* of the system, since ν_v is not zero for the 0–0 band, owing to the fact that the zero-point energies in the upper and lower states have in general different magnitudes and are different for the two isotopic molecules. The isotopic displacement for the 0–0 band would vanish only if there were no zero-point energy (old quantum theory). However, an isotopic displacement for the 0–0 band is actually observed in a number of cases, although, because of its comparative smallness, not in all the cases investigated. However, even then the existence of a displacement for the 0–0 band follows indirectly from the fact that the observed shifts of the other bands agree with formula (IV, 15) and not with the corresponding formula of the old quantum theory. In the latter, $\omega_0 v - \omega_0 x_0 v^2$ and $\omega_0 \rho v - \omega_0 x_0 \rho^2 v^2$ are used for the vibrational terms instead of the expressions in (IV, 15).

As an example of the difference between old and new quantum theory, the observed isotopic shifts in the v'-progression with $v'' = 0$, of the α bands of BO, corresponding to the two isotopes B^{10} and B^{11}, are given in Table 19. A

TABLE 19

ISOTOPIC DISPLACEMENTS IN THE v' = PROGRESSION WITH $v'' = 0$ OF THE α BANDS OF BO

[According to data of Jenkins and McKellar (373)]

Band	Observed Isotopic Displacement $B^{10}O - B^{11}O$ (cm^{-1})	Calculated from Quantum Mechanics (cm^{-1})	Calculated from Old Quantum Theory (cm^{-1})
0–0	− 8.6	− 9.08	0
1–0	+ 26.7	+ 26.29	+ 35.69
2–0	+ 60.8	+ 60.36	+ 70.09
3–0	+ 93.6	+ 93.14	+103.20
4–0	+125.2	+124.63	+135.01

shift of the 0–0 band is directly observed here. The third and fourth columns give the values calculated in the two ways described with half-integral and integral vibrational quanta. It can be seen that the observed values are all in agreement with the assumption of the half-integral vibrational quanta.[2] The same has been found to be true for all cases thus far investigated. *Thus the existence of the zero-point vibration is proved.*

The investigation of the isotope effect is sometimes of great value for the analysis of the vibrational structure of an extensive band system. Suppose we have, for example, a series of absorption bands whose intensity at first increases with decreasing wave length. Then, if the series does not begin with a very intense band, it is in general not possible to say offhand whether the first observed band is the 0–0 band of the system. Thus at first we can fix only a *relative* numbering of the individual bands. However, when an isotope effect is observed, the *absolute* numbering is easily found, since the isotopic displacement must almost (though not completely) vanish for the 0–0 band, and naturally the remaining shifts must also agree with the calculated values. In this way, for example, the vibrational numbering has been determined for the absorption bands of ICl [(255) and (552)] and Br$_2$ (133).

Sometimes, when the *carrier of* (that is, the molecule giving rise to) *a band system* has been in doubt, the observation of the isotope effect can lead to an unambiguous answer. While in absorption experiments in pure gases there can usually be no doubt about the carrier of a given absorption band system, in emission—in electric discharges, flames, and the like—band systems often appear that belong to molecules that are not chemically stable but are formed in the discharge or flame. In addition, impurities in discharges or flames may make themselves much more noticeable than their concentration would appear to warrant. Since the magnitude of the isotope effect depends on the mass of the two participating atoms, it can be used to decide between

---

[2] The very small, approximately constant, difference between the observed and the calculated values is due to an electronic isotope effect.

the different possibilities for the carrier of a band system. For example, the above-mentioned BO bands were at first taken to be BN bands, since they appear by excitation of BCl_3 vapor with active nitrogen. Mulliken (508) then showed, however, that the magnitude of the isotope shift was not compatible with this assumption, but was compatible only with the assumption that BO is the carrier of the band system, the oxygen being due to a slight impurity. In a similar manner, for example, it has been shown definitely that the two band systems appearing in the green and the violet spectrum of the ordinary carbon arc (see Fig. 7) are due to the C_2 and CN molecules, respectively, a question that was for a long time in doubt.

The investigation of the isotope effect in electronic band spectra has led, furthermore, to the *discovery of a number of new isotopes of very small abundance*. By using very long absorbing layers or, in emission, very long exposure times, it is possible to observe isotope bands that are very weak in comparison to the main bands.

The first rare isotope discovered by the use of band spectra was the *oxygen isotope* of mass 18. Already in 1927 Dieke and Babcock (186) had found an extremely weak band A' near the most intense atmospheric O_2 band A at 7596 Å (0–0 band), which appears in the solar spectrum. Both bands have exactly the same structure. Fig. 73 gives a spectrogram of this region of the solar spectrum. In spite of the identical structure, the A' band does not fit into the Deslandres table of the main atmospheric oxygen bands, being much closer to the A band than the 1–1 band, which would be the nearest band of the system. The explanation of this A' band remained a riddle until Giauque and Johnston (253) showed that it could be explained quantitatively if it was ascribed to a molecule $O^{16}O^{18}$, whose absorption bands could be calculated according to (IV, 15) from those of the ordinary O_2^{16} molecule. From the relative intensities of the two bands the *relative abundance* of the two isotopic oxygen atoms was estimated to be 1 : 630 [Childs and Mecke (154)]. Shortly after the discovery of O^{18}, Babcock (74) found a further band A'', five times weaker than A', which also accompanied the main atmospheric band A. This band was identified as an $O^{16}O^{17}$ band by Giauque and Johnston (254), and thereby the existence of an O^{17} isotope was proved.

Later, in addition to the 0–0 band, the 1–0 and 2–0 bands of the $O^{16}O^{18}$ molecule were also observed. Furthermore, it was established that every second line was *not* missing for the $O^{16}O^{18}$ molecule, as it is for $O^{16}O^{16}$. This difference is in

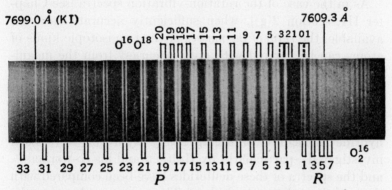

Fig. 73. Isotope Effect in the Atmospheric O_2 Band (A) λ7596 Å. The lines of ordinary O_2 are indicated below and those of the isotopic molecule (A' band) above. The numbers added to the leading lines are the K values (see pp. 245 and 304).

agreement with theory (see p. 150). Though most of the even-numbered lines of the A' band are covered by the strong (odd-numbered) lines of the A band, nevertheless a few of them can be seen in Fig. 73.

Furthermore, Naudé (527) has found in the NO absorption system weak bands which are to be ascribed to the isotopic molecules NO^{17} and NO^{18}. Finally, the existence of these isotopes has also been demonstrated by the mass spectroscope. In this way the relative abundance was found to be $O^{18} : O^{16} = 1 : 503$ [Smythe (640)].

As a result of the existence of the isotopes O^{17} and O^{18}, the chemical *atomic-weight scale* (based on the oxygen mixture = 16) does not agree exactly with the Aston mass-spectroscopic scale, which is based on $O^{16} = 16$. From the relative abundance of the isotopes, the following conversion formula is obtained:

$$A_{\text{Aston}} = A_{\text{chem.}} \, 1.000273.$$

Following the discovery of the oxygen isotopes, the rare isotopes of *carbon*, C^{13} [King and Birge (400)], and of *nitrogen*, N^{15} [Naudé (527)], were found also by means of their band spectra [see also the more recent work (306), (374), (379), (424), and (720a)].

As in the case of the rotation-vibration spectra [see Chapter III, section 2(g)], when sufficiently accurate data are available, the *ratio of the masses* of the two isotopic kinds of atoms can be derived with great accuracy from the magnitude of the isotope shift in electronic band spectra [see, for example, Birge (105) and Jenkins and McKellar (373)].

Since it has become possible to obtain the rare *hydrogen isotope of mass* 2 in a concentrated form, many diatomic hydride molecules containing heavy hydrogen have been investigated—particularly by Hulthén and his co-workers—and the spectra of these deuterides have been compared with those of the ordinary hydrides. The agreement between the observations and the theoretical formula (IV, 15) is, in general, excellent.

In some cases, however, small but definite *deviations* appear [see, for example, Watson (692)] that can be traced back to a small alteration of the potential curve under consideration in changing to the "heavy" molecule. This has been discussed theoretically by Kronig (423), Dieke (184), and Van Vleck (682). For hydrogen, the mass difference is so great and the mass itself so small that the difference in the nuclear motion associated with the electronic motion does have some effect—as in atomic spectra. To this must be added other secondary influences due to the finer interactions of the motions in the molecule (see the above references).

Tables of the band-spectroscopic isotope effects investigated until 1936 are given by Sponer (36).

3. ROTATIONAL STRUCTURE OF ELECTRONIC BANDS

General. While, in the foregoing section, we neglected the contribution of rotational energy to the emitted or absorbed frequencies and considered only the vibrational contribution, we shall now consider the *possible changes in the rotational state* for any given vibrational transition. In the expression

$$\nu = \nu_e + \nu_v + \nu_r$$

the quantity $\nu_0 = \nu_e + \nu_v$ is constant for a given vibrational transition, while ν_r is variable, corresponding to the different values of the rotational quantum number in the upper and lower states. All of the possible transitions for a constant value of ν_0 taken together form, as we shall presently see in greater detail, a *single band*. As in the case of rotation-vibration spectra, we have for such a band

$$\nu = \nu_0 + F'(J') - F''(J''), \qquad \text{(IV, 16)}$$

where $F'(J')$ and $F''(J'')$ are the rotational terms of the upper and lower state, respectively. The difference from the infrared and Raman spectra is that now F' and F'' belong to *different* electronic states and can therefore have very different magnitudes.

In the most general case previously dealt with (symmetrical top, taking into account the interaction of vibration and rotation) we have [see (III, 101 and 87)]

$$F(J) = B_v J(J+1) + (A - B_v)\Lambda^2 - D_v J^2(J+1)^2 + \cdots. \quad \text{(IV, 17)}$$

Here the term containing Λ^2 is constant for a given vibrational state of a given electronic state. As a result, this term in Λ^2 can be completely neglected in the calculation of the possible rotational transitions when we choose ν_0 in (IV, 16) appropriately. Therefore, in this chapter, in order to avoid introducing yet another special symbol, we shall understand $F(J)$ to mean the rotational energy measured from the rotational level having $J = 0$; that is,

$$F(J) = B_v J(J + 1) - D_v J^2(J + 1)^2 + \cdots. \quad \text{(IV, 18)}$$

Then, according to (IV, 16), we have

$$\nu = \nu_0 + B_v'J'(J' + 1) - D_v'J'^2(J' + 1)^2 + \cdots$$
$$- [B_v''J''(J'' + 1) - D_v''J''^2(J'' + 1)^2 \cdots]. \qquad \text{(IV, 19)}$$

The branches of a band. As *selection rules* we must apply those holding for the symmetrical top (see p. 126), for which now the upper and lower states can have *different* electronic angular momenta Λ. Thus, in the most general case, when at least one of the two states has $\Lambda \neq 0$,

$$\Delta J = J' - J'' = 0, \pm 1. \qquad \text{(IV, 20)}$$

When, however, $\Lambda = 0$ in both electronic states ($^1\Sigma - {}^1\Sigma$ transition; see Chapter V), the transition with $\Delta J = 0$ is forbidden and only $\Delta J = \pm 1$ appears, as for most infrared bands. Thus we have to expect *three or two series of lines* (*branches*), respectively, whose wave numbers are given by the following formulae (just as for the rotation-vibration spectra):

$$R \text{ branch}: \nu = \nu_0 + F'(J + 1) - F''(J) = R(J). \quad \text{(IV, 21)}$$
$$Q \text{ branch}: \nu = \nu_0 + F'(J) \qquad - F''(J) = Q(J). \quad \text{(IV, 22)}$$
$$P \text{ branch}: \nu = \nu_0 + F'(J - 1) - F''(J) = P(J). \quad \text{(IV, 23)}$$

Here the J's are the rotational quantum numbers in the lower state ($= J''$).

If we substitute (IV, 18) in (IV, 21–23), neglecting the small correction term in D and for brevity omitting the index v, we obtain the following, just as in the case of rotation-vibration spectra (see Chapter III):

$$\nu = \nu_0 + 2B' + (3B' - B'')J + (B' - B'')J^2 = R(J). \quad \text{(IV, 24)}$$
$$\nu = \nu_0 \qquad + (B' - B'')J + (B' - B'')J^2 = Q(J). \quad \text{(IV, 25)}$$
$$\nu = \nu_0 \qquad - (B' + B'')J + (B' - B'')J^2 = P(J). \quad \text{(IV, 26)}$$

As before, the P and R branches can be represented by a single formula,

$$\nu = \nu_0 + (B' + B'')m + (B' - B'')m^2, \quad \text{(IV, 27)}$$

where $m = -J$ for the P branch and $m = J + 1$ for the R branch. Thus, when no Q branch is present ($^1\Sigma - {}^1\Sigma$ transition), there is a *simple series of lines* whose separation changes regularly. This corresponds exactly to the simplest observed fine structures of bands described in Chapter II. Formula (IV, 27) has exactly the same form as the empirical equation (II, 8). The only essential difference compared to the infrared spectra is that now B' and B'' may have very different magnitudes and that, as a result, the quadratic term in (IV, 24–27) may be much greater (that is, there may be a much more rapid alteration in the separation of successive lines), in agreement with experiment.

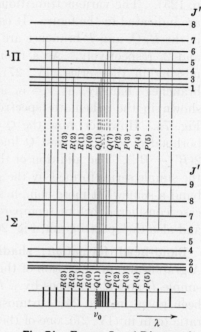

Fig. 74. Energy Level Diagram for a Band with P, Q, and R Branches. For the sake of clarity, in the spectrogram below, the lines of the P and R branches, which form a single series, are represented by longer lines than those of the Q branch. The separation of the lines in the Q branch has been made somewhat too large in order that the lines might be drawn separately. The convergence in the P and R branches is frequently much more rapid than drawn.

From Fig. 52, p. 119, which also holds for the present case (no Q branch), it follows immediately that the smallest value for J in the R branch is $J = 0$ and in the P branch $J = 1$. As a result, according to (IV, 24 and 26), no line appears in the position $\nu = \nu_0$. In agreement with experiment (see Figs. 18 and 19), there is a gap in the series of lines (IV, 27), the so-called *zero gap*, analogous to that in the infrared spectrum.

The case where all *three branches* (P, Q, and R) appear is represented by an energy level diagram in Fig. 74. In this figure it is assumed that $\Lambda = 1$ in the upper state and $\Lambda = 0$ in the lower state ($^1\Pi - {}^1\Sigma$ transition; see Chapter V). As a result, the lowest level in the upper state has $J = 1$ (see p. 125). The various transitions with $\Delta J = +1$, 0, and -1 are indicated in the figure. It can be seen that the *first lines* in the R, Q, and P branches are now those having $J = 0$, 1, and 2, respectively. As a result, there are now two lines missing in the series (IV, 27), formed by the R and P branches—namely, at $\nu = \nu_0$ and $\nu = \nu_0 - 2B''$. This is shown in the schematic spectrogram in the lower part of Fig. 74. However, now the Q *branch* begins in the neighborhood of ν_0. The first Q line ($J = 1$) lies at $\nu = \nu_0 + 2(B' - B'')$. The addition of the Q branch, which overlaps the simple series formed by the P and R branches, gives the band a somewhat more complicated appearance than in the case considered before (compare the lower part of Fig. 74 and also the spectrogram, Fig. 20).

Band-head formation; shading (degrading) of bands. A graphical representation of the simplest type of band with simple P and R branches by a *Fortrat diagram* has already been given in Fig. 24. In most cases, owing to the quadratic term in (IV, 27), one of the two branches "turns back" (broken part of the parabola in Fig. 24)—that is, forms a *band head*. This gives rise to the appearance so characteristic of most bands in the visible and ultraviolet regions. We can now consider in somewhat greater detail the conditions under which such band heads (corresponding to the vertex of the Fortrat parabola) appear and can calculate their separation from the zero line (band origin).

A head is formed in the R branch if in (IV, 24) the factor $(B' - B'')$ of the quadratic term in J is negative, since the linear and quadratic terms then have opposite signs in (IV, 24) and the same sign in (IV, 26). Thus, in this case the head lies on the short-wave-length side of the zero line and the band is *shaded (degraded) toward the red* (toward longer wave lengths). This is the case when $B' < B''$—

that is, when the nuclear separation in the upper state is greater than that in the lower [see (III, 82)]. Conversely, when $B' > B''$—that is, when the nuclear separation in the upper state is smaller than that in the lower—the factor $B' - B''$ is positive and the band head therefore lies in the P branch; the band is *shaded* (*degraded*) *toward the violet* (toward shorter wave lengths), as is the case in the example, Fig. 24.

The m value corresponding to the *vertex of the Fortrat parabola*—that is, to the band head (see Fig. 24)—is obtained by putting $\dfrac{d\nu}{dm} = 0$ in (IV, 27). This gives

$$m_{\text{vertex}} = -\frac{B' + B''}{2(B' - B'')}. \qquad \text{(IV, 28)}$$

If this is substituted in (IV, 27), we obtain for the separation between the zero line and the vertex

$$\nu_{\text{vertex}} - \nu_0 = -\frac{(B' + B'')^2}{4(B' - B'')}. \qquad \text{(IV, 29)}$$

Naturally, for m_{vertex} an integral value is not usually obtained. The actual head then lies at the nearest whole-numbered value of m—that is, at the nearest $\nu(m)$ in (IV, 27). However, for most practical purposes, (IV, 28 and 29) can be considered to apply to the band head.[3] It can now be seen from (IV, 28 and 29) that the *head lies at a distance from the zero line that is the greater, the smaller $B' - B''$ is.* If B' is very nearly equal to B'', the head may lie at such a great distance from the band origin that it is not observed, since for the corresponding m value the intensity of the lines may have decreased to zero (see section 4). This is almost always the case for infrared rotation-vibration bands (see Chapter III). However, such cases also occur occasionally in electronic bands—for example, for C_2 and CN.

---

[3] It is seen that the sign of $\nu_{\text{vertex}} - \nu_0$, according to (IV, 29), is in agreement with what has been said before—namely, that the band is shaded to the red if $B' < B''$, and to the violet if $B' > B''$.

If a Q branch is present in addition to the P and R branches, the Q branch can also be represented by a parabola [according to (IV, 25)]. Its vertex points in the same direction as that of the parabola of the P and R branches [same quadratic term in (IV, 24–26)]. This agrees with the empirical results discussed in Chapter II (see Fig. 25, p. 51, in which m is used instead of J). Whereas the lines of the P and R branches lie on one and the same parabola, the Q *branch forms a parabola by itself.* This is the reason that the series of lines in the Q branch intersects those of the P and R branches a number of times, while the latter two always run parallel (see p. 50). If B' and B'' are not very different, as in the example of the AlH band in Figs. 20 and 25 ($B' = 6.024$ and $B'' = 6.296$ cm^{-1}), the Q-branch parabola intersects the abscissa axis almost at right angles, owing to the smallness of the linear term in (IV, 25). This means that a *head* is formed at the beginning of the Q branch, as is clearly shown in the spectrogram, Fig. 20. Thus, bands having a Q branch very often show *two* heads either in the P and Q branches ($B' > B''$, shading to the violet) or in the R and Q branches ($B' < B''$, shading to the red). The latter is the case for the AlH band, as well as for the previously discussed PN bands, for some of which a second head (Q head) can be clearly seen in Fig. 9, p. 32, while for others it is hidden by the R head.

If B' is approximately equal to B'', according to (IV, 25) all the lines of the Q branch fall nearly in the same place (ν_0). We then have an intense, almost line-like Q branch, on either side of which P and R branches extend with approximately equal separation of the lines, as in the infrared spectrum of the symmetrical top. An example is the BH band at 4330 Å [see (451)].

If B' is very different from B'', the head of the Q branch does not appear clearly, since the vertex of the corresponding parabola then lies considerably below the ν axis.

For different bands of the same band system—that is, different $v'-v''$ combinations—the pairs of values B' and B'' are somewhat different, since, according to (III, 83), B_v

depends on v. The separation of the zero line (origin) from the band head therefore alters from band to band. This accounts for the fact that, in a Deslandres table, the differences between corresponding bands in two vertical or two horizontal rows sometimes do not agree quite exactly; as we have seen, the constancy of these differences is strictly derived only for zero rotational energy—that is, for the *band origins* ($J = 0$).[4] It cannot therefore hold rigorously for the band heads with their varying separations from the zero line and their varying J values. However, as long as the separation $\nu_{\text{head}} - \nu_0$ is itself small—that is, as long as B' and B'' are not too nearly the same—this correction makes little difference. For the PN bands discussed earlier, $\nu_{\text{head}} - \nu_0$ lies between 5.7 and 12.7 cm^{-1}.

According to what has been said above, the head of the Q branch lies very close to ν_0. Thus, in a band system in which Q branches appear whose heads can be measured, the Q *heads*, and not the P or R heads, should be used to determine the vibrational constants. Naturally, still more accurate values for the vibrational constants are obtained from the *band origins* themselves (for their determination, see p. 204).

When, as is usually the case, the difference between B_e' and B_e'' is not too small, the difference $B_v' - B_v''$ has the same sign for all the bands (owing to the smallness of the rotational constant α). All the bands of a band system are therefore *usually shaded in the same direction*.

However, if B_e' and B_e'' are only slightly different from each other, there may be, in one and the same band system, bands for which $B' - B''$ is positive as well as bands for which $B' - B''$ is negative—that is, bands that are shaded to the violet as well as bands that are shaded to the red. Such a case was first found for the violet CN bands [see Jenkins (366)]. The B_v curves for the upper and lower states of these bands are plotted in Fig. 75. It can be seen from this figure that the bands in the main sequence ($v' = v''$) are shaded to the violet as long as $v < 9$, since then $B' > B''$. On the other hand, for larger values of v, $B' < B''$; that

---

[4] The constancy of the differences also holds, as may easily be seen, for any other given rotational state J.

is, the bands are shaded to the red.   Thus a *reversal of the shading* takes place in the main sequence.   For the bands of the other sequences the direction of shading is found by shifting the B_v' curve by $|\Delta v|$ to the left or to the right, depending on whether $\Delta v = v' - v''$ is positive or negative.   The point of intersection with the (unshifted) B_v'' curve gives the point where a reversal of the shading takes place in the particular sequence.   The most intense bands of this system (with small v) are thus shaded to the violet (see the spectrogram, Fig. 7), whereas the weaker bands with larger v are shaded to the red.   The latter lie for the most part on the long-wave-length side of the corresponding sequences— that is, on the returning limb of the parabola that represents the bands of a sequence (see p. 173).   Some of these bands can be seen in Fig. 7 (broken leading lines).   As already remarked, they are called *tail bands*, since, before they were theoretically explained, they were thought to form the end of the preceding sequence of bands. In some cases bands in the neighborhood of the turning point of the shading ($B' \approx B''$) have no head at all and are of the same appearance as

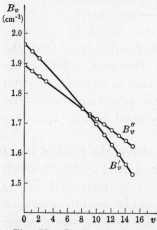

Fig. 75. B_v Curves for the Upper and Lower States of the Violet CN Bands According to the Data of Jenkins (366) and Jenkins, Roots, and Mulliken (377).

rotation-vibration bands [see, for example, Jenkins (366) and Coster and Brons (168) and (169)].

The B values of the different electronic states of a molecule run more or less parallel to the ω values.   The state with the larger value of B has in general the larger ω, and vice versa (see also Chapter VIII, p. 498).   Or, expressed in another way, the smaller the nuclear separation in an electronic state is, the greater is the force constant in it.   In addition, according to (III, 84), α_e/B_e is proportional to $\omega_e x_e/\omega_e$.   Therefore it is usually found that, when the ΔG curves of two electronic states intersect, the corresponding B_v curves also intersect, at similar v values.   Thus, when a reversal of the bands is observed in the sequences (formation of heads of heads), a reversal of the shading usually occurs also [for example, for CN (366) and N_2^+ (303), (168), and (169)].

Thus far, in the discussion in this section, we have neglected the *rotational constant D*, which is, of course, usually only a very small correction term. However, the introduction of this correction is necessary for accurate measurements, particularly for high J values. For the *P and R branches* we then obtain, from (IV, 18 and 21–23), omitting the subscript v [compare equation (III, 97) for the rotation-vibration bands],

$$\nu = \nu_0 + (B' + B'')m + (B' - B'' - D' + D'')m^2 \\ - 2(D' + D'')m^3 - (D' - D'')m^4 \qquad \text{(IV, 30)}$$

and for the *Q branch*

$$\nu = \nu_0 + (B' - B'')J(J + 1) - (D' - D'')J^2(J + 1)^2. \qquad \text{(IV, 31)}$$

It should be noted that now, in contrast to the case of rotation-vibration spectra, D' can be very different from D'' and the fourth-power term can therefore be important.

While in general the cubic and fourth-power terms do not alter the above considerations about the appearance of the bands, in extreme cases these terms can bring about a *change in shading in one and the same band*, particularly if the band is observed up to very high J values; for example, in consequence of these higher-power terms, not only might the P branch form a head on the long-wave-length side but the R branch might also form a head on the short-wave-length side, or even *two* heads might appear in one and the same branch. In principle, this follows directly from the fact that equations of the fourth degree, such as (IV, 30 and 31), can have, in general, two maxima and one minimum or two minima and one maximum. A more detailed investigation shows that two opposing heads can appear in a band when B' and B'' are very nearly equal, but, however, still sufficiently different that a "normal" head appears, and when, in addition, $D' - D''$ is large and has the same sign as $B' - B''$. Such cases have been observed, for example, for BeH [Watson (690)] and for the indium and gallium halides [Wehrli and Miescher (701) and (495)].

Combination relations; evaluation of the rotational constants. In principle, the rotational constants B' and B'' for electronic bands can be evaluated by comparing the empirical formula (II, 8) with (IV, 27) in the manner previously described for rotation-vibration bands (see p. 120). In practice a different procedure is used to obtain the rotational constants—namely, the employment of the *combina-*

tion relations or *combination differences*. As we shall see, these permit us to obtain separately the upper and lower rotational states from the observed band and then to evaluate the rotational constants separately.

First of all, we shall consider the case of a *band that has only a single P and a single R branch* and shall take the wave numbers of the lines as well as their correct numbering (position of the zero gap) as given. How the correct numbering can be derived in cases where it is not obvious will be discussed later. As an example, the wave numbers of the lines of the 0–0 band of the green BeO bands are given in Table 20, in which the J numbering (not the m numbering) is used (see p. 184).

It follows immediately from Fig. 52, p. 119, that the difference between the wave numbers of two lines with the same *upper* state is equal to the separation, $\Delta_2 F''(J)$, of one of the *lower*-state rotational levels from the next but one; for example, the difference between the lines $P(5)$ and $R(3)$ (upper state in both cases, $J = 4$) is equal to the separation of the rotational levels $J = 3$ and $J = 5$ in the lower state. Thus

$$R(J-1) - P(J+1) = F''(J+1) - F''(J-1)$$
$$= \Delta_2 F''(J). \qquad \text{(IV, 32)}$$

Correspondingly, it can be seen from Fig. 52 that the difference between the wave numbers of two lines with a common *lower* state is equal to the separation of one of the *upper*-state rotational levels from the next but one:

$$R(J) - P(J) = F'(J+1) - F'(J-1) = \Delta_2 F'(J). \qquad \text{(IV, 33)}$$

The correctness of the *combination relations* (IV, 32 and 33) may also be verified easily by substitution of (IV, 21 and 23).

It should be noted that (IV, 32 and 33) are *quite independent of the formula* (IV, 18) *for the rotational levels* and would also hold when irregularities, so-called *perturbations*, occur (see Chapter V, section 4). For the example in

TABLE 20

FINE STRUCTURE OF THE GREEN BeO BANDS

Wave numbers of the lines of the 0–0 band and combination differences for the bands 0–0, 0–1, and 2–1 after Rosenthal and Jenkins (602)

J	$R(J)$	$P(J)$	0–0 Band $\Delta_2F''(J)=R(J-1)-P(J+1)$	0–0 Band $\Delta_2F'(J)=R(J)-P(J)$	0–0 $\dfrac{\Delta_2F''(J)}{J+\frac12}$	0–0 $\dfrac{\Delta_2F'(J)}{J+\frac12}$	0–1 Band $\Delta_2F''(J)=R(J-1)-P(J+1)$	0–1 Band $\Delta_2F'(J)=R(J)-P(J)$	2–1 Band $\Delta_2F''(J)=R(J-1)-P(J+1)$	2–1 Band $\Delta_2F'(J)=R(J)-P(J)$
0	21,199.81									
1	202.88	21,193.25	9.84	9.63	6.560	6.420		9.44		
2	205.74	189.97	16.47	15.77	6.588	6.308	16.18	15.68		
3	208.52	186.41	23.08	22.11	6.594	6.317	22.71	21.93		
4	211.12	182.66	29.64	28.46	6.587	6.324	29.16	28.22	29.02	33.80
5	213.58	178.88	36.30	34.70	6.600	6.309	35.63	34.48		
6	215.58	174.82	42.93	40.76	6.605	6.271	42.19	40.68	42.16	46.09
7	217.71	170.65	49.23	47.06	6.564	6.275	48.59	46.94	48.65	52.19
8	219.65	166.35	55.78	53.30	6.562	6.271	55.04	53.15	55.09	58.39
9	221.43	161.93	62.37	59.50	6.565	6.263	61.49	59.48	61.57	
10	223.12	157.28	68.86	65.84	6.558	6.271	67.95	65.78	68.12	
11	224.62	152.57	75.42	72.05	6.558	6.265	74.59	71.98		
12	225.92	147.70	81.93	78.22	6.554	6.258	81.10	78.41		76.72
13	227.23	142.69	88.39	84.54	6.547	6.267	87.48	84.70	87.46	82.71
14	228.40	137.53	95.01	90.87	6.552	6.267	93.98	90.82	93.77	88.89
15	229.34	132.22	101.65	97.12	6.558	6.266	100.42	97.07	100.23	95.00
16	230.08	126.75	108.33	103.33	6.566	6.262	106.86	103.29	106.70	101.28
17	230.67	121.01	114.69	109.66	6.554	6.266	113.31	109.53	113.34	
18	230.94	115.39	121.27	115.55	6.555	6.246	119.73	115.75		
19		109.40								

$v' = 0$ $v'' = 0$ $v'' = 1$ $v'' = 1$

The R and P branches of the 0–0 band have been measured up to $J = 59$ and 61, respectively. For the 2–1 band a number of Δ_2F values cannot be obtained because of overlapping of the corresponding lines by others.

Table 20, the $\Delta_2 F''(J)$ and $\Delta_2 F'(J)$ values derived from the observed wave numbers of the lines are given in the fourth and fifth columns.

By forming $\Delta_2 F''(J) = R(J-1) - P(J+1)$ and $\Delta_2 F'(J)$ $= R(J) - P(J)$, *the two series of rotational terms have been separated from one another*, since, according to (IV, 32), the former depends only on the lower state and the latter, according to (IV, 33), depends only on the upper state. By adding corresponding $\Delta_2 F(J)$ values, we can obtain the position of the rotational terms in the lower as well as the upper state. However, it is generally not necessary to carry out this addition, since the *rotational constants B* (and possibly D), which determine the position of the rotational levels, can be obtained *from the combination differences* themselves. If we substitute the expression (IV, 18) for $F(J)$ and neglect the term in D, we obtain

$$\Delta_2 F(J) = F(J+1) - F(J-1)$$
$$= B_v(J+1)(J+2) - B_v(J-1)(J) = 4B_v(J+\tfrac{1}{2}). \quad \text{(IV, 34)}$$

(About the small correction terms due to D, see below.) Thus the combination differences $\Delta_2 F(J)$ form, to a first good approximation, a linear function of the rotational quantum number J, going through zero for $J = -\tfrac{1}{2}$. As an illustration, the values of $\Delta_2 F''(J)$ and $\Delta_2 F'(J)$ from Table 20 are represented graphically in Fig. 76. The agreement with a straight line is better than can be shown in a drawing made to this scale. From the slopes of these lines, according to (IV, 34), we can obtain $4B_v''$ and $4B_v'$, respectively.

Instead of determining $4B$ graphically, we can also calculate it from (IV, 34) by determining the mean value of $\Delta_2 F(J)/(J+\tfrac{1}{2})$. These quantities are given in the sixth and seventh columns of Table 20, and their constancy shows the accuracy of formula (IV, 34). From the figures in the table we obtain

$$B_0' = 1.569 \text{ cm}^{-1} \quad \text{and} \quad B_0'' = 1.642 \text{ cm}^{-1}.$$

If two (or more) bands with the same v' are measured, the combination differences $\Delta_2 F'(J)$ for the upper state of the two bands *must agree exactly* within the accuracy of measurement. This is illustrated by the energy level diagram of

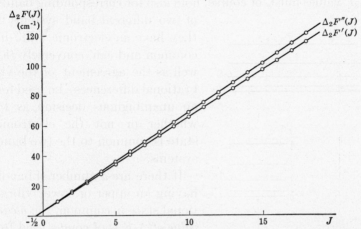

Fig. 76. $\Delta_2 F(J)$ Curves for the Upper and Lower States of the 0–0 Band of the Green BeO System.

Fig. 77. The combination differences $\Delta_2 F''(J)$ and $\Delta_2 F'(J)$, formed for the 0–1 band, of BeO are given in the eighth and ninth columns of Table 20. (In order to save space, the wave numbers of the band lines are omitted.) It can be seen that, owing to the fact that v' is the same, the $\Delta_2 F'(J)$ values for the two bands 0–0 and 0–1 agree very closely for each J value,[5] whereas the $\Delta_2 F''(J)$ values are different.

A corresponding state of affairs exists, of course, for bands having a common lower vibrational state. For them, the $\Delta_2 F''(J)$ must agree exactly for all values of J. To illustrate this, the $\Delta_2 F''$ and $\Delta_2 F'$ values for the 2–1 band are given in the tenth and eleventh columns of Table 20. It can be seen that the $\Delta_2 F''$ values agree with those of the 0–1 band, whereas the $\Delta_2 F'$ values are different.

---

[5] The accuracy of the wave numbers of the band lines is here about ± 0.1 cm^{-1}. Naturally the accuracy of the differences $\Delta_2 F$ is less. This should be allowed for when comparing the different $\Delta_2 F$ values in Table 20.

The agreement between corresponding combination differences for bands with the same lower or the same upper vibrational states forms an important and very sensitive *check on the correctness of an analysis*. Such an agreement between the Δ_2F values must, of course, hold also for corresponding bands of two different band systems if they have an electronic state in common and can, conversely (as well as the agreement of the vibrational differences), be used for an unambiguous decision as to whether or not the electronic state is common to the two band systems.

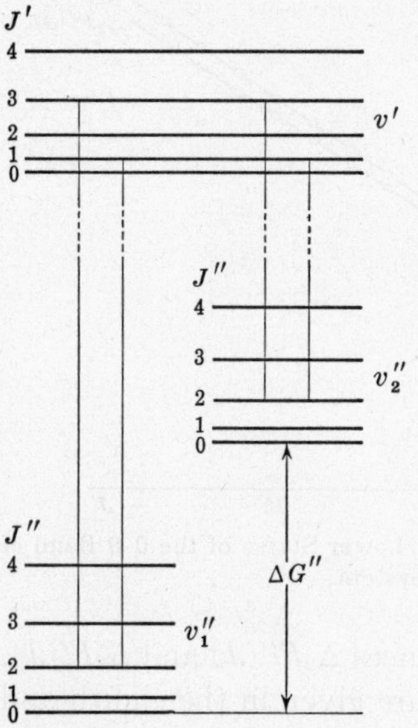

Fig. 77. Agreement of the Combination Differences for Two Different Bands with the Same Upper State. The agreement is shown for $J'' = 2$. For both lower levels, v_1'' and v_2'', for the P branch $J' = 1$ and for the R branch $J' = 3$; that is, the difference $R(J) - P(J)$ must be the same for the two bands $v' \rightarrow v_1''$ and $v' \rightarrow v_2''$ for the same J value.

If there are a number of bands having an upper or lower vibrational state in common, the *mean value of* Δ_2F is of course used for the determination of the corresponding B_v value. The B_v' and B_v'' values for the green BeO bands, determined in this way, are collected in Table 21. (Actually, in determining these B_v' and B_v'' values the correction due to the rotational constant D was allowed for in the manner described below.) It can be seen that the B_v *values decrease very nearly linearly* (see also the example

TABLE 21

ROTATIONAL CONSTANTS B_v OF BeO IN THE UPPER AND LOWER STATES OF THE GREEN BANDS

[Rosenthal and Jenkins (602)]

v	B_v''	B_v'
0	1.6422	1.5691
1	1.6232	1.5536
2	1.6052	1.5363

of HCl, p. 121), in agreement with the earlier formula (III, 83):

$$B_v = B_e - \alpha_e(v + \tfrac{1}{2}). \qquad \text{(IV, 35)}$$

A graphical representation of B_v curves has been given before in Fig. 75, which refers to CN.   In this figure, the B_v'' curve is linear over a very wide range, whereas the B_v' curve has a marked curvature.   However, the latter may also be regarded as linear for small values of v.

The *rotational constants* B_e for the unrealizable, completely vibrationless state, as well as α_e, are obtained from the observed B_v values in the manner described on p. 121.   In the example of the green BeO bands we find that

$$B_v' = 1.5771 - 0.0160(v' + \tfrac{1}{2}),$$
$$B_v'' = 1.6514 - 0.0186(v'' + \tfrac{1}{2}),$$

where the constant terms are the B_e values.   From these we can obtain the *moment of inertia* and the *internuclear distance* in the equilibrium position of the molecule (minimum of the potential curve) according to equation (III, 82).   Introducing the numerical values for all the constants into this formula gives

$$I_e = \mu r_e^2 = \frac{27.994}{B_e} \cdot 10^{-40} \text{ gm cm}^2 \qquad \text{(IV, 36)}$$

and

$$r_e = \frac{4.10653}{\sqrt{\mu_A B_e}} \cdot 10^{-8} \text{ cm}, \qquad \text{(IV, 37)}$$

where μ_A is the reduced mass in Aston atomic-weight units ($O^{16} = 16$).   It follows that, in the example of BeO,

$$I_e' = 17.75 \cdot 10^{-40} \text{ gm cm}^2, \quad \text{and} \quad r_e' = 1.362 \cdot 10^{-8} \text{ cm},$$

$$I_e'' = 16.95 \cdot 10^{-40} \text{ gm cm}^2, \quad \text{and} \quad r_e'' = 1.331 \cdot 10^{-8} \text{ cm}.$$

Apart from I_e and r_e, sometimes I_0 and r_0 are quoted. These are the values calculated from (IV, 36 and 37) when B_0

is used instead of B_e. They are the mean values of the moment of inertia and nuclear separation, respectively, in the lowest vibrational state of the molecule. In the example of BeO,

$$I_0' = 17.84 \cdot 10^{-40} \text{ gm cm}^2, \quad \text{and} \quad r_0' = 1.365 \cdot 10^{-8} \text{ cm,}$$

$$I_0'' = 17.05 \cdot 10^{-40} \text{ gm cm}^2, \quad \text{and} \quad r_0'' = 1.335 \cdot 10^{-8} \text{ cm.}$$

The rotational constants can be derived with even greater accuracy than by the above simplified procedure if band lines with high J values are also measured. For these lines it is necessary to *take into account the nonrigidity of the rotator*—that is, the rotational constant D. From (IV, 18) it follows that, instead of (IV, 34),

$$\Delta_2 F(J) = (4B_v - 6D_v)(J + \tfrac{1}{2}) - 8D_v(J + \tfrac{1}{2})^3. \quad \text{(IV, 38)}$$

Sometimes further terms with higher (odd) powers of $(J + \tfrac{1}{2})$ come in. These terms, however, need to be taken into account only in rare cases [see, for example, Jevons (34)]. The constant $6D_v$ in the first bracket of the above formula can be neglected for almost all purposes, since, in general, D is of the order of $10^{-5}B$. In the following we shall therefore use

$$\Delta_2 F(J) = 4B_v(J + \tfrac{1}{2}) - 8D_v(J + \tfrac{1}{2})^3. \quad \text{(IV, 39)}$$

The formula shows that for high J the $\Delta_2 F$ curve lies somewhat below the straight line $4B_v(J + \tfrac{1}{2})$. To be sure, this is scarcely noticeable in a drawing to the scale used in Fig. 76, since D is so small. However, if we subtract $4\tilde{B}_v(J + \tfrac{1}{2})$ from each of the $\Delta_2 F(J)$ values, where $\tilde{B}_v$ is an approximate value for B_v, the difference $\Delta_2 F(J) - 4\tilde{B}_v(J + \tfrac{1}{2})$ can be plotted on a much larger scale and the curvature becomes noticeable. This has been done in Fig. 78(a) for the lower state with $v'' = 0$ of the green BeO bands. In drawing the figure, additional higher $\Delta_2 F''(J)$ values not given in Table 20 have been used [see Rosenthal and Jenkins (602)]. In order to obtain an accurate value for B_v we have to draw a tangent to the curve for small J values (broken straight line). The slope of this line gives the correction $4\Delta B_v$, which has to be applied to the preliminary $4\tilde{B}_v$ in order to obtain a better value of $4B_v$. Since the figure can be drawn to a suitable scale, ΔB_v and, correspondingly, B_v itself can be very accurately determined. In the figure, $\widetilde{B}_0$ is assumed to be 1.6. From the drawing, $\Delta B_0 = 0.0423$ cm^{-1}, so that $B_0 = 1.6423$ cm^{-1}.

The deviation of the $\Delta_2 F$ curve from the broken straight line represents the correction term $8D_v(J + \frac{1}{2})^3$. Thus at least a preliminary value for D_v can be obtained if the deviation for a high value of J, say $J = 40$, is divided by $8(J + \frac{1}{2})^3$. In the present case the value of D_v so obtained is $8.33 \cdot 10^{-6}$cm^{-1}. Since the tangent to the $\Delta_2 F$ curve cannot be drawn very accurately, it is necessary to check the correctness of the D value so obtained by calculating

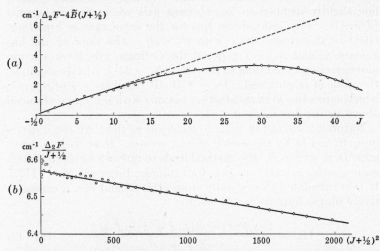

Fig. 78. Graphical Determinations of the Rotational Constants B and D for the state $v'' = 0$ of the Green BeO Bands. (a) $\Delta_2 F(J) - 4\widetilde{B}(J + \frac{1}{2})$ as a function of J with $\widetilde{B} = 1.6$. (b) $\Delta_2 F(J)/(J + \frac{1}{2})$ as a function of $(J + \frac{1}{2})^2$.

$8D_v(J + \frac{1}{2})^3$ for all J values and adding it to the observed $\Delta_2 F$ values. Since, according to (IV, 39),

$$\Delta_2 F(J) + 8D_v(J + \frac{1}{2})^3 = 4B_v(J + \frac{1}{2}), \qquad \text{(IV, 40)}$$

if D_v is chosen correctly, the sum to the left, plotted as a function of J, must give exactly a straight line, even for high J values. This result can be tested in a drawing of the same type as Fig. 78(a).

If the deviation of the $\Delta_2 F$ curve from a straight line cannot be determined with sufficient accuracy, the best procedure is to calculate D_v from the theoretical formula (III, 86), possibly allowing for the constant β_e [see (III, 85) and p. 116], instead of using the above empirical method. B_v can then be accurately determined from the slope of the line $\Delta_2 F(J) + 8D_v(J + \frac{1}{2})^3$ in the manner described. In this way, at any rate, a considerably more accurate B_v value is obtained than when D_v is completely neglected.

A *second graphical method* consists of plotting $\Delta_2 F(J)/(J + \frac{1}{2})$ against $(J + \frac{1}{2})^2$. According to (IV, 39),

$$\frac{\Delta_2 F(J)}{(J + \frac{1}{2})} = 4B_v - 8D_v(J + \frac{1}{2})^2. \qquad (IV, 41)$$

Without taking D_v into account, $\Delta_2 F(J)/(J + \frac{1}{2})$ would be a constant (see above). Owing to the D_v correction, we obtain a straight line slightly inclined to the abscissa axis when plotting against $(J + \frac{1}{2})^2$. Fig. 78(b) shows this for the same case as Fig. 78(a) (BeO in the ground state with $v'' = 0$). The slope of the line gives $8D_v$, and the intercept on the ordinate axis gives $4B_v$ [or, more precisely, according to (IV, 38), $4B_v - 6D_v$]. In the example, the value of D_v obtained is $D_0 = 8.31 \cdot 10^{-6}$ and $B_0 = 1.6421$ cm^{-1}, which agrees in a very satisfactory manner with the values obtained above by the first method.

Naturally, instead of using a graphical method, we could determine B_v and D_v by the *method of least squares*. If we wish to determine D_v as well as B_v, this method leads to rather long, even though quite simple, calculations [see, for example, Birge and Shea (112)]. If D is calculated theoretically from (III, 85 and 86), a comparatively simple formula for B_v results:

$$4B_v = \frac{\Sigma[\Delta_2 F(J) + 8D_v(J + \frac{1}{2})^3](J + \frac{1}{2})}{\Sigma(J + \frac{1}{2})^2}, \qquad (IV, 42)$$

where the summations are to be taken over all the J values for which $\Delta_2 F$ is known.

As an exercise the reader might try to derive the B values of the upper and lower vibrational states of the 0–0 CN band and the 1–0 rotation-vibration band of HCl according to one of the methods given. The necessary data are given in Tables 7 and 9, respectively.

In the calculation of moments of inertia and internuclear distances from the B values, the *Dunham correction* resulting from the finer interaction of vibration and rotation (see p. 116) must sometimes be taken into account for hydrides. However, for other molecules it can be neglected entirely unless still more accurate B values are obtained than are available at the present time [see, in this connection, Crawford and Jorgensen (173) and Dieke and Lewis (188)]. The finer interaction between rotation and electronic motion can also lead to a very small correction (see also

p. 252). Furthermore, in calculating the internuclear distance from the moment of inertia, we must remember that the moment of inertia of a system consisting of two point-like atoms at a distance r_e is somewhat different from that of a molecule consisting of two atomic nuclei and the electrons moving around them. However, this correction leads to an appreciable difference only for the hydrides and even then is very small [see Casimir (151)].

If a Q branch is also present in the bands under investigation (for example, $^1\Pi - {}^1\Sigma$ transitions; see p. 185 f.), additional combination relations are introduced, since now three lines have the same upper or lower state. These relations, which may be read directly from Fig. 74 and which may also be verified with the help of equations (IV, 21–23), are the following:

$$R(J) \quad -Q(J) \quad = F'(J+1) -F'(J) = \Delta_1 F'(J). \quad \text{(IV, 43)}$$

$$Q(J+1) -P(J+1) = F'(J+1) -F'(J) = \Delta_1 F'(J). \quad \text{(IV, 44)}$$

$$R(J) \quad -Q(J+1) = F''(J+1) -F''(J) = \Delta_1 F''(J). \quad \text{(IV, 45)}$$

$$Q(J) \quad -P(J+1) = F''(J+1) -F''(J) = \Delta_1 F''(J). \quad \text{(IV, 46)}$$

Thus from these combination differences we obtain the *separation of successive rotational levels* and not, as before, the separation between one and the next but one. It is seen that the first two combination differences are equal to each other and, similarly, the last two are equal to each other; that is,

$$R(J) - Q(J) \quad = Q(J + 1) - P(J + 1), \quad \text{(IV, 47)}$$

and

$$R(J) - Q(J+1) = Q(J) \quad - P(J + 1). \quad \text{(IV, 48)}$$

Table 22 gives as an example the wave numbers of the lines of the 4–11 band of the fourth positive group of CO. The fifth to eighth columns contain the differences (IV, 43–46). It can be seen that the combination relations (IV, 47 and 48) are well satisfied. In several other cases, there is a small systematic deviation for high J values which will be explained later (see p. 278).

Table 22

WAVE NUMBERS OF THE LINES AND COMBINATION DIFFERENCES IN THE 4-11 BAND OF THE FOURTH
POSITIVE GROUP OF CO

[After Gerö (249)]

J	$R(J)$	$Q(J)$	$P(J)$	$R(J) - Q(J) = \Delta_1 F''(J)$	$Q(J+1) - P(J+1) = \Delta_1 F''(J)$	$R(J) - Q(J+1) = \Delta_1 F'(J)$	$Q(J) - P(J+1) = \Delta_1 F'(J)$	$\dfrac{\Delta_1 F''(J)}{J+1}$	$\dfrac{\Delta_1 F'(J)}{J+1}$
0	48,338.37	.....	.....	.....	.....	3.37	.....	.....	3.37
1	340.94	48,335.00	.....	5.94	5.37	6.99	6.42	2.828	3.353
2	342.87	333.95	48,328.58	8.92	8.50	10.23	9.81	2.903	3.340
3	345.16	332.64	324.14	12.52	12.00	14.32	13.80	3.065	3.515
4	346.38	330.84	318.84	15.54	15.28	17.80	17.54	3.082	3.534
5	347.17	328.58	313.30	18.59	18.39	21.02	20.82	3.082	3.487
6	347.17	326.15	307.76	21.02	20.91	24.57	24.46	2.995	3.502
7	347.17	322.60	301.69	24.57	24.10	27.94	27.47	3.042	3.463
8	346.38	319.23	295.13	27.15	27.14	31.33	31.32	3.016	3.481
9	345.16	315.05	287.91	30.11	30.20	34.34	34.43	3.016	3.439
10	344.02	310.82	280.62	33.20	33.38	37.84	38.02	3.026	3.448
11	341.85	306.18	272.80	35.67	36.32	41.09	41.74	3.000	3.451
12	339.63	300.76	264.44	38.87	39.23	44.50	44.86	3.004	3.437
13	337.06	295.13	255.90	41.93	42.18	48.22	48.47	3.039	3.453
14	333.95	288.84	246.66	45.11	44.95	51.84	51.68	3.002	3.451
15	330.31	282.11	237.16	48.20	48.14	55.16	55.10	3.011	3.446
16	326.15	275.15	227.01	51.00	51.27	58.40	58.67	3.008	3.443
17	321.71	267.75	216.48	53.96	54.13	61.92	62.09	3.003	3.445
18	316.73	259.79	205.66	56.94	57.11	65.21	65.38	3.001	3.437
19	311.67	251.52	194.41	60.15	60.28	68.88	69.01	3.011	3.447
20	306.18	242.79	182.51						

The fulfillment of the relations (IV, 47 and 48) is an excellent *check* on the correctness of the analysis of a band. In addition, of course, if two or more bands are measured that have the same upper state, the differences (IV, 43 and 44) must agree exactly for each J value for these bands, while for bands with the same lower state the differences (IV, 45 and 46) must agree exactly. To these checks may be added those previously described in which $\Delta_2 F(J)$ was used.

Substituting $F(J) = B_v J(J + 1)$ in $\Delta_1 F(J) = F(J + 1) - F(J)$, we obtain

$$\Delta_1 F(J) = F(J + 1) - F(J) = 2B_v(J + 1). \quad (IV, 49)$$

Thus, to a first good approximation, the $\Delta_1 F(J)$ increase linearly with J, as did the $\Delta_2 F(J)$. The fulfillment of this relation is shown in the example of the CO band by the constancy of the $\Delta_1 F'(J)/(J + 1)$ and $\Delta_1 F''(J)/(J + 1)$ values given in the last two columns. These values were obtained by taking the means of corresponding $\Delta_1 F(J)$ values in the fifth and sixth and in the seventh and eighth columns, respectively. The value of $2B_v$ is obtained graphically from the slope of the line (IV, 49) or by calculation of the mean of the $\Delta_1 F(J)/(J + 1)$ values. The B_v values so obtained agree, of course, with those obtained from the $\Delta_2 F$ values. In the example in Table 22 we obtain from the $\Delta_1 F$ values

$$B_4' = 1.505, \qquad B_{11}'' = 1.723 \text{ cm}^{-1},$$

and from the $\Delta_2 F$ values

$$B_4' = 1.504, \qquad B_{11}'' = 1.722 \text{ cm}^{-1}.$$

In general, the determination of the B_v values from the $\Delta_2 F$ values is to be preferred (see Chapter V). The $\Delta_1 F$ values are used for the determination of rotational constants only when, for some reason, the P or the R branch is not observed or can be measured only inaccurately.

It can easily be seen that including the D *correction* in (IV, 18) gives

$$\Delta_1 F(J) = F(J+1) - F(J) = 2B(J+1) - 4D(J+1)^3. \qquad \text{(IV, 50)}$$

When this formula is used, for an accurate determination of the constants, it is necessary to employ a procedure similar to that previously explained for the $\Delta_2 F$ values (p. 198 f.). In the above numerical example, allowing for the D correction raises the B values by about 0.003 cm^{-1}.

Determination of the band origins (zero lines). As we have seen above, if we wish to determine the vibrational constants of a molecule very accurately, we must use the origins (zero lines) ν_0 and not the band heads. An approximate value for ν_0 is obtained, according to (IV, 24), when we subtract $2B'$ from the measured first line $R(0)$ of the R branch or $2B' + (3B' - B'')1 + (B' - B'')1^2$ from the second line $R(1)$ of the R branch, and so on. Thus, for example, from $R(0)$ of the 0–0 band of BeO (Table 20) we obtain $\nu_0 = 21,196.67$ cm^{-1}. Alternatively, corresponding calculations, using the lines of the P or Q branches, may be carried out.

For a more accurate determination of the origins the following procedure may be used, in which all the measurements are taken equally into account: If only P *and R branches* are present, $R(J - 1) + P(J)$ is formed for all the J values occurring. According to (IV, 24 and 26),

$$R(J - 1) + P(J) = 2\nu_0 + 2(B' - B'')J^2. \qquad \text{(IV, 51)}$$

[To take D into account, $-2(D' - D'')J^2(J + 1)^2$ would have to be added to this, but this correction can be neglected in most practical cases.] Thus, when $R(J - 1) + P(J)$ is plotted against J^2, a straight line is obtained whose intersection with the axis gives $2\nu_0$ and whose slope gives $2(B' - B'')$. In carrying out this graphical method, it is advantageous to subtract $2(\overline{B' - B''})J^2$ from $R(J - 1) + P(J)$, where $\overline{B' - B''}$ is an approximate value for $B' - B''$, and then to plot the difference $R(J - 1) + P(J) - 2(\overline{B' - B''})J^2$ against J^2. This is done in Fig. 79 for the 0–0 band of BeO (Table 20), taking $\overline{B' - B''} = 0.07$ cm^{-1}. The straight line obtained intersects the ordinate axis at 42,393.44 cm⁻¹. Therefore it follows that $\nu_0 = 21{,}196.72$ cm⁻¹. From the slope of the line an accurate value of $B' - B''$ can be obtained.

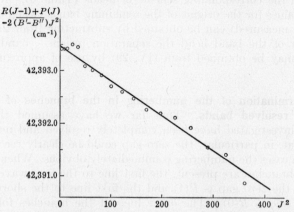

Fig. 79. Graphical Determination of the Zero Line of the 0–0 Band of the Green BeO System from $R(J - 1) + P(J)$.

If an intense Q *branch* is present, it is simplest to use this branch to determine ν_0, since, according to (IV, 25), for the Q branch

$$Q(J) = \nu_0 + (B' - B'')J(J + 1).$$

When we plot $Q(J)$ against $J(J + 1)$, we again obtain a straight line whose intersection with the ordinate axis gives ν_0 and whose slope gives $(B' - B'')$.

Table 23 gives as an example the scheme of band origins (Deslandres table) of the PN bands obtained in this way as far

TABLE 23

SCHEME OF BAND ORIGINS OF THE PN BANDS

[After Curry, Herzberg, and Herzberg (176)]

v'' v'	0	1	2	3
0	39,688.57	38,365.30	37,055.97	
	1088.51		1088.52	
1	40,777.08		38,144.49	36,849.18

as the fine structure of the bands has been investigated. It can be seen that the constancy of the differences between the bands in the two horizontal rows is fulfilled with much greater accuracy than in the corresponding scheme of heads (Table 6). Approximate values for the origins of the remaining bands (when Q heads are not measured) can be obtained by subtracting from the wave number of the band head the separation (origin − band head), which may be obtained from (IV, 29) by use of approximate B values.

Determination of the numbering in the branches of incompletely resolved bands. Thus far we have assumed that the bands investigated have been completely resolved and measured and that, in particular, the zero gap could be clearly recognized. In such cases the numbering is immediately obvious. When only P and R branches are present, the first line to the long-wave-length side of the zero gap is $P(1)$ and the first line to the short-wavelength side is $R(0)$. The other lines of the branches follow on from these in the order of their J values. If a Q branch is present, its first line is $Q(1)$ (assuming a $^1\Pi - {}^1\Sigma$ or $^1\Sigma - {}^1\Pi$ transition). This line lies very near one of the missing lines in the series formed by the P and R branches (see p. 186).

However, a complete resolution of a band is often not obtainable with the means available, particularly in the case of heavy molecules. In particular, in the neighborhood of the band head and the origin, the lines are often so close together that they cannot be separated by a spectrograph of limited resolving power. In such cases the numbering of the individual lines of the branches is by no means obvious. Yet there are various ways in which it may be found.

Let us assume that, in a certain case, two or three series of lines with regularly altering separation are observed at some distance from the head. It is generally easy to decide *which of these branches is the P branch, which is the Q branch, and which is the R branch.* According to our previous discussion (p. 188), the P and R branches always run approximately parallel, while the Q branch intersects the other two branches more or less frequently. The Q branch is therefore generally easily recognizable as such. At a large distance from the band head, the weaker of the two branches that run parallel to each other is the one that forms the head, since its lines have much higher J values; that is, for bands shaded to the red the weaker is the R branch and for bands shaded to the violet the weaker is the P branch [for an example, see Fig. 18(*b*)].

It is clear that, in general, if only P and R branches are present, we cannot obtain the correct numbering for an incompletely resolved band if it is the only band of the system that is measured. This is because in the Fortrat diagram the P and R branches form a single parabola, for which the position of the abscissa axis is not known if the zero gap is not known (see Fig. 24). For the various possible positions of the zero gap we obtain different linear terms in equation (II, 8)—that is, different B' and B'' values, between which, in general, a decision is not possible. If, however, two different bands of a system are measured that are known (from the vibrational analysis) to have, for example, the same upper state, then *for the correct numbering in both bands the combination differences $\Delta_2 F'$ must agree exactly for each J value.* This is a very sensitive criterion of whether the correct numbering has been found. A similar reasoning applies to $\Delta_2 F''$ when the two bands have the same lower state.

Thus, in order to find the numbering, we have to vary it systematically until we have found a numbering in the two bands for which the $\Delta_2 F'$ (or $\Delta_2 F''$ if the bands have the same lower state) coincide [see, for example, Pomeroy (567)]. First of all, we start with a preliminary (arbitrary) numbering in the two bands, in which, for example, the first observed line in each branch is numbered 1, the second 2, and so on, and then form the differences $R(J) - P(J)$ for both bands, assuming for a moment that the chosen numbering is the correct one. In general, the two sets of differences will not agree, even when they are displaced relative to one another. The numbering in one branch of the first band is then shifted by 1, the differences are again formed, the numbering is shifted by 2 units, the differences are again formed, and so on, the differences being compared each time with the unaltered differences of the second band. If an agreement is not obtained for any numbering of the first band, the relative numbering of the second band must also be altered systematically. If the two bands actually have the upper state in common, the differences $R(J) - P(J)$ must agree exactly for one relative numbering in this systematic testing, and, similarly, the differences $R(J - 1) - P(J + 1)$ must agree when they have the same lower state. Provided that no chance agreement occurs and the accuracy of measurement suffices, this procedure leads at all events to the desired end—that is, to a determination of the *relative numbering* of the two branches in the two bands.

It is then easy to find the *absolute numbering*, since successive combination differences, $\Delta_2 F$ (if they are the correct ones), must differ by $4B$, according to (IV, 34). Therefore, if we divide one of the combination differences in a series by the separation between successive differences, we obtain, according to (IV, 34), $J + \frac{1}{2}$ and thereby the absolute J value. (The data in Table 20 may serve to exemplify this.) We can also say that, if the combination differences are plotted against a preliminary numbering, the correct absolute numbering is that for which the straight line formed by the $\Delta_2 F$ values goes through the point $-\frac{1}{2}$ on the abscissa axis (see Fig. 76). When the correct absolute numbering is so obtained, the determination of the constants can be carried out in the manner described above.

When the numbering for two bands in a band system has once been found, the analysis of further bands is no longer so tiresome. If a third band has a state in common with one of the first two, we know beforehand one set of the correct combination differences that must appear in the third band. We can therefore determine the correct numbering in the third band simply by shifting its relative numbering. Even for a third band of the system that has no state in common with the two already analyzed, the numbering can easily be determined, since the combination differences must at least have similar magnitudes to those for the first two bands (since the B values in a system do not alter very much).

The procedure described above is always applicable. However, in some cases, the following procedures for the determination of the numbering may lead to the desired end more quickly.

If a Q *branch* is present in addition to P and R branches, the numbering can be found for a single band, even if the region of the zero gap is unresolved. In the Fortrat diagram the Q branch forms a parabola which has its vertex almost on the ν axis (see p. 50 f.). This point is approximately ν_0. Therefore, if we extrapolate the Q branch, observed at larger J values, to smaller J values, where it is no longer resolved (calculating with a constant second difference; see Table 7, p. 45), ν_0 must lie approximately at the position where the calculated branch forms a head. The *numbering of the Q branch* is thereby given (at least within one or two units), since at its head J is very nearly zero. When the P and R branches are now similarly extrapolated, we can also obtain their numbering, at least approximately, since ν_0 is now known. The numbering found can be checked by the combination relations (IV, 47 and 48). We may also use these combination relations alone in order to find the numbering if we try systematically in a manner similar to the above, but now within a single band. The absolute numbering then is obtained either from the relation $\Delta_1 F(J) = 2B(J + 1)$, or, as above, from the relation $\Delta_2 F(J) = 4B(J + \frac{1}{2})$.

Finding the numbering becomes particularly simple if so-called *perturbations* occur in the branches, as long as these perturbations are not too great. These perturbations, which will be discussed in greater detail in Chapter V, section 4, consist in the deviation of one line or several successive lines in a branch from a smooth curve and always appear at a corresponding position in the P and R branches—that is, at the same J' or the same J''. They are thus perturbations of the upper or lower rotational term series. Therefore, when this phenomenon appears, we can use it to determine which lines of the P and R branches correspond to each other —that is, have the same J' or J''. We can decide immediately which of the two cases we are dealing with if the disturbed band can be compared with another with the same upper or the same lower state. If the perturbation also occurs in the other band, the common state is the one that is perturbed; if it does not occur in the other band, the state not in common is the one that is perturbed. We thereby know whether the perturbed lines have the same J' or the same J'', and thus we obtain the *relative numbering*. The absolute numbering is obtained in the same manner as above.

The picking out of branches. In the case of singlet bands, which are the only ones considered in this chapter, the identification of branches is not difficult as long as the individual bands of a band system are fairly well separated from one another and do not overlap. Series of lines that form branches usually stand out fairly clearly (see Figs. 18–20). All we have to do in order to be sure that a particular series forms a branch is to see that the separation alters approximately linearly ($\Delta^2\nu$ = constant; see p. 43) and that the intensity changes regularly. As explained before, it is generally not difficult to decide which is the P, which is the R, and which is the Q branch (if the latter is present).

However, it often happens that the individual bands of a band system lie so close to one another that their *fine structures overlap*. In such cases the resultant fine structure may possibly have such a complex appearance that it is difficult to pick out a number of branches belonging to the same band. In such cases a procedure first given by Loomis and Wood (467) for the picking out of branches has proved very valuable. It is also valuable for multiplet bands (see Chapter V) with their large number of branches.

Let us assume that by inspection of the spectrogram a few lines have been found that apparently belong to one and the same branch. We then form the first and second differences for this "branch," and, keeping the second difference constant, we calculate the expected positions of further lines in this branch in both directions from the observed part. We then have a series of wave-number values that theoretically, at least, might represent a branch. For each line of this calculated branch we now form the differences with all the neighboring observed wave numbers and plot them in a diagram against the arbitrary running numbers in the branch. We obtain a diagram such as that shown in Fig. 80 for the case of an Na₂ band. If, as in the example, the originally

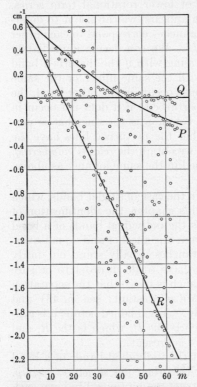

Fig. 80. Loomis-Wood Diagram of the 1–1 Band of the Blue-Green System of Na₂.

assumed branch is real, there must be points in the diagram lying in the neighborhood of the abscissa axis for every value of the running number. Thereby this one branch is completed as far as the data permit. At the same time, however, we obtain in the diagram the other branches belonging to the same band. Since the branches of a band all have the same quadratic term, $(B' - B'')J^2$, the distance between successive lines must be rather similar for large values of J, except if B' happens to be nearly equal to B''. Therefore the other branches must appear in the same diagram as series of points lying on smooth, slightly curved lines, as is the case in Fig. 80. It can be seen that, in the example, three branches are present. The two curves running at an angle to the abscissa axis correspond to the P and R branches, and the points lying in the neighborhood of the abscissa axis correspond to the Q branch (the branch from which we started). The latter intersects the P as well as the R branch. The points lying in between the three curves correspond to lines belonging to other bands. They form curves with such a large slope that they are difficult to recognize, since the separation of the lines in them is either much larger or much smaller than in the original band.

If the branches of a band have been determined in this manner for at least a part of their course, the numbering can be found by the procedure previously described and the band constants can be determined.

Isotope effect. As already mentioned in Chapter III, section 2(g), two isotopic molecules have somewhat different rotational constants. The formulae previously given

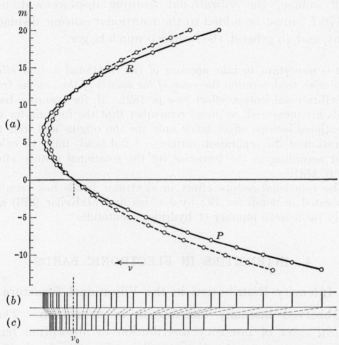

Fig. 81. **Fine Structure of the Bands of Two Isotopic Molecules.** (a) Fortrat parabolae. (b) and (c) Spectra of the lighter and the heavier isotopic molecule, respectively. In order to show the influence of the rotational isotope effect alone, the zero lines ν_0 of the two bands have been drawn one above the other.

still hold. We have only to take account of the fact that the rotational constants in the upper and lower states of a band may be quite different. As in the case of infrared bands, the *rotational isotopic displacement* is approximately *proportional to the distance from the origin*, the lines of the heavier isotope lying nearer to the origin. As an illustration, Fig. 81(a) gives the Fortrat diagram of a band for two isotopic molecules. The parabola corresponding to the heavier isotope is indicated by a broken line. Fig. 81(b) and (c) give schematically the corresponding spectrograms. It can be seen that in the head-forming branch the rotational isotopic displacement becomes zero on going through the origin again.

Of course, the vibrational isotopic displacement (see p. 176 f.) must be added to the rotational isotopic displacement, and, in general, the former is much larger.

It is important to take account of the rotational isotope effect if we wish to determine the *ratio of the masses of the isotopes* from the vibrational isotope effect (see p. 182). If, for example, band heads are measured, we must remember that the formula for the vibrational isotope effect holds only for the origins and that the alteration of the separation (origin − band head) must be calculated according to the formulae for the rotational isotope effect (see p. 154).

The rotational isotope effect in electronic bands has been investigated in detail for BO by Jenkins and McKellar (373) and lately for a large number of hydrides (deuterides).

4. INTENSITIES IN ELECTRONIC BANDS

(a) Intensity Distribution in the Vibrational Structure

Observed intensity distribution in absorption. *Three typical cases* of intensity distribution in absorption band series are represented schematically in Fig. 82. In the first case [Fig. 82(a)], coming from long wave lengths, the first band, the 0–0 band of the system, is very intense. Joining onto it, a few further bands of the $v'' = 0$ progression appear with very rapidly decreasing intensities. Such a case is observed, for example, for the atmospheric oxygen bands that appear in the red part of the solar spectrum. In the second case [Fig. 82(b)], the intensity of the bands in the progression $v'' = 0$ at first increases somewhat with decreasing wave length and then decreases slowly. The absorption bands of CO, whose spectrogram is reproduced in Fig. 14, exemplify such a case. In the third case [Fig. 82(c)], the first bands in the progression are not present at all (as may be shown, for example, by an investigation of the isotope effect; see above, p. 179). We then have a long series of bands drawing ever closer together until they come to a convergence limit, at which the previously mentioned continuum joins on. The maximum of the intensity lies either at very high v

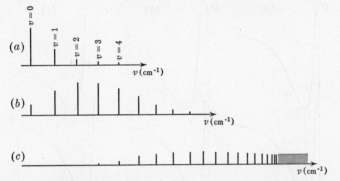

Fig. 82. **Three Typical Cases of Intensity Distribution in Absorption Band Series (Schematic).** For the sake of simplicity, the bands are drawn with the same separation in the three cases. Naturally, the cases would be observed only in different band systems, which would in general not have the same band separations.

values or possibly even in the continuum. An example of this kind of intensity distribution is presented by the I_2 absorption spectrum in Fig. 15. Between these three cases there are all possible transition cases. Thus, observation shows that for a given v'' the possible v' values vary greatly—that is, that there is *no strict selection rule for the vibrational quantum number v.*

The Franck-Condon principle. The different cases of intensity distribution are explained in an easily visualized manner by the *Franck-Condon principle.* Franck's main idea, which was developed mathematically and later given a wave mechanical basis by Condon, is the following: *The electronic jump in a molecule takes place so rapidly in comparison to the vibrational motion that immediately afterwards* *the nuclei have not altered appreciably either their relative position* (their separation) *or their velocity compared to the state immediately before.* The consequences of this assumption, which is confirmed by wave mechanics (see below), are most clearly seen by considering Fig. 83(a), (b), and (c), in which are drawn the potential curves that were assumed by Franck and Condon for the upper and lower electronic states

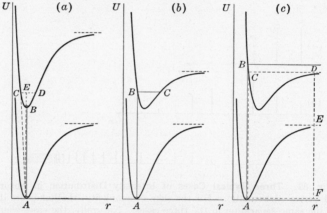

Fig. 83. Potential Curves Explaining the Intensity Distribution in Absorption According to the Franck-Condon Principle. In (c), *AC* gives the energy of the dissociation limit, *EF* the dissociation energy of the ground state, and *DE* the excitation energy of the dissociation products (see p. 409 f.).

in order to explain the three typical cases of intensity distribution.

In Fig. 83(a) the potential curves of the two electronic states have been so chosen that their *minima* lie *very nearly one above the other* (equal internuclear distance). In absorption, the molecule is initially at the minimum of the lower potential curve, if we disregard the zero-point vibration. It can be seen that at any rate for a transition to the minimum of the upper potential curve (0–0 band) the requirement of the Franck-Condon principle (only a small alteration of position and momentum) is fulfilled. On the other hand, a transition into a *high* vibrational state [*CD* in Fig. 83(a)] would be possible only when, at the moment of the electronic jump, either the position (transition from A to C) or the velocity (transition from A to E) or both alter to an appreciable extent. At the point E, of course, the molecule has the amount of kinetic energy EB. Only at the turning points C or D is the kinetic energy, and thereby the velocity, zero as in the initial state. Thus, on the basis of the Franck-Condon principle, a transition from $v'' = 0$ to such a high vibrational level is forbidden or at least highly improbable. For the level $v' = 1$, the necessary alteration of the position or the velocity during the electron jump is comparatively small. Therefore the 1–0 band can still appear, though with much smaller intensity than the 0–0 band. For the 2–0, 3–0, $\cdots$ bands the necessary alteration of position and velocity increases, and consequently a rapidly decreasing intensity is to be expected. Thus we obtain an intensity distribution of the type illustrated in Fig. 82(a).

In Fig. 83(b) the *minimum of the upper potential curve* lies *at a somewhat greater r value than that of the lower*. Therefore the transition from minimum to minimum (0–0 band) is no longer the most probable, since the internuclear distance must alter somewhat in such a transition. The most probable of the transitions is that from A to B in Fig. 83(b) (vertically upwards). For this transition there is no alteration in the internuclear distance at the moment of the "jump" and no alteration of the velocity. Thus, immediately after the electron jump the two nuclei still have their old distance from each other and zero relative velocity. Since, however, the equilibrium internuclear distance has a different value in the new electronic state, the nuclei start to vibrate between B and C. The vibrational levels whose left turning points lie in the neighborhood of B are the upper levels of the most intense bands. For still higher vibrational levels an appreciable alteration of the internuclear distance or velocity must take place, as a result of which the intensities of the bands decrease again with increasing v'. Thus the observed intensity distribution in the second case [Fig. 82(b)] is explained. The same intensity distribution results when the minimum of the upper potential curve lies at a somewhat smaller r value than in the ground state. However, this case is much rarer in absorption than that shown in Fig. 83(b).

In Fig. 83(c) the *minimum of the upper potential curve* lies *at a still greater internuclear distance.* The Franck-Condon principle is strictly fulfilled for the transition AB. However, the point B on the upper potential curve lies above the asymptote of this curve and therefore corresponds to the continuous region of the term spectrum of the upper state. After such an electron jump the atoms fly apart. Transitions to points somewhat below (that is, in the discrete region) and somewhat above B are also possible. Thus in this way the third case of intensity distribution can be explained.

Summarizing, we can say that in absorption *the most intense transition from $v'' = 0$ is always that corresponding to a transition from the minimum of the lower potential curve vertically upward.* In all cases in which a fine-structure analysis has been carried out, it has been found that the r_e values obtained actually have a magnitude that is in agreement with the conclusions obtained according to the above (Fig. 83) from the intensity distribution in the corresponding absorption bands.

The meaning and mode of action of the Franck-Condon principle can be demonstrated and made clearer by a *mechanical example.* If we bend a flexible strip of tin into the shape of the potential curve of the lower state and illustrate the motion of the molecule by the motion of a small cylindrical body rolling on this surface, the position of rest of the cylinder will be at the bottom of the channel thus formed. If the shape of the channel is now suddenly altered (corresponding to the electron jump), the cylinder, which at first, as a result of its inertia, did not alter its position, will in general no longer be at the minimum. It will therefore carry out vibrations about the new equilibrium position. The vibrations will be the more violent the more the equilibrium position has altered, and under some circumstances they may be so strong that the cylinder will fly out of the other side of the channel after traversing the curve once. This will be the case when the cylinder, immediately after the "electron jump," is above the asymptote of the new potential curve. On the other hand, it is clear that the cylinder will not be set in vibration when the position of the minimum does not alter.

Wave mechanical formulation of the Franck-Condon principle. As Condon (160) has shown, it follows also from wave mechanics that the *transitions vertically upward*

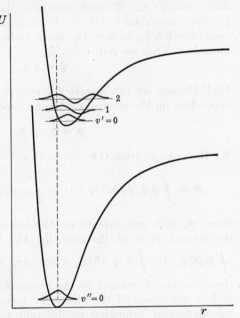

in the potential energy diagram correspond to the most intense absorption bands. However, we have to remember that, according to wave mechanics, an oscillator can never be quite at rest but that in the lowest vibrational state we have rather the probability density distribution given by Fig. 41. Therefore a transition "vertically upward" may take place within a certain range of r values, particularly since also in the various upper vibrational

Fig. 84.   Franck-Condon Principle According to Wave Mechanics. The potential curves are so drawn that the "best" overlapping of the eigenfunctions exists for $v' = 2$, $v'' = 0$ (see the broken vertical line).

levels a certain range of r values is possible (see the eigenfunctions in Fig. 84). This consideration makes it quite clear why instead of only one band a number of bands of the $v'' = 0$ progression appear in absorption with a more or less broad intensity maximum. The extent of the band series and of the continuum which may possibly join onto it is the greater the steeper the upper potential curve.

In wave mechanics, the transition probability between two states depends, according to (I, 17), on the corresponding matrix element of the electric moment (the so-called transition moment):

$$R = \int p\psi'\psi''^* d\tau, \tag{IV, 52}$$

where ψ' and ψ'' are the total eigenfunctions of the system in the upper and lower states and p is a vector with components $\Sigma e_i x_i$, $\Sigma e_i y_i$, and $\Sigma e_i z_i$. We now represent the total eigenfunction as a product, according to (IV, 5), leaving out, however, the rotational eigenfunction ψ_r, as may be shown to be allowable for the present purpose. Thus we put

$$\psi = \psi_e \psi_v. \tag{IV, 53}$$

Furthermore, we can resolve the electric moment p into one part depending on the electrons and one depending on the nuclei:

$$p = p_e + p_n. \tag{IV, 54}$$

We then obtain from (IV, 52), with $\psi_v^* = \psi_v$ [see (III, 32)],

$$R = \int p_e \psi_e' \psi_v' \psi_e''^* \psi_v'' d\tau + \int p_n \psi_e' \psi_v' \psi_e''^* \psi_v'' d\tau. \tag{IV, 55}$$

Since p_n does not depend on the co-ordinates of the electrons, the second term of the sum in (IV, 55) can also be written $\int p_n \psi_v' \psi_v'' d\tau_n \int \psi_e' \psi_e''^* d\tau_e$, where $d\tau_n$ and $d\tau_e$ are, respectively, the elements of volume of the space of the nuclear co-ordinates and of the space of the electronic co-ordinates. The electronic eigenfunctions belonging to different electronic states, like the vibrational eigenfunctions (see p. 14), are orthogonal to one another; that is $\int \psi_e' \psi_e''^* d\tau_e = 0$. We therefore obtain

$$R = \int \psi_v' \psi_v'' dr \int p_e \psi_e' \psi_e''^* d\tau_e, \tag{IV, 56}$$

where dr is substituted for $d\tau_n$, since the vibrational eigenfunctions ψ_v depend on the internuclear distance r only.

For a given electronic transition, neglecting the finer interaction of vibration and electronic motion, as is done in (IV, 53),

$$R_e = \int p_e \psi_e' \psi_e''^* d\tau_e = \text{constant}. \tag{IV, 57}$$

(The square of this expression is proportional to the *electronic transition probability*.)   (IV, 56) can therefore be written

$$R_{v'v''} = R_e \int \psi_{v'} \psi_{v''} dr, \qquad (IV, 58)$$

where we have added the indices $v'v''$ to R. Thus the probability of transition between the different vibrational states $v'v''$ of two given electronic states depends on the *integral over the product of the two vibrational eigenfunctions* (sometimes called the *overlap integral*).   The intensity is obtained from $R_{v'v''}$ according to (I, 18).

Let us first consider the *intensity of the 0–0 band* given by (IV, 58). As illustrated in Fig. 84, the eigenfunctions of the upper and lower states are bell-shaped curves. Obviously, the product of the two eigenfunctions for each value of r, and thereby also the integral of this product over all r values, is greatest if the minima of the two potential curves lie exactly one above the other (unlike the drawing). The more the minima are separated from each other, the smaller is the integral, and therefore the intensity of the 0–0 band, entirely in agreement with the result of the naïve Franck-Condon principle.

Obviously, if the minima of the two potential curves lie at equal internuclear distances, the value of the integral (IV, 58) for the 1–0 *band* is very small, since there are approximately as many positive as negative contributions to the integral (indeed, for the harmonic oscillator the integral is exactly zero). If we now imagine the potential curve for the upper state to be shifted to larger or smaller r values, the integral, and thereby the intensity of the 1–0 band, at first increases (whereas it decreases for the 0–0 band). The integral has a maximum value when the upper potential curve lies so that the maximum (or the minimum) of the upper vibrational eigenfunction lies vertically above the maximum of the lower eigenfunction. At the same time, the 0–0 band has already a smaller intensity. If the r values of the minima of the potential curves differ still more, the overlap integral for the 1–0 band, and thereby the intensity of the 1–0 band, decreases again.

Since the eigenfunctions for the higher vibrational states have broad maxima or minima at the position of the classical turning points of the motion and fluctuate rapidly between these turning points so that the contributions to the integral (IV, 58) cancel one another, *this integral has a maximum value for those vibrational levels in the upper state whose broad maximum or minimum lies* (roughly) *vertically above the maximum of the eigenfunction of the lower state* ($v'' = 0$).   The integral decreases for greater as well as smaller values of v'. It can be seen that this result agrees essentially with the results of the elementary conception of the Franck-Condon principle (see above). The extension of the progression of absorption bands with $v'' = 0$ to both sides of the maximum of intensity is determined mainly by the breadth of the eigenfunction of the ground state—that is, ultimately by the Heisenberg uncertainty principle (see p. 82).

In more exact calculations we have to make allowance for the fact that the relation (IV, 53) does not hold exactly and that therefore R_e is not completely independent of internuclear distance [see Coolidge, James, and Present (162), and Finkelnburg (222)].

Intensity distribution in emission (Condon parabola). According to the Franck-Condon principle, the variation of intensity in a *band progression with $v' = 0$ in emission* corresponds exactly to that in absorption: There is an intensity maximum lying at a v'' value that is the greater the greater the difference between the positions of the minima of the two potential curves (Fig. 83).

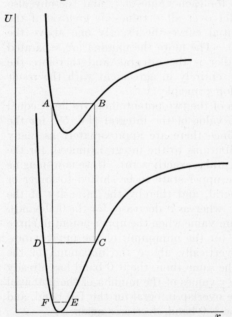

Fig. 85. Potential Curves for the Explanation of the Intensity Distribution in Emission According to the Franck-Condon Principle.

However, the intensity distribution is different for *band progressions in emission having $v' \neq 0$* (the same is true for the absorption band progressions with $v'' \neq 0$ that appear at higher temperatures). In order to understand this, let us consider Fig. 85. During the vibration in the upper state the molecule stays preferentially at the turning points A

and B of the vibrational motion, while the intermediate positions are passed through very rapidly. As a result, the *electron jump* takes place *preferentially at the turning points*. If it takes place at the turning point B and if there is to be no change in position and velocity, immediately after the jump the molecule will be at C, vertically below B, and C forms the right turning point of the new vibrational motion C–D. However, the electron jump can take place from A as well as from B. In this case, according to Franck and Condon, the transition takes place to F, and F forms the left turning point of the new vibrational motion E–F.

Thus we can see that there are *two v'' values* for which the probability of the transition from a given v' is a maximum. There are thus *two intensity maxima* to be expected in a v''-progression ($v' =$ constant), one at small v'' and a second at large v''. In Fig. 86 the estimated intensities of the PN bands (Table 6) are plotted in an array similar to a Deslandres

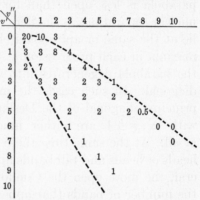

Fig. 86. Intensities and Condon Parabola in the Band System of PN.

table. It can be seen that there actually are two intensity maxima present in all the horizontal rows with the exception of that with $v' = 0$. We can see from Fig. 85 that the two maxima should separate from each other with increasing v' and, apart from that, go to higher v'' values. This is in exact agreement with observations (Fig. 86). If we join up the most intense bands in the array, we obtain a parabolic curve whose axis is the principal diagonal. It is called the *Condon parabola*. This Condon parabola can be obtained theoretically according to the above method of construction when the potential curves are known. The broken curve given in Fig. 86 is the theoretical curve, which, as we can see, reproduces the observed intensity maxima in the band progressions, $v' = $ constant, very well. It can also be seen quite clearly in Table 18 that the observed CO bands (which are naturally the most intense bands) lie on a parabolic curve.

On the basis of Fig. 85 it is clear that the separation of the two maxima in a progression $v' = $ constant, and thereby the width of the parabola, is the greater the farther the minima of the potential curves are separated from each other in the r direction. In the case of the PN bands the parabola is less open than for CO, since the difference in nuclear separations is smaller. If the two potential minima lie at the same or approximately the same r value, the two maxima in each progression $v' = $ constant fall together and the parabola degenerates into a straight line, the principal diagonal. In such cases the most intense bands lie in the principal diagonal of the Deslandres table, while the bands with $\Delta v = \pm 1$ are either much weaker or not observed at all. At the same time these are often the cases in which heads of heads and tail bands appear (see p. 174 f.). In general, the more open the Condon parabola is, the greater is the number of bands that appear in a band system (see the above examples of PN and CO). This is easily understood on the basis of the above considerations.

It is obvious that the Condon parabola will be well developed only when a large number of successive vibrational levels of the upper state are about equally populated. If, on the other hand, the level with $v' = 0$, for example, is preferentially excited, the Condon parabola derived in the above manner no longer gives the most intense bands in the system. However, it gives in every case the relative intensity maxima in the individual progressions $v' = $ constant. The dependence of the excitation of different vibrational states in the upper state of a band system on the special conditions of excitation—for instance, the electron velocity—has been investigated repeatedly [see, for example, Langstroth (439a)].

It is easily seen that the Condon parabola represents also

the maxima of intensity in the progressions with $v'' \neq 0$ occurring in *absorption*. However, only at a sufficiently high temperature is the Condon parabola well developed in absorption, since only then are the higher vibrational levels of the ground state sufficiently populated.

The wave mechanical explanation of the intensity distribution in a band progression $v' = $ constant will be clear if we consider, for example, the eigenfunctions $v = 10$ and $v = 4$ in Fig. 41 and regard them as belonging to two different electronic states. We can see that the integral (IV, 58) and thereby the intensity of the transition $(v' = 10 \rightarrow v'' = 4)$ will be a maximum if either the right broad maximum of the upper eigenfunction lies above the right maximum of the lower eigenfunction or the left maximum of the upper eigenfunction lies above the left maximum of the lower one (possibly also the left upper maximum above the right lower maximum). Therefore, for a given position of the potential curves and a given v' and varying values of v'' there is in general an *intensity maximum for two different values of v''*. However, we can also see that in forming the overlap integral (IV, 58) in this way a regular variation in the intensities in a progression $v' = $ constant does not necessarily follow. In fact, for a favorable relative position of the two eigenfunctions a band may be intense even if it lies *between the two maxima*, and, on the other hand, for an unfavorable position of the eigenfunctions a band may be abnormally weak in the neighborhood of the maximum. These considerations explain the observed facts that relatively intense bands occur at certain places inside the Condon parabola (see Fig. 86 and Table 18) and that, furthermore, in some resonance series $(v' = $ constant), as, for example, for Na_2 (Fig. 29), one or the other of the bands is missing or, on the other hand, has an abnormally high intensity. In the case of the Na_2 resonance series, W. G. Brown (136) has quantitatively tested and confirmed this explanation by a comparison of the observed intensities with those calculated on the basis of the eigenfunctions [see also Wehrli (700) and Bewersdorff (99)].

From a knowledge of the potential curves (and consequently of the vibrational eigenfunctions), according to (IV, 58) and (I, 18) the relative intensities of the various bands in a band system may be predicted theoretically for absorption or for thermal excitation in emission if the temperature is known, since then the distribution of the molecules over the various initial states is known [see Chapter III, section 2(e)]. Conversely, from a measurement of the relative intensities of bands with different v' in emission or different

v'' in absorption the temperature of a gas may be determined. This method of temperature determination may also be applied to electric discharges, although then only an effective temperature is obtained, which need not coincide with the actual temperature of the gas, since the population of the vibrational levels for non-thermal emission depends on the mechanism of excitation. There-fore the *"vibrational temperature"* thus obtained for discharges does not always agree with the *"rotational temperature"* discussed later [see, for example, Duffendack, Revans, and Roy (191)].

(b) Intensity Distribution in the Rotational Structure

The intensity in a branch of an electronic band varies in essentially the same way as in the rotation-vibration bands [see Chapter III, section 2(e)]. There is an *intensity max-imum*, which lies at a J value that is the higher the higher the temperature or the smaller B.

$^1\Sigma - {}^1\Sigma$ **transitions.** In the special case of $^1\Sigma - {}^1\Sigma$ transi-tions (see p. 184 f. and Chapter V) which have only a P and an R branch, the intensity relations are given quantitatively by the previous formulae (III, 114 and 115) and Fig. 57, p. 134. In this figure we naturally have to allow for the fact that in electronic bands one of the branches usually forms a head. However, this does not alter the intensities of the lines (see also Figs. 18 and 19). The diagrams in Fig. 57 refer to absorption. For emission we have only to exchange the letters P and R in this figure.

Strictly speaking, the formula (III, 115) for emission holds only in the case of *excitation by high temperature* (thermal collisions), since only then is the number of mole-cules in the different states given by the Boltzmann factor and the statistical weight. However, it has been found experimentally that the intensity distribution in emission bands occurring in electric discharges is of the same type. This is easily understood, since, when a molecule is excited by electron collision, no great change in the angular momen-tum of the system can be produced (owing to the smallness of the electron mass), and therefore the distribution of the molecules over the different rotational states in the upper electronic state is practically the same as in the ground state. But in the latter, owing to the numerous molecular collisions, the distribution corresponds to thermal equilibrium at a certain effective temperature, and therefore this will also be at least approximately the case in the upper state. We thus obtain the intensity distribution (III, 115). However, we must be quite clear that this *normal intensity distribution in discharges* results from the circumstance that the angular momentum is not strongly altered in excitation by electron collision. For other modes of excitation—for instance, by chemical reactions or by dissociation of polyatomic molecules in electrical discharges—large deviations from the normal thermal distribution can occur. This has been observed, for example, by Oldenberg (539) in the excitation of OH bands by discharges in H_2O vapor[6] and by Lochte-Holtgreven (447) in the excitation of C_2 and CH bands by discharges in hydrocarbons. In both cases, much higher rotational lines appear than we would expect on the basis of the temperature. The opposite case—namely, a preferential excitation of low rotational levels—has recently been observed by Schüler and Gollnow (626) for CuH in a hollow cathode discharge. Furthermore, large deviations from the thermal intensity distribution occur when molecular gases are excited by monochromatic light (see below), as well as when the molecule can predissociate (see Chapter VII).

How well the thermal intensity distribution holds in most cases of electric discharges is illustrated by Fig. 87. According to (III, 115),

$$\log \frac{I_{\text{em.}}}{J' + J'' + 1} = \log C - \frac{B'J'(J' + 1)hc}{kT}. \quad \text{(IV, 59)}$$

Here C contains the factor ν^4 (or, for absorption, ν; see p. 133); but, since, for a given band, ν covers only a very small range of values, C may be considered as constant for most prac-

---

[6] See also Lyman (471*b*).

tical cases.   The observed values of log $[I_{em.}/(K' + K'' + 1)]$ for the 0–0 band (λ3914) of the negative nitrogen group in an electric discharge are plotted against $K'(K' + 1)$ in Fig. 87. K is used instead of J, since the bands represent a $^2\Sigma - ^2\Sigma$ transition [see Chapter V, section 3(b)].   If the temperature is uniform, this should give a straight line whose slope is inversely proportional to the effective temperature.   It can be seen that this is actually the case.   Why two parallel straight lines are obtained instead of only one will be explained later.   Conversely, in this way we can *determine the*

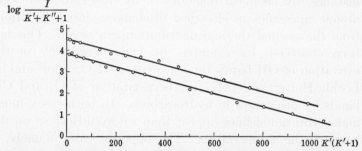

Fig. 87.   Log $[I/(K' + K'' + 1)]$ for the 0–0 Band of the Negative Nitrogen Bands Plotted Against $K'(K' + 1)$ [after Ornstein and van Wijk (549)].   The log $[I/(K' + K'' + 1)]$ values for corresponding lines of the P and R branches (with the same K') agree within the accuracy of the measurements, as they should.   They have therefore not been separately plotted, but rather their average has been plotted.

effective temperature in a light source (see Chapter VIII, section 2).

The *influence of temperature on the intensity distribution* in an electronic band can be clearly seen in Fig. 26, in which photographs of the $N_2{}^+$ band λ4278 at the three temperatures $-180°$ C., $20°$ C., and $400°$ C. are reproduced.   It can be seen very clearly how the maxima in the P and R branches shift and become flatter with increasing temperature and how the appearance of the band (development of the band head, distinctness of the zero gap) is thereby altered.   Still more marked differences in appearance are observed for bands occurring in the electric arc as well as in weak electric discharges—for instance, the CN bands.

Other transitions. If the quantum number Λ differs from zero in one or both of the participating electronic states, the intensity distribution in the P and R branches deviates from that represented in Fig. 57 only for small J values. However, in addition, a Q *branch* appears. We shall refrain from giving the explicit formulae developed by Hönl and London (329) for the intensities [see, for example, Weizel (33) and Jevons (34)] and shall give only a graphical representation of the intensity distri-

bution for two typical cases in Fig. 88(a) and (b).

The first case [Fig. 88(a)] represents a $^1\Pi - ^1\Sigma$ *transition* (see Chapter V). The same curves also hold qualitatively for other transitions for which $\Delta\Lambda \neq 0$. It is important to note that, according to theory, the lines of the Q branch in this case should have approximately double the in-

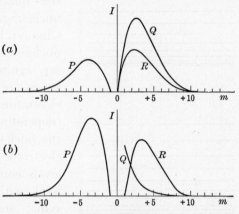

Fig. 88. Intensity Distribution in Bands with a Q Branch (Emission). (a) $^1\Pi - ^1\Sigma$ transition. (b) $^1\Pi - ^1\Pi$ transition. The running number m has been chosen as abscissa (see p. 184 f.). For the Q branch, $m = J$.

tensity of the corresponding lines of the P branch or the R branch. It can be seen qualitatively from the spectrogram Fig. 20 (p. 46) that this is actually the case. Also quantitatively, the calculated intensity distribution has been confirmed.

In the second case [Fig. 88(b)] $\Delta\Lambda = 0$ and $\Lambda = 1$ ($^1\Pi - ^1\Pi$ *transition*). In this case the intensity of the Q branch decreases very rapidly from the beginning without going through a maximum [it is approximately proportional to $(1/J)e^{-F(J)hc/kT}$. As a result, the Q branch is observed in such cases only when the region in the neighborhood of the zero line is well resolved. The same applies to other transitions having $\Delta\Lambda = 0$ and $\Lambda \neq 0$.

Intensity alternation. According to Chapter III, section 2(f), *for homonuclear molecules*, either the even-numbered or the odd-numbered rotational levels have the greater statistical weight if $\Lambda = 0$. The ratio of the weights of the "strong" and the "weak" levels is $(I + 1)/I$, where I is the quantum number of the nuclear spin. As we have seen in Chapter III, for a given homonuclear molecule the strong levels are symmetric and the weak levels are antisymmetric for all electronic states, or vice versa (depending on the statistics of the nuclei). Therefore, even in electronic transitions, only strong levels combine with strong and weak with weak [sym. ↔ antisym.; see (III, 119)]. Since, in addition, the selection rule $\Delta J = \pm 1$ holds, two electronic states with $\Lambda = 0$ (Σ states) can combine with each other only if in one the even-numbered levels are the "strong" levels and in the other the odd are the "strong" levels. This is shown in Fig. 89. It can be seen that, owing to the alternating statistical weights of the rotational levels in the upper as well as in the lower states, an *alternation of intensity* must occur, exactly as in the Raman spectra of homonuclear molecules. This alternation of intensities is very clearly seen in the spectrogram of the N_2^+ band (Fig. 26). From the magnitude of the

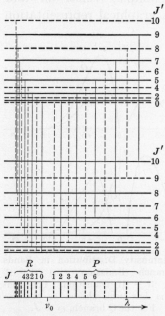

Fig. 89. Origin of the Intensity Alternation in an Electronic Band ($^1\Sigma - ^1\Sigma$) of a Homonuclear Molecule. The "strong" and "weak" levels and transitions are indicated by full and broken lines, respectively.

intensity alternation the nuclear spin can be derived, just as it can be from the rotational Raman spectrum [see Chapter III, section 2(f)]. If every alternate line is missing, the nuclear spin $I = 0$ (see p. 144).

The intensity alternation is the reason for the occurrence of the two parallel lines in Fig. 87, which refers to N_2^+. Their vertical separation $= 0.69 = \log_e 2$.   The points corresponding to alternate lines in the fine structure lie alternately on one and the other straight line in the diagram; that is, an intensity alternation in the ratio $2 : 1$ is present. Consequently, the spin of the N nucleus is $I = 1$.

Resonance series.   The resonance series form quite an extreme case of intensity distribution in the rotational structure of a band.   When only one quite definite rotational level in the upper state is excited by irradiation of the gas under consideration with an intense and sharp spectral line (for example, by irradiation of I_2 vapor with the green Hg line), we do not obtain bands in the fluorescence spectrum, but only single lines.   For instance, in a $^1\Sigma - {}^1\Sigma$ transition, we obtain doublets consisting of one line of the P branch and one line of the R branch. They are, as we can see from Fig. 52, the lines $R(J - 1)$ and $P(J + 1)$, where J is the rotational quantum number of the state excited by the irradiation. This kind of resonance series was first observed by Wood for Na_2 and I_2.   Fig. 29 shows such a *doublet resonance series* for Na_2 excited by the Cd line 5086 Å. According to (IV, 32 and 34), the *doublet separation* is given by

$$\Delta\nu = R(J - 1) - P(J + 1) = 4B_v''(J + \tfrac{1}{2}). \quad \text{(IV, 60)}$$

It changes from doublet to doublet in the resonance series corresponding to the alteration in B_v''. The rotational constant α can be calculated from this alteration.

For $^1\Pi - {}^1\Sigma$ transitions, as before, a doublet resonance series appears when the excitation is by means of a line of the P or R branch, whereas only a series of single lines appears when the excitation is by means of a line of the Q branch [in no case triplets, as one might think on the basis of Fig. 74 (see p. 278)]. A *singlet resonance series*, excited by the Cd line 4800 Å, is also present in the spectrogram in Fig. 29.

For heavier molecules, such as I_2, it may easily happen that the irradiating line, particularly when it is not very sharp, covers a number of absorption lines—for example, one of the P and one of the R branch. Naturally, if this is the case, we obtain a superposition of a number of resonance series [see, for example, Loomis (457)].

The investigation of resonance spectra is particularly useful as an aid to the fine-structure analysis of bands of heavier molecules, for which the rotational structure is not completely resolved. However, the rotational constants B_v'' can be obtained from (IV, 60) only if J is known, say on the basis of a partial analysis of the complete band.

By the addition of a gas that does not quench the fluorescence (for example, a rare gas), a *transition into other rotational states* of the excited molecules may be brought about *by collisions* before the fluorescence radiation is emitted so that ultimately, with sufficient pressure of the foreign gas, the complete bands may appear in spite of the excitation by a single line only. In this connection a particularly interesting phenomenon was observed by Wood and Loomis (721) for I_2—namely, that only every alternate line appears in the I_2 bands produced in this way. Since the prohibition sym. ↔ antisym. holds also for collisions (see p. 138), only lines with symmetrical upper levels (or only those with antisymmetrical upper levels) can appear in the fluorescence spectrum, even after collisions, if the originally excited state was a symmetrical (or antisymmetrical) state, whereas in absorption, or in fluorescence produced by white light, all the rotational lines appear, the nuclear spin of iodine not being zero.

Further details about resonance series can be found in Pringsheim [(37) and (573)].

CHAPTER V

Finer Details About Electronic States and Electronic Transitions

1. CLASSIFICATION OF ELECTRONIC STATES; MULTIPLET STRUCTURE

In general, each molecule has a number of band systems of the type discussed in the foregoing chapter and has therefore also a *number of electronic states*. In particular, the Rydberg series of bands that are observed in some cases (see Chapter II) cannot, according to the foregoing, be regarded as a single band system. They can only be explained as transitions from a Rydberg series of electronic states to a given electronic state where the potential curves are so situated relative to one another that, owing to the Franck-Condon principle, essentially only the 0–0 band appears for each band system. The existence of such *Rydberg series of electronic states* makes it appear probable from the very outset that the classification of the electronic states of diatomic molecules can be made in a similar manner to that of the atomic terms, which are, of course, "pure" electronic terms and form Rydberg series throughout.

Orbital angular momentum. Whereas the motion of the electrons in an atom takes place in a spherically symmetrical field of force, the motion in a diatomic molecule takes place in a *cylindrically symmetrical field* whose symmetry axis is the line joining the nuclei. Since there is a strong *electric* field between the nuclei, we have a situation quite analogous to that of an atom in an electric field. A *precession* of the electronic orbital angular momentum L takes place about the field direction (internuclear axis) with constant component $M_L (h/2\pi)$, where M_L can take only the values

$$M_L = L, \ L - 1, \ L - 2, \ \cdots, \ -L. \qquad (V, 1)$$

This precession is illustrated in Fig. 90.

In an electric field, states that differ only in the sign of M_L have the same energy, since the force on an electron in an electric field (unlike that in a magnetic field) does not depend on the direction or magnitude of its velocity; that is, the energy is the same for states that differ only in the sense of the rotation of the electrons about the internuclear

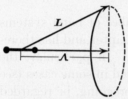

axis. In the molecules, therefore, only states with different $|M_L|$ will have different energy. The more the field deviates from spherical symmetry— that is, the stronger the interaction of L with the internuclear axis is—the faster is the precession of L and the greater is the energy difference between states with different $|M_L|$. In the molecule the interaction is generally very great. Consequently the energy difference between states with different $|M_L|$ is very great—in fact, so great that they can be called different electronic states. The stronger the field is, the

Fig. 90. Precession of the Orbital Angular Momentum L about the Line Joining the Nuclei. The position of the nuclei is indicated by the two heavy dots. The magnitude of the nuclear separation drawn in the diagram has, of course, nothing to do with the length of the vectors.

more the quantum number L loses its meaning as angular momentum, since the faster the precession takes place the less it is justified to regard L as constant in magnitude and direction. However, M_L, as component of the angular momentum in the direction of the line joining the nuclei, remains well defined. It is therefore more appropriate to classify the electronic states according to the value of $|M_L|$ than according to the value of L. Following the international nomenclature, we put

$$\Lambda = |M_L|. \qquad (V, 2)$$

This quantum number corresponds to the angular momentum vector Λ, which represents the *component of the electronic orbital angular momentum along the line joining the nuclei* and whose magnitude is $\Lambda(h/2\pi)$. It is therefore identical with the quantum number Λ, previously introduced in the treatment of the symmetrical top [see Chapter III, section 2(d)].

For a given value of L, the quantum number Λ can take the values

$$\Lambda = 0, \ 1, \ 2, \ \cdots, \ L. \tag{V, 3}$$

Thus in the molecule for each value of L there are $L + 1$ distinct states with different energy. However, often the value of L cannot be given at all, since the corresponding angular momentum L is not defined.

From what has been said above, it follows that electronic states of the molecule with $\Lambda \neq 0$ are *doubly degenerate*—that is, have a statistical weight equal to 2—since each state consists of two states, one with $M_L = +\Lambda$ and one with $M_L = -\Lambda$.

According as $\Lambda = 0, 1, 2, 3, \cdots$, the corresponding molecular state is designated a Σ, Π, Δ, Φ, $\cdots$ state, analogous to the mode of designation for atoms, but using Greek letters instead of italics for the symbols. It should be noted, however, that the Greek letters do not mean the same thing as the corresponding italic letters for the atom. They are only analogous.

It may be shown that, owing to the cylindrical symmetry of the field of the two nuclei, the *electronic eigenfunction* of the molecule may be rigorously represented by

$$\psi = \chi e^{+i\Lambda\varphi} \quad \text{or} \quad \psi = \bar{\chi}e^{-i\Lambda\varphi} \tag{V, 4}$$

as long as the nuclei can be thought of as fixed in space [see Wigner and Witmer (712) and Hund (348)]. In these functions, φ is the azimuth of one of the electrons about the line joining the nuclei as axis, starting from a fixed reference plane. χ and $\bar{\chi}$ are functions of the other co-ordinates, including the azimuths of the remaining electrons relative to the one electron. $\bar{\chi}$ differs from χ only in that the azimuthal angles mentioned are replaced by their negatives. The two functions (V, 4) correspond to the rotation of the electrons in one sense or the opposite sense, respectively, about the line joining the nuclei and thus for a given Λ and χ belong to the same eigenvalue (twofold degeneracy). It can be shown, furthermore, that $\Lambda(h/2\pi)$ actually is the angular momentum about the internuclear axis (see the similar proof in A.A., p. 49).

Owing to the linearity of the Schrödinger equation (I, 13), any *linear combination* of the two functions (V, 4),

$$\psi = a\chi e^{+i\Lambda\varphi} + b\bar{\chi}e^{-i\Lambda\varphi}, \tag{V, 5}$$

is also a solution belonging to the same eigenvalue. If $\Lambda = 0$ (Σ state), however, there is only one solution and ψ does not depend on φ.

Spin. It is to be expected that the resultant spin S will play a role for molecules quite analogous to that for atoms. This is confirmed by a wave mechanical calculation. Actually, it is observed that in some band systems all the bands are double or triple (see Chapter II). Just as for atoms, it seems reasonable to *explain this multiplet structure by the electron spin.*

As for atoms, the spins of the individual electrons form a *resultant* S, the corresponding quantum number S being *half integral or integral according as the total number of electrons in the molecule is odd or even.* Since the spin S is not affected by an electric field, in Σ states (similar to S states for atoms) it is fixed in space as long as the molecule does not rotate and if there is no external magnetic field. On the other hand, if $\Lambda \neq 0$ (Π, Δ, $\cdots$ states), a magnetic field in the direction of the internuclear axis results from the orbital motion of the electrons. This magnetic field brings about a *precession of S* about the field direction (that is, in this case the internuclear axis) *with constant component $M_S(h/2\pi)$.* For molecules, M_S is called Σ, in order to bring out the analogy better (this quantum number Σ must not be confused with the symbol Σ for terms with $\Lambda = 0$).[1] The values of Σ allowed by the quantum theory are (see Chapter I for M_S)

$$\Sigma = S, \; S - 1, \; S - 2, \cdots, \; -S. \tag{V, 6}$$

---

[1] It will be remembered that, correspondingly, for atoms the letter S is used both as the spin quantum number and as symbol for a term with $L = 0$.

That is to say, $2S + 1$ different values are possible. In contrast to Λ, the quantum number Σ can be positive and negative. It is not defined for states with $\Lambda = 0$—that is, Σ states.

Total angular momentum of the electrons; multiplets. The total electronic angular momentum about the internuclear axis, denoted by Ω, is obtained by adding Λ and Σ, just as the total electronic angular momentum J for atoms is obtained by adding L and S. Whereas, however, a vector addition has to be carried out for atoms, for molecules an algebraic addition is sufficient, since the vectors Λ and Σ both lie along the line joining the nuclei. Thus for the *quantum number of the resultant electronic angular momentum about the internuclear axis* we have

$$\Omega = |\Lambda + \Sigma|. \qquad (\text{V, 7})$$

If Λ is not equal to zero, according to (V, 6) there are $2S + 1$ different values of $\Lambda + \Sigma$ for a given value of Λ (that is, of Ω as well, if $\Lambda \geq S$). As a result of the interaction of S with the magnetic field produced by Λ, these different values of $\Lambda + \Sigma$ correspond to somewhat different energies of the molecular state. Thus *the term splits into a multiplet of $2S + 1$ components*, quite similar to the behavior for atoms. On the other hand, if Λ equals zero, there is no magnetic field in the direction of the internuclear axis (Σ is not defined) and consequently no splitting occurs. Σ states are single as long as the molecule does not rotate. Nevertheless $2S + 1$ is called the *multiplicity* of a state, quite independent of whether Λ is greater than 0 or not—that is, regardless of whether (without rotation) an actual splitting is present or not.

The addition of the vectors (the vector diagram) is illustrated in Fig. 91(a) for a term with $\Lambda = 2$ and $S = 1$, and in Fig. 91(b) the splitting of this term is shown, which, without spin, would be single.

The multiplicity is added to the term symbol as a left upper index, and the value of $\Lambda + \Sigma$ as a subscript (compare the similar nomenclature for atoms). Thus the example deals with a $^3\Delta$ term whose components would be designated $^3\Delta_3$, $^3\Delta_2$, and $^3\Delta_1$.

To a first good approximation, the components of a multiplet term of a molecule are *equidistant* (differing in this

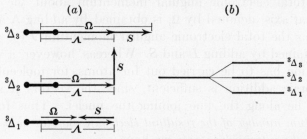

Fig. 91. (*a*) Vector Diagrams and (*b*) Energy Level Diagram for a $^3\Delta$ State (V = 2, S = 1). In (*b*), to the left the term is drawn without taking the interaction of Λ and S into account; to the right, taking account of it.

respect from atoms), since we have here a phenomenon quite analogous to the splitting of an atomic term with $L = 0$ and $S \neq 0$ in a magnetic field. The magnitude of the splitting is proportional to Λ, since the internal magnetic field is proportional to Λ. Thus, to a first approximation, the energy of a term component is

$$T_e = T_0 + A \cdot \Lambda \cdot \Sigma, \qquad (V, 8)$$

where T_0 is the energy of the "center of gravity" of the multiplet, and A, the *coupling constant*, is a measure of the strength of the interaction between orbital and spin angular momenta.

Thus far, with one or two exceptions, only *singlet, doublet, and triplet* terms have been observed for diatomic molecules. For singlet terms ($S = 0$) we have $\Omega = \Lambda$; for doublet terms ($S = \frac{1}{2}$) we have $\Omega = \Lambda \pm \frac{1}{2}$; for triplet terms ($S = 1$) we have $\Omega = \Lambda$ and $\Lambda \pm 1$. According to what has been said, molecules with an even number of electrons can have only odd multiplicities (singlet or triplet terms), and those with an odd number of electrons can have only even multiplicities (doublet terms). Thus for molecules, as well as for atoms, there is an *alternation of multiplicities*, which has always been confirmed by observation.

As for atoms, the *magnitude of the multiplet splitting* increases rapidly with increasing number of electrons. For BeH, for example, the splitting of the first excited $^2\Pi$ state is 2 cm^{-1}, while for HgH the splitting of the corresponding state is 3684 cm^{-1}.

Normal and *inverted* terms occur for molecules as for atoms —that is, terms for which the multiplet components lie in the order of their Ω values and terms for which they lie in the inverted order.

The spin does not alter the *twofold degeneracy of terms with* $\Lambda \neq 0$. Each of the multiplet components is now doubly degenerate, even those with $\Omega = 0$, as long as $\Lambda \neq 0$.

However, in contrast to terms with $\Omega \neq 0$, this degeneracy holds *only to a first approximation* for terms with $\Omega = 0$ and $\Lambda \neq 0$ (for example, $^3\Pi_0$ terms). If the mutual interaction of the electrons is taken into account, there results a very small splitting into two terms, which, in the example, are designated $^3\Pi_{0^+}$ and $^3\Pi_{0^-}$ (see below).

If $S > \Lambda \neq 0$, we obtain negative as well as positive values for $\Lambda + \Sigma$. As a result, according to (V, 7), some Ω values occur twice. However, these Ω values correspond to different energy values, according to (V, 8). For a $^4\Pi$ term, for example, the $\Lambda + \Sigma$ values $\frac{5}{2}, \frac{3}{2}, \frac{1}{2},$ and $-\frac{1}{2}$, are obtained; these [according to (V, 8)] correspond to four equidistant energy levels, although [according to (V, 7)] the last two have the same Ω.[2] Thus, as long as $\Lambda \neq 0$, molecular states have always the *full multiplicity*. This behavior is different from the behavior of atoms. It would therefore be better to use $\Lambda + \Sigma$ rather than Ω as an index to distinguish the multiplet components. Thus far, however, only very few quartets and higher multiplicities have been investigated for molecules [see Budó (140), Heimer (292), and Nevin (530)].

In the above discussion we have assumed an interaction of the electrons in a molecule of the same type as is assumed in the

---

[2] The term with $\Lambda + \Sigma = +\frac{1}{2}$, as well as that with $\Lambda + \Sigma = -\frac{1}{2}$, is doubly degenerate.

Russell-Saunders coupling for atoms—that is, a relatively small coupling between orbital angular momentum and spin. However, for heavy molecules, this coupling can become so strong that the quantum numbers Λ and Σ lose their meaning as angular momenta and only Ω retains its meaning (see below).

Symmetry properties of the electronic eigenfunctions. In the classification of molecular electronic states, in addition to the quantum numbers introduced above, the symmetry properties of the electronic eigenfunctions are of great importance. These symmetry properties depend on the symmetry properties of the molecule (but are not identical with them). We shall confine ourselves here to presenting the results [for a derivation see Kronig (31), van der Waerden (27), and Hund (348)].

For a diatomic molecule (and similarly for a linear polyatomic molecule), each plane through the line joining the nuclei is a symmetry plane of the nuclear frame. This fact, as shown by wave mechanical calculations, is the reason for the following property of the electronic eigenfunction of a Σ state: *For a reflection at any plane passing through the line joining the nuclei the eigenfunction either remains unaltered or changes sign.* In the first case, the state is called a Σ^+ state, and in the second case it is called a Σ^- state.

The same difference also exists for terms with $\Omega = 0$, if $\Lambda \neq 0$. For them there are always two components that do not exactly coincide (see above) and are designated 0^+ and 0^-.

The eigenfunctions of Σ states (and 0 states) according to (V, 4) do not depend on φ but only on the relative azimuths of the electrons. In the case of two electrons, an eigenfunction that changes sign for a reflection at any plane through the internuclear axis (Σ^-) is, for example, $\sin \varphi_{12}$, if φ_{12} is the angle between electrons 1 and 2, whereas $\cos \varphi_{12}$ is an example of an eigenfunction that does not change sign for such a reflection (Σ^+).

If the two nuclei in the molecule have the *same charge* (for example, $O^{16}O^{16}$, but also $O^{16}O^{18}$), the field in which the electrons move has, in addition to the symmetry axis, a *center of symmetry* (or we could also say a plane of symmetry at right angles to the internuclear axis); that is to say, the field remains unaltered by a reflection of the nuclei at this center of symmetry (midpoint of the internuclear axis). For brevity it is sometimes said that the *molecule* has a center of symmetry. A calculation shows (see below) that, in consequence of this symmetry, the *electronic eigenfunction remains unaltered or only changes its sign by reflection at the center of symmetry* (that is, by exchange of the co-ordinates of all the electrons, x_i, y_i, z_i, with $-x_i$, $-y_i$, $-z_i$). In the first case we speak of *even states* and in the second case of *odd states*. This character is indicated by adding g or u to the term symbol. Thus for like nuclei we have Σ_g, Σ_u, Π_g, Π_u, $\cdots$ states. States of the same multiplet have the same symmetry character.

It should be noticed that, according to the above, the distinction between even and odd electronic levels is independent of whether the molecule is homonuclear or not, provided the nuclei have the same charge. To a certain approximation, even the electronic eigenfunctions of molecules such as CN, for which the two nuclei differ only by one unit of charge, possess the symmetry property mentioned before.

The *connection between symmetry properties of the molecule and symmetry properties of the eigenfunctions* may be seen in the following way: If we effect a transformation of co-ordinates in the Schrödinger equation (I, 13), it goes over into

$$\sum_k \frac{1}{m_k} \left(\frac{\partial^2 \psi_{\text{tr.}}}{\partial x_k{}^2} + \frac{\partial^2 \psi_{\text{tr.}}}{\partial y_k{}^2} + \frac{\partial^2 \psi_{\text{tr.}}}{\partial z_k{}^2} \right) + \frac{8\pi^2}{h^2} (E - V_{\text{tr.}}) \psi_{\text{tr.}} = 0, \quad (V, 9)$$

where the subscript tr. indicates the transformed quantities. If the transformation of co-ordinates is such that the nuclear configuration remains unchanged—that is, if it is a symmetry operation (for example, reflection at a plane through the line joining the nuclei)—it means that $V_{\text{tr.}} = V$. In this case, the solutions of (V, 9) must be the same as those of (I, 13), since the equations have then exactly the same form. If ψ is a solution of (I, 13), $-\psi$ is also a solution and, therefore, for a given eigenvalue E, $\psi_{\text{tr.}}$ equals either ψ or $-\psi$. The probability density distribution $|\psi|^2$ of the electrons accordingly remains unaltered (as was to be expected) for all possible symmetry operations and has the same symmetry as the configuration of the nuclei. The foregoing discussion, however, applies only to *nondegenerate* electronic states (Σ states).

For *degenerate* states ($\Lambda \neq 0$), there exists the possibility that in a symmetry operation the eigenfunction ψ may go over into another of the functions belonging to the same eigenvalue (other than $-\psi$). For example, by reflection at a plane through the internuclear axis (exchange of all the azimuthal angles with their negative values), the first of the functions (V, 4) goes over into the second, and vice versa; that is, the eigenfunction does not remain unaltered or go over into its negative. However, linear combinations (V, 5) can easily be found such as remain unchanged or go over into their negatives by the reflection—namely, the functions

$$\psi^+ = \chi e^{i\Lambda\varphi} + \overline{\chi} e^{-i\Lambda\varphi}$$
$$\psi^- = \chi e^{i\Lambda\varphi} - \overline{\chi} e^{-i\Lambda\varphi}. \tag{V, 10}$$

It can be seen immediately that when all the φ are replaced by $-\varphi$, ψ^+ remains unaltered, whereas ψ^- goes over into $-\psi^-$. ψ^+ and ψ^- are linearly independent of each other and can therefore also be chosen as *the* two eigenfunctions of the degenerate state in place of (V, 4). That is to say, all the eigenfunctions of this state can be represented by

$$\psi = c\psi^+ + d\psi^-, \tag{V, 11}$$

where c and d are two constants.

According as the eigenfunction is ψ^+ or ψ^-, we may therefore also distinguish Π^+, Π^-, Δ^+, Δ^-, $\cdots$ states, similar to the Σ^+ and Σ^- states but with the difference that Π^+ and Π^- (and correspondingly the other pairs) have *exactly* equal energies, so that it is usually superfluous to make this distinction. However, if we take account of the influence of the rotation of the molecule (see below), a splitting takes place into two components with just the eigenfunctions ψ^+ and ψ^-, which then have somewhat different energies, and not into two components with eigenfunctions $\chi e^{i\Lambda\varphi}$ and $\overline{\chi} e^{-i\Lambda\varphi}$. According to (V, 10), each of the states Π^+ and Π^- (and correspondingly for larger Λ) contain, so to speak, rotations of the electrons in *both* senses, since both $e^{+i\Lambda\varphi}$ and $e^{-i\Lambda\varphi}$ occur in ψ^+ as well as in ψ^-.

It is to be noted that, for equal nuclear charges, electronic states that differ in the reflection character of their eigenfunctions with respect to the origin (even-odd) never have the same energy, independent of whether $\Lambda = 0$ or $\neq 0$, whereas, according to what has been said previously, states that differ only in the reflection character with respect to a plane going through the line joining the nuclei have different energy values only when $\Lambda = 0$ (Σ states).

2. COUPLING OF ROTATION AND ELECTRONIC MOTION

In section 1 we have considered the electronic motion quite independently of the rotation of the whole molecule and the vibration of the nuclei relative to each other; that is, we have regarded the nuclei as fixed (*two-center system*). If, however, as is the case for actual molecules, rotation and vibration take place at the same time as the electronic motion, these motions influence one another.

The mutual interaction of vibrational and electronic motions is essentially taken into account if the vibrational levels are so chosen as to fit the potential curve of the electronic state [see Chapter III, section 2(a)], since this potential curve gives the dependence of the electronic energy (including nuclear repulsion) on the internuclear distance. The mutual interaction of rotation and vibration has already been discussed in Chapter III, section 2(c). However, we must now consider more closely the *influence of rotational and electronic motions on each other*; that is, we must find out by what quantum numbers we can describe the rotational levels in the different types of electronic states, how their energies depend on these quantum numbers, and what symmetry properties the corresponding eigenfunctions possess.

(a) Hund's Coupling Cases

The different angular momenta in the molecule—electronic spin, electronic orbital angular momentum, angular momentum of nuclear rotation—form a resultant that is always designated J, as is the total angular momentum of the atom (in both cases disregarding nuclear spin). If the spin S and the orbital angular momentum Λ of the electrons are zero—that is, if we have a $^1\Sigma$ state—the angular momentum of the rotation of the pair of nuclei is identical with the total angular momentum J and we have the simple rotator previously treated (see Chapter III). In all other cases we have to distinguish different modes of coupling of the angular momenta, as was first done by Hund.

Hund's case (a). Hund's case (a) corresponds completely to the assumptions we made for the classification of the electronic states. Namely, in this case, it is assumed that the *interaction of the nuclear rotation with the electronic motion* (spin as well as orbital) is *very weak*, whereas the *electronic motion* itself is *coupled very strongly to the line joining the nuclei*. Even in the rotating molecule, Ω is then well defined and forms a resultant J with the angular momentum N of the rotation of the pair of nuclei. This is exactly the same case as was discussed previously for the symmetrical top [Chapter III, section 2(d)], except that now we have Ω in place of Λ. Fig. 92 gives the vector diagram for this case. J is a vector, constant in magnitude and direction. Ω and N rotate about this vector (nutation). At the same time, the precession of L and S takes place about the internuclear axis (see p. 231 f.), the precession in this case being assumed to be very much faster than the nutation of the figure axis whose frequency is given by (III, 20).

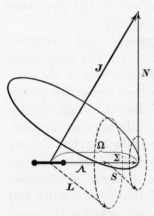

Fig. 92. Vector Diagram for Hund's Case (a). The nutation of the figure axis is indicated by the solid-line ellipse; the much more rapid precessions of L and S about the line joining the nuclei is indicated by the broken-line ellipses.

To a first approximation, the *rotational energy* in this case is [see Mulliken (512)]

$$F(J) = B_v[J(J + 1) - \Omega^2]. \qquad (V, 12)$$

This expression is quite similar to the formula (III, 101) holding for the symmetrical top, except that the term with A is omitted, since A is different for each electronic state and can therefore be included in the electronic energy. B_v

has the same value for every component of a given multiplet term except for very large multiplet splitting. Since J has the component Ω in the direction of the internuclear axis, it follows from quantum theory (see p. 23) that J is integral if Ω is integral—that is, for an even number of electrons (see section 1 of this chapter)—whereas J is half integral if Ω is half integral—that is, for an odd number of electrons. Naturally J cannot be smaller than Ω (compare Fig. 92). Therefore we have

$$J = \Omega,\ \Omega + 1,\ \Omega + 2,\ \cdots. \qquad (V, 13)$$

Levels with $J < \Omega$ do not occur. Since Ω is constant for a given multiplet component, the rotational energy, according to (V, 12), is practically the same as for the vibrating rotator, except that some of the first rotational levels are missing.

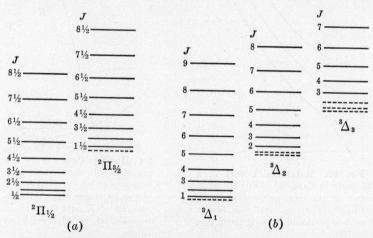

Fig. 93.   The First Rotational Levels of a $^2\Pi$ and a $^3\Delta$ State in Hund's Case (a).   The dotted levels do not occur, since J must be $\geqq \Omega$.   The Λ-type doubling [see section 2(b)] is ignored.

The electronic energy of the multiplet components is given, to a first approximation, by (V, 8). As an example, the rotational levels of a $^2\Pi$ and a $^3\Delta$ state in case (a) are represented in Fig. 93. The missing levels are indicated by broken lines. Fig. 94 gives a somewhat different representation of the rotational levels of a $^3\Pi$ term. The three curves representing the rotational levels can be brought into coincidence simply by a vertical shift, if case (a) holds strictly [see, however, section 2(b)].

Hund's case (b). As we have seen above, when $\Lambda = 0$, and $S \neq 0$, S is not coupled to the internuclear axis at all. This means that Ω is not defined. Therefore Hund's case (a)

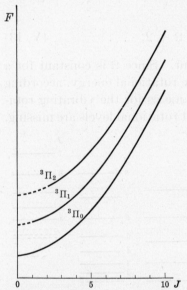

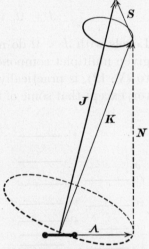

Fig. 94. Rotational Levels of a $^3\Pi$ State in Case (a). Only the solid parts of the curves correspond to actually occurring rotational levels. The Λ-type doubling is ignored (see Fig. 100).

Fig. 95. Vector Diagram for Hund's Case (b). The nutation of the figure axis, represented by the broken-line ellipse, is faster than the precessions of K and S about J, represented by the solid-line ellipse.

cannot apply here. Occasionally, particularly for light molecules, even if $\Lambda \neq 0$, S may be only *very weakly coupled to the internuclear axis*. This weak (or zero) coupling of S to the internuclear axis is the characteristic of Hund's case (b). In this case Λ (when it is different from zero) forms a resultant with N [in the same manner as Ω and N in case (a)] which is designated by K (see Fig. 95). The corresponding quantum number K can take the integral values

$$K = \Lambda, \ \Lambda + 1, \ \Lambda + 2, \ \cdots . \tag{V, 14}$$

K is the *total angular momentum apart from spin*. (In case $\Lambda = 0$, $K \equiv N$, and K can take all integral values from 0 up.)

K and S form a resultant J, the *total angular momentum including spin* (Fig. 95). The possible values of J for a given K are, according to the principles of vector addition (see Chapter I, p. 21), given by

$$J = (K+S), \ (K+S-1), \ (K+S-2), \ \cdots, \ |K-S|. \tag{V, 15}$$

Thus, in general (except when $K < S$), each level with a given K consists of $2S + 1$ *components*; that is, the number of components is equal to the multiplicity. As a result of the very weak coupling between K and S, these components have slightly different energies. The splitting increases with increasing K. The relation (V, 15) shows that J is again half integral for an odd number of electrons and integral for an even number of electrons.

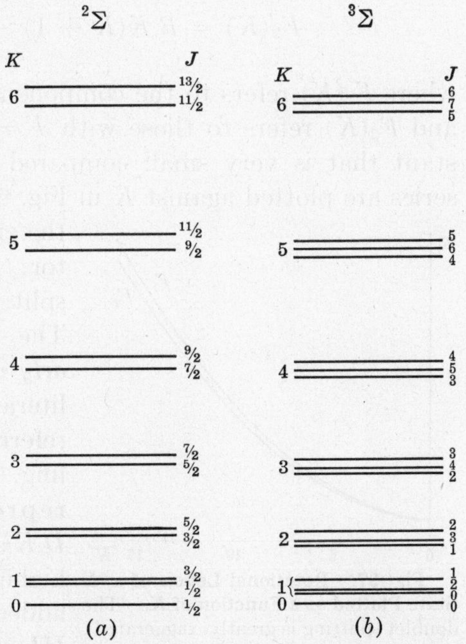

Thus far, with one or two exceptions, only cases with $S = \frac{1}{2}$ (doublets) and $S = 1$ (triplets) have been observed. Fig. 96 gives an energy level diagram for a $^2\Sigma$ and a

Fig. 96. First Rotational Levels (a) of a $^2\Sigma$ and (b) of a $^3\Sigma$ State. It should be noted that, for $^3\Sigma$, for a given K value, the levels do not lie in the order of their J values. The doublet or triplet splitting is drawn to a much larger scale than the separation of levels with different K.

$^3\Sigma$ state. It should be noted that, for Σ states ($\Lambda = 0$), the lowest rotational level ($K = 0$) has, according to (V, 15), only a single J value—namely, $J = S$ (that is, it is single)—in agreement with what was said above: Multiplet Σ states are single, like the S states of atoms, if the rotation is disregarded.

The *rotational energy* in the case of a $^2\Sigma$ *state* is given theoretically by [see Mulliken (512)]

$$F_1(K) = B_vK(K + 1) + \frac{\gamma}{2}K\,,$$

$$F_2(K) = B_vK(K + 1) - \frac{\gamma}{2}(K + 1),$$

$$\text{(V, 16)}$$

where $F_1(K)$ refers to the components having $J = (K + \frac{1}{2})$ and $F_2(K)$ refers to those with $J = (K - \frac{1}{2})$. γ is a constant that is very small compared to B_v. The two term series are plotted against K in Fig. 97. We have essentially the energy levels of the rotator; however, each level is split into two components. The *splitting increases linearly with K*. In the earlier literature this splitting is referred to as ρ-type doubling. For a more accurate representation a term $D_vK^2(K + 1)^2$ and possibly higher terms have to be added to (V, 16) [see Chapter III, section 2(b) and (c)].

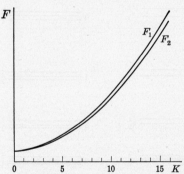

Fig. 97. Rotational Levels of a $^2\Sigma$ State Plotted as a Function of K.   The doublet splitting is greatly exaggerated .

For $^3\Sigma$ and $^4\Sigma$ states, more complicated formulae hold. They have been derived by Kramers (420a) [see also Mulliken (512), Hebb (284), and Schlapp (617)] and by Budó (140), respectively, but will not be given here. In both cases, as for $^2\Sigma$, the formula for the simple rotator holds for the mean of the component levels with the same K except for the lowest K values.

If $\Lambda \neq 0$, an additional term, which depends on Λ and K, has to be added to (V, 16) or the corresponding formula for triplet states [see Mulliken (512)].

Naturally, for *singlet states* the distinction between cases (a) and (b) is pointless. For them, $\Lambda = \Omega$ and $K = J$, and we have then the simple symmetrical top [see Chapter III, section 2(d)].

Cases (a) and (b) are the most important of the five coupling cases distinguished by Hund.

Hund's case (c). If the *coupling between L and S is stronger* than *that between L and the molecular axis*, we have Hund's case (c). It can occur for heavier molecules if the multiplet splitting is large. In this case, L and S form first a resultant J_a, and only this is space quantized with respect to the internuclear axis, with constant component Ω. For atoms this corresponds to the case of a weak electric field (no Paschen-Back effect). In this case Λ and Σ are not defined. Ω and the nuclear rotation N form a resultant J. The formula for the rotational levels is the same as in case (a)—namely, (V, 12). Fig. 98 gives the vector diagram for this coupling case.

Some subdivisions of case (c) are distinguished by Mulliken (513) but will not be considered here.

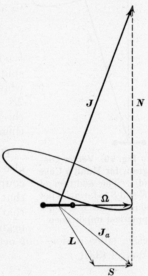

Fig. 98.   Vector Diagram for Hund's Case (c).   The precessions of L and S about J_a and of J_a about the line joining the nuclei has not been indicated by ellipses.

Hund's case (d). It may happen that L is *more weakly coupled to the internuclear axis than to the axis of rotation* of the molecule. Then the angular momentum N of the rotation of the nuclei is quantized. In this case it is designated by R, the corresponding quantum number taking the integral values $R = 0, 1, 2, \cdots$. R forms a resultant with L (Fig. 99) that is again designated by K, since it represents the total angular momentum apart from spin. For a given R, the quantum number K can take the values

$$K = (R + L), (R + L - 1), (R + L - 2), \cdots, |R - L|. \quad \text{(V, 17)}$$

Thus there are $2L + 1$ different K values for each R, except if $R \leqq L$.

K then combines with S to form a resultant J in the same way as in case (b). Practically, however, in case (d), the coupling between K and S is so small that S and therefore also J can be disregarded and we need to use only K.

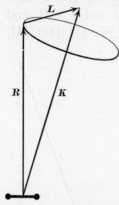

The *rotational energy* is given in this case, to a first approximation, by

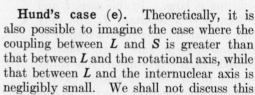

$$F(R) = B_v R(R + 1). \qquad \text{(V, 18)}$$

Each of the terms given by this formula is split into $2L + 1$ close components, each of which, strictly speaking, is further split into $2S + 1$ components. We shall not go into the complicated formulae for these splittings [see Weizel (33)].

Fig. 99. Vector Diagram for Hund's Case (d). The addition of K and S to form J is not shown, since it is not of practical importance.

Hund's case (e). Theoretically, it is also possible to imagine the case where the coupling between L and S is greater than that between L and the rotational axis, while that between L and the internuclear axis is negligibly small. We shall not discuss this case, since it does not occur in practice [see Mulliken (512) and Weizel (33)].

(b) Uncoupling Phenomena

Hund's coupling cases represent only idealized limiting cases. Actually they often reproduce the observed spectra to a good approximation. However, frequently small deviations, and, less frequently, large deviations, from them appear. These deviations have their origin in the fact that interactions which were neglected or regarded as small in the idealized coupling cases really have an appreciable magnitude and that the relative magnitude of the interactions alters with increasing rotation. Therefore, sometimes, with increasing rotation, a *transition* takes place *from one coupling case to another*. This phenomenon is called *uncoupling*.

Λ-type doubling. The interaction between the rotation of the nuclei and L, neglected in the discussion of coupling cases (a) and (b), produces a *splitting into two components for each J value* in the states with $\Lambda \neq 0$ which are doubly degenerate without rotation.[3] In general, this splitting increases with increasing rotation—that is, with increasing J. It is present for all states with $\Lambda \neq 0$ and is called Λ-*type doubling.* Such a splitting is shown in the energy level diagram in Fig. 58(*b*), p. 135, which applies to a ¹Π state. The two component levels with somewhat different energies, into which the one level of the ordinary rotator is split, have the same value of J, thus differing from, say, the two component

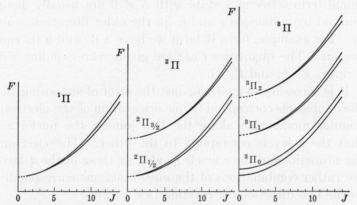

Fig. 100. Λ-Type Doubling for the First Rotational Levels of ¹Π, ²Π, ³Π. The parts of the curves corresponding to nonoccurring levels are dotted. The magnitude of the Λ-type doubling is exaggerated considerably.

levels into which each rotational level of a ²Σ state is split and which also show an increase in splitting with increasing rotation [see Fig. 96(*a*)].

For *multiplet states,* the rotational levels of each component of the multiplet, including those with $\Omega = 0$, split into two components. The behavior of the rotational terms for ¹Π, ²Π, and ³Π states is shown in (*a*), (*b*), and (*c*), respectively, of Fig. 100. The magnitude of the Λ splitting is much exaggerated in the figure. In general, it will amount to only a

---

[3] Degeneracies occurring in an atomic system are generally removed by external or internal perturbations (external electric or magnetic field or internal interactions).

fraction of a cm^{-1}. Only in special cases and for large J values will it reach a value of a few cm^{-1}. The splitting is relatively the greatest for terms with the smallest Ω (see the figure). In particular, for $\Omega = 0$ (in the case of a $^3\Pi$ state), it is relatively large even for small J and is approximately independent of J, in contrast to the other terms.

$^1\Delta$, $^2\Delta$, and $^3\Delta$ states behave in a similar way to the $^1\Pi$, $^2\Pi$, and $^3\Pi$ states (Fig. 100) except that the splittings are considerably smaller.

Following Mulliken (513), the two slightly different rotational term series of a state with $\Lambda \neq 0$ are usually distinguished by subscripts c and d (in the older literature a and b). For example, for a Π term we have a Π_c and a Π_d component. The quantities $F(J)$ are given corresponding subscripts: $F_c(J)$ and $F_d(J)$.

It is necessary to guard against the error of supposing that the c sublevels correspond to one orientation of the electronic angular momentum along the line joining the nuclei and that the d levels correspond to the other. The electronic eigenfunctions of the c levels as well as those of the d levels are rather combinations of the eigenfunctions corresponding to the two directions of rotation (see p. 240).

Kronig (421) and Van Vleck [(678) and (679)] have shown that, if the interaction of rotation and electronic motion is taken into account, the formula for a series of rotational levels belonging to a state with $\Lambda \neq 0$ is (omitting terms independent of J)

$$F_i(J) = B_v J(J + 1) + D_v J^2(J + 1)^2 + \cdots + \Phi_i(J), \quad (V, 19)$$

where the subscript i stands for c or d. In by far the most cases $\Phi_i(J)$ is a very small correction which may be represented by

$$\Phi_i(J) = \kappa_i + \delta_i J(J + 1) + \mu_i J^2(J + 1)^2 + \cdots, \quad (V, 20)$$

where $\mu_i \ll \delta_i$ and κ_i is of the order of magnitude of δ_i. From this it follows that, if κ_i is neglected, we can also write

$$F_i(J) = B_v^i J(J + 1) + D_v^i J^2(J + 1)^2 + \cdots, \quad (V, 21)$$

where $B_v{}^i$ and $D_v{}^i$ are *effective B and D values*,[4] which are related to the true B and D values according to the expressions

$$B_v{}^i = B_v + \delta_i,$$
$$D_v{}^i = D_v + \mu_i. \tag{V, 22}$$

Thus the rotational levels of each of the substates c or d may be represented in exactly the same manner as previously [formula (IV, 18)], and this is confirmed by experiment. However, the effective B and D values no longer have exactly the same physical meaning as before.

For $^1\Pi$ states or multiplet Π states belonging to case (b) (in the latter case J must be replaced by K in the formula), calculation shows that $\delta_d - \delta_c$ is of the same order of magnitude as δ. Therefore $(\mu_d - \mu_c)J^2(J + 1)^2$ may be neglected compared to $(\delta_d - \delta_c)J(J + 1)$, and, to a first good approximation, the Λ splitting is

$$\Delta\nu_{dc}(J) = F_d(J) - F_c(J) = qJ(J + 1), \tag{V, 23}$$

where

$$q = B_v{}^d - B_v{}^c = \delta_d - \delta_c. \tag{V, 24}$$

Thus, in contradistinction to the spin splitting for $^2\Sigma$ terms, the Λ-*type splitting increases quadratically with the rotational quantum number.*

Calculation shows that, for $^1\Delta$ states and multiplet Δ states of case (b), $\delta_d \approx \delta_c$. As a result, according to (V, 19–21), the splitting is proportional to $J^2(J^2 + 1)$, where the proportionality factor is very much smaller than δ. This means that for Δ states the Λ doubling is negligibly small for not too large J values.

The effective B values, $B_v{}^c$ and $B_v{}^d$, are the ones obtained from the empirical data. The *true B_v values*, which have to be known for the calculation of the moment of inertia and the internuclear distance, can be obtained from them only if δ_d and δ_c are separately known, while empirically only $q = \delta_d - \delta_c$ can be determined. Only in favorable cases can the quantities δ_d and δ_c be derived on the basis of theoretical formulae. Fortunately it has always been found that these quantities are very small compared to B and are actually of the order of magnitude of $B^d - B^c$ (that is, roughly $10^{-3} B$ or smaller). In practice, the *mean of $B_v{}^d$ and $B_v{}^c$*

---

[4] These are not to be confused with the symbols for isotopes used in equation (III, 130).

is used as an approximation for the true B_v value. It should be remarked that, in general, a term $\Phi(J)$ has also to be added to the usual formula for the rotational levels of $^1\Sigma$ states. This inclusion of $\Phi(J)$ has the result that, for $^1\Sigma$ states also, under some circumstances the experimentally derived B value is only an effective B value that deviates by a small amount from the true B value. The deviation—that is, $\Phi(J)$—is the greater (for Σ as well as Π, Δ, and like states) the closer other electronic states are found to the state under consideration (see p. 319).

For *multiplet states belonging to case* (a) (large multiplet splitting) the variation of the Λ-type doubling is different for the different multiplet components. For $^2\Pi$ states, the Λ-type doubling of the $^2\Pi_{\frac{1}{2}}$ component varies linearly with J, whereas for the $^2\Pi_{\frac{3}{2}}$ component it varies with the third power of J and for small J is very small compared to that of $^2\Pi_{\frac{1}{2}}$. As mentioned above, for $^3\Pi$ states, the Λ-type splitting of the $^3\Pi_0$ component is relatively large even for small J and is, to a first approximation, independent of J. The $^3\Pi_1$ component shows somewhat the same variation of the Λ-type splitting as a $^1\Pi$ term; that is, it is proportional to $J(J + 1)$, whereas the $^3\Pi_2$ component shows a splitting which is proportional to $J^2(J + 1)^2$ and which, for not too large J, is very much smaller than that of the two other triplet components (see Fig. 100).

A full discussion of Λ-type doubling, including intermediate cases, is to be found in a paper by Mulliken and Christy (523). Thus far, a complete analysis of Λ-type doubling has been carried out for only relatively few molecules.

Transition from case (b) to case (d) (L uncoupling). The Λ-type doubling discussed in the foregoing may be regarded as the beginning of a gradual transition of the coupling in the molecule from case (a) or case (b) to case (d). We shall now consider the complete transition, but only from case (b) to case (d), since this is the only one observed in practice—for example, for some electronic states of H_2 and He_2. For these molecules it happens fairly often that the interaction between the orbital angular momentum L and the internuclear axis is so small that for the higher rotational levels it is outweighed by the interaction with the rotational axis [case (d)]. While, without rotation, there are $L + 1$ terms with different Λ for a given value of L, of which those with $\Lambda \neq 0$ are doubly degenerate, for large rotation [in case (d)] there is a splitting into $2L + 1$ components—that is, there is no degeneracy. It is therefore clear that, at the beginning of the transition to case (d), a splitting of the levels that are degenerate with each other must take place—that is, just the Λ-*type doubling*.

In Fig. 101 the first rotational levels for the case $L = 1$ are drawn as an example, to the left for case (b) (strong coupling of L with the internuclear axis) and to the right for case (d) (vanishing coupling with the internuclear axis). If we now imagine, starting out from case (b), the coupling to be decreased successively (say by decreasing the nuclear separation in the molecule), the rotational levels to the left must eventually go over into those to the right and must do so in such a way that K, which in the

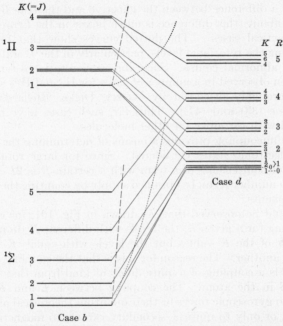

Fig. 101. **Transition from Case (b) to Case (d) for the Lowest Rotational Levels for $L = 1$.** The strength of the interaction between L and the internuclear axis decreases from left to right.

present case is equal to the total angular momentum J, remains unaltered for a given level and, in addition, in such a way that levels with equal K do not cross one another (see section 4). In this way we obtain the connecting lines drawn in Fig. 101, which naturally are supposed to reproduce only schematically the behavior of the levels for an alteration of the coupling conditions. We can see how in the $^1\Pi$ state the levels split with increasing uncoupling (Λ-type doubling) and finally go over into two levels with different R (but, of course, with equal K).

In a practical case, of course, the coupling does not alter for a particular level but rather changes from one level to the next, approaching case (d) for the higher rotational levels. This change of coupling from one level to the next is indicated by the broken-line curves in Fig. 101 for weak uncoupling and by the dotted curves for strong uncoupling. The points of intersection of these curves with the connecting lines between right and left give roughly the positions of the rotational levels. If we follow the broken-line curves, we can see immediately how the Λ-type doubling arises and how a difference between the effective and the true B value is brought about (this difference is much larger in the figure than in most practical cases). The dotted curves show that for strong uncoupling the rotational levels, particularly in the $^1\Pi$ state, follow quite an abnormal course. Such abnormal rotational term series have been observed in a number of cases for H_2 and He_2 and have been thoroughly discussed by Weizel, Dieke, Richardson, and others [see (33) and (47)]. Thus far, such cases have not been observed with certainty for other molecules.

The L uncoupling provides a means of determining the L value of the electronic states considered. Since for large rotation the number of components of a term with a certain R is $2L + 1$, the quantum number L can be obtained simply by counting the number of components.

It should be observed that, as drawn in Fig. 101, for complete uncoupling for a given R, the levels with different K do not lie in the order of the K values but the levels with equal $|K - R|$ lie near one another. The reason for this is that the coupling between L and R is a coupling of a quite different kind from that between L and S in the atom. The coupling between L and R is due mainly to gyroscopic forces or their quantum theoretical analogues and not, or only to quite a secondary extent, to magnetic forces (as is the coupling between L and S).

Transition from case (a) to case (b) (spin uncoupling). Whereas the multiplet Σ states always belong strictly to case (b), many *cases intermediate between* (a) *and* (b) occur for Π, Δ, $\cdots$ states. In most cases (apart from H_2, He_2, and some hydrides) case (a) is well fulfilled for no rotation or very small rotation; that is, S is so coupled with Λ that a resultant Ω is defined. If the multiplet splitting is not too great, however, as J increases, the rotational velocity of the molecule eventually becomes comparable with the precessional velocity of S about Λ (see Fig. 92), and finally, with still further increasing J, the influence of the molecular rotation predominates. Consequently, S *is uncoupled from the molecular axis* and forms with K (the resultant of Λ and N) the total angular momentum J, in accordance with case (b). This process is called *spin uncoupling*.

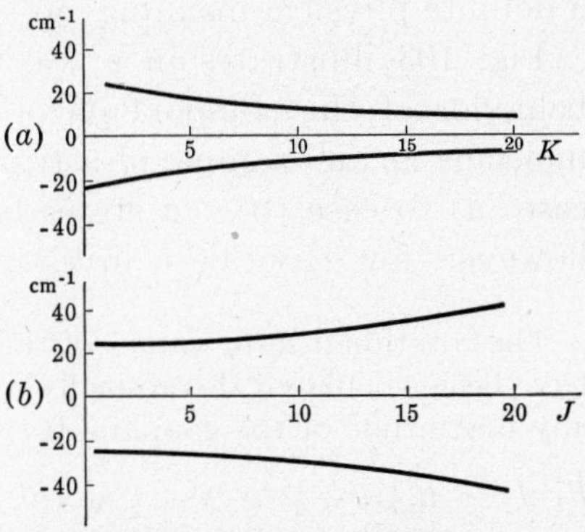

For large rotation [case (b)] there is then only a small splitting of the levels with

Fig. 102. Doublet Splitting in the $^2\Pi$ ($v = 0$) State of CN. (a) As a function of K and (b) as a function of J.

a given K, while for small rotation [case (a)] there is a much greater splitting. As an illustration, Fig. 102(a) shows the variation of the rotational term values in the $^2\Pi$ state of CN, the amount $BK(K+1)$ being subtracted from the observed values (using a mean B). It can be seen that the terms draw together with increasing K. We must, however, remember that for small rotation the angular momentum K is not defined, since then S is coupled to the molecular axis. However, in spite of that, we can at least formally assign

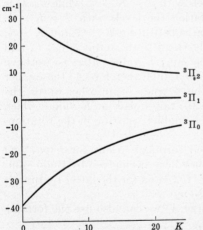

Fig. 103. Triplet Splitting in the $B\,^3\Pi$ ($v = 6$) State of N_2 as a Function of K. The three curves represent the three triplet components $^3\Pi_2$, $^3\Pi_1$, $^3\Pi_0$. The center component has been arbitrarily assumed to be constant, whereas actually it is given by $BK(K+1)$.

K values to the levels ($K = J \pm \tfrac{1}{2}$ for doublet terms) if we

extend the numbering used for large K values (where it has a definite physical meaning) to small K.

Fig. 103 illustrates in a way similar to Fig. 102(a) the behavior of the components of the $B\ {}^3\Pi$ state of the N_2 molecule as an example of a triplet state that changes from case (a) to case (b). Δ states behave in a similar manner; however, few have been investigated thus far.

The rotational term values of the components of doublet states have been calculated theoretically by Hill and Van Vleck (323) for any magnitude of the coupling between S and Λ. They obtained

$$F_1(J) = B_v\{(J+\tfrac{1}{2})^2 - \Lambda^2 - \tfrac{1}{2}\sqrt{4(J+\tfrac{1}{2})^2 + Y(Y-4)\Lambda^2}\},$$
$$F_2(J) = B_v\{(J+\tfrac{1}{2})^2 - \Lambda^2 + \tfrac{1}{2}\sqrt{4(J+\tfrac{1}{2})^2 + Y(Y-4)\Lambda^2}\}. \qquad (V, 25)$$

Here $Y = A/B_v$, where A, the coupling constant in (V, 8), is a measure of the strength of the coupling between the spin S and the orbital angular momentum Λ. $F_1(J)$ is the term series that forms for large rotation the levels with $J = K + \tfrac{1}{2}$, while $F_2(J)$ is that which forms for large rotation the levels with $J = K - \tfrac{1}{2}$. It can be seen from (V, 25), on substituting $K + \tfrac{1}{2}$ and $K - \tfrac{1}{2}$, respectively, that for sufficiently small Y the term values F_1 and F_2 are very nearly equal for the same K value—that is, we have case (b). The smaller the value of Y (and therefore A) the smaller are the values of K for which this is true; or, in other words, the transition from case (a) to case (b) takes place at K values which are the smaller the smaller is the doublet splitting in the rotationless state.

Similar but more complicated formulae result for *triplet and quartet states*. For the former they have been given by Budó (139) [see also Challacombe and Almy (152)] and for the latter by Brandt (124) and Budó (140) [see also Nevin (530)].

For *small spin uncoupling* (large A) we can also use the formula

$$F(J) = B_{\text{eff.}} J(J + 1)$$

instead of formula (V, 25) or the corresponding formula for triplet or quartet states, where the effective B is somewhat different for the different multiplet components. According to Mulliken (513), for doublet states

$$B_{\text{eff.}} = B\left(1 \pm \frac{B}{A\Lambda} + \cdots\right), \qquad (V, 26)$$

and for triplet states

for $\qquad \Sigma = 0, \; B_{\text{eff.}} = B,$

and for $\qquad \Sigma = \pm 1, \; B_{\text{eff.}} = B\left(1 \pm \dfrac{2B}{A\Lambda} + \cdots\right).$ $\qquad$ (V, 27)

It can be seen that the middle component of a triplet state gives approximately the true B value.

For any strength of the spin uncoupling, the mean of the two or three components with equal J follows exactly the simple formula

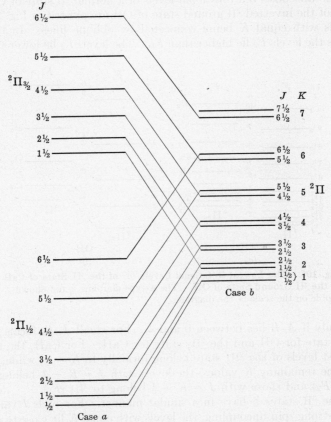

Fig. 104.   Transition of a $^2\Pi$ State from Case (a) to Case (b).

$F(J) = BJ(J + 1)$, with the true B value (if the Λ-type doubling is neglected).

In Fig. 104 the transition from case (a) to case (b) is illustrated by an energy level diagram for a $^2\Pi$ state, similar to Fig. 101 for the L uncoupling. From this figure we can see why levels with equal K draw together with increasing uncoupling. However, at the same time we can also see that levels with equal J *draw apart* with increasing J (that is, with increasing uncoupling), since they belong to different K values, and since the separation of successive levels at the right increases with increasing K. Therefore, if the splitting is plotted as a function of J (not K), we obtain Fig. 102(b) in place of Fig. 102(a) (see also Fig. 105).

The first observed rotational levels of a normal $^2\Pi$ state of CaH and of the inverted $^2\Pi$ ground state of OH are plotted in Fig. 105, levels with equal K being connected by oblique lines. In both cases the levels F_2 lie higher than F_1. The levels F_2 lie lower than

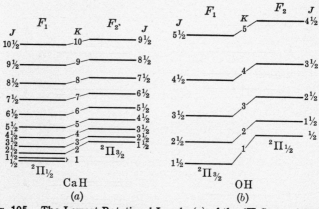

Fig. 105. **The Lowest Rotational Levels** (a) **of the** $^2\Pi$ **State of CaH and** (b) **of the** $^2\Pi$ **Ground State of OH.** The Λ-type doubling is not shown. It is negligible on the scale of the diagram.

F_1 only if A/B lies between 0 and 4. For small J, F_1 forms the $^2\Pi_{\frac{3}{2}}$ state for OH and the $^2\Pi_{\frac{1}{2}}$ state for CaH. For CaH, the two lowest levels of the $^2\Pi_{\frac{1}{2}}$ state belong formally to $K = 1$, while, for all the remaining K values, the levels with $J = K - \frac{1}{2}$ belong to $^2\Pi_{\frac{3}{2}}$ (F_2) and those with $J = K + \frac{1}{2}$ belong to $^2\Pi_{\frac{1}{2}}$ (F_1).

The $^3\Pi$ states behave in a similar manner. For high J values and strong spin uncoupling, the levels with equal K lie close to one another and in general (similar to doublet states) in the inverse order of the J values—that is, the level with $J = K - 1$ higher than that with $J = K$ and this higher than that with $J = K + 1$, independent of whether, for small J, the $^3\Pi$ state is normal or inverted [see Mulliken (513) and Jevons (34)]. For quartet states see Brandt (124).

Thus far, in considering spin uncoupling we have neglected the Λ-*type doubling* (that is, incipient L uncoupling), which takes place *simultaneously* and also increases with increasing rotation. This neglect is justified in many cases, at least approximately. However, cases do also occur in which the two uncouplings are of comparable magnitude. As an example, Fig. 106 gives the rota-

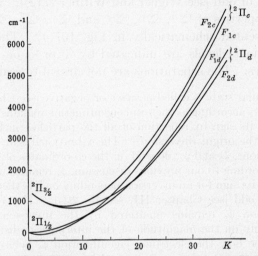

Fig. 106.   Spin Doubling and Λ-Type Doubling for the $^2\Pi$ State of CaH [after Mulliken and Christy (**523**)].   The ordinate gives the energy values for the component F_{1d}. The deviations of the other components, F_{1c}, F_{2c}, and F_{2d}, from the former are plotted on a 20-fold scale.

tional levels of the $^2\Pi$ state of CaH as a function of K. It is seen that for large K the Λ doubling is larger than the spin doubling. We cannot go into the complicated formulae holding for such cases [see Van Vleck (678) and Hebb (284)]. A full discussion is given by Mulliken and Christy (523).

(c) Symmetry Properties of the Rotational Levels

The symmetry properties of the rotational levels introduced in Chapter III, section 2(f)—positive-negative, and, for identical nuclei, symmetric-antisymmetric—are, as we have already mentioned, influenced by the symmetry of the electronic eigenfunctions. Now that we have become acquainted with the different kinds of electronic eigenfunctions, we can discuss this in greater detail.

Σ states. A more detailed discussion (see below) shows that *for Σ$^+$ states the even-numbered rotational levels are positive and the odd are negative*, whereas *for Σ$^-$ states the even are negative and the odd are positive*. For multiplet Σ states the character positive-negative depends on whether K (not J) is even or odd [see Wigner and Witmer (712)]. The symmetry properties of $^1Σ^+$, $^2Σ^+$, $^3Σ^+$ and $^1Σ^-$, $^2Σ^-$, $^3Σ^-$ states are represented schematically in Fig. 107(a). The successive rotational levels are indicated by $\oplus$ or $\ominus$ on the horizontal lines. The separations are not drawn to scale.

A molecular state is called positive or negative [see Chapter III, section 2(f)] according as the total eigenfunction remains unaltered or changes its sign by reflection of all the particles (including the nuclei) at the origin (inversion). The vibrational and rotational eigenfunctions, $ψ_v$ and $ψ_r$, depend on the co-ordinates of the nuclei only. According to our previous discussion, $ψ_r$ remains unchanged or changes its sign for an inversion depending on whether J (or K) is even or odd [see Chapter III, section 2(f)]. The vibrational eigenfunction $ψ_v$ remains unaltered by the inversion, since it depends only on the magnitude of the internuclear distance. In order to see how the electronic eigenfunction $ψ_e$ behaves for an inversion we must take account of the fact that an inversion is equivalent to a rotation of the molecule through 180° about an axis perpendicular to the internuclear axis, followed by a reflection at a plane perpendicular to this rotational axis and passing through the internuclear axis. The first operation does not influence $ψ_e$, since $ψ_e$ depends only on the co-ordinates of the electrons *relative* to the nuclei (as well as on the internuclear distance), whereas the second operation (which affects the electrons only) leaves $ψ_e$ unaltered for Σ$^+$ states and changes its sign for Σ$^-$ states (see the definition of Σ$^+$ and Σ$^-$ states, p. 238); that is, $ψ_e$ remains unaltered or changes its sign for an inversion depending on whether the electronic state is Σ$^+$ or Σ$^-$. From these considerations it follows that the total eigenfunction $ψ = ψ_e \cdot ψ_v \cdot ψ_r$ for a Σ$^+$ state remains unaltered or changes its sign for an inversion— that is, a rotational level of a Σ$^+$ state is positive or negative— according as the rotational quantum number is even or odd, whereas for Σ$^-$ states just the converse holds.

If the *nuclei* are *identical*, the positive rotational levels of the molecule are symmetric and the negative are antisymmetric for *even* electronic states (for example, Σ_g), and the negative are symmetric and the positive are antisymmetric for *odd* states (for example, Σ_u). These properties are represented in Fig. 107(*b*) for $^1\Sigma_g{}^+$, $^1\Sigma_u{}^+$, $^1\Sigma_g{}^-$, and $^1\Sigma_u{}^-$. Multiplet Σ states show a corresponding behavior.

An exchange of the nuclei can be brought about if all the particles are first reflected at the origin and then the electrons alone are reflected at the origin. In the first reflection, the eigenfunc-

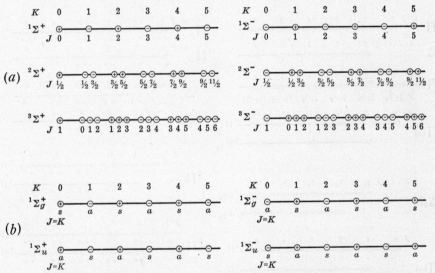

Fig. 107. Symmetry Properties of the Rotational Levels of Σ States. (*a*) For unlike nuclei. (*b*) For identical nuclei. In (*b*), *s* means symmetric and *a* means antisymmetric.

tion remains unchanged for positive terms but changes sign for negative terms. In the second reflection, the eigenfunction remains unaltered for even electronic states (see p. 239), whereas it changes sign for odd electronic states. In this way the above rule is obtained.

Π, Δ, ⋯ states. For Π, Δ, ⋯ states there is a twofold degeneracy without rotation, which, as we have seen, is removed with increasing rotation. A detailed investigation shows [see Wigner and Witmer (712)] that always *one com-*

ponent is positive and the other is negative, and, in fact, that it is alternately the upper and the lower that is positive, as is illustrated in Fig. 108(a) for $^1\Pi$ and $^1\Delta$. We can also see here the meaning of the earlier designation c and d for the Λ-doubling components. In both series (c and d), positive and negative levels alternate, as for Σ states. The one behaves like a Σ^+ state and therefore can be designated Π^+ (or Δ^+); the other behaves like Σ^- and can therefore be designated Π^- (or Δ^-).

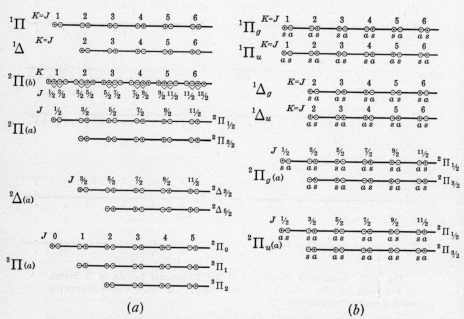

(a) $\hspace{6cm}$ (b)

Fig. 108. Symmetry Properties of the Rotational Levels of Π and Δ States.
(a) For unlike nuclei. $\quad$ (b) For identical nuclei.

Since the signs $+$ and $-$ are not very convenient as indices, in the following we shall use the subscript c for Π^+, Δ^+, $\cdots$, and the subscript d for Π^-, Δ^-, $\cdots$; thus, for example, $F_c(J)$ refers to Π_c—that is, Π^+. It should be noted that this nomenclature is not the same as Mulliken's (513).

The *electronic eigenfunctions* of the two Λ components, Π^+ and Π^- (or Π_c and Π_d), are given to a first approximation by (V, 10), even if the splitting is taken into account. Whether the Π^+ or the Π^- (and correspondingly the Δ^+ or Δ^-) term series lies higher depends on the position of neighboring electronic states [see Van Vleck (678) and Mulliken and Christy (523)].

Multiplet states with $\Lambda > 0$ behave in a similar way. As examples, the symmetry properties of the rotational levels of $^2\Pi$, $^2\Delta$, and $^3\Pi$ states are given in Fig. 108(a) for case (a). In addition, a $^2\Pi$ state in case (b) is represented. The other states in case (b) behave correspondingly.

If the *nuclei* are *identical*, we have again to distinguish even and odd states. As before, for even electronic states the positive levels are symmetric and the negative are antisymmetric and conversely for odd electronic states. Fig. 108(b) shows this for $^1\Pi_g$, $^1\Pi_u$, $^1\Delta_g$, $^1\Delta_u$, $^2\Pi_g$, and $^2\Pi_u$. Other states behave correspondingly.

3. TYPES OF ELECTRONIC TRANSITIONS

(a) Selection Rules

In order to determine the quantum numbers and symmetry properties introduced in the two foregoing sections, we have to know the selection rules for these quantum numbers and symmetry properties and compare the spectra predicted on their basis with the observed spectra. The selection rules are obtained by considering the integrals (I, 17). We must distinguish between selection rules that hold quite generally, independent of the coupling case to which the electronic state under consideration belongs, and those that hold only for a definite coupling case.

General selection rules. The selection rule for the total angular momentum J,

$$\Delta J = 0, \pm 1, \textit{with the restriction } J = 0 \nrightarrow J = 0, \quad \text{(V, 28)}$$

always holds (assuming dipole radiation), as for atoms.[5] Furthermore, the symmetry selection rules already men-

---

[5] For a proof see Kronig (31).

tioned in Chapter III hold quite generally: *Positive terms combine only with negative, and vice versa*, or symbolically

$$+ \leftrightarrow -, \quad + \nleftrightarrow +, \quad - \nleftrightarrow -, \qquad \text{(V, 29)}$$

and, for identical nuclei, *symmetric terms combine only with symmetric and antisymmetric only with antisymmetric*, or

$$s \leftrightarrow s, \quad a \leftrightarrow a, \quad s \nleftrightarrow a. \qquad \text{(V, 30)}$$

Finally, we have, in the case of nuclei with equal charge the selection rule that *even electronic states combine only with odd*; that is,

$$g \leftrightarrow u, \quad g \nleftrightarrow g, \quad u \nleftrightarrow u. \qquad \text{(V, 31)}$$

Thus, for example, $\Sigma_g \leftrightarrow \Sigma_u$, but $\Sigma_g \nleftrightarrow \Sigma_g$.

The proof for this selection rule is the same as that for (V, 29), which was given previously (p. 136 f.), except that we have to use the electronic eigenfunction instead of the total eigenfunction. In the case that not only the charge but also all other properties of the nuclei are the same (homonuclear molecules), (V, 31) follows immediately from (V, 29 and 30) if we take account of the fact (see Figs. 107 and 108) that for identical nuclei all the positive levels are symmetric and the negative antisymmetric in an even electronic state (and the opposite is the case in an odd one). But the rule (V, 31) is more general, holding also for such heteronuclear molecules as $O^{16}O^{18}$, even though the property symmetric-antisymmetric is not defined for them. However, if, in these cases, the influence of rotation is taken into account, (V, 31) no longer holds quite rigorously. To a certain approximation the rule (V, 31) holds even for molecules in which the nuclei have slightly different charge, such as CN (see p. 239). (V, 31) is independent of whether Λ is defined or not (see p. 247).

Selection rules holding for case (a) as well as case (b). Apart from the above quite general selection rules, there are some that hold in case (a) as well as in case (b) but not in other coupling cases. However, since these two coupling cases are by far the most frequent, these selection rules still have a fairly general significance.

In cases (a) and (b), the quantum number Λ is defined and for it there is the selection rule

$$\Delta\Lambda = 0, \pm 1. \qquad (V, 32)$$

This means that $\Sigma - \Sigma$, $\Sigma - \Pi$, $\Pi - \Pi$, $\Pi - \Delta$, $\cdots$ transitions but not $\Sigma - \Delta$, $\Sigma - \Phi$, $\Pi - \Phi$, $\cdots$ transitions can occur. The selection rule for Λ corresponds exactly to the selection rule for M_L for atoms in an electric or magnetic field (see p. 27).

Furthermore, Σ^+ *states cannot combine with* Σ^- *states;*[6] that is,

$$\Sigma^+ \longleftrightarrow \Sigma^+, \quad \Sigma^- \longleftrightarrow \Sigma^-, \quad \Sigma^+ \longleftrightarrow\!\!\!\!/ \; \Sigma^-. \qquad (V, 33)$$

However, Σ^+ as well as Σ^- states combine with Π states.

In cases (a) and (b) the resultant spin S is defined, and for the corresponding quantum number there is the selection rule (as for atoms)

$$\Delta S = 0. \qquad (V, 34)$$

This means that *only states of the same multiplicity combine with one another.* To be sure, this *prohibition of intercombinations* holds less and less rigorously with increasing number of electrons.

The possible electronic transitions, on the basis of the most important selection rules so far mentioned, are summarized in Table 24.

Selection rules holding only in case (a). We now come to the special selection rules that hold only if *both* the participating electronic states belong to the same coupling case. The relative simplicity of a large number of multiplet bands (compare, for example, the spectrogram Fig. 22) results from the fact that usually some of these special selection rules are fulfilled.

If both states belong to case (a), the following rule holds for the quantum number Σ:

$$\Delta\Sigma = 0. \qquad (V, 35)$$

---

[6] For a proof see Kronig (31).

TABLE 24

ALLOWED ELECTRONIC TRANSITIONS

Unequal Nuclear Charge	Equal Nuclear Charge
$\Sigma^+ \longleftrightarrow \Sigma^+$	$\Sigma_g^+ \longleftrightarrow \Sigma_u^+$
$\Sigma^- \longleftrightarrow \Sigma^-$	$\Sigma_g^- \longleftrightarrow \Sigma_u^-$
$\Pi \longleftrightarrow \Sigma^+$	$\Pi_g \longleftrightarrow \Sigma_u^+, \; \Pi_u \longleftrightarrow \Sigma_g^+$
$\Pi \longleftrightarrow \Sigma^-$	$\Pi_g \longleftrightarrow \Sigma_u^-, \; \Pi_u \longleftrightarrow \Sigma_g^-$
$\Pi \longleftrightarrow \Pi$	$\Pi_g \longleftrightarrow \Pi_u$
$\Pi \longleftrightarrow \Delta$	$\Pi_g \longleftrightarrow \Delta_u, \; \Pi_u \longleftrightarrow \Delta_g$
$\Delta \longleftrightarrow \Delta$	$\Delta_g \longleftrightarrow \Delta_u$
$\cdots$	$\cdots$

All the above transitions are possible as singlets, doublets, triplets, and so on, but intercombinations—singlet-triplet and similar transitions—are forbidden.

This means that in an electronic transition *the component of the spin along the internuclear axis does not alter.* Therefore, transitions such as $^2\Pi_{\frac{1}{2}} - {}^2\Pi_{\frac{1}{2}}$, $^2\Pi_{\frac{3}{2}} - {}^2\Pi_{\frac{3}{2}}$, $^2\Pi_{\frac{1}{2}} - {}^2\Delta_{\frac{3}{2}}$, $^2\Pi_{\frac{3}{2}} - {}^2\Delta_{\frac{5}{2}}$, $^3\Pi_0 - {}^3\Pi_0$, $\cdots$ but not $^2\Pi_{\frac{1}{2}} - {}^2\Pi_{\frac{3}{2}}$, $^2\Pi_{\frac{1}{2}} - {}^2\Delta_{\frac{5}{2}}$, $^3\Pi_0 - {}^3\Pi_1$, $\cdots$ take place. This selection rule corresponds exactly to the selection rule $\Delta M_S = 0$ for atoms in a strong electric or magnetic field (see p. 27). Like (V, 34) it holds to a very good approximation as long as the interaction between spin and orbital angular momentum is not too great.

Further, in case (a) for Ω, the total electronic angular momentum about the internuclear axis, we have

$$\Delta\Omega = 0, \pm 1 \qquad\qquad (V, 36)$$

(corresponding to the selection rule $\Delta M_J = 0, \pm 1$ for atoms). This selection rule adds nothing to (V, 32 and 35) as long as (V, 35) holds strictly. However, it still holds for strong interaction of spin and orbital angular momentum when (V, 35) and possibly even (V, 32) have lost their validity [Hund's case (c)].

If $\Omega = 0$ for both electronic states, the transitions with $\Delta J = 0$ are forbidden and only those with $\Delta J = \pm 1$ appear (corresponding to the rule for atoms: $M = 0 \leftrightarrow M = 0$ for $\Delta J = 0$). This means, for example, that no Q branch appears for the $^3\Pi_0 - {}^3\Pi_0$ component of a $^3\Pi - {}^3\Pi$ transition.

Apart from these selection rules, which state only whether or not a given transition can take place at all, the *intensities of the allowed lines* can also be calculated theoretically. The exact intensity formula may be found, for example, in Weizel (33) and Mulliken (513). Here we shall say only that, qualitatively, for an individual sub-band (corresponding to a definite Ω' and Ω'') the intensity distribution is given by Fig. 88(*a*), if $\Delta\Omega \neq 0$ (for example, $^2\Pi_{\frac{3}{2}} - {}^2\Delta_{\frac{5}{2}}$)— that is, an intense Q branch is present—whereas the intensity distribution for $\Delta\Omega = 0$ (for example, $^2\Pi_{\frac{3}{2}} - {}^2\Pi_{\frac{3}{2}}$) is given by Fig. 88(*b*)—that is, a weak Q branch is present whose intensity decreases rapidly with increasing J. If, in addition, Ω itself is zero, no Q branch is present (see above). The appearance or nonappearance of an intense Q branch can accordingly be used to establish whether or not $\Delta\Omega$ (and thereby $\Delta\Lambda$) differs from zero.

Selection rules holding only in case (b). If both states belong to case (b), the following rule for the quantum number K of the total angular momentum apart from spin holds:

$$\Delta K = 0, \pm 1, \qquad\qquad (V, 37)$$

with the added restriction

$$\Delta K = 0 \text{ is forbidden for } \Sigma - \Sigma \text{ transitions.} (V, 38)$$

This restriction follows immediately from the selection rules (V, 29 and 33) according to Fig. 107.

Furthermore, pronouncements can be made about the dependence of the *intensity* on J or K; for $\Delta\Lambda = 0$—that is, for $\Pi - \Pi$, $\Delta - \Delta$, $\cdots$ transitions [for $\Sigma - \Sigma$ transitions see (V, 38)]—if both states belong to case (b), the branches with $\Delta K = 0$ decrease very rapidly in intensity with increasing K [approximately proportional to $(1/K)e^{-E_r/kT}$; see

Fig. 88(b)] and therefore are often not observed. Also, in branches for which $\Delta J \neq \Delta K$, the intensity similarly falls off very rapidly with increasing K. These branches are often called *satellite branches*, since their lines always lie very near to those of the corresponding main branches with the same ΔK but having $\Delta J = \Delta K$. The intensity of satellite branches is always small compared to that of the main branches as long as case (b) applies.

Selection rules holding only in case (c). In case (c), besides the general selection rules (see above), we have

$$\Delta\Omega = 0, \pm 1. \qquad (V, 39)$$

Therefore we have transitions of the same kind as those given in Table 24 if we replace Λ by the quantum number Ω. Also, analogous to (V, 33), we have the rule $0^+ \leftrightarrow 0^-$. Furthermore, as in case (a), if both states have $\Omega = 0$, $\Delta J = 0$ is forbidden.

More general cases. The special selection rules thus far mentioned hold, as we have said, only if *both* participating states belong to one coupling case. However, if, for example, the one state belongs to case (a) and the other to case (b), all these special selection rules no longer hold and there remain only the selection rules holding for both coupling cases. It can therefore be seen that the number of transitions in such cases is very much greater.

As a result of the spin uncoupling usually present, it often happens that both states approach case (b), at least for large rotations. Then the special selection rules for case (b) hold as well as the general selection rules, at least for large rotation. Also it not infrequently happens that both electronic states belong to case (a) for small rotation and to case (b) for large rotation (see below).

(b) Allowed Electronic Transitions

In *designating a given electronic transition*, the upper state is always written first and then the lower. $^1\Pi - {}^1\Sigma$ thus means a transition for which the upper state is $^1\Pi$ and the lower $^1\Sigma$; $^1\Sigma - {}^1\Pi$ means a transition for which $^1\Sigma$ is the upper state and $^1\Pi$ is the lower state.[7]   Sometimes an arrow is used to indicate whether the transition under consideration is observed in emission or absorption: $^1\Pi \to {}^1\Sigma$ means a transition from $^1\Pi$ to $^1\Sigma$ in emission, and $^1\Pi \leftarrow {}^1\Sigma$ indicates a transition in absorption from the lower $^1\Sigma$ state to the upper $^1\Pi$ state.   Naturally, the validity of a selection rule is independent of which state is the upper and which is the lower.   This independence is indicated in the foregoing by a double arrow $\leftrightarrow$; for example, $\Pi \leftrightarrow \Sigma^+$ in Table 24 means that $\Pi - \Sigma^+$, as well as $\Sigma^+ - \Pi$, is possible.

If several electronic states of a molecule are known, some of which may be of the same type, they are distinguished by a letter $X, A, B, \cdots, a, b, \cdots$, in front of the term symbol or by one or more asterisks added to it.   Thus we describe transitions by symbols such as $A\,^1\Pi - X\,^1\Sigma$ or $B\,^1\Sigma - X\,^1\Sigma$ or $\Pi^{**} - \Sigma^*$ and so on. X is frequently used for the ground state of the molecule in question.   Instead of this brief characterization of the various electronic states of the molecule also the complete electronic configurations are used (see Chapter VI).   The following discussion of the various types of electronic transitions is, of course, independent of these additional symbols.

$^1\Sigma - {}^1\Sigma$ transitions.   For singlet transitions, there is no object in distinguishing between cases (a) and (b).   They can therefore be treated equally well according to the one or the other case.   If we adopt case (b), in addition to the general rules (V, 28–31 and 33), we have, for $^1\Sigma - {}^1\Sigma$, the special rule (V, 38) : $\Delta K = 0$ is forbidden, or, since here $J = K$, $\Delta J = 0$ is forbidden.   Thus only the transitions with $\Delta J = \Delta K = \pm 1$ appear, and we obtain the band structure already treated in detail in the foregoing chapter— namely, *a single P and a single R branch* (see Figs. 19, 24,

---

[7] This nomenclature is the converse of that for atomic spectra.   This difference is connected with the fact that for atoms the energies of the quantum states are usually negative, since they are given relative to the ionized state, whereas for molecules they are positive, since they are given relative to the lowest state.

and 52)—which is fairly often observed experimentally. In Fig. 109(a) the branches are represented in a manner somewhat different from that in which they were previously. It can be seen that the selection rule $+ \leftrightarrow -$ is fulfilled for both branches. Fig. 109(a) holds for a $^1\Sigma^+ - {}^1\Sigma^+$ transition. For a $^1\Sigma^- - {}^1\Sigma^-$ transition, $+$ and $-$ must be everywhere interchanged; this interchange, however, does not alter the transitions appearing. It is therefore not possible to decide from the spectrum alone which of the two cases is the actual one.

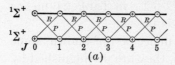

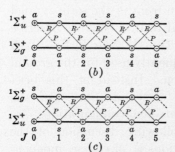

Fig. 109. $^1\Sigma - {}^1\Sigma$ Transitions. (a) $^1\Sigma^+ - {}^1\Sigma^+$. (b) $^1\Sigma_u^+ - {}^1\Sigma_g^+$. (c) $^1\Sigma_g^+ - {}^1\Sigma_u^+$. The values of J given refer to the upper as well as the lower state. In diagrams (b) and (c), the transitions corresponding to the antisymmetrical levels are indicated by broken lines.

Examples of $^1\Sigma - {}^1\Sigma$ transitions are the previously discussed BeO bands (602) and the CuH bands (290), of which Fig. 19 gives a spectrogram.

For *like nuclei*, the even-odd symmetry has to be considered. Therefore only the transitions $^1\Sigma_u^+ - {}^1\Sigma_g^+$, $^1\Sigma_g^+ - {}^1\Sigma_u^+$, $^1\Sigma_u^- - {}^1\Sigma_g^-$, and $^1\Sigma_g^- - {}^1\Sigma_u^-$ are possible. The first two of these are represented in Fig. 109(b) and (c). In all four cases the transitions with $\Delta K = \Delta J = \pm 1$ are in agreement with the rule $+ \leftrightarrow -$ as well as with the rule sym. $\leftrightarrow$ antisym. The origin of the intensity alternation has already been explained by Fig. 89. The alternation is indicated in Fig. 109(b) and (c) by full and broken lines. If $+$ and $-$ are everywhere interchanged, Fig. 109(b) represents a $^1\Sigma_g^- - {}^1\Sigma_u^-$ transition and Fig. 109(c) a $^1\Sigma_u^- - {}^1\Sigma_g^-$ transition.

It can be seen from Fig. 89 that the strong lines of the P branch form the continuation of the series of the weak lines rather than the strong lines of the R branch. Thus, if alternate lines are entirely missing (nuclear spin $I = 0$), the P

and R branches (unlike the behavior for molecules with unequal nuclei) do not appear to form a single series—that is, if we take no account of the missing lines. This is an unambiguous criterion of whether or not alternate lines are missing in a band.

Examples of $^1\Sigma_u{}^+ - {}^1\Sigma_g{}^+$ transitions are the longest-wavelength absorption band systems of the alkali vapors [for Li_2 see (64); for Na_2 see (233)], the ultraviolet P_2 bands [see (311) and (69)], and a number of band systems of H_2 [see (47)] and He_2 [see (33)], which also exhibit examples of $^1\Sigma_g{}^+ - {}^1\Sigma_u{}^+$ transitions. $^1\Sigma^- - {}^1\Sigma^-$ transitions have not yet been observed.

In Chapter III it was shown that for a given homonuclear molecule (even when it is ionized) either always the symmetric or always the antisymmetric levels have the greater statistical weight, depending on whether the nuclei follow Bose statistics or Fermi statistics. Thus, according to Fig. 109(*b*) and (*c*), for one and the same molecule $^1\Sigma_u{}^+ - {}^1\Sigma_g{}^+$ is distinguished from $^1\Sigma_g{}^+ - {}^1\Sigma_u{}^+$ by the fact that for the one the even-numbered (or odd-numbered) rotational lines are the more intense and for the other the odd (or even) are the more intense. Therefore, if the statistics of the nuclei is known, we can decide between the two transitions mentioned on the basis of the observed alternation of intensities or, conversely, can draw conclusions concerning the *nuclear statistics* if the type of the electronic states is known. However, we cannot decide between $^1\Sigma_u{}^+ - {}^1\Sigma_g{}^+$ and $^1\Sigma_g{}^- - {}^1\Sigma_u{}^-$ in this way, nor between $^1\Sigma_g{}^+ - {}^1\Sigma_u{}^+$ and $^1\Sigma_u{}^- - {}^1\Sigma_g{}^-$.

For H_2, for example, it is found theoretically (see Chapter VI) that the ground state is $^1\Sigma_g{}^+$. It is observed that, in the $^1\Sigma_u{}^+ - {}^1\Sigma_g{}^+$ bands that have the ground state of the molecule as lower state, the odd-numbered rotational lines—that is, those corresponding to the antisymmetric levels—are the stronger. From this it follows that the H *nuclei (protons) follow Fermi statistics*. For D_2 the intensity alternation is just the opposite; therefore the D *nuclei (deuterons) follow Bose statistics* [compare also the discussion in Chapter III, section 2(f)].

$^2\Sigma - {}^2\Sigma$ **transitions.** $^2\Sigma$ states always belong strictly to case (*b*), and therefore for $^2\Sigma - {}^2\Sigma$ transitions $\Delta K = \pm 1$ always holds ($\Delta K = 0$ is forbidden). The separation of the two sublevels with $J = K + \frac{1}{2}$ and $J = K - \frac{1}{2}$ for a given K is, in general, very small compared to the separation of successive rotational levels. Therefore, with not too great resolution, we have exactly the same band structure as for $^1\Sigma - {}^1\Sigma$ bands, as Fig. 110 shows, except that the lines are now numbered by K instead of J. There is a P and an R branch, for which exactly the same formulae hold as previously (see Chapter IV, section 3). Because of this fact we were able to use the violet CN bands, which represent a $^2\Sigma - {}^2\Sigma$ transition, as an example of the simplest type of band in Chapter II.

However, with larger resolution, as we can also see from Fig. 110, each "line" of the P and R branches, according to the rule $\Delta J = 0, \pm 1$, is split into three components. For one of these—namely, that with $\Delta J = 0$—ΔJ is unequal to ΔK. Therefore, according to the previous discussion (p. 268), the intensity of these components falls off very rapidly

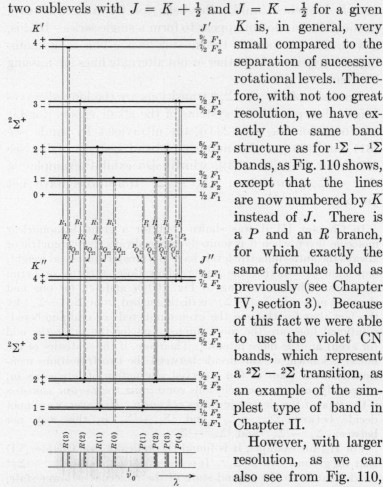

Fig. 110. Energy Level Diagram for the First Lines of a $^2\Sigma^+ - {}^2\Sigma^+$ Band, with Schematic Spectrum. The numbers in brackets behind P and R in the schematic spectrum at the bottom give the K'' values. The full designation of the branches (see below) is written on the vertical lines representing the transitions. The doublet splitting has been much exaggerated.

with increasing K. For this reason they are indicated by broken lines in Fig. 110. Thus, in practice, except for very small K, a splitting of each of the lines (single for small dispersion) into two components of about equal intensity and a separation increasing with increasing K is to be expected (full lines in Fig. 110). In other words there is a *doublet P* and a *doublet R branch*.

Such bands occur for many molecules. The best-known *example* is provided by the violet CN bands, one of which is shown in the spectrogram, Fig. 18. The splitting into doublets is just noticeable in the spectrogram for the largest K values. Also the violet SiN (372) and CP (77) bands and a large number of hydride bands are of this type.

The two branches indicated by broken lines in Fig. 110 have $\Delta J = 0$ and are thus to be called Q branches. However, as may be seen from the figure, the lines lie close to the other two lines with equal K and ΔK (they form satellite branches). These Q *branches* therefore have the *form of an R or a P branch* and not that of a Q branch whose Fortrat parabola would have its vertex on the ν axis. Such branches are consequently called *R-form Q branches* or *P-form Q branches* [abbreviated ${}^R Q$, ${}^P Q$ branches; see Mulliken (515)].

If we again distinguish the term components having $J = K + \frac{1}{2}$ by the subscript 1 and those having $J = K - \frac{1}{2}$ by the subscript 2 (see p. 246), we obtain for the four *main branches*

$$R_1(K) = F_1'(K + 1) - F_1''(K), \qquad \text{(V, 40)}$$

$$R_2(K) = F_2'(K + 1) - F_2''(K), \qquad \text{(V, 41)}$$

$$P_1(K) = F_1'(K - 1) - F_1''(K), \qquad \text{(V, 42)}$$

and

$$P_2(K) = F_2'(K - 1) - F_2''(K), \qquad \text{(V, 43)}$$

and correspondingly for the two *satellite branches*

$${}^R Q_{21}(K) = F_2'(K + 1) - F_1''(K), \qquad \text{(V, 44)}$$

and

$${}^P Q_{12}(K) = F_1'(K - 1) - F_2''(K). \qquad \text{(V, 45)}$$

The subscript 21 or 12 of ${}^R Q$ or ${}^P Q$ is to indicate that the transition takes place from a term of the series F_2 to one of the series F_1, or vice versa.

It appears from (V, 40–43) and also from Fig. 110 that the *combination differences* (IV, 32 and 33) must be formed either between R_1 and P_1 or between R_2 and P_2. Therefore, for example, for different bands with the same lower state, the values of $R_1(K-1) - P_1(K+1)$ [and, correspondingly, $R_2(K-1) - P_2(K+1)$] must agree exactly even if perturbations are present. On the other hand, $R_1(K-1) - P_1(K+1)$ is only approximately equal to $R_2(K-1) - P_2(K+1)$. If perturbations are present, this relation need not hold at all.

According to (V, 16) and (V, 40–43), the *line splitting* in the P and R branches is

$$\Delta\nu_{12}(P) = P_1 - P_2 = (\gamma' - \gamma'')K - \tfrac{1}{2}(\gamma' + \gamma''),$$
$$\Delta\nu_{12}(R) = R_1 - R_2 = (\gamma' - \gamma'')K + \tfrac{1}{2}(3\gamma' - \gamma''). \qquad \text{(V, 46)}$$

Thus the splitting of the lines in the branches increases linearly with K (as does the splitting of the terms), the magnitude of the splitting depending essentially on the difference of the splitting factors in the upper and lower states. This difference can be derived very accurately from the observed splitting of the branches even if, as is usually the case, these values are very small and, as a result, the doublets are not resolved for very small K values. In this case, the splitting in the P and in the R branches for equal K

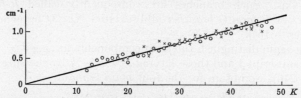

Fig. 111. Doublet Splitting in the P and R Branches of the 3–0 Band of the Violet CP System $(^2\Sigma - {}^2\Sigma)$. The small circles refer to the P branch, and the crosses refer to the R branch.

is practically the same. Fig. 111 gives as an example the splitting in the 3–0 band of the $^2\Sigma - {}^2\Sigma$ system of CP in its dependence on K. It can be seen that the linear relations (V, 46) are well fulfilled. From the slope of the straight line we obtain $\gamma_3' - \gamma_0'' = 0.0263$ cm^{-1}.

From (V, 16) follows for the $\Delta_2 F$ values (again disregarding terms with D_v)

$$\Delta_2 F_1(K) = 4B_v(K+\tfrac{1}{2}) + \gamma, \quad \Delta_2 F_2(K) = 4B_v(K+\tfrac{1}{2}) - \gamma, \qquad \text{(V, 47)}$$

which means that the $\Delta_2 F$ curves for the two components of a $^2\Sigma$ state form parallel lines whose vertical separation is 2γ. In

principle, the values of γ for the upper and lower states can therefore be separately derived from the observed $\Delta_2 F$ values. In
practice, however, the magnitude of γ is often smaller than the
accuracy of the $\Delta_2 F$ values. In the above example of CP (Fig.
111), from the mean of the differences of corresponding $\Delta_2 F$
values, $2\gamma_0'' = -0.034$ is obtained for the lower state, while the
accuracy of the individual $\Delta_2 F$ values is only ± 0.05 cm^{-1}. The
rotational constant B_0'' is 0.796 cm^{-1}. Thus we see that γ represents only a small correction term.

At any rate, it can be seen from (V, 47) that, if there is no
perturbation, the value of B_v for a $^2\Sigma$ state, and consequently the
moment of inertia and internuclear distance, can be derived without a knowledge of γ if we simply use the mean value of $\Delta_2 F_1$ and
$\Delta_2 F_2$. For this,

$$\tfrac{1}{2} [\Delta_2 F_1(K) + \Delta_2 F_2(K)] = 4B_v(K + \tfrac{1}{2}) + \cdots, \quad (V, 48)$$

from which the constant B_v can be obtained as described on p. 194 f.

The symmetry properties for $^2\Sigma - {}^2\Sigma$ transitions of *homonuclear molecules* are quite analogous to those for $^1\Sigma - {}^1\Sigma$
transitions if we replace J by K in the previous discussion,
since states with equal K have the same symmetry properties
(see Fig. 107, p. 261). Thus now the two components of the
doublets are alternately both strong and both weak; either
the lines with even-numbered K are strong and those with
odd K are weak, or vice versa.[8] Thus also for homonuclear
molecules, a $^2\Sigma - {}^2\Sigma$ band under small dispersion has the
same appearance as a $^1\Sigma - {}^1\Sigma$ band.

Thus far the sole example of $^2\Sigma - {}^2\Sigma$ bands for homonuclear molecules is afforded by the so-called negative
nitrogen bands (N_2^+). Fig 26 shows one of these bands
under small dispersion (no resolution of the doublets). The
intensity alternation is clearly to be seen.

$^3\Sigma - {}^3\Sigma$ **transitions.** $^3\Sigma - {}^3\Sigma$ transitions are entirely
analogous to $^2\Sigma - {}^2\Sigma$ transitions. With small dispersion
the bands consist of a single P and a single R branch, as do
$^1\Sigma - {}^1\Sigma$ bands. With larger dispersion, each "line" is

---

[8] By determining which case occurs, we can again decide whether the lower
state is $^2\Sigma_g^+$ or $^2\Sigma_u^+$.

resolved into three approximately equally intense components. Thus there are in all *six main branches*. Apart from that, *six very weak satellite branches*, for which $\Delta J \neq \Delta K$, appear. We shall not go into the structure of these bands in detail. It may only be remarked that, unlike the case of $^2\Sigma - {}^2\Sigma$ transitions, for $^3\Sigma - {}^3\Sigma$ the splitting of the lines is not simply a linear function of K (see p. 246).

The only $^3\Sigma - {}^3\Sigma$ bands thus far known for unlike nuclei are the SO bands [Martin (482)].

For *identical nuclei*, $^3\Sigma - {}^3\Sigma$ transitions behave in a manner similar to $^2\Sigma - {}^2\Sigma$ transitions. The intensity alternation is again determined by K. The best-known example of a $^3\Sigma - {}^3\Sigma$ transition for identical nuclei is the ultraviolet absorption band system of O_2 (Schumann-Runge bands), for which every alternate triplet in the P and R branches is missing, since the nuclear spin of the oxygen atom is zero [see Mulliken (510), and Lochte-Holtgreven and Dieke (449)].

Since in these O_2 bands the even-numbered rotational lines are missing and since the O nucleus follows Bose statistics, the lower state—that is, the ground state of the O_2 molecule—must be a $^3\Sigma_g{}^-$ or a $^3\Sigma_u{}^+$ state. The electron configuration (see Chapter VI) shows that it can only be a $^3\Sigma_g{}^-$ state (see Fig. 172, p. 474).

Thus far, $\Sigma - \Sigma$ transitions of still higher multiplicities have not been observed. According to what has been said, it would be easy to predict their structure.

$^1\Pi - {}^1\Sigma$ **transitions.** For a $^1\Pi - {}^1\Sigma$ transition the distinction between case (a) and case (b) is again pointless. According to what has been said on p. 263 f., transitions with $\Delta J = 0$ as well as $\Delta J = \pm 1$ are now possible and we obtain (according to the discussion in Chapter IV) *one P, one Q, and one R branch*. As long as the Λ-type doubling of the $^1\Pi$ state can be neglected, the band structure is given exactly by formulae (IV, 21–26). It must be remembered that, in a $^1\Pi$ state, according to (V, 13) the smallest J value is $J = 1$. As a result, the lines $P(1)$ and $Q(0)$ do not occur (see Fig. 74).

If we take account of the Λ-*type doubling*, we might at first think that each line of the three branches P, Q, and R

would split into two components. However, this has never been observed. The reason for this becomes clear when we remember the selection rule (V, 29): $+ \leftrightarrow -$. It then follows immediately from Fig. 112(a) that only simple branches are to be expected; in the upper state one of the two components of a Λ-type doublet is $+$ and the other is $-$, and therefore a given lower state can combine only with the one or the other, according as the lower state is $-$ or $+$. Thus

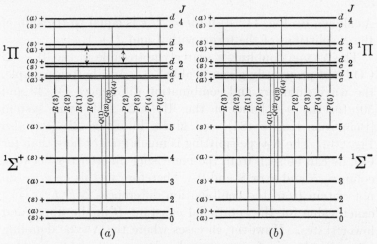

Fig. 112. Energy Level Diagram for the First Lines of (a) a $^1\Pi - {}^1\Sigma^+$ Transition and (b) a $^1\Pi - {}^1\Sigma^-$ Transition. For the sake of clarity, the Λ-type doubling in the $^1\Pi$ state has been greatly exaggerated. The broken arrow to the left in (a) gives $R(2) - Q(2)$, and the one to the right gives $Q(3) - P(3)$. Their difference gives the sum of the Λ doublings for $J = 2$ and $J = 3$ in the upper state. The designations s and a, added in parentheses, hold for a $^1\Pi_u - {}^1\Sigma_g$ transition for identical nuclei.

line doublets do not appear. In the kind of Λ-type doubling assumed in Fig. 112, the lines of the Q branch always have the *lower* Λ component as upper state, whereas the lines of the P and R branches have the *upper* Λ component as upper state. If the Λ-type doubling were such that the order of $+$ and $-$ in the $^1\Pi$ state was reversed, the lines of the Q branch would start from the upper component and those of the P and R branches would start from the lower component.

Thus, since the lines of the P and R branches always have a somewhat different upper state from the lines of the Q branch, it follows that the combination relations (IV, 47 and 48) no longer hold exactly. A so-called *combination defect* occurs—that is to say,

$$R(J) - Q(J) = Q(J+1) - P(J+1) + \varepsilon \approx \Delta_1 F'(J), \quad (V, 49)$$

and

$$R(J) - Q(J+1) = Q(J) - P(J+1) + \varepsilon \approx \Delta_1 F''(J). \quad (V, 50)$$

As shown by Fig. 112(a) for $J = 2$, ε is equal to the sum of the Λ splittings of the terms with J and $J + 1$.

The Λ-type doubling is scarcely noticeable in the $^1\Pi - {}^1\Sigma$ CO band previously given (Table 22). As a better example, the wave numbers and combination differences (V, 49 and 50) for the 0–0 band of the $^1\Pi - {}^1\Sigma$ AlH band system [Bengtsson-Knave (84)] are given in Table 25 (see also Fig. 20). The Λ-type splitting is much greater here than for CO, as can be seen from the increasing difference ε between columns 5 and 6 or 8 and 9. Therefore in this case we do not obtain from the combination differences $\Delta_1 F(J)$ a very exact value for the rotational constant B in the upper and lower states. However, in cases where the Λ-type doubling is small (that is, for most molecules except the hydrides), the error in B is not very great. For an exact determination of the B values, the $\Delta_2 F$ values given by (IV, 32–34) must be used.

It can be seen from Fig. 112(a) that the $\Delta_1 F''$ values for different bands with the same lower state need not agree exactly, since the Λ-type doubling in the different upper states may be of different magnitude, whereas the $\Delta_2 F''$ values must always agree exactly, even if perturbations are present.

We can now also understand the fact (see p. 229 f.) that the resonance series corresponding to absorption bands with P, Q, and R branches ($^1\Pi - {}^1\Sigma$) do not consist of triplets but only singlets or doublets, depending on whether excitation is by a Q line or a P or R line. Since, as shown above, the

TABLE 25

WAVE NUMBERS OF THE LINES AND COMBINATION DEFECTS IN THE AlH BAND 4241 Å

[0–0 band of the $^1\Pi$–$^1\Sigma$ system according to Bengtsson-Knave (84)]

J	R(J)	Q(J)	P(J)	R(J)−Q(J)	Q(J+1)−P(J+1)	ε	R(J)−Q(J+1)	Q(J)−P(J+1)
0	23,483.54	....	....	.....	.....	.....	13.34	25.14
1	494.36	23,470.20	....	24.16	24.01	0.15	25.29	37.65
2	505.18	469.07	23,445.06	36.11	35.91	0.20	37.85	50.24
3	515.46	467.33	431.42	48.13	47.87	0.26	50.50	62.65
4	525.09	464.96	417.09	60.13	59.72	0.41	63.06	75.02
5	534.00	462.03	402.31	71.97	71.37	0.60	75.62	87.14
6	542.20	458.38	387.01	83.82	82.82	1.00	88.14	99.64
7	549.59	454.06	371.24	95.53	94.46	1.07	100.71	111.73
8	556.03	448.88	354.42	107.15	105.83	1.32	113.05	123.78
9	561.55	442.98	337.15	118.57	116.93	1.64	125.42	135.80
10	566.10	436.13	319.20	129.97	128.03	1.94	138.74	147.68
11	569.51	428.36	300.33	141.15	138.87	2.28	149.96	159.46
12	571.55	419.55	280.68	152.00	149.42	2.58	162.04	171.10
13	572.39	409.51	260.09	162.88	159.92	2.96	174.06	182.60
14	571.55	398.33	238.41	173.22	169.89	3.33	185.93	193.91
15	569.00	385.62	215.73	183.38	179.52	3.86	197.77	205.06
16	564.58	371.23	191.71	193.35	189.08	4.27	209.33	216.24
17	557.97	355.25	166.17	202.72	198.14	4.58	220.82	
18	548.80	537.15	139.01	211.65	....	.....	232.27	
19	....	316.53						

upper state of a Q line is different from that of the P and R lines with the same upper J value, for excitation by a Q line only Q lines can appear in fluorescence; that is, we have a singlet resonance series, whereas for excitation by a P or R line both P and R lines but no Q lines appear in fluorescence (doublet resonance series).[9]

While, as for $^1\Sigma - {}^1\Sigma$ transitions, the $\Delta_2 F''$ values yield directly the *rotational constants* B'' and D'' of the *lower* ($^1\Sigma$) state, only the effective B' and D' of the one component of the *upper* state, designated by d, are obtained from $\Delta_2 F_d' = R(J) - P(J)$ [see Fig. 112(a)]. The effective B' and D' values of the other component of the upper state, designated by c, can be obtained only with the help of the Q branch—for example, by using the method described on p. 205 for obtaining $B' - B''$ from the Q branch (assuming the previously determined B''), or from

$$\Delta_2 F_c'(J) = Q(J+1) - Q(J-1) + R(J-1) - P(J+1), \quad (V, 51)$$

a relation that may be easily verified by referring to Fig. 112(a).

In equations (V, 49 and 50), ε is the sum of the splittings of two successive levels. The splitting of one level is very nearly one half of this. Therefore, according to (V, 23 and 24), we have

$$\tfrac{1}{2}\varepsilon = (B_v^d - B_v^c)J(J+1) = qJ(J+1). \quad (V, 52)$$

The $\varepsilon/2$ values derived from Table 25 are represented graphically in Fig. 113. It can be seen that the quadratic dependence on J (solid

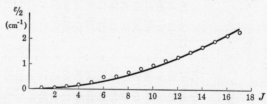

Fig. 113. Λ-Type Doubling in the $^1\Pi$ State of AlH. The points are observed (see Table 25). The curve corresponds to a quadratic increase of the splitting.

curve) is well fulfilled. The value of the Λ-type doubling constant q obtained is $q = 0.0080$ cm^{-1}. The value of B_v is the mean of B_v^c and B_v^d (see p. 251 f.); in the present case $B_0 = 6.020$ cm^{-1}.

[9] On the other hand, for a $^1\Sigma - {}^1\Pi$ transition (see below) triplet resonance series would indeed occur by excitation with a line of any one of the three branches; but such a case has not yet been observed.

Fig. 112(a) holds for a $^1\Pi - {}^1\Sigma^+$ transition. A $^1\Pi - {}^1\Sigma^-$ transition, represented in Fig. 112(b), is completely analogous except that the upper states of the P and the R branches on the one hand, and of the Q branch on the other, are interchanged, since in the lower state $+$ and $-$ are interchanged.

Since initially we do not know the order of $+$ and $-$ in the $^1\Pi$ state, we cannot decide whether we are dealing with $^1\Pi - {}^1\Sigma^+$ or $^1\Pi - {}^1\Sigma^-$ from a single band system alone (without knowledge of the electronic structure of the molecule). However, if two different $^1\Sigma$ states combine with one and the same $^1\Pi$ state, we can decide from the band structure alone whether the two $^1\Sigma$ states have like or unlike symmetry, as may be readily seen by comparing Fig. 112(a) and (b). Therefore, if the symmetry (Σ^+ or Σ^-) of the one state can be determined on the basis of electronic structure (see Chapter VI), that of the other can also be determined. At the same time we obtain the order $+$ $-$ or $-$ $+$ for the Λ components of the $^1\Pi$ state. Multiplet Π and Σ states can be treated in a similar manner.

The *intensity distribution* in the three branches of $^1\Pi - {}^1\Sigma$ bands is given by Fig. 88(a) (see the discussion, p. 227).

Examples of $^1\Pi - {}^1\Sigma^+$ transitions (other than the CO and AlH bands already mentioned) are the BH bands [(451), (667), and (63)], the red and infrared bands of BeO (320), and the PN bands (see Chapter IV). Thus far an example of a $^1\Pi - {}^1\Sigma^-$ transition is not known with certainty. (For further details see the authors cited.)

For *homonuclear molecules* every second line in the branches is weak or missing, as for $^1\Sigma - {}^1\Sigma$ transitions. This can be seen immediately from Fig. 112, in which the symbols s and a, which would apply to a $^1\Pi_u - {}^1\Sigma_g^+$ and a $^1\Pi_u - {}^1\Sigma_g^-$ transition, respectively, have been added in parentheses. The intensity alternation would be just the opposite for $^1\Pi_g - {}^1\Sigma_u$ transitions.

Examples of $^1\Pi_u - {}^1\Sigma_g^+$ transitions are the Werner bands of H_2, which appear both in emission and absorption (380), several other band systems of H_2 (47), the Lyman-Birge-Hopfield bands of N_2 (697), and the blue-green absorption systems of Li_2 (282) and Na_2 (467). A number of $^1\Pi_g - {}^1\Sigma_u^+$

transitions are observed for He₂ [see Weizel (33)]. Thus far $^1\Pi - {}^1\Sigma^-$ transitions have not been found for homonuclear molecules.

$^1\Sigma - {}^1\Pi$ **transitions.** The rotational structure of a $^1\Sigma - {}^1\Pi$ transition is of exactly the same type as that of a $^1\Pi - {}^1\Sigma$ transition. Three branches, P, Q, and R, appear. As examples, a $^1\Sigma_g^+ - {}^1\Pi_u$ and a $^1\Sigma_g^- - {}^1\Pi_u$ transition are represented schematically in Fig. 114, the intensity alterna-

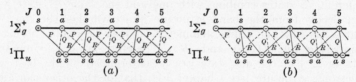

Fig. 114. $^1\Sigma - {}^1\Pi$ **Transitions.** (a) $^1\Sigma_g^+ - {}^1\Pi_u$. (b) $^1\Sigma_g^- - {}^1\Pi_u$. The broken-line transitions correspond to the antisymmetric levels.

tion being indicated by broken and full lines. For unequal nuclei the distinction between s and a and broken and full lines in the figure has to be disregarded. For $^1\Sigma_u - {}^1\Pi_g$, s and a have everywhere to be interchanged.

The *main difference between $^1\Pi - {}^1\Sigma$ and $^1\Sigma - {}^1\Pi$ transitions* is that for the former the lines $P(1)$ and $Q(0)$ are missing, whereas, for the latter, $R(0)$ and $Q(0)$ are missing (see Figs. 112 and 114). Apart from that, there is a difference in the intensity distribution [see, for example, Jevons (34)]; for small J values, for $^1\Pi - {}^1\Sigma$ the R branch is more intense than the P branch, and for $^1\Sigma - {}^1\Pi$ the P branch is the more intense, independent of whether the transition is observed in absorption or emission (see p. 133 f.). Therefore, for an observed transition with single P, Q, and R branches, we can decide whether $^1\Pi$ or $^1\Sigma$ is the lower state from the band structure alone only if the region in the neighborhood of the zero line is resolved and it can be decided which of the two lines, $R(0)$ and $P(1)$, is missing or which of the branches P and R is the more intense for the first J values. Only if other band systems of the same molecule (or analogous systems of an analogous molecule) are observed is a distinction possible without resolution of the region in the neighborhood of the zero line.

The best-known example of a $^1\Sigma^+ - \,^1\Pi$ transition is to be found in the Ångström bands of CO in the visible region [(165) and (619)] (see Fig. 11). Another example is the AlH band at 4752 Å (85). For like nuclei such transitions have been observed only for H_2 (47) and He_2 (33). A $^1\Sigma^- - \,^1\Pi$ transition has been found for AlH by Holst (326).

$^2\Pi - \,^2\Sigma$ **transitions.** Whereas a $^2\Sigma$ state always belongs to case (b), a $^2\Pi$ state can belong either to case (a) or to case (b) or to cases intermediate between (a) and (b).

We shall consider first those $^2\Pi - \,^2\Sigma$ transitions for which the $^2\Pi$ *state belongs to case* (b). It is clear that, if the doublet separation in both states is so small that the doublet components cannot be separated in the spectrogram, exactly the same band structure will be obtained as for a $^1\Pi - \,^1\Sigma$ transition—that is, one P, one Q, and one R branch, the Q branch being the most intense. For somewhat greater doublet splitting *each line of the three branches is split into two components* (similar to the fine structure of $^2\Sigma - \,^2\Sigma$ transitions). This is illustrated by Fig. 115 (solid lines). The levels in the upper and lower states can be numbered by the quantum number K, for which the selection rule (V, 37) holds. The three doublet branches correspond to the three ΔK values, $+1$, 0, and -1. These branches are designated R_1, R_2, Q_1, Q_2, P_1, and P_2 in the way indicated in Fig. 115.

In addition to these main branches there are also four *satellite branches* (broken lines in Fig. 115), for which $\Delta J \neq \Delta K$, and whose intensity decreases very rapidly with increasing K (see p. 268). Their designation as $^RQ_{21}$, $^QR_{12}$, $^QP_{21}$, and $^PQ_{12}$ will be clear from what was previously said for $^2\Sigma - \,^2\Sigma$ transitions. They have the same form as the six main branches, and, for a small doublet splitting of the $^2\Sigma$ state, their lines lie very close to the corresponding lines of the main branches. These satellite branches are very seldom observed in case (b).

As for $^1\Pi - \,^1\Sigma$ transitions, the Λ-*type doubling* produces no additional doubling of the lines for $^2\Pi - \,^2\Sigma$ bands, but only a combination defect (difference between the upper states of the main Q branches and those of the main R and P branches). As may easily be verified from Fig. 115, relations quite similar to (V, 49 and 50) hold individually for the branches distinguished by the subscript 1 and for those distinguished by the subscript 2.

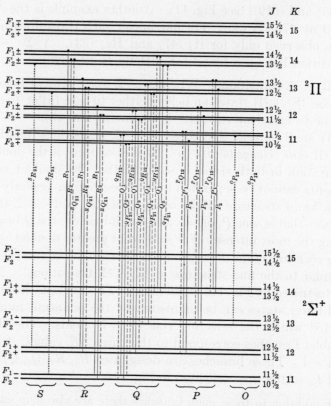

Fig. 115.   Energy Level Diagram for a $^2\Pi(b) - {}^2\Sigma^+$ **Band.** The levels are drawn only for medium K values (11 to 15), since, in general, case (a) is approached for small K values.   A number of consecutive lines are drawn for each branch. In the upper state, two levels occur for each J and K value, owing to the Λ-type doubling. Often in the upper state, the order of F_1 and F_2 is opposite to that drawn. The broken-line branches are satellite branches; the dotted branches (with $\Delta K = -2$) do not appear in a strict case (b).   The last dotted vertical line to the right should go to the lower of the two levels with $K = 12$, $J = 12\frac{1}{2}$ (not $J = 11\frac{1}{2}$).

If the $^2\Pi$ *state belongs to case* (a) (large separation between $^2\Pi_{\frac{1}{2}}$ and $^2\Pi_{\frac{3}{2}}$), the selection rule $\Delta K = 0, \pm 1$ no longer applies and all transitions in accord with the selection rules $\Delta J = 0$, ± 1, and $+ \leftrightarrow -$ are possible and appear with comparable intensities. We can now divide each of the bands of a $^2\Pi - {}^2\Sigma$ transition into *two sub-bands* $^2\Pi_{\frac{1}{2}} - {}^2\Sigma$ and $^2\Pi_{\frac{3}{2}} - {}^2\Sigma$, which are separated from each other by the amount of the doublet splitting of the $^2\Pi$ state. Correspondingly, for each band, there are *two zero lines* whose separation is approximately constant for different bands of a band system.

In Fig. 116, a $^2\Pi(a) - {}^2\Sigma^+$ transition is illustrated by means of an energy level diagram. In this diagram the splitting of the $^2\Pi$ state had to be drawn on a smaller scale than the separation of the rotational levels. It is seen from the figure that for each sub-band six branches are possible, making *twelve branches* in all.

In by far the most actual cases the $^2\Pi$ state belongs neither strictly to case (a) nor strictly to case (b), but usually to a *transition case* which approximates case (a) for small rotation, while for large rotation a transition to case (b) gradually takes place. This transition takes place at J values that are the lower the smaller is the doublet splitting in the rotationless state (see p. 256). In Fig. 117(a), (b), and (c), three typical cases of $^2\Pi - {}^2\Sigma$ bands are represented by Fortrat diagrams. Fig. 117(a) represents the band 4400 Å of CdH, for which the doublet splitting is so great that the approximation to case (a) is very good. Correspondingly, all twelve branches (six in each sub-band) are observed. Fig. 117(b) gives a MgH band which approaches the opposite limiting case [case (b)] very closely. Only the six above-mentioned branches, which draw together pair-wise with increasing J, are observed. Finally, Fig. 117(c) gives an intermediate case, a red CN band (see the spectrogram Fig. 23), for which the doublet splitting in the $^2\Pi$ state, without rotation, has an intermediate value. Since in this case the doublet splitting in the $^2\Sigma$ state is fairly small, the branches P_1 and Q_{12}, Q_1 and R_{12}, P_{21} and Q_2, and Q_{21} and R_2 fall pair-wise so close together that they are not resolved. Therefore each sub-band shows only four branches, of which two form heads, as can be seen from the diagram. Thus these bands have *four heads*, as shown by the spectrogram Fig. 23.[10] These inter-

---

[10] Sometimes, however, particularly if B' and B'' are very different from each other, only the shortest- or longest-wave-length head is prominent.

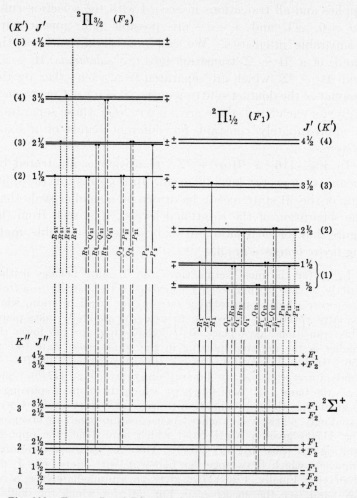

Fig. 116. Energy Level Diagram for the First Lines of a $^2\Pi(a) - {}^2\Sigma^+$ Band. In actuality the spin-doublet splitting in the upper state is often much larger than that drawn, while, on the other hand, the spin-doublet splitting in the lower state and the Λ-doublet splitting in the upper state is in general much smaller. If the $^2\Pi$ state belongs strictly to case (a), the dotted and broken-line transitions are of the same intensity as the full-line transitions; however, in going over to case (b), they change over into the satellite branches given there.

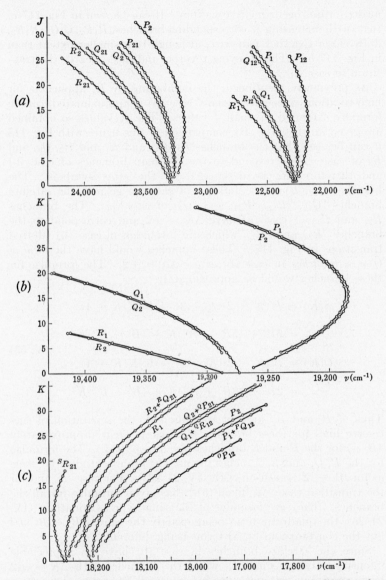

Fig. 117.   Fortrat Diagrams of Typical $^2\Pi - {}^2\Sigma$ Bands. (a) CdH band at 4400 Å. (b) MgH band at 5203 Å. (c) CN band at 5473 Å (see Fig. 23). The ordinate is J or K, respectively, and not m, as in previous Fortrat diagrams.

mediate cases occur relatively often. It can be seen in Fig. 117(c) that, with increasing J, corresponding branches, P_1P_2, Q_1Q_2, R_1R_2, draw closer together pair-wise, although to a smaller extent than in Fig. 117(b). This drawing together indicates clearly the transition to case (b).

As previously mentioned, the numbering by K, applicable for high rotation [since then usually case (b) is approximated] can be formally extended to small J values. The K values so obtained are given in Fig. 116. By comparison of this figure with Fig. 115 it can be seen that the branches P_1, Q_1, and R_1 and P_2, Q_2, and R_2 of case (a) correspond to the six main branches of case (b) and therefore can be designated by the same symbols. The branches Q_{12}, R_{12}, P_{21}, and Q_{21} of case (a) go into the satellite branches $^PQ_{12}$, $^QR_{12}$, $^QP_{21}$, and $^RQ_{21}$ of case (b). The branches R_{21} and P_{12} of case (a) have $\Delta K = \pm 2$ and correspond to the branches $^SR_{21}$ and $^OP_{12}$, which are forbidden in case (b) (dotted transitions in Fig. 115). These branches would have the *form of O or S branches* in case (b), since $\Delta K = \pm 2$. The formulae for these branches would be approximately

$$S(K) = B'(K + 2)(K + 3) - B''K(K + 1)$$

$$= 6B' + (5B' - B'')K + (B' - B'')K^2,$$

$$\text{(V, 53)}$$

$$O(K) = B'(K - 2)(K - 1) - B''K(K + 1)$$

$$= 2B' - (3B' + B'')K + (B' - B'')K^2.$$

Thus, if B' and B'' are not too different, the separation of successive lines for these branches is twice as great (approximately $4B$) as for the P and R branches (see also p. 95 f.). The formulae for the P, Q, and R branches in case (b) are essentially the same as for $^1\Pi - {}^1\Sigma$ transitions [see (IV, 24–26)]. For case (a) and for the transition cases Mulliken (513) has given formulae for all the branches. They are formulae of the same type as equations (IV, 24–26), the quadratic term being exactly the same $[(B' - B'')J^2]$ but the constant and linear terms being different.

Since the satellite branches in case (b) have an appreciable intensity only for small K, while the branches with $\Delta K = \pm 2$ have zero intensity, and since in almost all $^2\Pi$ states, at least for large rotation, a transition to case (b) takes place, it follows that in $^2\Pi - {}^2\Sigma$ transitions for large rotation only the six main branches will appear with appreciable intensity. Accordingly, Fig. 117(c) shows that the branches $^SR_{21}$ and $^OP_{12}$ in the CN band are observed only for low K values. Further details concerning intensities in the individual branches are given by Earls (197).

In the *analysis* of $^2\Pi - {}^2\Sigma$ bands each individual sub-band is dealt with in the manner previously described for singlet bands (see p. 191 f.). For large J, the three most intense branches of one sub-band are the branches P_1, Q_1, and R_1 and of the other P_2, Q_2, and R_2, whose correct numbering and identification can be tested by combination relations similar to (IV, 47 and 48). The $\Delta_2 F''$ values and from them the rotational constants of the lower state ($^2\Sigma$) are obtained from (see Fig. 116)

$$\Delta_2 F_1''(K) = R_1(K-1) - P_1(K+1),$$
$$\Delta_2 F_2''(K) = R_2(K-1) - P_2(K+1). \tag{V, 54}$$

As explained above for $^2\Sigma - {}^2\Sigma$ transitions, $\Delta_2 F_1''$ and $\Delta_2 F_2''$ differ in general only by a small constant amount, 2γ. From the mean of the $\Delta_2 F''$ values very accurate B and D values for the lower state may be obtained.

There is an excellent *check* if the *satellite branches* are also observed. From Fig. 116 it can be seen that the following must hold:

$$R_1(K-1) - P_1(K+1) = R_{21}(K-1) - P_{21}(K+1),$$
$$R_2(K-1) - P_2(K+1) = R_{12}(K-1) - P_{12}(K+1). \tag{V, 55}$$

These combination relations hold exactly, even allowing for Λ-type doubling.

Furthermore, if the satellite branches are observed, the *doublet splitting* for each rotational level of the lower state can be determined quite independent of any assumption about its variation—in fact, from four different combinations, namely, according to Fig. 116,

$$F_1''(K) - F_2''(K) = R_{12}(K) - Q_1(K) = Q_{12}(K) - P_1(K)$$
$$= R_2(K) - Q_{21}(K) = Q_2(K) - P_{21}(K). \tag{V, 56}$$

From these individual doublet separations the spin-coupling constant γ is obtained according to (V, 16).

For the *upper* state we have to evaluate

$$\Delta_2 F_i'(K) = R_i(K) - P_i(K). \tag{V, 57}$$

From these combination differences, as for $^1\Pi - {}^1\Sigma$ transitions, we again obtain the effective B and D values for only one Λ component of $^2\Pi_{\frac{1}{2}}$ and $^2\Pi_{\frac{3}{2}}$, respectively. The effective B and D values for the other Λ component can be obtained in a manner corresponding to that indicated above for $^1\Pi - {}^1\Sigma$; the magnitude of the Λ-type doubling can be obtained similarly.

Which of the two components of the upper state is $^2\Pi_{\frac{1}{2}}$ and which is $^2\Pi_{\frac{3}{2}}$—that is, whether the $^2\Pi$ term found is *normal* or *inverted*—can be decided in two different ways. First, it can be decided from the magnitude of the Λ-type doubling (that is, from the combination defect) in the two sub-bands; according to p. 252, for $^2\Pi_{\frac{3}{2}}$ the Λ doubling is considerably smaller than for $^2\Pi_{\frac{1}{2}}$, at least for small J values [case (a)]. Second, it can be decided from the fact that the missing lines in the neighborhood of the zero gap are different for the two sub-bands, as may be seen from Fig. 116.

The magnitude of the spin-doublet splitting in the $^2\Pi$ state can also be derived from the observed branches. Suitable combinations for this purpose may be read from Figs. 115 and 116. Details concerning the analysis of $^2\Pi - {}^2\Sigma$ bands are given, for example, by Almy and Horsfall (63).

Examples of $^2\Pi - {}^2\Sigma$ transitions, apart from those already mentioned, are the α bands of BO (373), for which the upper state is an inverted term. Further transitions of this type are observed for the alkaline-earth hydrides [BeH (541), MgH (277), CaH (342a), SrH (694a), and BaH (233b and 239), as well as ZnH (652), CdH (658), and HgH (353)]. These have normal $^2\Pi$ states. Mulliken (513) gives a full discussion of the fine structure of $^2\Pi - {}^2\Sigma$ bands as well as of the intensity distribution.

Figs. 115 and 116 are drawn for the case $^2\Pi - {}^2\Sigma^+$. Naturally, $^2\Pi - {}^2\Sigma^-$ transitions are quite analogous, but with a corresponding alteration of the $+-$ symmetry (see above for $^1\Pi - {}^1\Sigma^-$). Thus far, examples of $^2\Pi - {}^2\Sigma^-$ transitions are not known.

For *like nuclei*, $^2\Pi - {}^2\Sigma$ transitions could occur only for ionized molecules. However, they have not been observed thus far. In each sub-band they would show an intensity alternation like the $^1\Pi - {}^1\Sigma$ transitions.

$^2\Sigma - {}^2\Pi$ **transitions.** For $^2\Sigma - {}^2\Pi$ transitions exactly the same branches appear as for $^2\Pi - {}^2\Sigma$. As before, for medium doublet splitting of the $^2\Pi$ state, each band has four characteristic heads. The only differences are that the relative intensity of the branches is somewhat different and that, at the beginning of the branches, other lines are missing. The reader can easily derive the latter on the basis of the energy level diagram.

Examples of $^2\Sigma - {}^2\Pi$ transitions are the ultraviolet OH bands (661), the HCl$^+$ bands (536), the NO γ bands (618), and the Baldet-Johnson bands of CO$^+$ (142) [see Fig. 11(a)]. These are all $^2\Sigma^+ - {}^2\Pi$ transitions. Two examples of $^2\Sigma^- - {}^2\Pi$ transitions are known—namely, the CH band at 3900 Å [see Mulliken (513)] and an MgH band at 4400 Å [Guntsch (277)].

$^3\Pi - {}^3\Sigma$ **and** $^3\Sigma - {}^3\Pi$ **transitions.** In the general case—that is, if the $^3\Pi$ state approaches case (a)—these transitions are still more complicated than the $^2\Pi(a) - {}^2\Sigma$ transitions. Each component of the $^3\Sigma$ term can combine with each component of the $^3\Pi$ term, every combination giving rise to one P, one Q, and one R branch. Therefore, in this general case there are $3 \times 3 \times 3 = 27$ *branches*. All 27 branches for such a transition were first found and analyzed by Pearse (557) in the PH band at 3400 Å. The well-known first positive group of N$_2$ (see Fig. 8, p. 31) forms a further example of such a structure [Naudé (528)].

If the $^3\Pi$ state approaches case (b), many of the 27 branches disappear or are very weak. There are then only *nine main branches*, a P, a Q, and an R branch for each of the three triplet components, since in this case all the branches with $\Delta J \neq \Delta K$ have a vanishingly small intensity (see p. 268). An example of this is the NH band at 3300 Å [Funke (240)].

We cannot go into any details about the structure of these bands here. Apart from the references already given, the reader is referred to the papers of Dieke and Mauchley (190), Budó [(139) and (141)], Challacombe and Almy (152), and Gilbert (260), where also details may be found concerning the determination of the rotational constants and the multiplet splittings.

$\Pi \leftrightarrow \Sigma$ **transitions of higher multiplicities.** The only observed case of $\Pi \leftrightarrow \Sigma$ transitions of a multiplicity higher than 3 is a $^4\Sigma - {}^4\Pi$ transition of O$_2{}^+$, the so-called first negative bands of oxygen. Nevin (530) has identified in each of three of these bands 40 of the 48 possible branches and has determined the rotational constants. A theoretical discussion of the structure of $^4\Sigma - {}^4\Pi$ transitions is given by Budó (140).

$^1\Pi - {}^1\Pi$ **transitions.** Ignoring Λ-type doubling, a $^1\Pi - {}^1\Pi$ transition has a P, a Q, and an R branch like a $^1\Pi - {}^1\Sigma$ transition; but here the Q branch is weak and decreases rapidly in intensity with increasing J, since $\Delta\Lambda = 0$ (see

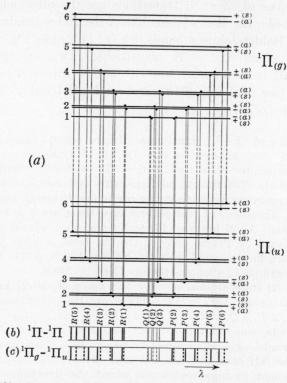

Fig. 118. **Energy Level Diagram for the First Lines of a $^1\Pi - {}^1\Pi$ Transition.** The Λ-type doubling of the levels, as well as of the lines, is much exaggerated. The B values in the upper and lower states are taken as equal. Consequently the spacing of the lines in the Q branch could not be drawn to scale. The schematic spectrogram (c) refers to the case of identical nuclei, the lines corresponding to the antisymmetrical levels being broken.

p. 267). If we take account of the Λ-type doubling, each line splits into two components, as Fig. 118 shows (this is different from a $^1\Pi - {}^1\Sigma$ transition, where no line splitting is produced by the Λ-type doubling of the levels; see Fig. 112). The reason that, for a given $J' - J''$ combination, only two lines result and not four, lies in the selection rule $+ \leftrightarrow -$, as can be seen immediately from Fig. 118. A $^1\Pi - {}^1\Pi$ band thus has *six branches*, of which the two Q branches are very weak.

As can be seen from Fig. 118, the *first lines* of the branches are $P(2)$, $Q(1)$, and $R(1)$. Thus in the series (IV, 27), formed by the P and R branches, three lines are missing (see lower part of Fig. 118), and not just one line, as for $\Sigma - \Sigma$ transitions.

If the region of the zero line and the head is not resolved and only the P and R branches are observed at large J values, a $^1\Pi - {}^1\Pi$ band has the same appearance, for a superficial examination, as a $^2\Sigma - {}^2\Sigma$ band. However, in a $^2\Sigma - {}^2\Sigma$ transition, the splitting of the lines increases linearly with K (see p. 274), whereas, in a $^1\Pi - {}^1\Pi$ transition, in general it increases *quadratically* with J, since the Λ-type doubling of each $^1\Pi$ state increases quadratically with J (see p. 251). Thus, in this way we can distinguish between the two types of transitions if it is not already clear, from a knowledge of the carrier of the band system or from other reasons, whether we are dealing with a doublet or a singlet transition.

The sole example of a $^1\Pi - {}^1\Pi$ transition thus far known for unlike nuclei is the AlH band at 3380 Å [Holst (325)].

In calculating the rotational constants, lines having the same component of the Λ-type doublet as upper or lower state, respectively, have to be used to form separately the $\Delta_2 F$ values for the one or the other Λ component of the two $^1\Pi$ states. In this way the effective B and D values of the two components of the two states are obtained (B^c, B^d, D^c, D^d). Their means give a very good approximation to the true B and D, respectively (see p. 251 f.).

The magnitude of the splitting of the line components is equal to the sum or difference of the Λ-type doublet separations of the upper and lower states (see Fig. 118). Therefore, since the Q branches are in general not observed to sufficiently high J values, the magnitude of the Λ-type doubling for the individual levels cannot be determined directly from the line splittings. However, an approximate value can be obtained from the effective B values according to (V, 23 and 24).

For *homonuclear molecules*, $^1\Pi_u$ can combine only with $^1\Pi_g$. In Fig. 118(a) the designation s and a, which would correspond to a $^1\Pi_g - {}^1\Pi_u$ transition, is added in brackets (for $^1\Pi_u - {}^1\Pi_g$ s and a would have to be exchanged everywhere). In the schematic spectrogram in Fig. 118(c) the lines corresponding to the antisymmetric levels are indicated by broken lines. It can be seen that, as a result of the different statistical weights of the s and a levels, here again strong and weak levels alternate in a given branch. However, now there are always two branches, with opposite intensity alternation, lying close together. Consequently, if the Λ-type doublets are not resolved, a resultant branch with no apparent intensity alternation appears. When the nuclear spin is zero, every second line is missing in each individual branch [broken lines in Fig. 118(c)]. However, even then, as may be seen from the figure, for a casual inspection only a single branch without any missing lines would appear to be present. But the figure shows that then the even-numbered lines are displaced to one side and the odd-numbered lines to the other side of a mean position. This effect is called *"staggering."* This staggering is also to be expected to a smaller degree if no lines are missing but only an intensity alternation is present and the Λ-type doublets are unresolved, since an unresolved doublet, consisting of a strong and a weak line, will appear to be shifted toward the side of the stronger line.

The only example thus far known of $^1\Pi - {}^1\Pi$ transitions for molecules with identical nuclei is the C_2 band system discovered by Deslandres and d'Azambuja in the violet and near ultraviolet and analyzed by Dieke and Lochte-Holtgreven (189) and Kopfermann and Schweitzer (418). It is a $^1\Pi_g - {}^1\Pi_u$ transition [see Fig. 118(c)]. The staggering is clearly observed in the fine structure of the individual bands.

$^2\Pi - {}^2\Pi$ **transitions.** When *both* $^2\Pi$ *states* of a $^2\Pi - {}^2\Pi$ transition belong to *case* (a), the selection rule $\Delta\Sigma = 0$ holds (see p. 265). As a result, a $^2\Pi - {}^2\Pi$ band splits into *two sub-bands*, $^2\Pi_{\frac{1}{2}} - {}^2\Pi_{\frac{1}{2}}$ and $^2\Pi_{\frac{3}{2}} - {}^2\Pi_{\frac{3}{2}}$. As Fig. 119(a) shows

in detail, each sub-band has a structure similar to that of a
$^1\Pi - {}^1\Pi$ transition; that is, each sub-band has six branches,
which form three close pairs, two P, two Q, and two R
branches, the two Q branches being very weak. Thus a

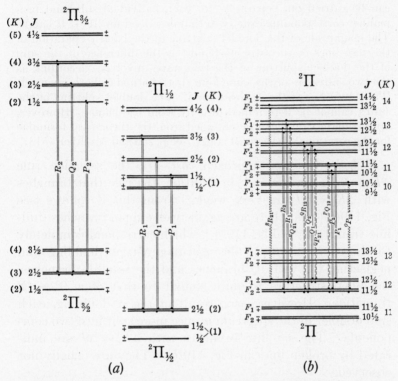

Fig. 119. Energy Level Diagram Explaining the Fine Structure of a
$^2\Pi - {}^2\Pi$ Band. (a) In Hund's case (a) $[{}^2\Pi(a) - {}^2\Pi(a)]$. (b) In Hund's case
(b) $[{}^2\Pi(b) - {}^2\Pi(b)]$. Only one line of each branch is given. The designations
of the branches are given only for each pair of Λ-doublet components together.
The dotted branches in (b) do not appear when both $^2\Pi$ states belong strictly
to Hund's case (b).

$^2\Pi(a) - {}^2\Pi(a)$ band has twelve branches in all. Since the
Λ-type doubling is always small and since the Q branches
are very weak, each sub-band has only one head and thus
each band has two heads. The separation of the two heads
is approximately constant for all the bands of a system.

The two sub-bands differ in the number of missing lines at the beginning of the branches and in the magnitude of the Λ-type doubling, which is appreciably greater for $^2\Pi_{\frac{1}{2}}$ than for $^2\Pi_{\frac{3}{2}}$. Owing to this difference we can decide which sub-band is $^2\Pi_{\frac{1}{2}} - {}^2\Pi_{\frac{1}{2}}$ and which is $^2\Pi_{\frac{3}{2}} - {}^2\Pi_{\frac{3}{2}}$. The determination of the rotational constants can be carried out separately for each individual sub-band in a manner corresponding exactly to that described for $^1\Pi - {}^1\Pi$ bands. The magnitude of the doublet splitting of the band (separation of the zero lines of the two sub-bands) is the difference or the sum of the doublet splitting of the two states involved, according as the two states are of the same kind (both normal or both inverted) [Fig. 119(a)] or of the opposite kind. The doublet splitting of the states cannot be determined directly from the bands. However, approximate values can be obtained from the theoretical formulae for the rotational levels in $^2\Pi$ states [see p. 256 and Mulliken (513)].

If *both* $^2\Pi$ *states* approach *case* (b), the selection rule $\Delta K = 0, \pm 1$ holds and, in addition, the rule that branches with $\Delta K \neq \Delta J$ are very weak. From this it follows [see Fig. 119(b)] that there are again twelve main branches [full-line transitions in Fig. 119(b)], which correspond completely to those of case (a). Disregarding Λ-type doubling and neglecting the weak Q branches and the satellite branches, the band structure is quite similar to that of a $^2\Sigma - {}^2\Sigma$ transition. However, as a result of the Λ doubling, each spin doublet in the spectrum is once more split into two components. The satellite branches with $\Delta K \neq \Delta J$ are indicated by broken lines in Fig. 119(b). They are usually not observed.

It may happen that, in both $^2\Pi$ states, *case* (a) holds *for small J* and *case* (b) holds *for large J*. Then, as may easily be verified by a comparison of Figs. 119(a) and (b), the twelve branches of case (a), present for small J, change over into the twelve main branches of case (b) for large J. For large J there are characteristic doublet branches (disregarding Λ-type doubling) which separate from each other with decreasing rotation.

For *homonuclear molecules* the intensity alternation in each of the two sub-bands is entirely analogous to that of a $^1\Pi - {}^1\Pi$ transition.

Thus far, four *examples* of $^2\Pi - ^2\Pi$ transitions have been investigated in detail—namely, bands of NO, MgH, SiF, and O_2^+, the latter corresponding to a $^2\Pi_u - ^2\Pi_g$ transition. In the MgH bands [Guntsch (275)], both $^2\Pi$ terms approach case (b) very closely, while the above-mentioned intermediate case occurs for the NO bands [Jenkins, Barton, and Mulliken (369)]. Most probably, case (a) applies to both participating states of the PO and NS bands corresponding to those of NO, but their fine structure has not yet been investigated.

If one $^2\Pi$ state approaches case (a) and the other approaches case (b), neither the rule $\Delta\Sigma = 0$ nor the rule $\Delta K = 0, \pm 1$ holds. The satellite branches with $\Delta K \neq \Delta J$ [drawn with broken lines in Fig. 119(b)], as well as the branches with $\Delta K = \pm 2$ (drawn with dotted lines), appear with appreciable intensity. In all there are twenty-four branches, as Fig. 119(b) shows, which always lie in pairs (Λ-type doubling), the eight Q branches being very weak. The ultraviolet O_2^+ bands [Stevens (653) and v. Bozóky (123)] and the α bands of SiF [Eyster (210)] furnish examples of such a case. As can be seen from Fig. 119(b), the spin-doublet splitting of the lower and upper states can be calculated directly from the branches in such a case. For details, the references given above should be consulted.

$^3\Pi - ^3\Pi$ **transitions.** For a $^3\Pi - ^3\Pi$ transition, everything is quite analogous to a $^2\Pi - ^2\Pi$ transition except that, if both $^3\Pi$ states belong to case (a), there are *three sub-bands* instead of two—namely, $^3\Pi_0 - ^3\Pi_0$, $^3\Pi_1 - ^3\Pi_1$, and $^3\Pi_2 - ^3\Pi_2$. Therefore each band has three heads and consists of three R and three P branches if we disregard the Λ-type doubling and the weak Q branches.[11] The same holds if both terms belong to case (b) or change uniformly from case (a) to case (b) with increasing rotation. In the latter case, for large K, there is a triplet P branch and a triplet R branch (disregarding Λ-type doubling). These branches are very clearly seen in the spectrogram of the N_2 band in Fig. 22, which represents such a transition. It can be seen

---

[11] The $^3\Pi_0 - ^3\Pi_0$ sub-band has no Q branch (see p. 267).

further that the triplets separate from one another with decreasing K, finally forming three separate heads. Fig. 120 shows how the six branches originate.

The N_2 band is an example of a $^3\Pi_u - {}^3\Pi_g$ *transition*

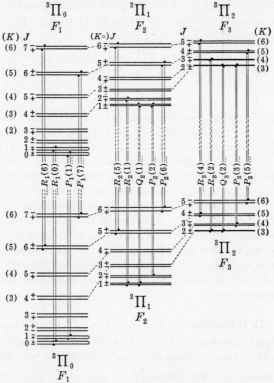

Fig. 120. Energy Level Diagram Explaining the Fine Structure of a $^3\Pi - {}^3\Pi$ Transition. For the upper as well as the lower state a very rapid transition from case (a) to case (b) is assumed. The Λ-type doubling is greatly exaggerated. The first line of every branch, as well as one line with a larger J value, is drawn except for the Q branches, which are not observed for higher J values. It is seen how for larger J the triplet R and triplet P branches arise. For a molecule with identical nuclei, in the upper state all the positive levels are symmetric and the negative antisymmetric ($^3\Pi_g$), and in the lower state the negative levels are symmetric and the positive antisymmetric ($^3\Pi_u$) or the converse is true ($^3\Pi_u - {}^3\Pi_g$). The K values are not given for the lowest levels, since they are not defined in case (a). Of course, formally it is possible to continue the K values from the higher levels to the lower, but the K values thus obtained do not always correspond to the true K values that one would obtain if a transition to case (b) were actually carried out. For example, strictly speaking, the three lowest levels of $^3\Pi_0$ belong to $K = 1$.

(identical nuclei). An intensity alternation cannot be noticed in Fig. 22, since the Λ-type doublets are not resolved (compare the behavior of $^1\Pi - {}^1\Pi$). With somewhat greater resolution, this splitting, and at the same time the intensity alternation, has been found in each individual branch [(344), (446), and (167)]. The first lines of the weak Q branches have also been observed [Guntsch (274)].

The Swan bands of C_2 (see Fig. 7) and a system of ultra-violet C_2 bands form $^3\Pi_g - {}^3\Pi_u$ transitions with a structure quite similar to the N_2 bands [(390), (635), (139), and (227)], except that even for large dispersion there is no intensity alternation but only a "staggering," owing to the zero nuclear spin of carbon (see the discussion for $^1\Pi - {}^1\Pi$).

For unlike nuclei $^3\Pi - {}^3\Pi$ transitions have been observed and analyzed for TiO [Christy (155)] and ZrO [Lowater (471)].

The theoretical intensity distribution in $^3\Pi - {}^3\Pi$ bands has been calculated by Budó (141).

In evaluating the rotational constants, first of all the combination differences $\Delta_2 F(J)$ for the upper and lower states are separately determined for the three sub-bands and then the B and D values are determined from the mean of the $\Delta_2 F(J)$ values [see Budó (139)].

$\Pi \leftrightarrow \Delta$ transitions. For $^1\Pi \leftrightarrow {}^1\Delta$ *transitions* we obtain exactly the same *six branches* as for $^1\Pi - {}^1\Pi$ transitions (Fig. 118). It is therefore unnecessary to reproduce a special energy level diagram. The only differences are that now the two Q branches are very intense ($\Delta\Lambda \neq 0$; see p. 227) and that more lines are missing near the zero gap. As may easily be seen, the first lines are $P(2)$, $Q(2)$, and $R(2)$ for $^1\Pi - {}^1\Delta$ and $P(3)$, $Q(2)$, and $R(1)$ for $^1\Delta - {}^1\Pi$.

The spectrogram of the NH band at 3240 Å, reproduced in Fig. 21, represents a $^1\Pi - {}^1\Delta$ transition [see Pearse (558) and Dieke and Blue (187)]. The six branches, which form three close pairs, not resolved for small J, can be clearly seen. Furthermore it can be seen that the lines $P(1)$, $R(0)$, $R(1)$, $Q(0)$, and $Q(1)$ are indeed missing. Further bands of this kind have been observed for H_2 and He_2 [see Richardson (47) and Weizel (33)].

$^2\Pi \longleftrightarrow {}^2\Delta$, $^3\Pi \longleftrightarrow {}^3\Delta$, $\cdots$ transitions are analogous to $^2\Pi - {}^2\Pi$, $^3\Pi - {}^3\Pi$, $\cdots$ transitions, except that now the Q branches are very intense. As long as both states belong to the same coupling case, there are twelve intense main branches for $^2\Pi \longleftrightarrow {}^2\Delta$ and eighteen intense main branches for $^3\Pi \longleftrightarrow {}^3\Delta$ which fall closely together in pairs (Λ-type doubling). In the most general case—that is, if both terms belong to different coupling cases—there are twenty-four branches for $^2\Pi \longleftrightarrow {}^2\Delta$ and fifty-four branches for $^3\Pi \longleftrightarrow {}^3\Delta$.

Examples of a $^2\Delta - {}^2\Pi$ transition are the CH band at 4315 Å (513) and the corresponding SiH band (593). Examples of $^3\Delta \longleftrightarrow {}^3\Pi$ transitions have not yet been investigated.

$\Delta - \Delta$ transitions. $^1\Delta - {}^1\Delta$ transitions resemble $^1\Pi - {}^1\Pi$ transitions in all details, with the exception that one more line is missing at the beginning of each of the branches and that the Λ-type doubling is much smaller. Up to the present time such transitions have not been observed with certainty.

Similarly, $^2\Delta - {}^2\Delta$ and $^3\Delta - {}^3\Delta$ transitions resemble $^2\Pi - {}^2\Pi$ and $^3\Pi - {}^3\Pi$ transitions, respectively, except for the missing lines and the Λ-type doubling. Gaydon and Pearse (245) have found one component, $^2\Delta_{\frac{5}{2}} - {}^2\Delta_{\frac{5}{2}}$, of a $^2\Delta - {}^2\Delta$ transition in the spectrum of NiH [see also A. Heimer (288)]. Mahanti (477) has tentatively identified the VO bands occurring in an electric arc containing vanadium as a $^2\Delta - {}^2\Delta$ transition. $^3\Delta - {}^3\Delta$ transitions have not yet been found experimentally.

Band structures in cases (c) and (d). Thus far, in our discussion of different band types, it has always been assumed that the participating electronic states belong to case (a) or case (b) or a case intermediate between them. Since *case* (c) may be regarded as a case (a) with extremely large multiplet splitting, the band structures in case (c) are quite similar to those in case (a), with only the difference that S and Σ are no longer "good" quantum numbers and, as a result, the selection rules $\Delta S = 0$ and $\Delta \Sigma = 0$ no longer apply. The electronic states combine according to the selection rule $\Delta \Omega = 0, \pm 1$. The structure of a band with given Ω' and Ω'' is then of exactly the same type as that of the above-described singlet bands: Transitions with $\Delta \Omega = 0$ and $\Omega \neq 0$ have a structure similar to that of a $^1\Pi - {}^1\Pi$ transition; with $\Delta \Omega = 0$ and $\Omega = 0$ similar to that of a $^1\Sigma - {}^1\Sigma$ transition; with $\Delta \Omega = \pm 1$ similar to that of $^1\Pi - {}^1\Sigma$ or $^1\Delta - {}^1\Pi$ transitions, respectively, according as one $\Omega = 0$ or not. Σ states always belong to case (b), even when all the other states of the molecule under consideration belong to case (c).

An important example is afforded by the visible absorption bands of the halogens, which have the appearance of $^1\Sigma - ^1\Sigma$ transitions, but for which in actuality the upper state is a $^3\Pi_{0^+}$ component of a $^3\Pi$ term with extremely large splitting [see Mulliken (516)]. Therefore they may also be designated $0^+ - 0^+$ transitions.

In *case* (d) the band structure is similar to that for $\Sigma - \Sigma$ transitions, each line being split into a number of components, corresponding to the coupling of L and R. A pure case (d) is, however, quite rare. On the other hand, transition cases from (a) or (b) to (d) are relatively frequent. In these cases the band structure is quite complicated. Since such structures occur in practice only for the higher excited states of H_2 and He_2, we shall not attempt a full discussion here. Extended discussions are to be found in Weizel (33).

General remarks on the technique of the analysis of multiplet bands. It is not always easy to decide to which of the types discussed above the bands of an empirically observed band system belong. The first step in the analysis is always the picking out of branches in the manner previously described (see p. 209). The number (and kind) of branches found gives in itself a good indication of the band type, but we must naturally allow for the fact that possibly some of the branches may have eluded observation. The most probable is chosen from among the various possible band types, and then an attempt must be made to find the numbering of the lines in the branches by calculation of the combination differences in the manner previously described. If the combination differences and the variation of the splitting of the levels obtained from the line splittings (if such splittings occur) agree in all details with those to be expected theoretically on the basis of the assumed band type, then the bands examined must actually belong to this type, and the kind of electronic states participating is thereby established. The rotational constants for the two electronic states can then be determined in the manner indicated above for the individual band types. If deviations from the theoretical expectations occur, the other possible band types must be tried out.

If, for example, we observe a band system whose bands at some distance from the band head are resolved into two doublet branches which run parallel to each other and whose splitting increases with increasing rotation, we may have a $^2\Sigma - ^2\Sigma$ or a $^1\Pi - ^1\Pi$ transition if we assume that the Q branches are too weak to be observed for the $^1\Pi - ^1\Pi$ transition. Which of the two cases we actually have can be decided by following the variation of the doublet splitting in the branches. If it increases linearly with an arbitrary running number, we have a $^2\Sigma - ^2\Sigma$ transition; if it increases quadratically, we have a $^1\Pi - ^1\Pi$ transition.

An investigation of the multiplet structure is necessary if we wish to determine the moment of inertia and internuclear distance of a diatomic molecule and also, as we shall see in Chapter VII, if we wish to determine the heat of dissociation of a molecule. However, just these quantities are of the greatest importance in the applications of band spectra. The material available in this field is already quite plentiful; however, considering the number of possible diatomic molecules and their possible electronic states, it is still very scanty.

(c) Forbidden Electronic Transitions

Apart from the transitions treated in the foregoing subsection, under certain conditions transitions also appear that contradict the selection rules discussed in subsection (a). They are called *"forbidden" transitions*. They can be observed in absorption by using extremely thick layers (considerably thicker than are necessary for the ordinarily allowed transitions). In emission they appear only under quite special conditions of excitation. In addition to the weak occurrence of whole band systems in violation of some electronic selection rule, also certain branches that are forbidden by the ordinary selection rules may appear very weakly in the bands of an otherwise nonforbidden band system. In what follows we shall discuss only the first type of forbidden transitions.

The appearance of forbidden transitions may have one of the three following reasons (see also A.A., p. 154):

1. The selection rule that is violated may be true *only to a first approximation*.

2. The selection rule may hold strictly for dipole radiation but not for *quadrupole radiation* or *magnetic dipole radiation*.

3. The selection rule may hold only for the completely free and uninfluenced molecule and may be violated in the presence of external fields, collisions with other molecules, and the like (*enforced dipole radiation*).

Violation of approximate selection rules.   The first case occurs for the selection rule $\Delta S = 0$, which holds less and less strictly with increasing atomic number.   Actually, *singlet-triplet intercombinations* have been observed even for such a relatively light molecule as CO.   In this example, we have a $^3\Pi - {}^1\Sigma$ transition (Cameron bands), which can be observed by use of an absorbing layer of 1 m or more at atmospheric pressure, whereas a fraction of a millimeter suffices as absorption path for the corresponding allowed $^1\Pi - {}^1\Sigma$ transition [see Hopfield and Birge (332) and Gerö, Herzberg, and Schmid (252)].   Similar intercombinations have also been observed for N_2 [Vegard (684) and Kaplan (396)], the Ga and In halides [Miescher and Wehrli (495) and (701)], and the halogen molecules [Mulliken (516)].   For the heavier molecules they represent fairly intense absorption and emission bands [transition to coupling case (c)].   For the theoretical intensity distribution in $^3\Pi \leftrightarrow {}^1\Sigma$ bands, see Budó (141).

Another example is the violation of the selection rule that $\Delta K = 0$ is forbidden for $\Sigma - \Sigma$ transitions.   For all diatomic molecules this rule holds to a very good approximation but not absolutely rigorously.   However, for ordinary $\Sigma - \Sigma$ transitions ($\Sigma^+ - \Sigma^+$ and $\Sigma^- - \Sigma^-$) the $+ \leftrightarrow -$ rule (V, 29) leads to the same result as the above selection rule, and therefore transitions violating it are rigorously forbidden for dipole radiation.   But, for $\Sigma^+ - \Sigma^-$, transitions with $\Delta K = 0$ (and similarly $\Delta K = \pm 2$) are just the ones allowed by the $+ \leftrightarrow -$ rule (see Fig. 107).   Now the rule $\Sigma^+ \leftrightarrow\!\!\!\!/ \,\Sigma^-$ holds only in a certain approximation (it is rigorous only if the molecule does not rotate) and therefore the *forbidden $\Sigma^+ - \Sigma^-$ transitions* may occur very weakly with $\Delta K = 0$ (and, if $S \neq 0$, also with $\Delta K = \pm 2$).   A system of very weak absorption bands of O_2 in the near ultraviolet is such a forbidden transition—namely, $^3\Sigma_u^+ \leftarrow {}^3\Sigma_g^-$ [(310) and (569)].

Quadrupole and magnetic dipole radiation.   For quadrupole as well as magnetic dipole radiation, with reference to the $+ -$ symmetry, the following selection rule holds [see Van Vleck (681)]:

$$+ \leftrightarrow +, \quad - \leftrightarrow -, \quad - \leftrightarrow\!\!\!\!/ \, +, \qquad \text{(V, 58)}$$

which is just the opposite of (V, 29).   For J the same selection rule (V, 28) holds for magnetic dipole radiation as for electric dipole radiation, whereas for quadrupole radiation

$$\Delta J = 0, \pm 1, \pm 2$$
$$(J = 0 \leftrightarrow J = 0, \quad J = \tfrac{1}{2} \leftrightarrow J = \tfrac{1}{2}, \quad J = 1 \leftrightarrow J = 0). \tag{V, 59}$$

Thus far, forbidden transitions of this kind have not been found for heteronuclear molecules; however, they have been found for homonuclear molecules. For these, of course, the rule *sym.* ↔ *antisym.* remains unaltered. Therefore, according to (V, 58), as can be seen from Fig. 107(*b*), only the transitions *g–g* and *u–u* can appear as magnetic dipole or quadrupole radiation, whereas the transitions *g–u*, which are the allowed transitions for ordinary dipole radiation, cannot occur.

The best-known and most important example is furnished by the *atmospheric oxygen bands* that appear in the red solar spectrum and form a $^1\Sigma_g^+ - {}^3\Sigma_g^-$ transition [Mulliken (510) and (514)]. Since here the whole atmosphere acts as an absorbing layer, the

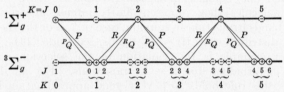

Fig. 121. Origin of the Branches of the Red Atmospheric Oxygen Bands ($^1\Sigma_g^+ - {}^3\Sigma_g^-$). The levels indicated by broken circles do not occur for O_2. The actual order of the triplet components in the lower state for low K values is not that given. Actually the levels with $J = K \pm 1$ lie close together and below $J = K$.

bands appear with great intensity in the solar spectrum, in spite of the fact that they are "forbidden." As can be seen from the spectrogram in Fig. 73, the bands consist of two *R*-form branches and two *P*-form branches. The origin of these branches is explained by Fig. 121. Since the nuclear spin of oxygen is 0, only the symmetric levels, which are here the positive, occur in both states and therefore (V, 58) is *ipso facto* fulfilled. It is seen that just four branches of the observed type (two of them being *Q* branches but of *R* and *P* form, respectively) are obtained if the selection rule $\Delta J = 0, \pm 1$ is assumed. No transitions with $\Delta J = \pm 2$ are found. Therefore [see (V, 59)] it follows that we have a case of magnetic dipole radiation and not quadrupole radiation [Van Vleck (681)]. A more detailed calculation shows that the absolute intensity of the bands is in agreement with this conclusion.[12]   Quadrupole radiation would be about one thousand times weaker than magnetic dipole radiation.[13]

Another forbidden transition, also involving magnetic dipole radiation, has been observed for oxygen—namely, an atmospheric oxygen band appearing in the infrared at 1.27 μ and representing a $^1\Delta_g - {}^3\Sigma_g^-$ transition [Ellis and Kneser (203), Herzberg (312), and Van Vleck (681)].

As has been mentioned before, rotation-vibration spectra of homonuclear molecules (rigorously forbidden as ordinary dipole radiation) may occur as quadrupole radiation.   Although they are not electronic transitions, the above selection rules hold for them. It can be seen immediately from these selection rules and from Fig. 107 that transitions with $\Delta J = 0$ and ± 2 (Q, S, and O branches) are possible between two vibrational levels of a given Σ_g or Σ_u state.   However, in consequence of their extremely small intensity, such transitions have thus far not been observed [see (315)].

Enforced dipole radiation.   Thus far, only a few examples of enforced dipole radiation are known, and they have not been explained in detail.   It is once more the oxygen molecule that shows several such transitions at high pressure and in the liquid state.   Since these transitions do not occur at small pressures and correspondingly great thicknesses, their occurrence at high pressures can only be explained as being due to the close approach of the molecules to one another.   We shall not go into details here, but only refer to the papers (202), (612), and (219).

Condon (161) has discussed theoretically the possibility of the occurrence of rotation-vibration spectra of homonuclear molecules due to the presence of an external electric field.

---

[12] The intensity is reduced in this case by a factor of about 1000 compared to ordinary magnetic dipole radiation, owing to the fact that the transition is an intercombination (singlet-triplet).

[13] It will be noticed that the atmospheric oxygen bands represent a $\Sigma^+ - \Sigma^-$ transition.   But in this case the occurrence of the transitions is not due to the fact that the rule $\Sigma^+ \leftrightarrow\!\!\!/ \;\Sigma^-$ is not a rigorous selection rule (see above), since the transition $^1\Sigma_g^+ - {}^3\Sigma_g^-$ is rigorously forbidden as electric dipole radiation because both states are even (g).   However, for molecules with unequal nuclei $\Sigma^+ \longleftrightarrow \Sigma^-$ transitions may occur very weakly not only as electric dipole radiations, owing to the fact that the rule $\Sigma^+ \leftrightarrow\!\!\!/ \;\Sigma^-$ is not rigorous, but also as quadrupole or magnetic dipole radiation.   The fine structure in these two types of $\Sigma^+ \longleftrightarrow \Sigma^-$ transitions is quite different, as can be easily derived from Fig. 107 and the selection rules (V, 29 and 58). But, as mentioned before, $\Sigma^+ \longleftrightarrow \Sigma^-$ transitions have not yet been observed for molecules with unequal nuclei.

4. PERTURBATIONS

Observed phenomena. We have already mentioned briefly in several connections that sometimes perturbations are observed in the otherwise smooth course of a branch. In such cases one line or several successive lines deviate more or less strongly from formula (II, 8). Sometimes even a splitting into two lines appears, or for multiplet bands the multiplet splitting may be abnormally great at one place in the band. A type of perturbation also appears in which the intensity suddenly becomes abnormally small at a certain place in the band. *Displacement* and *weakening* in intensity can also appear simultaneously. When the perturbations appear for a number of successive J values, they usually have a *resonance-like* behavior; the deviation from the normal course increases rapidly to a maximum with increasing J and then decreases rapidly again to zero.

As an *example*, a spectrogram of the CN band λ3921 Å is reproduced in Fig. 122(a). The deviation (in cm^{-1}) from the regular course in the P branch is represented graphically in Fig. 122(b). It can be seen clearly from the spectrogram as well as from the graphical representation that the doublet splitting, which is unnoticeable for small K, suddenly increases very rapidly at $K = 12$ and then decreases again to a small value. However, only the one doublet component is influenced.

It is clear that the perturbations in the band fine structure are due to *perturbations in the rotational term series* either of the upper or of the lower state.[14] Corresponding to this, if a perturbation appears, for example, at a certain point in a P branch of a band, it will also be observed for the same J' or J'' value in the corresponding R branch of the band and will have the same type and magnitude, as is clearly seen in Fig. 122(a) for the CN band. Furthermore, the perturbation also appears in other bands of the same system

---

[14] The perturbations are quite similar to the perturbations appearing in atomic spectra (see A.A., p. 170).

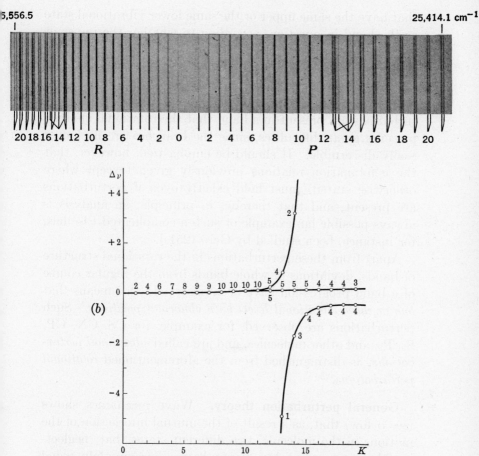

Fig. 122. **Perturbation in the 11–11 Band λ3921 Å of the Violet CN System after Jenkins (366).** (a) Spectrogram.* (b) Graphical representation of the perturbation in the *P* branch. The long leading lines in (a), on which the *K* values are written, give the unperturbed doublet components, and the shorter give the perturbed. In each case the latter are joined to the former. In (b) the deviation $\Delta\nu$ of the lines of the *P* branch from the regular course is given. The numbers on the curve are the estimated intensities of the respective lines.

* The author is greatly indebted to Professor F. A. Jenkins for this spectrogram.

that have the same upper or the same lower vibrational state as the band in question, according to whether the upper or the lower state is perturbed.

The *magnitude of the perturbations* is at times considerable. Deviations up to 20 cm^{-1} from the normal position have been observed. In rare cases, so many and such strong perturbations are present in a band that the rotational analysis presents great difficulties, since the branches are no longer easily discernible. It should be emphasized, however, that the combination relations previously given (except where otherwise stated) must hold exactly even if perturbations are present, and that thereby, in principle, an analysis is always possible [an example of such a complicated case has, for instance, been studied by Gerö (251)].

Apart from these perturbations in the rotational structure of bands, deviations of whole bands from the regular course of a band progression have been observed; this means that *one or more vibrational levels have abnormal positions*. Such perturbations are observed, for example, for CS, CN, CP, S_2, P_2, and other molecules, and are called *vibrational perturbations*, as distinguished from the aforementioned *rotational perturbations*.[15]

General perturbation theory. Wave mechanics shows (see below) that, as a result of the mutual interaction of the motions in the molecule, two different states that (neglecting the interaction) by chance have approximately equal energies influence each other strongly, the influence being the stronger the closer they lie together. This results in the levels *"repelling" each other*; that is, the higher is displaced upward and the lower downward by an equal amount. In addition, each of the two states assumes properties of the other; both states form a kind of *hybrid*.

The mutual repulsion of two states of approximately equal

---

[15] Bulthuis and Coster (145) have doubted the justification of distinguishing between vibrational and rotational perturbations, since they have essentially the same origin (see below). However, it appears useful from the experimental standpoint to make such a distinction, since experimentally there is a characteristic difference between the two.

energy immediately gives an explanation for the appearance of perturbations. We need only to assume the following: At the position at which the deviation from the normal course in a series of levels is observed there happens to lie still another level which might, for example, belong to another electronic state, and this level *displaces* one of the levels of the first series *from its "normal" position,* as indicated in Fig. 123. We shall see that the correctness of this explanation of perturbations has been confirmed by a large amount of experimental material.

Fig. 123. Explanation of Perturbations. The level $J = 4$ of the left series is perturbed by the level to the right, which has nearly the same energy but belongs to a different series of levels. The direction of the shift (repulsion) is indicated by the small arrows.

As previously mentioned, in the wave mechanical treatment of an atomic system (for example, of a molecule), we must always start out with an idealized model in which a number of the interactions actually present are neglected. For example, in the molecule the finer interaction between electronic motion and rotation (as well as vibration) is at first usually neglected. There is then a quite general wave mechanical procedure (the perturbation theory), which allows us to calculate the alteration of the eigenvalues and the eigenfunctions resulting if we go over from the model without interaction to that taking account of the interaction.

Let us assume that the wave equation of the unperturbed system (for example, of the molecule *without* taking account of the finer interaction),

$$\sum \frac{1}{m_k}\left(\frac{\partial^2\psi}{\partial x_k{}^2} + \frac{\partial^2\psi}{\partial y_k{}^2} + \frac{\partial^2\psi}{\partial z_k{}^2}\right) + \frac{8\pi^2}{h^2}(E - V)\psi = 0, \qquad (V, 60)$$

is readily soluble. Let its eigenvalues and eigenfunctions be

$$E_1{}^0,\ E_2{}^0,\ E_3{}^0,\ \cdots, \qquad \psi_1{}^0,\ \psi_2{}^0,\ \psi_3{}^0,\ \cdots \qquad (V, 61)$$

For the "perturbed" system—that is, *taking account* of the interaction in question—the Schrödinger equation is

$$\sum \frac{1}{m_k}\left(\frac{\partial^2\psi}{\partial x_k{}^2} + \frac{\partial^2\psi}{\partial y_k{}^2} + \frac{\partial^2\psi}{\partial z_k{}^2}\right) + \frac{8\pi^2}{h^2}(E - V)\psi + W\psi = 0. \qquad (V, 62)$$

Here $W\psi$ is the *"perturbation term"* representing the interactions. In the simplest case, W is a factor depending on the co-ordinates —that is, an addition to the potential energy V. However, it may also be a differential operator; that is, $W\psi$ may contain derivatives of ψ. However, the special form need not concern us here.

We shall designate the unknown eigenvalues and eigenfunctions of the "complete" wave equation (V, 62) by

$$E_1,\ E_2,\ E_3,\ \cdots,\qquad \psi_1,\ \psi_2,\ \psi_3,\ \cdots. \qquad (V, 63)$$

The perturbation theory now shows how these "true" eigenvalues and eigenfunctions can be expressed by the unperturbed eigenvalues and eigenfunctions and the perturbation function. Up to the *second* approximation, it is found that the *eigenvalues* are [see, for example, Pauling and Wilson (23)]

$$E_n = E_n{}^0 + W_{nn} + \sum_{\substack{i=0 \\ i \neq n}}^{\infty} \frac{|W_{ni}|^2}{E_n{}^0 - E_i{}^0}. \qquad (V, 64)$$

In this equation

$$W_{ni} = \int \psi_n{}^0 W \psi_i{}^0 * d\tau \qquad (V, 65)$$

are the so-called *matrix elements of the perturbation function W*. To a *first* approximation, the perturbation theory gives for the true *eigenfunctions* [16]

$$\psi_n = \psi_n{}^0 + \sum_{\substack{i=0 \\ i \neq n}}^{\infty} \frac{W_{in}}{E_n{}^0 - E_i{}^0} \psi_i{}^0. \qquad (V, 66)$$

It can be seen immediately from (V, 64 and 66) (and it is also plausible) that for a sufficiently small perturbation function W the true eigenvalues and eigenfunctions lie very close to the approximate eigenvalues and eigenfunctions. The deviations depend on the eigenfunctions and eigenvalues of all the other states of the system as well as on the magnitude of the perturbation function. Thus we have the aforementioned *interaction of the "unperturbed" states of the system*, which, strictly speaking, according to (V, 64 and 66), exists between *all* states of the system. However, as may be seen from the formulae, the alteration of the energy values

---

[16] Quite generally, $\psi_n = \sum_i a_{in} \psi_i{}^0$, since the functions $\psi_i{}^0$ form a complete orthogonal system and any function can be developed into a series of functions of such a complete orthogonal system.

and of the eigenfunctions is the greater the smaller is the separation $E_n{}^0 - E_i{}^0$ of the two levels influencing each other. If we have started from a very good approximate solution (for example, for the molecule, from the model of the vibrating rotator), the interaction is very small, except when the two interacting levels lie very close together—that is, when they are approximately in resonance.

It follows from (V, 64) that a level is displaced upward or downward according as the perturbing level lies below or above the perturbed level. Naturally, the *perturbing term* is also influenced, and, by exchanging i with n in (V, 64), it can be seen that it is displaced upward if it lies higher than the perturbed term and downward if it lies lower. The magnitude of its displacement is exactly equal and opposite to that of the perturbed term (since $W_{ni}{}^* = W_{in}$, as is easily seen). We can therefore also say that two *neighboring states always "repel" each other, the repulsion being the greater the closer the states lie to each other.* It must be emphasized, however, that this mode of expression is somewhat inexact, since the true states of an atomic system naturally do not repel each other. Repulsion and interaction take place only for the approximate model, in which the finer interactions have not yet been taken into account.

Formula (V, 64) is only an approximation. If the energy difference between two of the unperturbed levels approaches zero, the displacement $E_n - E_n{}^0$ does not approach infinity, as it might appear to do from (V, 64). In this case we must rather employ another method of approximation, in which the two perturbing levels are regarded, in zero approximation, as degenerate with respect to each other, and the influence of the remaining levels lying at greater distances is completely neglected. If δ is the original separation of the two levels, the actual separation, ε, resulting from the interaction is then found to be [see, for example, Dieke (185)]

$$\varepsilon = \frac{\delta}{2} \pm \sqrt{|W_{ni}|^2 + \frac{\delta^2}{4}}. \qquad (V, 67)$$

In this equation, terms with W_{nn} and W_{ii} are neglected, since the zero approximation can always be chosen so that they are zero. If the two unperturbed levels fall exactly together ($\delta = 0$), according to (V, 67) there is a shift of $\pm W_{ni}$ from the original position (and not ∞). As above, the shift decreases with increasing δ. Formula (V, 67) also holds for larger δ as long as the influence of levels other than n and i can be neglected.

Selection rules for perturbations. According to what has been said thus far, if such a resonance (that is, perturbation) occurs for one level, we should expect it to occur a number of times in the same series of rotational or vibrational levels. Since the perturbing level belongs also to a series of rotational (or vibrational) levels, there is, as is illustrated in Fig.

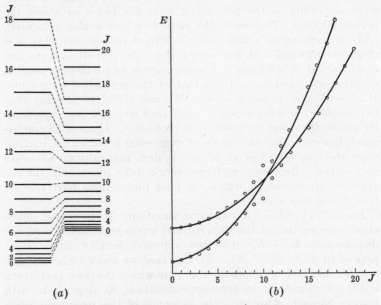

Fig. 124. Two Overlapping Rotational Term Series. (a) Energy level diagram. (b) Term curves. In (a), only the unperturbed levels are drawn, which are represented in (b) by the full-line curves. The position of the perturbed levels is indicated in (b) by the circles. However, the deviations from the curves have been drawn to a larger scale than the curve itself.

124(a), a number of places in which two levels, one from each of the series, have approximately equal energies (in the figure for $J = 7, 8, 9, 10, 12, 14,$ and 16 of the left series). We should therefore expect that perturbations would occur very frequently rather than be the exception. That this is not the case is due to the fact that *selection rules*, similar to those for the combination of two states by a quantum jump, hold for the interaction of two states. These have been

derived by Kronig (421). For diatomic molecules they are
as follows:

1. Both states must have the *same total angular momentum
J*; that is, $\Delta J = 0$.

2. Both states must have the *same multiplicity* ($\Delta S = 0$).
Naturally, this rule holds only as rigorously as it holds for
transitions with radiation; that is, for larger multiplet splitting, states of different multiplicity may perturb each other,
even though only to a smaller extent.

3. The Λ *values* of the two states *may differ only by* 0 *or*
±1. For large multiplet splitting—that is, when Λ is no
longer defined—this selection rule is replaced by $\Delta \Omega = 0$
or ±1.

4. *Both terms* must be *positive* or *both must be negative*
($+ \leftrightarrow -$).

5. For identical nuclei, both terms must have the *same
symmetry in the nuclei* ($s \leftrightarrow a$).

The derivation of the selection rules follows on the basis of
formulae (V, 64–67). According to these formulae, the occurrence
of an interaction depends not only on the smallness of the energy
difference between the two states but also on the magnitude of
W_{ni}. It can be shown that W_{ni} is zero for cases that do not correspond to the above selection rules [see Kronig (421)].

Dieke (185) has designated perturbations for which $\Delta \Lambda = \pm 1$
as A perturbations and those for which $\Delta \Lambda = 0$ as B perturbations.

Rotational perturbations. We shall first apply Kronig's
selection rules to the *mutual perturbation of two rotational
term series*. As may be seen from Fig. 124(a), the first selection rule obviously imposes a considerable restriction on the
possibilities of perturbation. A noticeable perturbation will
take place only if, *for one and the same J in both states*, the
levels have about the same height. In the figure this is the
case for $J = 10$. The separation for corresponding levels is
appreciably greater for higher and lower J values, and therefore the perturbation is considerably smaller if at all noticeable. The positions of the levels expected as a result of the
mutual repulsion of terms with equal J are given qualita-

tively in Fig. 124(b) for the two different rotational term series of Fig. 124(a). Naturally, in this figure it is assumed that the other selection rules (2–5) are also fulfilled (see below). The full-line curves give the regular course of the levels which would be expected without allowing for the perturbation; the small circles give the actual perturbed levels. It is seen that in both term series the deviations from the normal course increase at first in a resonance-like manner and then spring over to the other side of the smooth curve and decrease rapidly again. This behavior is exactly in agreement with observations (see Fig. 122).

If, as fairly often happens, only one line (or one level) in a series has an abnormal position, this may result either from the fact that the interaction is small and is therefore noticeable only for the level with the maximum perturbation or from the fact that the B values of the two series influencing each other are so different that an approximate agreement of the energies exists only for one J value.

It is seen from Fig. 124 that the course of the perturbations in the two term series must be *exactly opposite*. In a number of cases—for example, CN [Rosenthal and Jenkins (603)], He$_2$ [Dieke (183)], and CuH [T. Heimer (292)]—in addition to the perturbed levels, the perturbing levels have been found in other band systems and always the above theoretical conclusion—that the perturbations must always occur at equal J and with equal and opposite magnitudes—has been confirmed.

The perturbation in the CN band reproduced in Fig. 122(a) is due to a perturbation in the lower $^2\Sigma$ state of the band, which is brought about by the level $v' = 6$ of a $^2\Pi_{\frac{3}{2}}$ state (component of upper state of the red CN bands). Both term series are represented graphically in Fig. 125. It can be seen that, on the basis of the selection rule $\Delta J = 0$, only one component of the $^2\Sigma$ state will be perturbed in the neighborhood of $K = 14$. However, as Fig. 125 shows, a perturbation of the other doublet component by the same $^2\Pi_{\frac{3}{2}}$ state begins at higher J. We may also notice that only one Λ-doublet component is perturbed in the $^2\Pi_\frac{3}{2}$ state (see below). The $^2\Pi_\frac{1}{2}$ component of the $^2\Pi$ state produces perturbations for other vibrational levels of the $^2\Sigma$ state.

In consequence of selection rules 2–4 (p. 313), *certain electronic states* (or their components) *cannot perturb each other at all.* However, the above-discussed regularities remain unchanged. Selection rule 2 says, for example, that a triplet state cannot perturb a singlet state. Selection rule 3 says, for example, that a Δ state cannot perturb a Σ state. From the fourth selection rule it follows, for example, as we can see from Fig. 107, that a Σ^- state cannot perturb a Σ^+ state, and vice versa, since for equal J the $+-$ symmetry is not the same. From the same selection rule it also follows that a Σ state can perturb only the one Λ-doublet component of a Π state, since the $+-$ symmetry for equal J is the same only for one Λ component. This is shown clearly for the $^2\Pi_\frac{3}{2}$ state of CN in Fig. 125. On the other hand, both Λ components are influenced by the mutual perturbation of two Π states.

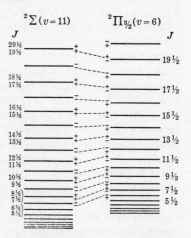

Fig. 125. Energy Level Diagram for the Perturbation in the CN Band Fig. 122. The spin doublets of the $^2\Sigma$ state, as well as the Λ doublets of the $^2\Pi$ state, have not been drawn separated. However, the splitting is indicated by giving the symmetry $+-$, as well as the J values for the spin doublets. In order to avoid confusion, the J values are given only for every other level. The levels which, according to the selection rules, can perturb each other are joined by broken lines.

As a result of selection rules 4 and 5, if the nuclei are alike, the terms participating in the perturbation must either both be even or both be odd (see Figs. 107 and 108). For example, a Π_u term cannot perturb a Π_g term.

From what has been said, we can see that from the type of perturbations found in an electronic state it is possible to draw certain conclusions about the type of the electronic state causing the perturbations. A more complete discussion is given by Ittmann (357), Brons (131), Coster and Brons (166), and Schmid and Gerö (620).

Since each of the electronic states, the perturbing and the perturbed, has a series of vibrational levels, it is to be expected that a resonance favoring a perturbation must reoccur more or less periodically. The first example of such a periodicity was observed for the $N_2{}^+$ bands [Herzberg (302)], for which a characteristic perturbation appears for $v' = 1, 3, 5,$ and 8 [see also (169) and (131)]. Schmid and Gerö [(250) and (623)] have given a convenient method for representing the perturbations in the different vibrational levels. The values $T_e + G(v) + F(J)$ of the different vibrational levels of the perturbing and the perturbed electronic states are plotted against $J(J + 1)$. Two sets of intersecting lines for the two electronic states are obtained, as is illustrated by Fig. 126, which refers to CN. The points of intersection correspond to positions of equal J for the two states—that is, to positions of maximum perturbation. In such a diagram, if the points of perturbation of only one of the states are known, in favorable cases the lines representing the rotational levels for the perturbing state can be found and thereby its vibrational and rotational constants can be determined approximately [see Coster and Brons (166), Schmid and Gerö (620), (250), and (623), and Kovács (419)].

Fig. 124(b) has been drawn under the assumption that the quantity W_{ni} in (V, 64) is constant for the whole region of perturbation. As Kronig has shown, this approximation is closely fulfilled only if $\Delta\Lambda = 0$—that is, if both electronic states are of the same type (B perturbations, according to Dieke). On the other hand, if $\Delta\Lambda = \pm1$ (A perturbations), Kronig has shown that to a first approximation W_{ni} is proportional to J; that is, the perturbation is zero for $J = 0$ even if the two levels are very close to each other. It is appreciable only for larger J values. Owing to this dependence, after the maximum perturbation the shift does not go back to zero again at higher J values, whereas it does go back to zero for $\Delta\Lambda = 0$, for which case W_{ni} is constant (see Fig. 124). In this way we can distinguish experimentally between the two cases, $\Delta\Lambda = 0$ and $\Delta\Lambda = \pm1$ [see Ittmann (357), Brons (131), and Dieke (185)]. Thus it follows, for example, that for the perturbation of CN, represented in Fig. 122, $\Delta\Lambda$ must be equal to ±1 (A perturbation), since the perturbation does not go back to zero. In this case, as mentioned before, direct observation of the perturbing state has shown it to be a $^2\Pi_{\frac{3}{2}}$ state, which, considering that the perturbed state is $^2\Sigma$, confirms the above result.

Thus far we have considered only the perturbation of the energy levels. However, according to (V, 66), there is associated with this

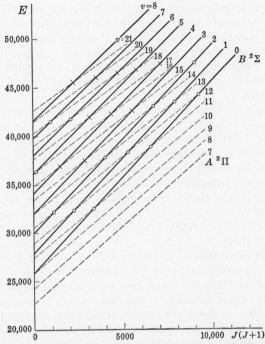

Fig. 126. Rotational Energy Levels and Perturbations in the $B\,^2\Sigma$ and $A\,^2\Pi$ States of the CN Molecule [Adaptation of a Figure by Schmid, Gerö, and Zemplén (624a)]. The ordinates give the energy above the ground state of CN; the abscissae are $J(J+1)$. The solid straight lines represent the energy of the rotational levels of the $B\,^2\Sigma$ state, and the broken straight lines represent those of the $A\,^2\Pi$ state. The small circles indicate the points of observed perturbations; the short dashes indicate points of intersection for which no perturbations have been observed because the corresponding bands have not been analyzed.

an *alteration of the eigenfunctions* which becomes the greater the smaller the separation $\delta = E_n^{\,0} - E_i^{\,0}$ becomes. If δ is very small, (V, 66) can no longer be used. The perturbation method, in which the two neighboring levels are in zero approximation regarded as degenerate with respect to each other (see above), then gives

$$\psi_n = a\psi_n^{\,0} + b\psi_i^{\,0}, \quad \psi_i = c\psi_n^{\,0} + d\psi_i^{\,0}, \qquad \text{(V, 68)}$$

where, for not too small δ, the coefficients a and d are found to be nearly 1, while b and c are very small [in agreement with (V, 66), if we consider in it only the two states n and i]. On the other hand, for very small δ all the coefficients are found to be of the order of 1 (in particular, for $\delta = 0$, $a = b = c = -d = 1/\sqrt{2}$), so that then (that is, for large perturbation) the true eigenfunctions of the perturbed states are mixtures of the two unperturbed eigenfunctions. We speak then of a *mixing of the eigenfunctions* (or also of *hybrid formation*). Thus, strictly speaking, for strong perturbation we can no longer say which of the perturbed states corresponds to the unperturbed state with the eigenfunction $\psi_i{}^0$ and which to the state with $\psi_n{}^0$.

As a result of this mixing of the eigenfunctions, the perturbed level assumes the properties of the perturbing level, and vice versa. If, therefore, in an electronic transition $A \rightarrow B$, a vibrational level of the state B is perturbed by a vibrational level of a state C, which normally would not combine with A (say as a result of the Franck-Condon principle), the state C is nevertheless able to combine with A in the perturbation region, since it has assumed the properties of B. The result of this is that *extra lines* appear in the perturbation region. Apart from the regular lines of the transition $A \rightarrow B$ there will be some lines of the transition $A \rightarrow C$—namely, just those that go to the strongly perturbing levels. Such extra lines are recognizable in Fig. 122(a). We can see that for $K = 13$ and 14 there are three lines each instead of the ordinary two [namely, apart from the center line, which is not perturbed, there is one line in the upper branch of the curve in Fig. 122(b), as well as one in the lower]. It is obviously impossible to distinguish, on the basis of the spectrum alone, whether—for example, at $K = 13$ (or 14) in Fig. 122—the line in the upper or the lower branch of the curve is the extra one—that is, corresponds to a level of the perturbing state.

Hand in hand with the mixing of the eigenfunctions, there goes an *alteration of the intensity of the lines* under consideration, since the intensity depends on the eigenfunctions. Only the sum of the intensities of the regular and extra lines is equal to the normal unperturbed intensity, as may be seen qualitatively from Fig. 122(b), in which the estimated intensities are given. We may also say that the extra lines "*borrow*" their intensity from the regular lines. Thus perturbations in the usual intensity distribution occur, and under some circumstances may appear alone if the extra lines are not observed (see above).

Extended discussions of examples of perturbations are given, for instance, by Stenvinkel (652) and T. Heimer (292). Recently, theoretical investigations of different types of perturbations have been carried out by Budó and Kovács [(142) and (420)].

According to the above [see formula (V, 64)], if two electronic states are fairly widely separated, the perturbation between them is small and affects all the rotational levels in nearly the same manner, since $E_n^0 - E_i^0$ is approximately the same for all of them. If the perturbed state is a $^1\Sigma$ state, this perturbation is simply made manifest by a very slight alteration in the rotational constants of this state from the unperturbed values. On the other hand, if a $^1\Pi$ state is perturbed—for example, by a $^1\Sigma$ state lying at some distance from it—only the one Λ component is slightly perturbed (see above) and thereby a splitting of the Λ-type doublets results which increases with increasing J. This splitting is the ordinary Λ-type *doubling*. It is produced by the same influence that also produces the ordinary perturbations—the *finer interaction of electronic motion and rotation* in the molecule. Therefore the same formulae and selection rules as given above apply. On the basis of these considerations, the Λ-type doubling has been treated quantitatively by Van Vleck (679) and Kronig (421); in fact, the formulae previously given were obtained in this manner. We can now see why, as was mentioned earlier, the magnitude of the Λ-type doubling depends on the distance of the state considered from neighboring electronic states as well as on the type of the latter. Similar considerations apply to spin uncoupling.

Vibrational perturbations (intersection of potential curves). The essentials of the explanation of vibrational perturbations are already implied in the above considerations. We have only to add another point, which is of a certain importance also for rotational perturbations; namely, in the above selection rules for the perturbations we have left the vibrational quantum number out of consideration. It now appears (see below) that there is no strict selection rule for it, but that an analogue to the Franck-Condon principle holds [see Hulthén (343), Weizel (704), Herzberg (309), and Dieke (183)]: *Two vibrational states belonging to two different electronic states and lying at approximately the same height will influence each other strongly only if the system could go over from the one state to the other without a large alteration of position and momentum*—that is, if the levels lie in the neighborhood of the intersection of the potential curves of the two electronic states. This is illustrated by Fig. 127(a) and (b). According to the above rule, no great perturbation can take place between the levels A and B in this figure, whereas a large perturbation is to be expected between the levels C and D, provided that also the Kronig selection rules are fulfilled. In this case the perturbation may be appreciable

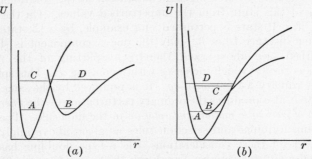

Fig. 127.   Potential Curves Explaining Vibrational Perturbations.

even if the energy resonance is not very sharp. It will then generally have about the same magnitude for a large number of successive rotational levels. In particular, if $\Delta\Lambda = 0$ (see below), it may happen that all the observed rotational levels from $J = 0$ up are displaced by about the same amount. Thus in that case we have what was called above, empirically, a *vibrational perturbation*.

According to our previous discussion, the magnitude of the perturbation between two states depends on the matrix element, W_{ni}, as well as on the energy difference. W_{ni} can be split into two parts, one depending on the electronic and rotational eigenfunctions and the other depending on the vibrational eigenfunction (similar to the transition moment for radiation; see p. 218 f.). The latter is found to be

$$W_{ni}^{v} = \int \psi_{n}^{v} W^{v} \psi_{i}^{v} \, dr, \qquad (V, 69)$$

where W^{v} is the part of the interaction energy depending on the internuclear distance; that is, W^{v} represents the finer interaction between vibration and electronic motion. According to (V, 69), a *strong perturbation* will occur only *if the vibrational eigenfunctions overlap in a suitable manner*.

For the levels A and B in Fig. 127(a), the eigenfunctions practically do not overlap at all, which means that $W_{AB}{}^v$ is very nearly zero and a perturbation does not occur, even if the resonance is very sharp. The same holds for the levels A and B in Fig. 127(b), although to a smaller extent, since the vibrational eigenfunctions between the turning points are not zero. In this case, for favorable energies of the two levels, a small rotational perturbation may become noticeable. On the other hand, for the levels C and D in the neighborhood of the points of intersection of the potential curves [Fig. 127(a) and (b)] a very favorable mutual overlapping of the eigenfunctions occurs, giving a large value to the integral (V, 69) (as is the case for the ordinary Franck-Condon principle; see p. 219). Therefore, if the Kronig selection rules are also fulfilled, a large perturbation can appear. In such cases, the perturbation can be quite considerable, even if the energy condition $E_i{}^0 \approx E_n{}^0$ is not very well fulfilled.

If we imagine, for example, the two rotational term series in Fig. 124(a) shifted relative to each other by about half the height of the figure, then $E_n{}^0 - E_i{}^0$ is of nearly the same magnitude for all the pairs of rotational levels with equal J. If at the same time the Franck-Condon principle is well fulfilled, the relatively large value of the denominator in the last term of (V, 64) can be compensated by a correspondingly large value of W_{ni} (owing to the large value of $W_{ni}{}^v$). According as $\Delta\Lambda = 0$ or ± 1, we obtain two different cases (see above). For $\Delta\Lambda = \pm 1$, W_{ni}, and thereby the perturbation, is zero for $J = 0$ (A perturbation) and increases with increasing J. In this case, the perturbation makes itself manifest in that the *effective B value* for this state *does not fit in with the smooth course of the B values* of the neighboring vibrational states. If, however, $\Delta\Lambda = 0$ (B perturbation) all the rotational levels (including the level with $J = 0$) are displaced by nearly the same amount with respect to the unperturbed positions. Thus in this case there is a vibrational perturbation—that is, a *deviation from the smooth course of the vibrational states.*

Thus *vibrational perturbations* appear only if $\Delta\Lambda = 0$. However, they do not always appear if $\Delta\Lambda = 0$, but only if at the same time the separation of the unperturbed levels is relatively great, so that $E_n{}^0 - E_i{}^0$ is approximately the same for all the rotational states, and if, in addition, $W_{ni}{}^v$ in (V, 69) is very large, as is the case in the neighborhood of the points of intersection of the potential curves.

The effect of the *mixing of the eigenfunctions* in the case of vibrational perturbations is, according to (V, 68), that a vibrational state in the neighborhood of a point of intersection of the potential curves has three instead of two broad maxima of its eigenfunction (see Fig. 41). As a result of this mixing of the eigenfunctions, it may sometimes be doubtful to which of the two electronic states each of the two mutually perturbing vibrational levels is to be ascribed (compare the analogous behavior for rotational perturbations).

In Fig. 128(a) *two intersecting potential curves* (with $\Delta\Lambda = 0$) are reproduced. Near the point of intersection they are dotted. The unperturbed vibrational levels are indicated by dotted lines unless

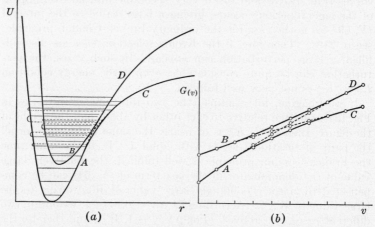

Fig. 128. **Perturbed and Unperturbed Vibrational Levels of Two Electronic States Having Intersecting Potential Curves.** (a) Potential curves. (b) Dependence of the vibrational energy on the vibrational quantum number. The unperturbed curves and levels, as far as they do not coincide with the perturbed, are indicated by broken lines. In (a), corresponding perturbed and unperturbed levels are joined by a bracket. The perturbed levels are deliberately not continued right up to the potential curves on the right, since it cannot be unambiguously said to which limb of the potential curve they are to be ascribed (see text).

they coincide with the corresponding perturbed vibrational levels, which are indicated by full lines. In Fig. 128(b) the unperturbed vibrational levels [$G(v)$] are given by the two intersecting dotted curves as a function of a relative running number that is so chosen that we have equal running numbers for the two states at the point of intersection of the potential curves. The perturbed levels (full lines) have been drawn under the simplifying assumption that only levels with the same relative running number perturb one another, an assumption that amounts approximately to assuming that only those levels that have the same r for the right turning point of the classical vibrational motion perturb one another. While the Franck-Condon principle, as we have seen above, does hold for perturbations, it is actually never so exact as to exclude the mutual perturbation of levels with slightly different turning points, and therefore actually also levels of relative running numbers differing by one unit will perturb one another.[17] Thus the actual course of the perturbed levels [full-line curves in Fig. 128(b)] will in general not be as regular as it is drawn.

At any rate it can be seen that as a result of the perturbation the correlation of the series of levels above and below the point of intersection is no longer unambiguous. The observations give only the positions of the vibrational levels and not directly the potential curves. Therefore it may happen that on the basis of the observed levels we can just as well assume that the levels of limb A belong to limb C and those of B belong to D (full curves) as that A belongs to D and B belongs to C (dotted curves), particularly if in the intermediate region the levels are not as regular as drawn. Under the first assumption the perturbation in the smooth course is produced by the *approach* of the unperturbed potential curves, and under the second assumption it is produced by their *intersection*. If, however, a large number of vibrational levels on the limbs A and D can be represented by one and the same formula of the usual kind (and correspondingly those on the limbs B and C), we can assume with some justification that "originally" there has been an intersection.

In many cases, vibrational levels of the two electronic states are observed only below the point of intersection, and it is only their extrapolation that points to the existence of an intersection of the potential curves. We can be certain that such an intersection has some physical meaning only when the vibrational levels are observed quite close to the point of intersection and show a quite regular course.

As an example, we may refer to the case of the upper $^1\Sigma$ state of the AgH bands. Bengtsson and Olsson (86) found the ΔG curve given in Fig. 129 for this state, which shows a sharp bend at about $v = 5$, while, for example, the curve for the ground state has quite a normal course. The explanation of this bend is to be sought in the vibrational levels under consideration lying in the neighborhood of the point of intersection of two potential curves

---

[17] In the case that the two $G(v)$ curves are very steep and intersect at a small angle, the above assumption gives a good approximation, since then only levels with equal relative running number will have approximately equal energy and thus will perturb one another.

(with $\Delta\Lambda = 0$). It can be seen from Fig. 128(b) that, when we approach the point of intersection along the curve B, the slope of the ΔG curve (that is, the curvature of the G curve) alters rapidly and in such a way that the slope becomes smaller. Similar cases, in which the slope of the ΔG curve suddenly *increases* strongly and for which, therefore, the levels approach the point of intersection on the curve A in Fig. 128(b), have been observed for N_2 (147) and Br_2 (132).

An interaction of two states with $\Delta\Lambda = 0$ (different from that of states with $\Delta\Lambda = \pm 1$) is present even if we consider only the electronic motion in the field of two fixed centers (or, in other words, if we neglect completely the interaction of rotation and electronic motion—that is, for $J = 0$; see above). Von Neumann and Wigner (529) have shown that, in this two-center problem, *states with the same* Λ, if also the other symmetry properties $(+, -; g, u)$ are the same, cannot intersect if the internuclear distance is changed infinitely slowly ("adiabatically"), but *always "avoid"*

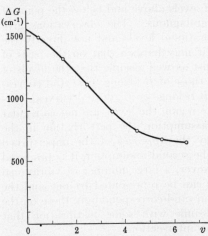

Fig. 129. ΔG Curve for the Upper $^1\Sigma$ State of AgH [after Bengtsson and Olsson (86)].

each other. If in a certain zero approximation two potential curves of two states with the same Λ and the same symmetry properties cross, in higher approximation this intersection is avoided [see Fig. 128(a)]; that is, the upper curve on the right of the point of intersection goes over into the upper curve on the left and the lower curve on the right goes over into the lower curve on the left. This is a result of the aforementioned repulsion of the unperturbed states, which is largest at the point of intersection. States with equal Λ and the same symmetry properties are called *states* (terms) *of the same species.* Fig. 130 shows several pairs of potential curves of two states of the same species, which in all four cases avoid each other. We can see that in Fig. 130(a) there would be scarcely any point in assuming that "originally" (that is, neglecting the finer interaction of the electrons) an intersection was present, whereas in Fig. 130(c) and (d) it appears very well possible and in Fig. 130(b) doubtful.

Fig. 130(*d*) illustrates the case where an "attractive" potential curve in zero approximation is crossed by a "repulsive" potential curve. As the figure shows, the lower of the resulting potential curves can have a maximum if the interaction is not too strong. Thus far, such *potential curves with a maximum* have been observed in very few cases only—for example, AlH and BH [Herzberg and Mundie (317)].

The preceding considerations show clearly the *limitations of the concept of potential curves* for the representation of the vibrational motion and the vibrational levels of a diatomic molecule. The concept of potential curves is based on the fact (see p. 157) that in general the electronic motion is very fast compared to the nuclear vibrations. However, when the potential curves of two states of the same species intersect each other or approach each other so

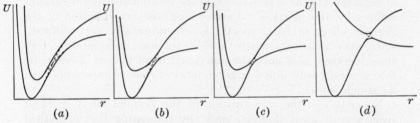

Fig. 130. **Different Cases of "Avoidance" of Potential Curves of the Same Species.** The broken parts of the curves give the course of the potential energy in zero approximation, and the full curves give the true course.

that their separation is of the same order as, or smaller than, the separation of successive vibrational levels, the frequency of the going over from the one to the other electronic state is of the same order as the vibrational frequency, and therefore it is no longer a good approximation to consider the vibrational motion of the nuclei as taking place in the *average* field produced by the electrons at various internuclear distances; or, in other words, electronic and vibrational motion can no longer be separated. We may not even be able to decide to which electronic state a given "vibrational" state belongs.

The energy levels are the primary observable quantities. The potential curves are rigorously defined only for the nonvibrating molecule (two-center system, adiabatic change of nuclear separation), which does not correspond to reality. But they are yet extremely useful in correlating and systematizing the energy levels. We may also say that by the observed vibrational levels only certain points on the potential curves are defined (the turning points).

If, therefore, the interaction of two states with intersecting (zero approximation) potential curves is slight, as in Fig. 130(c), so that only one or a few points lie off the smooth course of vibrational levels, we may with some justification speak of the *occurrence of an intersection* [see also Weizel (704) and Heitler (293)].

5. ZEEMAN EFFECT

The investigation of the effect of a magnetic field on the spectrum (Zeeman effect) plays practically no part in the analysis of molecular spectra (other than in the analysis of atomic spectra). Whereas sometimes, in atomic spectra, an unambiguous determination of the electronic transition giving rise to certain lines can be made only with the help of an investigation of the Zeeman effect, in band spectra the investigation of the rotational structure always suffices for this purpose. Furthermore, the investigation of the Zeeman effect of band spectra is experimentally very difficult, since, even without a magnetic field, the lines in a band lie very close together, and since the individual band lines in a magnetic field generally split into a larger number of closer components than do atomic lines.

Nevertheless, the investigation of the Zeeman effect in band spectra is of great interest, since, by comparing the theoretical splitting patterns with those observed, we can test the theories previously developed. Only the most important points will be dealt with here; for details the reader is referred to the review by Crawford (171) [see also Jevons (34)].

Up to the present time, an appreciable effect of an *electric* field on band lines (*Stark effect*) has been observed only for the H_2 spectrum [(641), (402), (472), and (580)]. We shall refrain here from a discussion of the Stark effect and refer the reader to the theoretical work of Penney (560), MacDonald (473), and Kiuti and Hasunuma (402a).

General remarks on the term splitting in a magnetic field. In a magnetic (or an electric) field, the total angular momentum J of the molecule can have only certain orientations (*space quantization*) such that the component in the field direction is $M \cdot h/2\pi$, where

$$M = J, J - 1, \cdots, -J$$

(see Fig. 3 and p. 23). If an interaction between the field and the molecule exists, a precession of J takes place at the corresponding angle, about the field direction as axis (see Fig. 2, p. 18). In addition, the states with different M have somewhat *different energies in the field*—namely (see A.A., p. 98),

$$W = W_0 - \bar{\mu}_H \cdot H, \qquad (V, 70)$$

where W_0 is the energy of the molecule in the absence of the field, $\bar{\mu}_H$ is the mean value of the component of the magnetic moment in the field direction, and H is the field strength. The magnetic moment μ is due almost entirely to the motion of the electrons and therefore depends on their angular momenta. For $^1\Sigma$ states, the total spin and orbital angular momentum of the electrons and thereby also μ are zero. Therefore, to a first good approximation, $^1\Sigma$ states are not affected by a magnetic field, although, of course, the space quantization of J still takes place.

Zeeman effect in Hund's case (a). In Hund's case (a) (see p. 242) the electronic angular momenta are strongly coupled to the internuclear axis. With the resultant angular momentum $\Omega = |\Lambda + \Sigma|$ in the internuclear axis, there is associated a *magnetic moment*, which, owing to the double magnetism of the electron

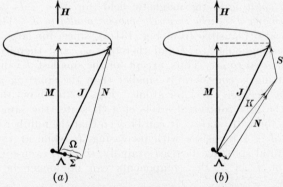

Fig. 131. Vector Diagrams of the Molecule in a Magnetic Field. (a) In Hund's case (a). (b) In Hund's case (b). The ellipses indicate the precession of J in the magnetic field. At the same time, the much faster precession (or nutation) of the other vectors takes place about J (see Figs. 92 and 95).

(A.A., p. 108), is *proportional to* $(\Lambda + 2\Sigma)$. As for atoms, the value of the proportionality factor is simply equal to the value of the Bohr magneton $\mu_0 = (e/2mc)(h/2\pi)$. Thus, for a $^1\Pi$ state, for example, there is a magnetic moment of exactly one Bohr magneton $(1\mu_0)$ in the line joining the nuclei; for a $^2\Pi_{\frac{3}{2}}$ state it is $2\mu_0$; for a $^2\Pi_{\frac{1}{2}}$ state it is $0\mu_0$; and so on.

For the splitting in a magnetic field it is the time average $\bar{\mu}_H$ of the component of the magnetic moment in the field direction that matters [see (V, 70)]. Since the nutation of Ω about J takes place very rapidly compared to the precession of J about the field direction, we can obtain $\bar{\mu}_H$ by first forming $\bar{\mu}_J$, the time average of the component of μ in the direction of J, and then taking its component in the field direction. Fig. 131(a) shows the vector diagram. It can be seen from this diagram that

$$\bar{\mu}_J = (\Lambda + 2\Sigma)\mu_0 \cos(\Omega, J) = (\Lambda + 2\Sigma)\mu_0 \frac{\Lambda + \Sigma}{\sqrt{J(J+1)}}. \qquad (V, 71)$$

Correspondingly, for $\bar{\mu}_H$

$$\bar{\mu}_H = \bar{\mu}_J \cos(H, J) = \bar{\mu}_J \frac{M}{\sqrt{J(J+1)}}$$

$$= \frac{(\Lambda + 2\Sigma)(\Lambda + \Sigma)M}{J(J+1)} \mu_0. \qquad (V, 72)$$

This formula, in combination with formula (V, 70), shows that the *maximum splitting* in the magnetic field (for $M = \pm J$) *decreases with increasing J nearly inversely proportionally to J*. This conclusion is also plausible from Fig. 131(a), since, for large J, Ω is almost perpendicular to J and therefore $\bar{\mu}_J$, and thereby $\bar{\mu}_H$, is small compared to μ_0. Thus, except for the smallest J values, the total splitting is considerably smaller than the splitting $\mu_0 H$ for the normal Zeeman effect for atoms. Fig. 132(a) shows the splitting for the first rotational levels of a $^1\Pi$ state (the same figure also holds for a $^3\Pi_1$ state). It can be seen that the number of components $2J + 1$ increases with increasing J, while at the same time the total splitting decreases rapidly, so that, even for as low a value of J as 5, the components can no longer be drawn separately.

It is clear from this that well-resolved splitting patterns in the spectrum are to be expected only for lines with very low J values. The patterns to be expected, on the basis of the selection rule $\Delta M = 0, \pm 1$, for the first lines of the three branches of a $^1\Sigma - {}^1\Pi$ transition are drawn in Fig. 133. Since the splitting in the $^1\Sigma$ state is vanishingly small, the line splitting gives directly the term splitting in the $^1\Pi$ state. We cannot discuss here the theoretical calculation of the intensities of the Zeeman components [see Crawford (171)]. But the theoretical values are indicated in Fig. 133 for the example by the heights of the vertical lines. For the CO Ångström bands, which represent such a $^1\Sigma - {}^1\Pi$ transition, the theoretical splitting patterns have been confirmed quantitatively by experiment, at least for the first two lines of each of the three branches, and a qualitative agreement has been found for the further lines whose splitting patterns cannot be fully resolved. For further examples see Crawford (171).

It should be noted that, as long as there is no uncoupling, the splitting is quantitatively the same for all like transitions, inde-

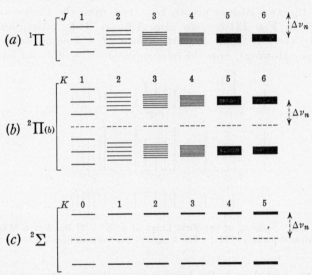

Fig. 132. **Term Splitting in a Magnetic Field.** (a) $^1\Pi(^3\Pi_1)$. (b) $^2\Pi(b)$. (c) $^2\Sigma$. The position of the levels without field is indicated by broken lines. For comparison, the magnitude of the splitting in the normal Zeeman effect $\Delta\nu_n$ is given to the right by the broken-line arrow.

pendent of the special molecular constants. This behavior is analogous to that of atoms.

Zeeman effect in Hund's case (b). In Hund's case (b), the orbital angular momentum of the electrons is coupled to the internuclear axis, whereas the spin is coupled to the rotational axis [see Fig. 131(b)]. The time average $\bar{\mu}_J$ of the magnetic moment in the direction of J is composed of the contributions of μ_Λ and μ_S. As a result of the nutation of Λ about K and of the precession of K about J, the contribution of μ_Λ is $\Lambda\mu_0 \cos(\Lambda, K) \cos(K, J)$ [where $\cos(\Lambda, K) = \Lambda/\sqrt{K(K+1)}$], while the contribution of μ_S is $2\sqrt{S(S+1)}\mu_0 \cos(S, J)$. (The factor 2 comes from the double magnetism of the electron.) Therefore, for the component in the field direction, we obtain [multiplying by $\cos (J, H) = M/\sqrt{J(J+1)}$]

$$\bar{\mu}_H = \left[\frac{\Lambda^2}{\sqrt{K(K+1)}} \cos (K, J) \right.$$
$$\left. + 2\sqrt{S(S+1)} \cos (S, J) \right] \frac{M}{\sqrt{J(J+1)}} \mu_0, \tag{V, 73}$$

where the two cosines are to be taken from the obtuse-angled triangle in Fig. 131(b) (see also A.A., p. 110). According to (V, 73), there is again a splitting into $2J + 1$ equidistant components. However, now the *total splitting* ($M = \pm J$) for large J,

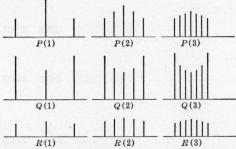

Fig. 133. Splitting of the First Lines of a $^1\Sigma - ^1\Pi$ Band in a Magnetic Field [after Crawford (**171**)]. The length of the vertical lines gives the intensity.

when the first term in the bracket is small, is *approximately independent of J* and is of the order of magnitude of the normal Zeeman splitting.

To be sure, it very often happens in case (b) that the coupling between S and K is so small that these two angular momenta are uncoupled even by a small field. The *molecular analogue to the Paschen-Back effect* then appears (see A.A., p. 112); S and K are space quantized independently of each other in the field direction. As a result, $\bar{\mu}_H$ is given by the simpler formula

$$\bar{\mu}_H = \frac{\Lambda^2 \mu_0}{\sqrt{K(K+1)}} \cos (K, H) + 2\sqrt{S(S+1)} \mu_0 \cos (S, H)$$
$$= \frac{\Lambda^2 M_K}{K(K+1)} \mu_0 + 2 M_S \mu_0, \tag{V, 74}$$

since $\cos (K, H) = M_K/\sqrt{K(K+1)}$ and $\cos (S, H) = M_S/\sqrt{S(S+1)}$. The first term in (V, 74) corresponds exactly to $\bar{\mu}_H$ for case (a), if in (V, 72) we put $\Sigma = 0$, $J = K$, and $M = M_K$. Formula (V, 74) holds as long as the multiplet splitting is small compared to the Zeeman splitting. As in case (a), the first term in (V, 74) decreases rapidly with increasing K, whereas the second term is independent of K. Fig. 132(b) shows the splitting of a $^2\Pi$ state in this coupling case. For higher K there is practically only a splitting into two components (or, in general, $2S + 1$) corresponding to $M_S = \pm\frac{1}{2}$, with a separation $2\mu_0 H$. Fig. 132(c) gives the splitting for a $^2\Sigma$ term. Here the first term in (V, 74) is zero, since $\Lambda = 0$, and there remains only a splitting into two components, independent of K. Only in higher approximation, as a result of the interaction between K and S, does there appear a very small splitting of each component with a given M_S into $2K + 1$ components, which is of the same order of magnitude as the doublet splitting without field. In Fig. 132(c) this is indicated only by a broadening of the levels. Triplets and higher multiplets behave correspondingly.

If the doublet (multiplet) splitting without field is appreciably greater than the normal Zeeman splitting, formula (V, 73) holds; that is, a splitting of each doublet (multiplet) component into $2J + 1$ components takes place, the total splitting being of the order of $2\Delta\nu_n$.

When the Paschen-Back effect is present in both states participating in a transition, the selection rule $\Delta M_S = 0$ holds (see p. 27); that is, for doublet states $M_S = +\frac{1}{2}$ in the upper state combines only with $M_S = +\frac{1}{2}$ in the lower state, and correspondingly for $M_S = -\frac{1}{2}$. Since, however, the Zeeman splitting due to S in the upper and lower states is the same, it means that actually the line splitting in a doublet or triplet band of case (b) in a magnetic field is of exactly the same type as that for a corresponding singlet transition. In particular, for a $^2\Sigma - ^2\Sigma$ transition, no Zeeman splitting is to be expected; for $^2\Sigma \leftrightarrow ^2\Pi$, only a splitting for small K values is to be expected; and so on. Actually, the lines of the violet CN bands ($^2\Sigma - ^2\Sigma$), for example, show no splitting in a magnetic field.[18] Furthermore, the triplet bands of the He$_2$ molecule, for which the triplet splitting is vanishingly small, show exactly the same Zeeman splitting as the corresponding singlet bands of He$_2$.

Other cases. For *transition cases* between coupling cases (a) and (b), which in practice usually occur for multiplet states with $\Lambda \neq 0$, the behavior in a magnetic field is much more complicated.

---

[18] To be sure, the lines with very high K, which without field are split into doublets, show a small diminution of the doublet separation in a field. This behavior may be understood theoretically by taking into account the interaction of S and K.

Hill (322) has given detailed formulae for these cases [see also Crawford (171)]. The splitting for the different J values depends strongly on $Y = A/B$, where A is the spin-coupling constant (see p. 256) and B is the rotational constant. As an example, consider a $^2\Pi$ term that belongs to case (a) for small rotation but goes to case (b) for larger J. Here the splitting for the $^2\Pi_{\frac{1}{2}}$ component is zero as long as case (a) is a good approximation, since $\mu = 0$, whereas, if case (b) is approximated, both components show the same kind of splitting. The line splitting of the individual band lines would be correspondingly complicated in these cases. Such experimental data as there are confirm the theoretical results [Crawford (171)].

For the molecules H_2 and He_2, the transition to *case* (d) is also important. In this case, L is quantized with respect to the rotational axis, and therefore the Zeeman splittings for the singlet states also (including $^1\Sigma$ if $L \neq 0$) are of the order of the normal Zeeman splitting even for large K. The behavior of the splitting in intermediate cases, which actually occur more often than the limiting cases, is very complicated. It will not be discussed here.

Finally, the *Zeeman splitting of perturbed lines* must be mentioned. It has been found experimentally that perturbed lines are much more strongly influenced by a magnetic field than the neighboring normal lines of the same band. This is easily understood from the fact that only levels with equal M can perturb each other. As long as no magnetic field is present, this selection rule for perturbations plays no part, since all the levels with different M and equal J coincide, and therefore it was not mentioned in our previous discussion of perturbations. However, in a magnetic field, the splitting of the perturbing state is in general different from that of the perturbed state, and therefore the interaction of the individual component levels of the perturbed and the perturbing state is not the same for all values of M, since their separation varies. Therefore a large perturbation of some component levels can be indirectly brought about by the field, and thus a comparatively large line splitting in the field is observed. The magnitude and type of the interaction naturally depend very strongly on the kind of terms perturbing each other, and therefore an investigation of the Zeeman effect of perturbed lines lends itself to determining the type of the perturbing term. Thus far, however, there is very little material in this field [see Crawford (171) and Schmid and Gerö (620)].

Magnetic rotation spectra. According to the theory of the Faraday effect (that is, the magnetic rotation of the plane of polarization), when linearly polarized light goes through a gas that is in a longitudinal magnetic field, a rotation of the plane of polarization takes place if the wave length of the incident light lies very close to an absorption line of the gas considered and if the absorption line considered is split in the magnetic field. This effect, first discovered for a monatomic gas by Macaluso and Corbino, was first found for a diatomic gas—namely, Na_2—by Wood (719).

In Wood's experiments white light is sent through two crossed Nicols, between which is placed a tube filled with Na_2 vapor. As long as there is no magnetic field, no light goes through the system. However, when a longitudinal magnetic field is applied, a small part of the light does go through—namely, that part for which the plane of polarization has been rotated. An investigation of the spectrum of this transmitted light shows that it consists of individual bright lines or narrow bands whose positions agree very closely with those of the heads of the absorption bands of the vapor. However, the spectrum is much *simpler than the absorption spectrum*, since, instead of each band, there is only one line or at most a very narrow band. Such *magnetic rotation spectra* have also been found and investigated for a number of other molecules, including I_2, Br_2, K_2, and Bi_2. In particular, with their help, Loomis and co-workers [(463)–(465), (459), and (462)] have followed the vibrational quanta for the upper state of the alkali molecules to considerably higher v' values than was possible by the absorption spectrum.

From what has been said, the explanation for the magnetic rotation spectra of diatomic molecules is clear: Since a rotation of the plane of polarization takes place only in the immediate neighborhood of such absorption lines as show a noticeable Zeeman effect, in general *only the lines in a band with the lowest J values lead to a magnetic rotation*. Therefore, only in their immediate neighborhood is light transmitted by the crossed Nicols (unless the magnetic field is extremely strong). That is why only part of each band appears in the magnetic rotation spectrum. This effect is strengthened if the head of the band lies at low J values, since then part of the light that gives strong magnetic rotation lies just outside the band, and is therefore not absorbed by the gas.

According to the preceding discussion, magnetic rotation spectra should appear only for band systems showing a noticeable Zeeman effect. Actually, the absorption systems of the alkalis that have been particularly thoroughly investigated are $^1\Pi - {}^1\Sigma$ transitions, which show a marked Zeeman splitting for small J (see above). For $^1\Sigma - {}^1\Sigma$ transitions there should be no magnetic rotation spectrum. However, in two cases—the red Na_2 absorption bands and the infrared K_2 absorption bands, which represent such transitions—weak magnetic rotation spectra have been found. It has been shown by Carroll (150) that the explanation for this apparent contradiction to the theory lies in the fact that the upper $^1\Sigma$ state of the bands is perturbed by a $^3\Pi$ state. The perturbed levels of the $^1\Sigma$ state assume to a certain extent the properties of the $^3\Pi$ state—that is, they have a magnetic moment (whereas the nonperturbed levels have none)—and are therefore split in the magnetic field. In consequence of this, the perturbed lines (and only these) will produce a magnetic rotation. In agreement with this explanation the magnetic rotation lines observed in these band systems do not in general lie in the neighborhood of the zero lines of the bands, as is the case for $^1\Pi - {}^1\Sigma$ magnetic rotation spectra.

It should be noted that the appearance of a magnetic rotation spectrum is a much more sensitive criterion for the existence of a Zeeman splitting than the direct observation of the line splitting in a magnetic field.

CHAPTER VI

Building-Up Principles, Electron Configurations, and Valence

By the experimental investigation of band spectra, a number of electronic states have been found for many diatomic molecules. In this chapter we shall attempt to derive the type and energy of these states theoretically. This theoretical investigation leads to results of great value in the study of heats of dissociation and dissociation processes of molecules (see Chapter VII) and for an understanding of chemical valence.

The *manifold of electronic states*—that is, the totality of the energy levels of a molecule—can be obtained, as for atoms, by the *successive bringing together of the parts* (*building-up principle*). Whereas, however, the building up of the atom can take place only in one way, for a molecule there are three different possibilities:

1. The molecule may be built up by *bringing together the whole atoms* of which it consists; that is, we can investigate the question of what kind of molecular states result from given states of the separated atoms. When we have carried this out for all possible combinations of atomic states, we obtain the total manifold of the states of the molecule.

2. Instead of beginning with infinitely large separation, as in 1, we may start with zero nuclear separation; that is, we can *split the so-called united atom*. This procedure is naturally purely hypothetical, but, in spite of that, it is suitable for the determination of the term manifold.

3. Finally, we may employ a procedure analogous to that used for atoms: We *add the individual electrons* one after another *to the nuclei*, which are regarded as fixed, and con-

sider in which "orbits" or quantum cells the electrons will arrange themselves. The different possible electronic arrangements (electron configurations) then give the possible states as for atoms.

1. DETERMINATION OF THE TERM MANIFOLD FROM THE STATES OF THE SEPARATED ATOMS

Wigner and Witmer (712), on the basis of quantum mechanics, have derived rules for determining *what types of molecular states result from given atomic states.* According to the theory, these *correlation rules* should hold rigorously and be complete—that is, should give all the molecular states. Actually, cases contradicting them have thus far not been observed. To be sure, in many cases, the empirical data do not suffice for an unambiguous test of the theory. We have rather to use the Wigner-Witmer correlation rules as a help in correlating correctly the observed molecular states with those of the separated atoms. This procedure is absolutely safe, however, provided we assume the validity of quantum mechanics for molecules.

Unlike atoms. When two atoms with L and S values equal to L_1, S_1, and L_2, S_2, respectively, are brought up to each other, an (inhomogeneous) electric field results in the direction of the line joining the nuclei, producing a space quantization of L_1 and L_2 with reference to this direction such that the components are M_{L_1} and M_{L_2} (see p. 26). The resultant orbital angular momentum about the line joining the nuclei is therefore $M_{L_1} + M_{L_2}$, and the quantum number Λ of the molecule thus formed is

$$\Lambda = \left| M_{L_1} + M_{L_2} \right|. \tag{VI, 1}$$

By combination of all the possible M_{L_i} values we obtain all the possible Λ values.

In general, the different orientations of the L_i and thus the different Λ values correspond to different energies in the electric field; in fact, the difference in energy will be the greater the stronger the field—that is, the smaller the internuclear distance. Thus, from a given combination of the states of the separated atoms there results a number of different states of the whole system. The quantum number Λ of the resultant orbital angular momentum retains its meaning even for a close approach of the two atoms, such as in the actual molecule, where the L_i and M_{L_i} of the individual atoms have completely lost their meaning as angular momenta. Thus in this way, by starting out with large nuclear separation, where the L_i and M_{L_i} are well defined, we can derive the number and type of the resulting molecular states.

It should be noted that states which differ only in the sign of both M_{L_1} and M_{L_2} (and thus also of $M_{L_1} + M_{L_2}$) have equal energies as long as $M_{L_1} + M_{L_2} \neq 0$. They correspond to the two components of a molecular state with $\Lambda \neq 0$ which are degenerate with each other (see p. 233). For $\Lambda = M_{L_1} + M_{L_2} = 0$, however, each combination corresponds to a different molecular state (Σ state).

Let us consider as an example the case of an atom in an S state ($L_1 = 0$) approaching an atom in a D state ($L_2 = 2$). Then $M_{L_1} = 0$, while M_{L_2} can take the values 2, 1, 0, -1, and -2. According to (VI, 1), we have the Λ values 2, 1, and 0, where the values 2 and 1 occur twice. Thus we obtain a Δ, a Π, and a Σ state which have different energies. Similarly, from an S state and a P state we obtain the molecular states Π and Σ. If both $L_i \neq 0$, we obtain in general a number of like states.

The resulting molecular states for most of the cases occurring in practice are given in Table 26. When several states of the same kind result, their number is given in parentheses after the term symbol. Furthermore, for Σ states it is indicated whether they are Σ^+ or Σ^- states. As Wigner and Witmer have shown, this depends on the L_i values as well as on whether the atomic terms are even or odd—that is, whether Σl_i is even or odd. Consequently, the indices g and u are added to the atomic terms in the table. It can be seen from the table that, whenever both atoms have $L \neq 0$, the number of resulting molecular states is rather large.

TABLE 26

MOLECULAR ELECTRONIC STATES RESULTING FROM GIVEN STATES OF THE SEPARATED (UNLIKE) ATOMS

[According to Wigner and Witmer (712); see also similar tables in Mulliken (514).]

States of the Separated Atoms	Molecular States
$S_g + S_g$ or $S_u + S_u$	Σ^+
$S_g + S_u$	Σ^-
$S_g + P_g$ or $S_u + P_u$	Σ^-, Π
$S_g + P_u$ or $S_u + P_g$	Σ^+, Π
$S_g + D_g$ or $S_u + D_u$	Σ^+, Π, Δ
$S_g + D_u$ or $S_u + D_g$	Σ^-, Π, Δ
$S_g + F_g$ or $S_u + F_u$	Σ^-, Π, Δ, Φ
$S_g + F_u$ or $S_u + F_g$	Σ^+, Π, Δ, Φ
$P_g + P_g$ or $P_u + P_u$	$\Sigma^+(2)$, Σ^-, $\Pi(2)$, Δ
$P_g + P_u$	Σ^+, $\Sigma^-(2)$, $\Pi(2)$, Δ
$P_g + D_g$ or $P_u + D_u$	Σ^+, $\Sigma^-(2)$, $\Pi(3)$, $\Delta(2)$, Φ
$P_g + D_u$ or $P_u + D_g$	$\Sigma^+(2)$, Σ^-, $\Pi(3)$, $\Delta(2)$, Φ
$P_g + F_g$ or $P_u + F_u$	$\Sigma^+(2)$, Σ^-, $\Pi(3)$, $\Delta(3)$, $\Phi(2)$, Γ
$P_g + F_u$ or $P_u + F_g$	Σ^+, $\Sigma^-(2)$, $\Pi(3)$, $\Delta(3)$, $\Phi(2)$, Γ
$D_g + D_g$ or $D_u + D_u$	$\Sigma^+(3)$, $\Sigma^-(2)$, $\Pi(4)$, $\Delta(3)$, $\Phi(2)$, Γ
$D_g + D_u$	$\Sigma^+(2)$, $\Sigma^-(3)$, $\Pi(4)$, $\Delta(3)$, $\Phi(2)$, Γ
$D_g + F_g$ or $D_u + F_u$	$\Sigma^+(2)$, $\Sigma^-(3)$, $\Pi(5)$, $\Delta(4)$, $\Phi(3)$, $\Gamma(2)$, H
$D_g + F_u$ or $D_u + F_g$	$\Sigma^+(3)$, $\Sigma^-(2)$, $\Pi(5)$, $\Delta(4)$, $\Phi(3)$, $\Gamma(2)$, H

The precise rule concerning Σ^+ and Σ^- states is as follows: The number of Σ^+ states is one larger than the number of Σ^- states when $L_1 + L_2 + \Sigma l_{i_1} + \Sigma l_{i_2}$ is even, and it is one smaller than the number of Σ^- states when $L_1 + L_2 + \Sigma l_{i_1} + \Sigma l_{i_2}$ is odd.

The way in which the six states resulting from the combination $P + P$ of the separated atoms arise is illustrated by vector diagrams in Fig. 134. The two lower left configurations leading to Σ states differ only in the sign of both M_{L_i} values. In zero approximation they are degenerate with each other, as is each of the two combinations belonging to the Δ and the two Π states. Whereas, however, the Δ and Π states retain their twofold degeneracy, even when the finer interaction of the two atoms is taken into account, the states with $\Lambda = 0$ which are in zero approximation degenerate with each other split into two different Σ states when this interaction is allowed for. One of these is Σ^+ and the other is Σ^-. It would, however, be wrong to assume that the Σ^+ term corresponded to the one configuration and the Σ^- term to the other. Both configurations are, so to speak, contained in both states (compare the similar situation discussed on p. 240).

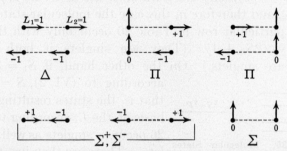

Fig. 134. **Vector Diagrams Showing the Determination of Molecular States from the Combination $P + P$ of the Separated Atoms.** The arrows represent the orientations of the L_i of the separated atoms. The numbers $+1$, 0, -1 indicate the M_{L_1} and M_{L_2} values. It can easily be verified by the reader that all the quantum theoretically possible orientations have been drawn. For simplicity the approximate values, $L_i(h/2\pi)$, have been used for the magnitude of the L_i [not the rigorous values $\sqrt{L(L+1)}(h/2\pi)$; see p. 24].

Whether the Σ state given by the third configuration with $\Lambda = 0$ is a Σ^+ or a Σ^- state depends on whether the atomic states have the same symmetry (both even or both odd) or the opposite symmetry (see the above rule).

We have yet to determine the *multiplicity* of the resulting molecular states. Let us assume that the coupling of the L_i to the field between the nuclei is strong compared to the coupling between L_i and S_i. Then, since the spin is not influenced by an electric field, the two spin vectors S_1 and S_2 of the separated atoms add together to a resultant S, the resultant spin vector of the molecule. The corresponding quantum number is (see p. 22)

$$S = (S_1 + S_2), (S_1 + S_2 - 1),$$
$$(S_1 + S_2 - 2), \cdots, |S_1 - S_2|. \tag{VI, 2}$$

For a given orientation of the L_i, each of the values of S in (VI, 2) is possible; that is, *each of the states given in Table 26 can occur with each of the multiplicities $(2S + 1)$ given by*

(VI, 2). Naturally the states with different multiplicities have different energies.

If, for example, one of the two atomic states is a singlet state ($S_1 = 0$), only one S value of the molecule is possible, $S = S_2$, and therefore in this case the molecular states given in the particular row in Table 26 occur only with the multiplicity ($2S_2 + 1$). (They are singlets if both atomic states are singlets.) On the other hand, if $S_1 = S_2 = \frac{1}{2}$,

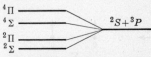

according to (VI, 2), $S = 1$ or 0; that is, the states resulting on the basis of the L_i according to Table 26 occur as singlets as well as triplets. There are then just twice as many states. If $S_1 = S_2 = 1$, $S = 2$ or 1 or 0. The states in Table 26 then occur as quintets

Fig. 135. Molecular States Resulting from $^2S + {}^3P$ (Schematic). To the right, for large nuclear distances; to the left, in the molecule.

as well as triplets and singlets. If $S_1 = \frac{1}{2}$ and $S_2 = 1$, $S = \frac{3}{2}$ or $\frac{1}{2}$; that is, the states occur as quartets or as doublets. Further examples can easily be formed by the reader. The molecular states resulting from an atom in a ^2S state and an atom in a ^3P state are represented schematically in an energy level diagram in Fig. 135.

It can be seen from these considerations that the manifold of the molecular states is much greater than that of the states of the separated atoms.

If the coupling between the L_i and S_i in the separated atoms is strong compared to the coupling of the L_i to the internuclear axis, a space quantization of the J_i's ($J_i = L_i + S_i$) rather than the L_i's takes place in the electric field produced when the atoms approach each other. The electronic angular momentum along the internuclear axis of the molecule (inclusive of spin)—that is, Ω—is then obtained by adding the M_{J_i} values. Analogous to (VI, 1), we have

$$\Omega = |M_{J_1} + M_{J_2}|. \qquad (VI, 3)$$

To every combination of M_{J_i} values corresponds a different molecular state, except that states differing only in the sign of both M_{J_1} and M_{J_2} form a degenerate pair as long as $\Omega \neq 0$. The Λ

value of the molecule in this kind of coupling is not defined but only the Ω value [case (c); see p. 247].

When both J_i are integral, the resulting Ω values for a given combination of J_i values are the same as the Λ values for the same combination of L_i values (see Table 26). Also the conditions for 0^+ and 0^- states are the same as for Σ^+ and Σ^-. For example, for $J_1 = 1$ and $J_2 = 1$, if both atomic states are even we obtain the Ω values 2, 1, 1, 0^+, 0^+, 0^- for the resulting molecular states.

When both J_i are half integral, the Ω values can be obtained in an analogous way from (VI, 3). In this case the number of states with $\Omega = 0$ is even, and half of them are 0^+ and the other half 0^-. For example, for $J_1 = \frac{3}{2}$, $J_2 = \frac{3}{2}$, we obtain the Ω values 3, 2, 2, 1, 1, 1, 0^+, 0^+, 0^-, 0^-; or, for $J_1 = \frac{3}{2}$, $J_2 = \frac{1}{2}$, we obtain the Ω values 2, 1, 1, 0^+, 0^-.

When one J_i is integral and the other half integral, again it is easy to form all possible $M_{J_1} + M_{J_2}$ values and determine Ω from (VI, 3). Here $\Omega = 0$ does not occur.

Naturally, for given L_1, S_1 and L_2, S_2 of the separated atoms the possible Ω values resulting from (VI, 3) are the same as those obtained from the Λ and S values resulting from (VI, 1) and (VI, 2).

Like atoms. If the nuclei of the two atoms that are brought together have the same charge, we have to distinguish whether the two atoms are in the same state or not. If they are *in the same state*, we obtain exactly the same molecular states as for unlike atoms [see Table 26 and (VI, 2)]. However, for like nuclei we have also the symmetry property *even* or *odd* of the electronic eigenfunctions (see p. 239). General rules for determining which of the resulting states are even and which are odd have been derived by Wigner and Witmer [see also Mulliken (514)]. Here we shall give in Table 27 only the resulting term types for the cases occurring in practice.

If the two atoms (for equal nuclear charge) are *not in the same state*, for large separation of the nuclei there is a resonance between those two states of the whole system for which either the one or the other atom is in the higher excited state. According to Table 26 and relation (VI, 2), the same molecular terms result from both combinations of states. For example, from $^1S_g + {}^1P_u$ we get $^1\Sigma^+$ and $^1\Pi$.

TABLE 27

MOLECULAR ELECTRONIC STATES RESULTING FROM LIKE STATES OF THE SEPARATED ATOMS FOR EQUAL NUCLEAR CHARGE

[According to Wigner and Witmer (712); see also Mulliken (514).]

States of the Separated Atoms*	Molecular States
$^1S + {}^1S$	$^1\Sigma_g{}^+$
$^2S + {}^2S$	$^1\Sigma_g{}^+, {}^3\Sigma_u{}^+$
$^3S + {}^3S$	$^1\Sigma_g{}^+, {}^3\Sigma_u{}^+, {}^5\Sigma_g{}^+$
$^4S + {}^4S$	$^1\Sigma_g{}^+, {}^3\Sigma_u{}^+, {}^5\Sigma_g{}^+, {}^7\Sigma_u{}^+$
$^1P + {}^1P$	$^1\Sigma_g{}^+(2), {}^1\Sigma_u{}^-, {}^1\Pi_g, {}^1\Pi_u, {}^1\Delta_g$
$^2P + {}^2P$	$^1\Sigma_g{}^+(2), {}^1\Sigma_u{}^-, {}^1\Pi_g, {}^1\Pi_u, {}^1\Delta_g, {}^3\Sigma_u{}^+(2), {}^3\Sigma_g{}^-, {}^3\Pi_g, {}^3\Pi_u, {}^3\Delta_u$
$^3P + {}^3P$	Singlet and triplet terms as for $^2P + {}^2P$; in addition, $^5\Sigma_g{}^+(2), {}^5\Sigma_u{}^-, {}^5\Pi_g, {}^5\Pi_u, {}^5\Delta_g$
$^1D + {}^1D$	$^1\Sigma_g{}^+(3), {}^1\Sigma_u{}^-(2), {}^1\Pi_g(2), {}^1\Pi_u(2), {}^1\Delta_g(2), {}^1\Delta_u, {}^1\Phi_g, {}^1\Phi_u, {}^1\Gamma_g$
$^2D + {}^2D$	Singlets as for $^1D + {}^1D$; in addition, $^3\Sigma_u{}^+(3), {}^3\Sigma_g{}^-(2), {}^3\Pi_u(2), {}^3\Pi_g(2), {}^3\Delta_u(2), {}^3\Delta_g, {}^3\Phi_u, {}^3\Phi_g, {}^3\Gamma_u$
$^3D + {}^3D$	Singlets as for $^1D + {}^1D$, triplets as for $^2D + {}^2D$, and quintets like singlets

* Whether the atomic state is even or odd is of no importance here, since both atoms are in the same state.

However, we also get the same from $^1P_u + {}^1S_g$—that is, when the excitation energies of the two like atoms are interchanged. Thus we have two $^1\Sigma^+$ and two $^1\Pi$ terms that have equal energies for large nuclear distance. Consequently, as a result of the interaction of the two atoms, as the internuclear distance becomes smaller we get four different states of different energy. A detailed calculation shows that one of each of the pairs of like states is even and the other is odd.[1] Thus, in the example $^1S_g + {}^1P_u$, for like atoms we obtain the states $^1\Sigma_g{}^+$, $^1\Sigma_u{}^+$, $^1\Pi_g$, and $^1\Pi_u$. Similarly, in more complicated cases *each of the states occurring for unlike atoms* [see Table 26 and relation (VI, 2)] *occurs twice for like atoms, once as an odd and once as an even state.* It is therefore not necessary to give a special table.

---

[1] Of course, the odd state does *not* correspond to the excitation of one atom and the even to the excitation of the other.

For the case that the L_i and S_i are strongly coupled [case (c)], again analogous relations hold. If the atoms are in the same state and if J is integral, we can use Table 27 if we substitute J for L and Ω for Λ and consider the singlet states only. For half-integral J we supplement the table by the two following examples: If both atoms are in the same state with $J = \frac{1}{2}$, we obtain the molecular states 1_u, $0_g{}^+$, $0_u{}^-$, where the numbers give the Ω values. For $J_1 = J_2 = \frac{3}{2}$ we obtain 3_u, 2_u, 2_g, 1_u, 1_g, 1_u, $0_g{}^+$, $0_u{}^-$, $0_g{}^+$, $0_u{}^-$. If the atoms are in unlike states, as before each of the states occurring for unlike atoms occurs twice, once as an odd and once as an even state.

2. DETERMINATION OF THE TERM MANIFOLD FROM THE STATES OF THE UNITED ATOM

Unlike atoms. If we imagine the nucleus of an atom to be split into two unlike nuclei, then, for a small separation of the resulting nuclei, this splitting has the same influence on the states of the system as an external electric field. If L and S are the orbital angular momentum and spin of the united atom, the following holds for the resulting molecule (see Chapter V, section 1):

$$\Lambda = |M_L| = L, L - 1, L - 2, \cdots, 0. \qquad \text{(VI, 4)}$$

The spin S of the molecule remains the same as in the atomic state from which the molecular state results. Thus, if we have, for example, a ^3D_g state of the magnesium atom, we get the molecular states $^3\Delta$, $^3\Pi$, and $^3\Sigma$ if we imagine the nucleus to be divided into a Be and an O nucleus or into a B and an N nucleus, and so on. Whether the resulting Σ state is a Σ^+ or a Σ^- state depends, as a more detailed calculation shows, upon whether $L + \Sigma l_i$ for the united atom is even or odd. Therefore we obtain in our example $^3\Sigma^+$, since $L + \Sigma l_i$ is even for ^3D_g.

If L and S are very strongly coupled in the united atom, there is no uncoupling of L and S when the nuclei are separated. A state of the united atom with given J will then split into the molecular states with

$$\Omega = |M_J| = J, J - 1, J - 2, \cdots, \tfrac{1}{2} \text{ or } 0, \qquad \text{(VI, 5)}$$

where the lowest Ω value is $\frac{1}{2}$ or 0, depending on whether J is half integral or integral. In the latter case the state with $\Omega = 0$ is a 0^+ or 0^- state according as $J + \Sigma l_i$ is even or odd.

Like atoms. For a splitting of the united atom into atoms with nuclei of equal charge—for example, splitting of the Mg atom into C + C—we get exactly the same states as for unlike atoms, except that the symmetry property even or odd has to be added. Calculation shows that the resulting molecular states are all even or all odd according as the state of the united atom is an even or an odd one. In the above example we therefore get, for C_2, $^3\Delta_g$, $^3\Pi_g$, and $^3\Sigma_g{}^+$.

3. DETERMINATION OF THE TERM MANIFOLD FROM THE ELECTRON CONFIGURATION

(a) Quantum Numbers of the Individual Electrons

As we have seen in Chapter II, p. 35, the spectrum of the He_2 molecule especially (but also that of some other molecules, such as H_2 and N_2) exhibits Rydberg series of bands instead of the vibrational series usually observed. Obviously, these band series result from transitions from a *Rydberg series of electronic states* (see Chapter I, p. 9) to a lower electronic state.

For atoms, Rydberg series of terms correspond to the excitation of a single electron to orbits with different principal quantum numbers. It is natural to attempt to ascertain whether or not a similar explanation is applicable to molecules. For this purpose we must investigate in somewhat greater detail the *motion of the individual electrons in the molecule* and the corresponding quantum numbers.

Single electron in a rotationally symmetric electric field. We shall first consider the motion of a single electron at a large distance from the molecular core consisting of the two nuclei and the remaining electrons (for example, an electron moving about $He_2{}^+$). We shall suppose the nuclei to be held fixed at a certain distance from each other. Such a system is called a *two-center system*. The field of force acting on the outer electron may be regarded, to a good approximation, as rotationally symmetric about the internuclear axis. We shall assume here that it is exactly rotationally symmetric.

The investigation of the Schrödinger equation (I, 12) for the motion of an electron in such a field of force (V rotationally symmetric and approaching zero for large separations) shows that, as for atoms, it is soluble for every positive energy value E but only for certain discrete negative E values. $E = 0$ corresponds to an infinitely large separation of the electron from the core, without relative kinetic energy.

As for an atom, the *continuous region of positive E values* corresponds to the *removal or capture of an electron* (ionization or recombination) with a kinetic energy which is not zero even at an infinite distance from the core, whereas for the discrete negative E values the electron cannot leave the field of the core. The *negative E values* thus correspond to the *stationary electronic states* of the system. Wave mechanical considerations show that, if we disregard electron spin, the stationary states can be characterized by three quantum numbers, of which, however, only one is precisely defined for all separations of the two nuclei. The latter quantum number is the exact analogue of the quantum number Λ, previously introduced for the electronic state of the whole molecule, and is designated by λ. The corresponding vector $\boldsymbol{\lambda}$ *represents the component of the orbital angular momentum of the electron about the internuclear axis and has the magnitude* $\lambda(h/2\pi)$. Thus if $\lambda \neq 0$, the electron rotates about the internuclear axis (even according to wave mechanics). The possible values of λ are 0, 1, 2, 3, $\cdots$. According to which of these values an electron has, it is called a σ, π, δ, φ, $\cdots$ electron, respectively.

The other two quantum numbers can be defined only approximately, and, in fact, this can be done in two different ways, depending on whether we start out from the case of very small internuclear distance ($r \rightarrow 0$) or very large internuclear distance ($r \rightarrow \infty$).

In the united atom—that is, for $r = 0$—the possible states of an electron are defined by the *quantum numbers n and l* (see p. 19). If the united atom is now split in such a way that the distance between the two nuclei is still small, the possible electronic orbits are the same as for the united atom in an electric field (Stark effect). In this case (small nuclear separation) the quantum numbers n and l are still approximately defined. The orbital angular momentum l of the electron is space quantized in the field and precesses with constant component $m_l(h/2\pi)$ about the field direction (see Fig. 90, which shows the corresponding behavior for L).[2] States with different $|m_l|$ have somewhat different

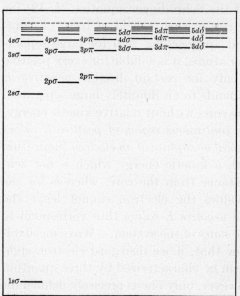

Fig. 136.   Energy Levels of a Single Electron in the Field of Two Fixed Centers at a Small Distance from Each Other (Schematic). Further term series with higher values of l and λ would join on to the right. The broken line above represents the ionization limit. It should be noted that states with equal n and equal l have only slightly different energies.

energies. $|m_l|$ is the *quantum number* λ, already introduced above, which retains its meaning as orbital angular momentum about the internuclear axis for any nuclear separation. Thus λ, for a given value of l, can take the values

$$\lambda = l, l - 1, l - 2, \cdots, 0. \tag{VI, 6}$$

[2] In the old Bohr interpretation this would mean that the plane of the elliptical orbit (which is perpendicular to l) can have only certain inclinations to the internuclear axis and rotates about this axis in such a way that the angle is kept constant.

States with $\lambda \neq 0$ are doubly degenerate, since a positive and a negative m_l having the same magnitude correspond to one and the same λ.

The *energy level diagram for an electron* for the case of small nuclear separation is drawn schematically in Fig. 136. In this diagram the values of the three quantum numbers are given by symbols such as $2s\sigma$, $3p\sigma$, $4d\pi$, and so on, in which the number gives the n value, the Roman letter gives the l value (as for atoms), and the Greek letter gives the λ value (see above). With increasing separation of the two nuclei (centers), the splitting between the states with different λ for the same n and the same l becomes greater and n and l lose more and more their meaning as quantum numbers. However, according to the Ehrenfest adiabatic law (see A.A., p. 86), the number of states is not thereby altered. Therefore, in the manner described, we can at least obtain the *manifold of the states of an electron even for intermediate nuclear distances.*

For very large separation of the two nuclei, which we designate by A and B, the one electron considered may be either with A or with B. Suppose it has the quantum numbers n and l in the particular atom. As the atoms approach, an electric field is produced, in which once more a space quantization of l takes place such that its component in the internuclear axis is equal to $m_l(h/2\pi)$. $|m_l| = \lambda$ is again the orbital angular momentum of the electron about the internuclear axis. Symbolically, we write the n and l values that the electron has in the separated atoms after the symbols giving the λ value (sometimes in parentheses), thus: $\sigma 1s$ or $\sigma(1s)$, $\pi 3d$ or $\pi(3d)$, and so on. When possible, the atom from which the electron under consideration comes is also indicated—for example, $\sigma 1s_A$, $\sigma 1s_B$, and so on. It should be noted that the quantum numbers n and l that an electron has in one of the separated atoms are in general not the same as those it would have in the united atom.

According to quantum mechanics, we cannot speak of definite orbits of the electron about the two nuclei but can only give the *probability of finding the electron at the various positions in the molecule.* This probability is given by the square of the magnitude of the *eigenfunction* of the wave equation belonging to the energy value considered (see p. 13).   In order to illustrate the form of the eigenfunctions of the lowest states, their *nodal surfaces*—that is, the surfaces on which they have the value zero—are given in two cross

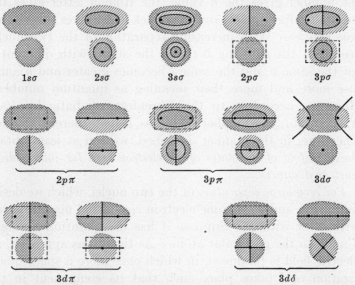

Fig. 137. Nodal Surfaces of the Eigenfunctions of an Electron in the Field of Two Fixed Centers [after Weizel (703)] (Schematic).   In each case, two cross sections are drawn, the one containing the line joining the nuclei and the other at right angles to it. The sign of the eigenfunction (− or +) is indicated by single and cross hatching. When the plane of the drawing is a nodal plane, this is indicated by a broken-line rectangle. In this case, the hatching gives the sign immediately in front of the plane of the drawing.   For π and δ electrons there are two eigenfunctions corresponding to the twofold degeneracy.

sections in Fig. 137 according to Weizel (703). Strictly speaking, the figure holds only for the case in which the core consists only of the two nuclei; however, qualitatively, it holds also for the more general case considered here (rotationally symmetric electric field). The nodal surfaces are planes through the internuclear axis, or rotational ellipsoids or rotational hyperboloids with the nuclei as foci. The hyperboloids degenerate in some cases into a plane perpendicular to the internuclear axis. The sign of the eigenfunction is indicated by different shading; it is opposite on the two opposite sides of a nodal surface.

If the two nuclei in the core have *unequal charges*, a given eigenfunction has different magnitudes at two points symmetrically placed with respect to the midpoint. It is obvious that the probability density in the neighborhood of the more strongly charged nucleus is the greater.

If, however, the two nuclei have *equal charges*, the eigenfunction has the same magnitude at two points placed symmetrically with respect to the midpoint (see also p. 238 f.) and can at most differ in sign. Corresponding to the earlier nomenclature, the states of the electron (for equal nuclear charge) are called *even* (g) or *odd* (u) according as the eigenfunction remains unaltered or changes sign by reflection at the origin. Symbolically, we write σ_g, σ_u, π_g, π_u, $\cdots$. We can easily see from Fig. 137 that for an even l of the united atom (s, d, $\cdots$ electrons) the eigenfunctions have the property g and for odd l (p, f, $\cdots$ electrons) they have the property u. At infinite nuclear separation always two states, such as $\pi 2p_A$ and $\pi 2p_B$, have the same energy if $A = B$. As the atoms approach, this degeneracy is removed and we obtain in the example a π_g and a π_u state. Other states of the electron behave correspondingly. Therefore, for large nuclear separations and equal nuclear charge we use the designation $\pi_u 2p$, $\pi_g 2p$, and so on. The property g–u for equal nuclear charge is exactly defined for any internuclear distance.

To the three quantum numbers λ, n, and l (the last two corresponding either to the separated atoms or to the united atom) must naturally be added the *quantum number s of the electron spin*, which behaves in quite the same way as for atoms for any distance between the two nuclei.

The eigenfunctions dealt with above refer to the motion of the electron apart from spin. They are also called *orbital wave functions*, and the corresponding states are called *orbitals* [see Mulliken (517)].   However, it should be noted that we cannot speak of actual orbits in wave mechanics.

For the subsequent discussion it is important to establish *in what way the orbitals alter in the transition from small to*

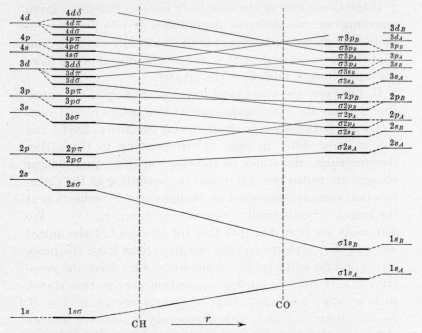

Fig. 138.   Correlation of Electronic Orbitals in a Two-Center System for Unequal Nuclear Charges.   To the extreme left and the extreme right are given the orbitals in the united and separated atoms, respectively, and, beside them, those in the molecule for very small and very large nuclear separations, respectively.   The region between corresponds to intermediate nuclear separations. The vertical broken lines give the approximate positions in the diagram that correspond to the molecules indicated.   It should be noticed that the scale of r in this and the following figure is by no means linear but becomes rapidly smaller on the right-hand side.   Owing to this change of scale, the straight connecting lines between right and left do not correspond to a linear energy change with r but to one that is closer to reality, even though it is an admittedly poor approximation.

large nuclear distances and, in particular, into which orbitals of the one limiting case those of the other limiting case go over.   Thus far, an exact calculation for intermediate nuclear distances has been carried out only for the case of $H_2{}^+$, for which the core consists of only the two nuclei [see

Morse and Stueckelberg (505), Teller (663), and Hellmig (296)]. However, for the more general cases we can obtain at least an approximate idea of the relative energies of the orbitals and the dependence of the energy on the nuclear distance when we *interpolate between the limiting cases* in the following way:

In Fig. 138, for the case of *unequal nuclear charges* the rela-

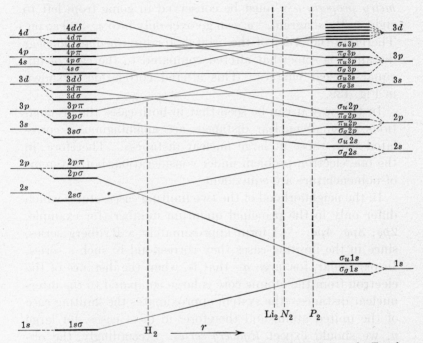

Fig. 139. Correlation of Electronic Orbitals in a Two-Center System for Equal Nuclear Charges. See the remarks for Fig. 138.

tive energies of the possible orbitals of an electron in the two limiting cases are represented by horizontal lines to the right and the left, respectively. We have now to consider that a σ orbital to the left can go over only into a σ orbital to the right, a π orbital can go over only into a π orbital, and so on. Also, theory shows that two different σ orbitals (and correspondingly for π, δ, and so on) cannot intersect if the nuclear distance is changed (see also p. 324). The *correlation* between left and right is then unambiguously given; the lowest σ orbital to the right goes into the lowest σ orbital to the left, the second lowest σ orbital to the right goes into the second lowest to the left, and so on. π, δ, $\cdots$ orbitals behave correspondingly.   This correlation is indicated in Fig. 138 by the connecting lines.

In the case of *equal nuclear charges*, in addition, the *symmetry property g–u* must be conserved in going from left to right in the diagram. σ_u can go over only into σ_u, and so on. Therefore the order of the orbitals for intermediate nuclear distances is somewhat altered compared to the case of unequal nuclear charges.   This altered correlation is shown in Fig. 139.

In this way it can be seen that in both cases the designations at small nuclear distances are unambiguously correlated with those at large nuclear distances.   Therefore, in the one electron problem under consideration, both systems of nomenclature are equivalent.

In the neighborhood of the two limiting cases, states which differ only in the principal quantum number (for example, $2p\sigma$, $3p\sigma$, $4p\sigma$, $\cdots$) form approximately a Rydberg series, since in the limiting cases they correspond to such a series. In particular, for large n—that is, when the distance of the electron from the atomic core is large compared to the internuclear distance—the system approximates the limiting case of the united atom, and therefore, in most cases, for large n, we should expect *Rydberg series*.   Accordingly, the observed Rydberg series of electronic states for He_2, N_2, and others are actually to be interpreted as terms of a single electron (emission electron) moving in the field of a molecular core.   From the limit of the Rydberg series we can obtain an accurate value for the ionization potential of the molecule under consideration (as for atoms).

In solving the wave equation (I, 12) for an electron in a rotationally symmetric field, it is advantageous to introduce cylindrical co-ordinates z, ρ, and φ, where the z axis is the internuclear axis, ρ is the perpendicular distance from the internuclear axis, and φ is

the azimuth against a fixed plane through the internuclear axis.
The expression $\dfrac{\partial^2\psi}{\partial x^2} + \dfrac{\partial^2\psi}{\partial y^2}$ in (I, 12) then goes over into $\dfrac{\partial^2\psi}{\partial\rho^2} + \dfrac{1}{\rho}\dfrac{\partial\psi}{\partial\rho}$
$+ \dfrac{1}{\rho^2}\dfrac{\partial^2\psi}{\partial\varphi^2}$ (see any text on partial differential equations). Consequently the wave equation becomes

$$\frac{\partial^2\psi}{\partial z^2} + \frac{\partial^2\psi}{\partial\rho^2} + \frac{1}{\rho}\frac{\partial\psi}{\partial\rho} + \frac{1}{\rho^2}\frac{\partial^2\psi}{\partial\varphi^2} + \frac{8\pi^2 m}{h^2}(E - V)\psi = 0, \quad \text{(VI, 7)}$$

where V depends only on z and ρ. In consequence the solution can be written as a product of a function of z and ρ, and a function of φ alone.

$$\psi = \chi(z, \rho) \cdot f(\varphi). \tag{VI, 8}$$

Substituting in (VI, 7) and multiplying by $\rho^2/[\chi(z, \rho) \cdot f(\varphi)]$, we obtain

$$\frac{\rho^2}{\chi}\frac{\partial^2\chi}{\partial z^2} + \frac{\rho^2}{\chi}\frac{\partial^2\chi}{\partial\rho^2} + \frac{\rho}{\chi}\frac{\partial\chi}{\partial\rho}\frac{8\pi^2 m\rho^2}{h^2}[E - V(z,\rho)] = -\frac{1}{f}\frac{\partial^2 f}{\partial\varphi^2},$$

where the left-hand side depends on ρ and z only, whereas the right-hand side depends on φ only. Therefore both sides must be equal to a constant, which we call λ^2. Consequently for $f(\varphi)$ we have the differential equation

$$\frac{d^2 f(\varphi)}{d\varphi^2} + \lambda^2 f(\varphi) = 0,$$

whose solution is

$$f(\varphi) = e^{\pm i\lambda\varphi}. \tag{VI, 9}$$

Since ψ is to be single-valued everywhere, we must require that $f(\varphi + 2\pi) = f(\varphi)$. This, according to (VI, 9), is possible only when λ is an integer. λ is the quantum number introduced previously. As shown by the above considerations, it is exactly defined for every internuclear distance. Substituting $e^{\pm i\lambda\varphi}$ in (VI, 8), we obtain

$$\psi = \chi(z, \rho)\, e^{\pm i\lambda\varphi}. \tag{VI, 10}$$

The possibility of taking out the factor $e^{\pm i\lambda\varphi}$ is due to the fact that the potential energy of the system is independent of φ. A more detailed calculation shows that $\lambda(h/2\pi)$ is indeed the orbital angular momentum about the internuclear axis (see a similar proof in A.A., p. 49). Thus for $\lambda > 0$ there is, even wave mechanically, a rotation of the electron about the internuclear axis, although there are no definite orbits.

According to (VI, 10), there are two eigenfunctions for one and the same χ and a given $\lambda \neq 0$ (twofold degeneracy). For $\lambda = 0$ there is only one eigenfunction, which is rotationally symmetric about the internuclear axis. For $\lambda \neq 0$, instead of the two functions (VI, 10), we may also use any linear combination of them (see p. 234), for example $\chi(z, \rho) \cos \lambda\varphi$ and $\chi(z, \rho) \sin \lambda\varphi$, both of which have λ nodal planes through the internuclear axis (at different angles for the former and the latter; see Fig. 137).

Quantum numbers corresponding to the function χ can be exactly defined only when χ can be resolved into a product of two functions, each depending on only one co-ordinate. This resolution is possible in the limiting cases (united atom or separated atoms), in which χ can be resolved into a product of two functions, one of r alone and one of ϑ alone, where r and ϑ are polar co-ordinates—that is, $r \ (= \sqrt{z^2 + \rho^2})$ is the distance from the center and ϑ (= arc tan ρ/z) is the angle against the z axis (internuclear axis). Therefore we can define the quantum numbers n and l (see above) exactly in these limiting cases and approximately also in the neighborhood of the limiting cases. However, in the region of intermediate nuclear distances, n and l cannot in general be exactly defined. Only when the core consists of only two nuclei (for example, $H_2{}^+$) can χ be resolved into a product $f(\mu) \cdot g(\nu)$, where μ and ν are elliptical co-ordinates [see, for example, Weizel (33)]. Correspondingly, in this case, in addition to λ, we can exactly define, for any internuclear distance, two further quantum numbers, which are in a fixed relation to the n and l values of the united atom or of the separate atoms. However, we shall not discuss this in detail here.

In many cases the eigenfunctions of a single electron in a molecule (*molecular orbitals*) can be approximated by a *linear combination of the orbital wave functions of the separate atoms* (atomic orbitals). In the case of *equal nuclear charges*, for example, the orbital $\sigma 2p$ for large internuclear distance has the same energy for each of the two atoms (see above). For smaller internuclear distances there is a splitting into $\sigma_g 2p$ and $\sigma_u 2p$. Let $\psi_A(\sigma 2p)$ and $\psi_B(\sigma 2p)$ be the orbital wave functions of the $\sigma 2p$ electron in the atoms A and B, respectively. For equal nuclear charges, these two functions are of exactly the same form and can be brought into coincidence by a shift AB. It can then be shown that the molecular orbital wave functions of $\sigma_g 2p$ and $\sigma_u 2p$ are given to a first approximation by

$$\psi_{AB}(\sigma_g 2p) = \psi_A(\sigma 2p) + \psi_B(\sigma 2p),$$
$$\psi_{AB}(\sigma_u 2p) = \psi_A(\sigma 2p) - \psi_B(\sigma 2p). \qquad \text{(VI, 11)}$$

For other orbitals, similar relations hold, except that for π, φ, $\cdots$ orbitals, $+$ and $-$ are exchanged. In order to introduce this mode of representation of molecular orbital wave functions directly into the symbol, Mulliken (519) writes, for example, for the above two orbits, instead of $\sigma_g 2p$ and $\sigma_u 2p$, $(\sigma 2p + \sigma 2p,\ \sigma_g)$ and $(\sigma 2p - \sigma 2p,\ \sigma_u)$, or, in short, $(\sigma + \sigma,\ \sigma_g)$ and $(\sigma - \sigma,\ \sigma_u)$, and similarly in other cases.

For *unequal nuclear charges* at very large internuclear distances, the eigenfunctions $\psi_A(\sigma 2p)$ and $\psi_B(\sigma 2p)$ (and correspondingly for other orbitals) are no longer of exactly the same form. For smaller internuclear distances the orbital wave function is, as in the previous case, a mixture of the two eigenfunctions (linear combination). However, the coefficients are no longer simply $+1$ or -1, but we have

$$\psi_{AB}(\sigma 2p_A) = a\psi_A(\sigma 2p) + b\psi_B(\sigma 2p),$$
$$\psi_{AB}(\sigma 2p_B) = c\psi_A(\sigma 2p) - d\psi_B(\sigma 2p),$$

(VI, 12)

where $a > b$ and $d > c$. The difference between a and b (and c and d) is the greater the greater the difference in nuclear charges. These eigenfunctions are also indicated by Mulliken in the symbols for the orbital by writing $(\sigma 2p_A + \sigma 2p_B,\ \sigma)$ and $(\sigma 2p_A - \sigma 2p_B,\ \sigma)$, respectively, where the $2p$ is omitted when it is self-evident. Other cases are similar.

Several electrons. To a certain approximation the considerations of the foregoing section can be applied to all the electrons of a molecule, since to a first approximation the motion of each individual electron can be regarded as a *motion in a rotationally symmetric field*—namely, that obtained by averaging over the different positions of the other electrons. However, in actuality, the field acting on the one electron naturally depends on the *momentary* positions of the other electrons and is therefore not strictly rotationally symmetric. This deviation is the less important the larger the distance of the electron under consideration from the remaining electrons.

Thus to a certain approximation we can characterize each individual electron in the molecule by the quantum numbers introduced above (see also Figs. 137–139). The electrons may be in any of the possible orbitals discussed above. A certain *electron configuration* of the molecule is defined by stating the quantum numbers of all the electrons in the molecule. States with different electron configurations have different energies. Actually, as we shall see, for a given electron configuration, we obtain in general several different energy states of the system.

If two or more electrons in a molecule have the same quantum numbers (apart from spin) and the same symmetry g or u, they are called *equivalent electrons*.

(b) The Pauli Principle in the Molecule

In the molecule, as well as in the atom, the number of electrons that can be in the same orbital is limited by the Pauli principle. In the atom this principle says that no two electrons can have the same set of the four quantum numbers n, l, m_l and m_s, or, since m_s can take only the values $+\frac{1}{2}$ and $-\frac{1}{2}$, that not more than two electrons can have the same set of the three quantum numbers n, l, and m_l.

The adaptation of this principle to the molecule is immediately clear from the foregoing considerations if we remember that the number of states of an atomic system is not altered by an alteration of the coupling conditions. Therefore we can start out from the behavior for very small internuclear distances, where the quantum numbers n and l are well defined. Since then $\lambda = |m_l|$, it follows that for given n and l there can be only two electrons with $\lambda = 0$ ($m_l = 0$, $m_s = \pm\frac{1}{2}$), while there can be four electrons for each $\lambda \neq 0$ ($m_l = +\lambda$, $m_s = \pm\frac{1}{2}$ and $m_l = -\lambda$, $m_s = \pm\frac{1}{2}$). In Table 28 these relations are represented for the different n and l values in a manner analogous to that used for atoms in Table 3. The energy increases from left to right. Thus *a σ shell of a molecule is closed with two electrons, a π shell with four electrons, and similarly a δ shell with four electrons,* and so on.

The same results are obtained if we start out from *widely separated nuclei*. Then, for unequally charged nuclei, the order of the shells is given by

$$\sigma 1s_A, \ \sigma 1s_B, \ \sigma 2s_A, \ \sigma 2s_B, \ \sigma 2p_A, \ \sigma 2p_B, \ \pi 2p_A, \ \pi 2p_B, \cdots, \quad \text{(VI, 13)}$$

TABLE 28

PAULI PRINCIPLE IN THE MOLECULE (FOR SMALL INTERNUCLEAR DISTANCE)

n	1	2				3									4
l	0	0	1			0	1			2					...
λ	0	0	0	1		0	0	1		0	1		2		...
m_l	0	0	0	$+1$	-1	0	0	$+1$	-1	0	$+1$	-1	$+2$	-2	...
m_s	↑↓	↑↓	↑↓	↑↓	↑↓	↑↓	↑↓	↑↓	↑↓	↑↓	↑↓	↑↓	↑↓	↑↓	...
	$1s\sigma$	$2s\sigma$	$2p\sigma$	$2p\pi$		$3s\sigma$	$3p\sigma$	$3p\pi$		$3d\sigma$	$3d\pi$		$3d\delta$		...

and as before, on the basis of the Pauli principle, each σ shell can contain only two electrons and each π, δ, $\cdots$ shell only four electrons. For equal nuclear charges, it is true, we have at first, for example, four equivalent $1s$ electrons of the two separated atoms; however, as soon as the atoms approach each other, the distinction between g and u appears. Two of the $1s$ electrons become σ_g, and the other two become σ_u, which go over into different orbitals of the united atom (see Fig. 139), and again only two σ electrons are equivalent. The other electrons behave correspondingly.

Thus, when we have, for example, a system with six electrons, for small internuclear distance these cannot all go into the $1s\sigma$ orbital but give as the lowest state $1s\sigma^2 2s\sigma^2 2p\sigma^2$. For large internuclear distance, when the nuclear charges are equal, the lowest configuration is $\sigma_g^2(1s)\sigma_u^2(1s)\sigma_g^2(2s)$.

(c) Derivation of the Term Type from the Electron Configuration

Terms of nonequivalent electrons. In the following we shall assume that the orbital angular momenta of the individual electrons are more strongly coupled with one another and the spins with one another than each individual orbital angular momentum with the corresponding spin (this coupling corresponds to the Russell-Saunders coupling for atoms). Then we can derive the terms resulting from a given electron configuration in the following way. The *resultant orbital angular momentum about the internuclear axis, Λ, is equal to the sum of the individual orbital angular momenta λ_i;* that is,

$$\Lambda = \Sigma\lambda_i. \qquad (VI, 14)$$

The *resultant spin is equal to the sum of the individual spins;* that is,

$$S = \Sigma s_i. \qquad (VI, 15)$$

All the vectors in (VI, 14) lie along the internuclear axis, and therefore we have a simple *algebraic* addition. In this addition we have to take into account the fact that the two opposite directions are possible for each individual vector. In (VI, 15) we have to add *vectorially* in the same way as for atoms (see p. 21 f.). S is integral or half integral according as the number of electrons is even or odd.

For nonequivalent electrons, the Pauli principle is satisfied *ipso facto* and need not be considered in the vector addition.

If we have, for example, a single π electron, $\Lambda = \lambda = 1$ and $S = \frac{1}{2}$; that is, we have a $^2\Pi$ state. If there is a π and a σ electron, Λ is again 1 but S can now, according to (VI, 15), take the values 1 and 0 and we have a $^3\Pi$ and a $^1\Pi$ state. Similar considerations hold for a single δ electron and for the configuration $\sigma\delta$.

If we have a π and a δ electron, the two λ_i's can have either the same or opposite directions—that is, $\Lambda = 3$ or 1. Since the spin can be 1 or 0, as before, we obtain the states $^1\Pi$, $^3\Pi$, $^1\Phi$, and $^3\Phi$. The vector addition of the λ_i for this case is represented diagrammatically in Fig. 140(a). To zero approximation—that is, neglecting the finer interaction of the electrons (see p. 355)—the four states drawn have equal energies. On the other hand, when this interaction is taken into account, the energy of the two states with $\Lambda = 3$ is somewhat different from that of the states with $\Lambda = 1$.

However, the degeneracy of the two components of the Π state or of the Φ state, respectively, remains even when the interaction of the electrons is taken fully into account.

In Fig. 140(b) the addition of the λ_i vectors for two π electrons is represented. The result is that Λ can be 2 or 0. Each of these two values results in two ways. The degen-

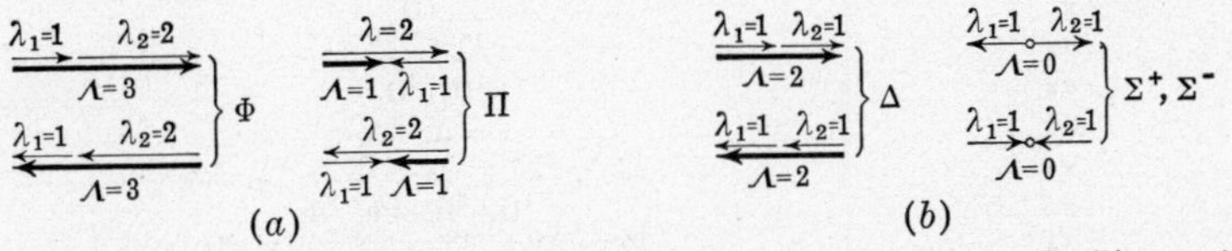

Fig. 140. Vector Addition of the λ_i to Give Λ. (a) $\lambda_1 = 1, \lambda_2 = 2$. ($b$) $\lambda_1 = 1$, $\lambda_2 = 1$. The λ_i are represented by light arrows, and the Λ by heavy arrows.

eracy of the two states with $\Lambda = 0$, in contrast to that of the two states with $\Lambda = 2$, does not, however, persist when the finer interaction of the electrons is taken into account, but the states split into a Σ^+ and a Σ^- state (Σ states, as we have seen, are always nondegenerate). We therefore obtain for the terms of two nonequivalent π electrons, if we also allow for spin, $^1\Sigma^+$, $^3\Sigma^+$, $^1\Sigma^-$, $^3\Sigma^-$, $^1\Delta$, and $^3\Delta$.

These examples, together with some others, are collected in Table 29.

The energy difference between corresponding states of different multiplicity is due to Heisenberg's resonance (as for atoms)— that is, to the electrostatic interaction of the electrons. In spite of that, we can always proceed *as though* it were due to a coupling energy of the spins. This procedure is usually applied for atoms (see A.A., p. 129) and has also been used implicitly in the above discussion for molecules.

Terms of equivalent electrons. If the electrons whose terms we wish to determine are equivalent, we have to take account of the *Pauli principle* when adding the λ_i and the s_i; that is, the electrons must differ either in m_l or in m_s.

For *two equivalent σ electrons*, since the m_l are equal, the spins must be antiparallel, so that only a single term results— namely, a $^1\Sigma$ state ($\Lambda = 0$, $S = 0$)—whereas for two non-equivalent σ electrons we obtain $^1\Sigma$ and $^3\Sigma$.

TABLE 29

TERMS OF NONEQUIVALENT ELECTRONS

[After Hund (347)]

Electron Configuration	Molecular Electronic Terms
σ	$^2\Sigma^+$
π	$^2\Pi_r$
$\sigma\sigma$	$^1\Sigma^+,\ ^3\Sigma^+$
$\sigma\pi$	$^1\Pi,\ ^3\Pi_r$
$\sigma\delta$	$^1\Delta,\ ^3\Delta_r$
$\pi\pi$	$^1\Sigma^+,\ ^3\Sigma^+,\ ^1\Sigma^-,\ ^3\Sigma^-,\ ^1\Delta,\ ^3\Delta_r$
$\pi\delta$	$^1\Pi,\ ^3\Pi,\ ^1\Phi,\ ^3\Phi_r$
$\delta\delta$	$^1\Sigma^+,\ ^3\Sigma^+,\ ^1\Sigma^-,\ ^3\Sigma^-,\ ^1\Gamma,\ ^3\Gamma_r$
$\sigma\sigma\sigma$	$^2\Sigma^+,\ ^2\Sigma^+,\ ^4\Sigma^+$
$\sigma\sigma\pi$	$^2\Pi,\ ^2\Pi,\ ^4\Pi_r$
$\sigma\sigma\delta$	$^2\Delta,\ ^2\Delta,\ ^4\Delta_r$
$\sigma\pi\pi$	$^2\Sigma^+(2),\ ^4\Sigma^+,\ ^2\Sigma^-(2),\ ^4\Sigma^-,\ ^2\Delta(2),\ ^4\Delta_r$
$\sigma\pi\delta$	$^2\Pi(2),\ ^4\Pi,\ ^2\Phi(2),\ ^4\Phi_r$
$\pi\pi\pi$	$^2\Pi(6),\ ^4\Pi(3),\ ^2\Phi(2),\ ^4\Phi_r$
$\pi\pi\delta$	$^2\Sigma^+(2),\ ^4\Sigma^+,\ ^2\Sigma^-(2),\ ^4\Sigma^-,\ ^2\Delta(4),\ ^4\Delta(2),^2\Gamma(2),\ ^4\Gamma_r$

The numbers in parentheses give the number of states of the type given if this number is not 1. The subscripts r indicate regular (normal) multiplets (see p. 237).

For *two equivalent π electrons*, if the two λ_i vectors are parallel [see Fig. 140(b)], on the basis of the Pauli principle the spins must be antiparallel. (If the spins were parallel, the two electrons would be alike in all four quantum numbers, n, l, m_l, and m_s.) Thus only a $^1\Delta$ and no $^3\Delta$ state can result. On the other hand, if the λ_i have opposite directions, the spins may be parallel or antiparallel and there results a $^1\Sigma$ as well as a $^3\Sigma$ state. A more detailed investigation shows that, of the Σ^+ and Σ^- states derived above for nonequivalent electrons, for equivalent electrons the former can occur only as singlet and the latter as triplet. We have thus the three states $^3\Sigma^-$, $^1\Delta$, and $^1\Sigma^+$. On the basis of the Hund rule,

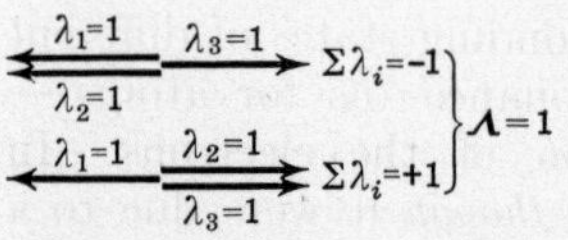

Fig. 141. Vector Diagram for the Configuration π^3. In order to avoid confusion, the resultant Λ has not been drawn. Since the electrons are equivalent, orientations of the λ_i, in which only the subscripts i are interchanged, are not to be counted as different from the two given.

$$\lambda_1=1 \quad \lambda_3=1$$
$$\lambda_2=1 \qquad \Sigma\lambda_i=-1$$
$$\lambda_1=1 \quad \lambda_2=1$$
$$\lambda_3=1 \qquad \Sigma\lambda_i=+1$$
$$\Lambda=1$$

which holds for molecules as well as for atoms (see A.A., p. 135), the state with greatest multiplicity, $^3\Sigma^-$, lies lowest.

For *three equivalent π electrons* (π^3), the three λ_i can have only the two relative orientations given in Fig. 141, both of which give $\Lambda = 1$—that is, a Π term. Since, owing to the Pauli principle, two of the electrons must always have antiparallel spin directions, the total spin can be only $S = \frac{1}{2}$; that is, only a $^2\Pi$ state results.

If *four equivalent π electrons* are present (π^4), the shell under consideration is closed (see p. 356); the λ_i must, in consequence of the Pauli principle, form antiparallel pairs. Therefore $\Lambda = 0$. Similarly, the s_i must also form antiparallel pairs, and, as a result, S is also equal to zero. We therefore obtain only a single $^1\Sigma$ state.

TABLE 30

TERMS OF EQUIVALENT ELEC-
TRONS

[After Hund (347)]

Electron Configuration	Molecular Electronic Terms
σ^2	$^1\Sigma^+$
π^2	$^1\Sigma^+$, $^3\Sigma^-$, $^1\Delta$
π^3	$^2\Pi_i$
π^4	$^1\Sigma^+$
δ^2	$^1\Sigma^+$, $^3\Sigma^-$, $^1\Gamma$
δ^3	$^2\Delta_i$
δ^4	$^1\Sigma^+$

The subscripts i indicate inverted multiplets.

These and other examples are collected in Table 30. The number of equivalent electrons is indicated by the exponent of the symbol in question. *Closed shells* always give a single $^1\Sigma$ state (similar to atoms, where they give a ^1S state).

Electron configurations with equivalent and nonequivalent electrons. If equivalent as well as nonequivalent electrons are present in an electron configuration, we first form separately the resultant Λ and S values for the equivalent electrons (Λ_e, S_e) and those of the nonequivalent electrons (Λ_n, S_n) and then add the Λ_e, S_e, Λ_n, and S_n in the same manner as discussed above for the addition of the λ_i and the s_i. In forming these resultants, we can always leave closed shells out of account, since they give $\Lambda = 0$ and $S = 0$. Table 31 gives the results for the most important cases.

Table 31

TERMS OF ELECTRON CONFIGURATIONS WITH EQUIVALENT AS WELL AS NONEQUIVALENT ELECTRONS

[After Hund (347) and Mulliken (514)]

Electron Configuration	Molecular Electronic Terms
$\pi^2\sigma$	$^2\Sigma^+,\ ^2\Sigma^-,\ ^2\Delta,\ ^4\Sigma^-$
$\pi^2\pi$	$^2\Pi_r,\ ^2\Pi_i(2),\ ^2\Phi_r,\ ^4\Pi_r$
$\pi^2\delta$	$^2\Sigma^+,\ ^2\Sigma^-,\ ^2\Delta_r,\ ^2\Delta_i,\ ^2\Gamma_r,\ ^4\Delta_r$
$\pi^2\sigma\sigma$	$^1\Sigma^+,\ ^1\Sigma^-,\ ^1\Delta,\ ^3\Sigma^+,\ ^3\Sigma^-(2),\ ^3\Delta,\ ^5\Sigma^-$
$\pi^2\sigma\pi$	$^1\Pi(3),\ ^1\Phi,\ ^3\Pi_r(2),\ ^3\Pi_i(2),\ ^3\Phi_r,\ ^5\Pi_r$
$\pi^2\sigma\delta$	$^1\Sigma^+,\ ^1\Sigma^-,\ ^1\Delta(2),\ ^1\Gamma,\ ^3\Sigma^+,\ ^3\Sigma^-,\ ^3\Delta(3),\ ^3\Gamma,\ ^5\Delta$
$\pi^2\pi\pi$	$^1\Sigma^+(3),\ ^1\Sigma^-(3),\ ^1\Delta(4),\ ^1\Gamma,\ ^3\Sigma^+(4),\ ^3\Sigma^-(4),\ ^3\Delta(5),\ ^3\Gamma,\ ^5\Sigma^+,\ ^5\Sigma^-,\ ^5\Delta$
$\pi^2\pi^2$	$^1\Sigma^+(3),\ ^1\Sigma^-,\ ^1\Delta(2),\ ^1\Gamma,\ ^3\Sigma^+,\ ^3\Sigma^-(2),\ ^3\Delta(2),\ ^5\Sigma^+$
$\pi^3\sigma$	$^1\Pi,\ ^3\Pi_i$
$\pi^3\pi$	$^1\Sigma^+,\ ^1\Sigma^-,\ ^1\Delta,\ ^3\Sigma^+,\ ^3\Sigma^-,\ ^3\Delta$
$\pi^3\delta$	$^1\Pi,\ ^1\Phi,\ ^3\Pi,\ ^3\Phi$
$\pi^3\pi^2$	$^2\Pi_i,\ ^2\Pi_r,\ ^2\Pi,\ ^2\Phi_i,\ ^4\Pi_i$
$\pi^3\pi^3$	$^1\Sigma^+,\ ^1\Sigma^-,\ ^1\Delta,\ ^3\Sigma^+,\ ^3\Sigma^-,\ ^3\Delta_i$
$\pi^3\pi^2\sigma$	$^1\Pi(3),\ ^1\Phi,\ ^3\Pi_i(2),\ ^3\Pi_r(2),\ ^3\Phi_i,\ ^5\Pi_i$
$\pi^3\pi^3\sigma$	$^2\Sigma^+(2),\ ^2\Sigma^-(2),\ ^2\Delta,\ ^2\Delta_i,\ ^4\Sigma^+,\ ^4\Sigma^-,\ ^4\Delta_i$

The subscripts r and i indicate regular (normal) and inverted multiplets, respectively.

Like atoms. For molecules consisting of like atoms (equal nuclear charge), everything is just as before (Tables 29–31) except that in addition we have to determine whether the resulting states are even or odd. According to what has previously been said, it is clear that the terms of a given electron configuration must either all be even or all be odd. They are *even if the number of "odd" electrons* (σ_u, π_u, $\cdots$) *is even*, whereas they are *odd if the number of "odd" electrons is odd*.

(d) Term Manifold of the Molecule

General. The representation of the electronic structure of a molecule by electronic configurations is, as has been mentioned, only an approximation—sometimes, in fact, only a poor approximation. In spite of that, on the basis of the Ehrenfest adiabatic law we can derive therefrom the *correct manifold of electronic states* of any molecule.

In order to obtain on this basis the term manifold for a given molecule—that is, for a given number of electrons—we have first of all to place the electrons in the lowest possible orbitals (shells) as far as is allowed by the Pauli principle, thus obtaining the ground state, and then bring one or more of the outer electrons into higher orbitals, and in each case determine the resulting term types from Tables 29–31. If we know the relative energies of the orbitals, we can obtain in this way not only the term manifold but also, though quite roughly, the *relative positions of the terms*.

It will be realized that this procedure corresponds exactly to the procedure for determining the term manifold of atoms (Bohr's building-up principle). However, the difference is that for molecules the order of the orbitals *depends on the internuclear distance and on the nuclear charge*. If these are altered—that is, in different molecules—considerable alterations in the order of the orbitals result, as is illustrated by Figs. 138 and 139. The larger the internuclear distance and the larger the nuclear charge, the farther to the right lies in these figures the vertical line that gives the order of the orbitals. For unlike atoms (Fig. 138), in addition, the relative positions of the orbitals at large internuclear distances depend greatly on the degree of dissimilarity of the atoms. The order holding for some molecules is indicated by broken vertical lines in Figs. 138 and 139.[3] The position of this vertical line for a given molecule cannot be given theoretically with any certainty but is in general better taken from experiment. Naturally, these lines are so drawn that for atoms of the second period of the periodic system, Li to F, the *K* electrons in the molecule have practically the same energy as in the separated atoms, and correspondingly for the *L* electrons for the atoms of the next period.[4]

---

[3] Representation by such a vertical line is, of course, a very rough approximation. It may very well be that the higher orbitals in a given molecule correspond to a different vertical line than the lower ones.

[4] Strictly speaking, owing to the splitting $\sigma_g 1s - \sigma_u 1s$, we have in a diatomic molecule two X-ray *K* levels instead of the one for the atom. However, the splitting is so small in comparison to the total energy of the X-ray levels that it has not hitherto been observed with certainty.

H₂ and the hydrides. As examples, let us consider first the H_2 molecule and the diatomic hydrides. Their internuclear distances are very small (for H_2, 0.74 Å), and so it can be assumed that they approach fairly closely the united

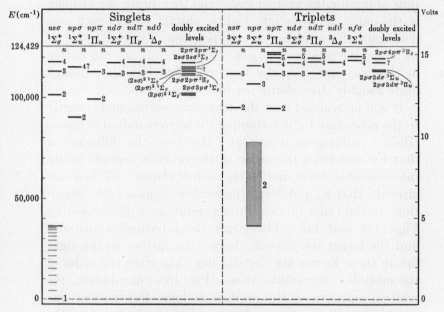

Fig. 142.   Diagram of the Observed Electronic States of the H_2 Molecule.
The data for most of the ordinary states are taken from Richardson (47), and those for the doubly excited states from Richardson (586), and Richardson and Rymer (587). For the ground state, the vibrational levels, which are observed up to the limit, are also indicated (shorter horizontal lines). Above each column (with exception of the doubly excited states) the orbital of the excited electron and the term type is given. The numbers by the terms give the n values. The state $2p\sigma\ ^3\Sigma_u$ is the unstable state resulting from two normal atoms. The corresponding continuum is indicated by hatching. It should, of course, extend up to infinity.

atom. Actually, with this assumption there is an excellent agreement between the observed electronic states and those predicted theoretically on the basis of the building-up principle.[4a] Thus for the order of the electronic shells we have to use the left side of Figs. 138 and 139.

[4a] In addition, the magnitude of the Λ doubling and of the multiplet splitting fits very well with this assumption [see Mulliken and Christy (523)].

The *ground state of* H_2 is the state in which both electrons are in the lowest orbital, $1s\sigma$ $(=\sigma_g 1s)$. This is a $^1\Sigma_g{}^+$ state (see Table 30). Most of the *excited states* result from one of the electrons going from the lowest orbital to one of the higher orbitals $2s\sigma$, $2p\sigma$, $2p\pi$, $\cdots$. In each case a singlet and triplet state result whose Λ value, according to Table 29, is equal to the λ of the one excited electron (emission electron). The analysis of the observed H_2 spectrum, which proved at first very difficult, since no pronounced bands appear, has been considerably advanced during the last decade by the work of Richardson, Dieke, Weizel, and their co-workers, and has led to the discovery of a large number of electronic states [see Richardson (47)]. Fig. 142 is an energy level diagram of the observed electronic states of the H_2 molecule. It was found that most of the observed states can be explained without difficulty as being due to the excitation of one electron to various orbitals. A comparison of Fig. 142 with Fig. 136 shows how good the agreement between theory and experiment is. In addition to these normal terms a number of states have been found that correspond to the excitation of both electrons. They are also given in Fig. 142, together with the electron configurations to which they are due. One or two observed states are as yet unexplained because not sufficient data are known for them. For some of the normal states longer Rydberg series, which have led to an accurate determination of the ionization potential, have been found.

In Table 32 are collected the lowest and the first excited electronic configurations to be expected on the basis of Fig. 138 for most of the *diatomic hydride molecules* thus far known. The resulting electronic states are also given. LiH, for example, has four electrons for which, according to the Pauli principle, the energetically lowest configuration is $(1s\sigma)^2 (2s\sigma)^2$. This configuration gives a $^1\Sigma^+$ state, which is indeed observed as the ground state of LiH. The two $1s\sigma$ electrons form the K shell of the Li atom, which is only slightly influenced by the molecule formation. Because of this, only the

TABLE 32

ELECTRON CONFIGURATIONS AND TERM TYPES OF THE LOWEST STATES OF DIATOMIC HYDRIDES

Molecule	Lowest Electron Configuration	First Excited Electron Configuration
LiH, BeH+	$K(2s\sigma)^2$ $^1\Sigma^+$	$2s\sigma 2p\sigma$ $^1\Sigma^+$ [$^3\Sigma^+$]
NaH, MgH+	$KL(3s\sigma)^2$ $^1\Sigma^+$	$3s\sigma 3p\sigma$ $^1\Sigma^+$ [$^3\Sigma^+$]
KH	$KLM_{sp}(4s\sigma)^2$ $^1\Sigma^+$	$4s\sigma 3d\sigma$ $^1\Sigma^+$ [$^3\Sigma^+$]
CuH, ZnH+	$KLM\ (4s\sigma)^2$ $^1\Sigma^+$	$4s\sigma 4p\sigma$ $^1\Sigma^+$ [$^3\Sigma^+$]
AgH, CdH+	$KLMN_{spd}(5s\sigma)^2$ $^1\Sigma^+$	$5s\sigma 5p\sigma$ $^1\Sigma^+$ [$^3\Sigma^+$]
AuH, HgH+	$KLMNO_{spd}(6s\sigma)^2$ $^1\Sigma^+$	$6s\sigma 6p\sigma$ $^1\Sigma^+$ [$^3\Sigma^+$]
BeH, BH+	$K(2s\sigma)^2 2p\sigma$ $^2\Sigma^+$	$(2s\sigma)^2 2p\pi$ $^2\Pi_r$
MgH, AlH+	$KL(3s\sigma)^2 3p\sigma$ $^2\Sigma^+$	$(3s\sigma)^2 3p\pi$ $^2\Pi_r$
CaH	$KLM_{sp}(4s\sigma)^2 3d\sigma$ $^2\Sigma^+$	$(4s\sigma)^2 3d\pi$ $^2\Pi_r$
ZnH	$KLM\ (4s\sigma)^2 4p\sigma$ $^2\Sigma^+$	$(4s\sigma)^2 4p\pi$ $^2\Pi_r$
SrH	$KLMN_{sp}(5s\sigma)^2 4d\sigma$ $^2\Sigma^+$	$(5s\sigma)^2 4d\pi$ $^2\Pi_r$
CdH	$KLMN_{spd}(5s\sigma)^2 5p\sigma$ $^2\Sigma^+$	$(5s\sigma)^2 5p\pi$ $^2\Pi_r$
BaH	$KLMN_{spd}O_{sp}(6s\sigma)^2 5d\sigma$ $^2\Sigma^+$	$(6s\sigma)^2 5d\pi$ $^2\Pi_r$
HgH	$KLMNO_{spd}(6s\sigma)^2 6p\sigma$ $^2\Sigma^+$	$(6s\sigma)^2 6p\pi$ $^2\Pi_r$
BH	$K(2s\sigma)^2(2p\sigma)^2$ $^1\Sigma^+$	$(2s\sigma)^2 2p\sigma 2p\pi$ $^1\Pi$, $^3\Pi$
AlH	$KL(3s\sigma)(3p\sigma)^2$ $^1\Sigma^+$	$(3s\sigma)^2 3p\sigma 3p\pi$ $^1\Pi$, $^3\Pi$
InH	$KLM_{spd}(5s\sigma)^2(5p\sigma)^2$ $^1\Sigma^+$	$(5s\sigma)^2 5p\sigma 5p\pi$ $^1\Pi$ [$^3\Pi$]
CH	$K(2s\sigma)^2(2p\sigma)^2 2p\pi$ $^2\Pi_r$	$(2s\sigma)^2 2p\sigma(2p\pi)^2$ [$^4\Sigma^-$], $^2\Delta$, $^2\Sigma^+$, $^2\Sigma^-$
SiH	$KL(3s\sigma)^2(3p\sigma)^2 3p\pi$ $^2\Pi_r$	$(3s\sigma)^2 3p\sigma(3p\pi)^2$ [$^4\Sigma^-$], $^2\Delta$, [$^2\Sigma^+$], [$^2\Sigma^-$]
SnH	$KLMN_{spd}(5s\sigma)^2(5p\sigma)^2 5p\pi$ $^2\Pi_r$	$(5s\sigma)^2 5p\sigma(5p\pi)^2$ [$^4\Sigma^-$], $^2\Delta$, [$^2\Sigma^+$], [$^2\Sigma^-$]
NH	$K(2s\sigma)^2(2p\sigma)^2(2p\pi)^2$ $^3\Sigma^-$, $^1\Delta$, $^1\Sigma^+$	$(2s\sigma)^2 2p\sigma(2p\pi)^3$ $^3\Pi$, $^1\Pi$
PH	$KL(3s\sigma)^2(3p\sigma)^2(3p\pi)^2$ $^3\Sigma^-$, [$^1\Delta$], [$^1\Sigma^+$]	$(3s\sigma)^2 3p\sigma(3p\pi)^3$ $^3\Pi$, [$^1\Pi$]
BiH	$KLMNO_{spd}(6s\sigma)^2(6p\sigma)^2(6p\pi)^2$ [$^3\Sigma^-$], [$^1\Delta$], $^1\Sigma$	?
OH	$K(2s\sigma)^2(2p\sigma)^2(2p\pi)^3$ $^2\Pi_i$	$(2s\sigma)^2 2p\sigma(2p\pi)^4$ $^2\Sigma^+$
HS, HCl+	$KL(3s\sigma)^2(3p\sigma)^2(3p\pi)^3$ $^2\Pi_i$	$(3s\sigma)^2 3p\sigma(3p\pi)^4$ $^2\Sigma^+$
HBr+	$KLM(4s\sigma)^2(4p\sigma)^2(4p\pi)^3$ $^2\Pi_i$	$(4s\sigma)^2 4p\sigma(4p\pi)^4$ $^2\Sigma^+$
HF	$K(2s\sigma)^2(2p\sigma)^2(2p\pi)^4$ $^1\Sigma^+$	$(2s\sigma)^2(2p\sigma)^2(2p\pi)^3 3s\sigma$ [$^3\Pi$], [$^1\Pi$]
HCl	$KL(3s\sigma)^2(3p\sigma)^2(3p\pi)^4$ $^1\Sigma^+$	$(3s\sigma)^2(3p\sigma)^2(3p\pi)^3 4s\sigma$ [$^3\Pi$], [$^1\Pi$]
HBr	$KLM(4s\sigma)^2(4p\sigma)^2(4p\pi)^4$ $^1\Sigma^+$	$(4s\sigma)^2(4p\sigma)^2(4p\pi)^3 5s\sigma$ [$^3\Pi$], [$^1\Pi$]
HI	$KLMN_{spd}(5s\sigma)^2(5p\sigma)^2(5p\pi)^4$ $^1\Sigma^+$	$(5s\sigma)^2(5p\sigma)^2(5p\pi)^3 6s\sigma$ [$^3\Pi$], [$^1\Pi$]

For the excited electron configurations the closed atomic shells have not been repeated. The states in brackets have not been observed. M_{sp} means that in the M shell only the subgroups $3s$ and $3p$ are closed, and similarly in other cases.

symbol K is written for it in Table 32. The excited states of LiH are obtained if one electron is brought from the $2s\sigma$ shell into higher shells. The lowest excited state is $K\ 2s\sigma\ 2p\sigma$, which gives a $^1\Sigma^+$ and a $^3\Sigma^+$ state, of which only the former has been observed thus far. The electronic states of the other alkali hydrides and of the ions of the alkaline earths are the same except that the principal quantum number is increased correspondingly (see Table 32). An extended discussion of the lower states of the alkali hydrides is given by Mulliken (520).

For CH, with seven electrons, the lowest electronic configuration is $K(2s\sigma)^2\ (2p\sigma)^2\ (2p\pi)$, which gives a $^2\Pi$ state as ground state, in agreement with experiment. The lowest excited state is obtained if an electron goes from the $2p\sigma$ shell into the $2p\pi$ shell. According to Table 31, the states given in Table 32 are then obtained, and are all observed with the exception of the $^4\Sigma^-$ state. The electronic states of SiH are similar except that the principal quantum number is one higher. However, for SiH, apart from the $^2\Pi$ ground state, only the excited $^2\Delta$ state is known.

In Table 32 the other hydrides have been treated in a similar manner. The states that have not been observed are in brackets. Only in a few cases have higher excited states also been observed, although theoretically, as for H_2, a large number of term series with higher n values would naturally be expected. A contradiction to the scheme is not known.

Molecules with nuclei of equal charge. In Table 33 the electron configurations for the ground states of the most important molecules with nuclei of equal charge are given as they are obtained from Fig. 139. In this table the nomenclature adapted to the separated atoms is used. Atomic shells that are not influenced by the molecule formation are given by the symbols $K, L, \cdots$ [Lennard-Jones (441)].

For He_2 in the lowest state the four electrons go into the orbitals $\sigma_g 1s$ and $\sigma_u 1s$, which they just fill. However, as we

TABLE 33

ELECTRON CONFIGURATIONS AND TERM TYPES OF THE GROUND STATES OF MOLECULES COMPOSED OF ATOMS WITH EQUAL OR NEARLY EQUAL NUCLEAR CHARGE

Z	Molecule	Lowest Electron Configuration	State	P_b	P_a	Diff.	D_0 (Volts)
1	H_2^+	$\sigma_g 1s\ (= 1s\sigma)$	$^2\Sigma_g^+$	$\tfrac{1}{2}$	0	$\tfrac{1}{2}$	2.649
2	H_2	$(\sigma_g 1s)^2$	$^1\Sigma_g^+$	1	0	1	4.478
3	He_2^+	$(\sigma_g 1s)^2(\sigma_u 1s)$	$^2\Sigma_u^+$	1	$\tfrac{1}{2}$	$\tfrac{1}{2}$	(3.0)
4	He_2	$(\sigma_g 1s)^2(\sigma_u 1s)^2$	$^1\Sigma_g^+$	1	1	0	0
6	Li_2	$KK(\sigma_g 2s)^2$	$^1\Sigma_g^+$	1	0	1	1.14
8	$[Be_2]$	$KK(\sigma_g 2s)^2(\sigma_u 2s)^2$	$[^1\Sigma_g^+]$	1	1	0	
10	$[B_2]$	$KK(\sigma_g 2s)^2(\sigma_u 2s)^2(\pi_u 2p)^2$	$[^3\Sigma_g^-]$	2	1	1	
12	$C_2(BeO)$	$\left\{\begin{array}{l}KK(\sigma_g 2s)^2(\sigma_u 2s)^2(\pi_u 2p)^3\sigma_g 2p \\ KK(\sigma_g 2s)^2(\sigma_u 2s)^2(\pi_u 2p)^4\end{array}\right.$	$^3\Pi_u$ / $^1\Sigma_g^+$	3	1	2	(3.6)
13	$N_2^+(CO^+,\ CN,\ BO,\ BeF)$	$KK(\sigma_g 2s)^2(\sigma_u 2s)^2(\pi_u 2p)^4\sigma_g 2p$	$^2\Sigma_g^+$	$3\tfrac{1}{2}$	1	$2\tfrac{1}{2}$	6.351
14	$N_2(CO)$	$KK(\sigma_g 2s)^2(\sigma_u 2s)^2(\pi_u 2p)^4(\sigma_g 2p)^2$	$^1\Sigma_g^+$	4	1	3	7.384
15	$O_2^+(NO)$	$KK(\sigma_g 2s)^2(\sigma_u 2s)^2(\pi_u 2p)^4(\sigma_g 2p)^2\pi_g 2p$	$^2\Pi_g$	4	$1\tfrac{1}{2}$	$2\tfrac{1}{2}$	6.48
16	O_2	$KK(\sigma_g 2s)^2(\sigma_u 2s)^2(\pi_u 2p)^4(\sigma_g 2p)^2(\pi_g 2p)^2$	$^3\Sigma_g^-$	4	2	2	5.082
18	F_2	$KK(\sigma_g 2s)^2(\sigma_u 2s)^2(\pi_u 2p)^4(\sigma_g 2p)^2(\pi_g 2p)^4$	$^1\Sigma_g^+$	4	3	1	(2.8)
20	Ne_2	$KK(\sigma_g 2s)^2(\sigma_u 2s)^2(\pi_u 2p)^4(\sigma_g 2p)^2(\pi_g 2p)^4(\sigma_u 2p)^2$	$^1\Sigma_g^+$	4	4	0	0
22	Na_2	$KKLL(\sigma_g 3s)^2$	$^1\Sigma_g^+$	1	0	1	0.763
30	$P_2(SiS)$	$KKLL(\sigma_g 3s)^2(\sigma_u 3s)^2(\sigma_g 3p)^2(\pi_u 3p)^4$	$^1\Sigma_g^+$	4	1	3	5.033
32	S_2	$KKLL(\sigma_g 3s)^2(\sigma_u 3s)^2(\sigma_g 3p)^2(\pi_u 3p)^4(\pi_g 3p)^2$	$^3\Sigma_g^-$	4	2	2	(3.6)
34	Cl_2	$KKLL(\sigma_g 3s)^2(\sigma_u 3s)^2(\sigma_g 3p)^2(\pi_u 3p)^4(\pi_g 3p)^4$	$^1\Sigma_g^+$	4	3	1	2.481

Z = number of electrons, P_b = number of bonding electron pairs, P_a = number of antibonding electron pairs, and D_0 = dissociation energy. Molecules and states in square brackets have not been observed. The D_0 values do not refer to molecules in parentheses.

shall see later, this state is unstable. But a large number of excited states, in which an electron goes from the $\sigma_u 1s$ orbital into higher orbitals, are stable. The observed electronic states of He_2 agree very well with those to be expected theoretically, as particularly the extensive investigations of Weizel and Dieke have shown. The observed Rydberg series correspond to the transition of the one electron (the emission electron) to similar excited states with different n. The energy level diagram is similar to that of H_2 in Fig. 142.

For the C_2 *molecule*, with its 12 electrons, two different electronic configurations are given for the ground state in Table 33. The first (giving $^1\Sigma_g{}^+$) corresponds to the one that would be expected if the electrons are brought into the lowest possible orbitals. Accordingly, the second (giving $^3\Pi_u$) should correspond to an excited state. Actually, however, it is found that the absorption spectrum of the C_2 molecule consists of the Swan bands [Klemenc (405)], whose lower state is $^3\Pi$. Thus $^3\Pi$ is the ground state of C_2. The explanation of this apparent contradiction is to be sought in the fact that, at the internuclear distances coming into question here, the orbitals $\pi_u 2p$ and $\sigma_g 2p$ have not very different energies (as Fig. 139 also shows). When the interaction of the electrons is taken into account, it may very well happen that the $^3\Pi_u$ state resulting from $\pi_u{}^3\sigma_g$ lies lower than the $\pi_u{}^4\ {}^1\Sigma_g{}^+$ state.[5]

For the N_2 *molecule*, with 14 electrons, in the lowest state both the $\pi_u 2p$ and the $\sigma_g 2p$ orbitals are completely filled (see Table 33), and therefore the ground state is a $^1\Sigma_g{}^+$ state, in agreement with observation. The excited states of N_2 are obtained if we bring an electron from one of the outermost orbitals that are filled in the ground state into the different higher orbitals. However, the electronic configurations of the observed excited states of N_2 are not yet completely understood.

---

[5] A similar situation arises in some cases in applying the building-up principle to atoms, although for larger numbers of electrons only.

If an electron is completely removed from the N_2 molecule, we obtain the three states $^2\Sigma_g{}^+$, $^2\Pi_u$, and $^2\Sigma_u{}^+$ of the $N_2{}^+$ *molecule* according as the electron is removed from the $\sigma_g 2p$, the $\pi_u 2p$, or the $\sigma_u 2s$ shell, respectively. These three states have indeed been observed as the three lowest electronic states of $N_2{}^+$,[6] where the $^2\Sigma_g{}^+$ state forms the ground state, as would be expected.

For the O_2 *molecule*, the two additional electrons go into the $\pi_g 2p$ shell, which is not, however, thereby closed. According to Table 30, we obtain the three states $^3\Sigma_g{}^-$, $^1\Delta_g$, and $^1\Sigma_g{}^+$ for the configuration $(\pi_g 2p)^2$. These three states have indeed been found as low-lying states, $^3\Sigma_g{}^-$ being the ground state (see p. 360 f.).

The electronic configurations of the remaining molecules given in Table 33 scarcely need any further elaboration.

Other molecules. If the nuclei have *unequal charges*, the distinction between g and u disappears. The order of the orbitals also alters to some extent (Fig. 138 instead of Fig. 139). However, the differences thereby introduced are small if the difference in nuclear charge amounts to only a few units. The electron configurations of the ground state and the excited states are then usually the same as for the corresponding molecules having equal nuclei and the same number of electrons. Correspondingly, some molecules with unlike nuclei have been added in parentheses after the corresponding molecules with equal nuclei in Table 33. Their electronic configurations are obtained from those given simply by omitting g and u.

The case of the *molecules with* 13 *electrons*, CO^+, CN, BO, and BeF, is particularly characteristic. For them, not only the ground states, $^2\Sigma$, but also the first two excited states, $^2\Pi$ and $^2\Sigma$, are the same as those of $N_2{}^+$. Likewise, a great similarity (not only spectroscopic) exists between N_2 and

---

[6] The $^2\Pi_u$ state has not been directly observed, but its existence has been inferred from the perturbations that it produces in the $^2\Sigma_u{}^+$ state. Naturally, a separation of a $\sigma_g 2s$ electron from N_2 also leads to a state of $N_2{}^+$. However, as Fig. 139 shows, this state lies very high and has not yet been observed.

CO, which both have 14 electrons, as well as between O_2^+ and NO, which both have 15 electrons. There is a small difference between the molecules C_2 and BeO, with 12 electrons. As mentioned before, for C_2 the two outermost shells have almost the same energy, and therefore we have two electron configurations which theoretically may form the ground state. The second configuration in Table 33 is the one that actually forms the ground state ($^3\Pi_u$) of C_2. For BeO the two shells have no longer so nearly the same energy, and therefore it is the first configuration that forms the ground state, in agreement with the experimental fact that it is a $^1\Sigma^+$ state.

Molecules with the same number of electrons are called *isosteric molecules* after Langmuir. The similarity of their empirical energy level diagrams and the similarity of their physical and chemical properties can easily be understood theoretically, as we have seen here, from a consideration of the electronic configurations. For molecules, if the nuclei are not too different, just as for atoms (for example, Li, Be$^+$, B^{++}, and so on), the electronic configurations and thereby the energy level diagram are *determined* essentially *only by the number of electrons*. If, on the other hand, we build up the molecule from the separate atoms, the similarity of isosteric molecules is by no means so easily understood. N_2 and CO, for example, result from the atomic states $^4S + {}^4S$ and $^3P + {}^3P$, respectively. From $^4S + {}^4S$ four different molecular states result, and from $^3P + {}^3P$ 18 result (see Tables 26 and 27). That ultimately a similar energy level diagram should result for N_2 and CO is not obvious when considered in this way.

If the two atoms that form a molecule belong to different periods of the periodic system and thus have *very different nuclear charges*, we can proceed in the following way: We take no account of those closed shells of the separate atoms that we should expect to be practically uninfluenced by molecule formation and consider only the electrons outside these closed shells [see Lennard-Jones (441)]. It is to be expected that these electrons will arrange themselves in orbitals similar to those for the corresponding molecules consisting of atoms from the second period of the periodic system. However, these orbitals can no longer be designated in the same way. Following Mulliken (514), we introduce the nomenclature $z\sigma$, $y\sigma$, $w\pi$, $x\sigma$, and $v\pi$ for the orbitals corresponding to the orbitals $\sigma_g 2s$, $\sigma_u 2s$, $\pi_u 2p$, $\sigma_g 2p$, and $\pi_g 2p$. A molecule such as SiO has the same number of outer electrons as CO or N_2. We should therefore expect as electronic configuration and term type for the ground state

$$(KKL)(z\sigma)^2(y\sigma)^2(w\pi)^4(x\sigma)^2 \; {}^1\Sigma^+$$

and for the first excited state

$$(KKL)(z\sigma)^2(y\sigma)^2(w\pi)^4(x\sigma)(v\pi) \; {}^1\Pi, \; {}^3\Pi,$$

and indeed ${}^1\Sigma^+$ is observed as the ground state and ${}^1\Pi$ as the first excited state. The same holds for the molecules CS and PN, which are isosteric with SiO.

For the molecules SiN and CP there is one outer electron less, and we obtain, corresponding to $N_2{}^+$, CN, and so forth, the three low-lying states ${}^2\Sigma$, ${}^2\Pi$, and ${}^2\Sigma$, according as the electron is removed from the $x\sigma$, $w\pi$, or $y\sigma$ orbital of the above configuration. For CP all three states, and for SiN the two ${}^2\Sigma$ states, have been observed, the energy difference being very similar to that for CN. The halides of the alkaline earths and the oxides of the earths also have the same number of outer electrons. Thus for them the same low-lying states are to be expected. Some of them have been observed.

Other groups of molecules with the same number of outer electrons can be treated in a similar manner. However, for the heavier molecules the theoretical predictions are more ambiguous, particularly for the excited states, since more and more orbitals in the separated atoms and therefore a fortiori in the molecule have approximately equal energy. For the P_2 molecule, for example, the first excited singlet state is different from that of N_2 [see (311)]. This difference can be understood qualitatively but cannot be predicted with certainty, since we can only interpolate the order of the orbitals for intermediate internuclear distances.

In order to arrive at a better theoretical understanding of the electronic structure of diatomic molecules, particularly of their excited states, much more experimental material is needed. At present, in most cases only a few electronic states are known for a given molecule. A great deal of further detailed work is necessary before the knowledge of the electronic structure of molecules reaches the stage already attained by our knowledge of the electronic structure of atoms.

4. STABILITY OF MOLECULAR ELECTRONIC STATES; VALENCE

According to the three methods treated in the foregoing (sections 1, 2, and 3), a very large number of molecular electronic states results. However, thus far we have not considered the question of *which of these numerous molecular states are stable and which are unstable*—that is to say, how the potential energy varies with changing internuclear distance in the individual cases—whether there is a minimum or not. This question of stability is, of course, of particular interest to the spectroscopist and the chemist. It is, however, very much more difficult to answer from theory than the question of which states are at all possible.

Closely connected with the question of the stability of the individual molecular states is the question of the stability of the molecule itself. We say that a molecule is *physically stable* if its ground state is stable—that is, if the ground state has a potential minimum (with an energy that is smaller than the energy of the separated atoms in their ground states). This physical stability is to be distinguished from *chemical stability*, which is possessed by a given molecule only if, even on collision with like molecules at low temperatures, it is stable for an appreciable length of time. Molecules such as CN, CH, OH, P_2, and others are physically but not chemically stable, since, although they appear in chemical reactions and in electric discharges, they do not form a stable gas at ordinary temperatures.

The fact that for many molecules only a few electronic states are observed appears at first to be in contradiction to the large term manifold demanded by theory. Although this has its basis partly in the inadequacy of the observational material obtained up to the present time, the main reason is that a large number of the states theoretically predicted are unstable and thereby escape observation. However, it should be noted that *the unstable states* (without a potential minimum) are *no less real than the stable states* and under suitable conditions may also make themselves known by continuous or diffuse spectra (see Chapter VII).

The question of stability and instability of molecular states is obviously closely connected with the question of the *nature of chemical valence*. We shall therefore take the opportunity of discussing this simultaneously, insofar as it refers to diatomic molecules.

Also closely related to the foregoing are these questions: Which of the theoretically predicted electronic states corresponds to a given observed molecular state? Into which atomic states does a given molecular state dissociate (see Chapter VII)? The latter is important for the practical applications.

In discussing the stability of molecules, three types of binding are generally distinguished: *homopolar or atomic binding, heteropolar or ionic binding*, and *polarization or van der Waals' binding*.[7] There are, however, transition cases between each two that can be as well described by the one as by the other type.

(a) Homopolar Binding (Atomic Binding)

Whereas ionic binding can be explained on a classical basis [see subsection (b)], the fact that neutral atoms can attract one another strongly and form very stable (homopolar) molecules, such as, for example, H_2, N_2, and CO, has first been explained on the basis of quantum mechanics.

Except for the simplest cases (H_2^+ and H_2), the theoretical discussion of the stability of molecular states deals with the

---

[7] In the chemical literature, the atomic binding is frequently referred to as *covalent binding*, and the ionic binding as *electrovalent binding*. Unfortunately, the same nomenclature is not used by all authors in this connection. In particular, sometimes under the name *homopolar molecules* are understood only those diatomic molecules that consist of like atoms, while all others are called *heteropolar*. However, it appears to be advantageous, and corresponds to the usage of many authors, to use *homopolar molecule* and *homopolar binding* as synonymous with *atomic molecule* and *atomic binding*; and *heteropolar molecule* and *heteropolar binding* as synonymous with *ionic molecule* and *ionic binding*, as is always done in the following. Sometimes, in addition, the names *polar* and *nonpolar molecules* are used—that is, molecules with or without a dipole moment. The latter are those with like atoms.

problem of a system consisting of a rather large number of particles (electrons and nuclei).   There is no hope of solving this problem rigorously, but various factors must be neglected in order to arrive at a solution.   According to the type of approximation used, we are led to different valence theories.   Often the approximations are very questionable, and in such cases the results obtained can only be called daring extrapolations.   However, when the different valence

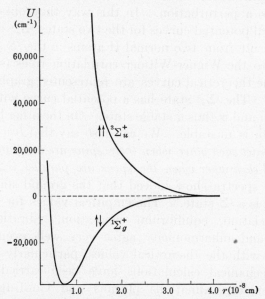

Fig. 143.   Potential Curves of the Two Lowest States of the H_2 Molecule. For the repulsive state, the theoretical data of Coolidge, James, and Present (162) have been used.

theories agree in their predictions in a given case, we can suppose that the rigorous solution would also lead to the same result [see, for this point, Van Vleck and Sherman (683)].

Two methods for the theoretical discussion of homopolar binding have proved to be the most important in the course of the development of the subject—the *method of Heitler and London* (partly extended by Slater and Pauling), which starts out from the separated atoms, and the *method of Hund and Mulliken* (partly extended by Herzberg and Lennard-Jones), which starts out from the orbitals of the individual electrons in the nuclear frame.

Treatment of the H_2 molecule according to Heitler and London. Heitler and London (295) have obtained a solution of the wave equation for the H_2 molecule by starting out from the state of the separated atoms as zero approximation and then introducing the interaction of the two atoms as a perturbation. In this way they obtained the theoretical potential curves for the two states $^1\Sigma_g{}^+$ and $^3\Sigma_u{}^+$, which result from two normal H atoms in the ^2S state according to the Wigner-Witmer correlation rules (see Table 27). The theoretical curves are represented graphically in Fig. 143. The $^1\Sigma_g{}^+$ state has a potential curve with a deep minimum and is thus a stable state. On the other hand, the $^3\Sigma_u{}^+$ state is unstable. We can also say that *two hydrogen atoms attract each other when their spins are antiparallel* ($^1\Sigma$) *and repel each other when the spins are parallel* ($^3\Sigma$). The observed spectra show indeed that the ground state of the molecule is a $^1\Sigma$ state.[8] The empirical values for the heat of dissociation, equilibrium separation, vibrational frequency, and anharmonicity agree very well, even quantitatively, with the theoretical values, particularly after the wave mechanical calculations have been carried through to higher approximations [James and Coolidge (361), Richardson (585), and Beutler and Jünger (96)]. For example, the best experimental value (see Chapter VII) for the heat of dissociation of H_2 in the ground state is

---

[8] Without an assumption about the statistics of the nuclei the spectrum does not allow us to decide what kind of a $^1\Sigma$ state the ground state of H_2 is. But on the assumption, which is confirmed by scattering experiments, that the protons follow Fermi statistics it follows from the spectrum that the ground state of hydrogen is either $^1\Sigma_g{}^+$ or $^1\Sigma_u{}^-$, of which the former is in agreement with the Heitler-London theory as well as with the electron configuration (see p. 365; compare also the discussion on p. 271). Conversely, if the theoretical result that the ground state is $^1\Sigma_g{}^+$ is accepted, it follows immediately that the protons follow Fermi statistics (see p. 271).

$D_0(H_2) = 36,116 \pm 6$ cm^{-1}, while the best theoretical value is $36,104 \pm 105$ cm^{-1}. The unstable $^3\Sigma_u^+$ state has also been observed. It is the lower state of the extensive continuous spectrum of hydrogen (see Chapter VII).

According to Heitler and London, the essential reason for the strong attraction in the H$_2$ molecule is the *"exchange degeneracy"*—that is, the fact that, for very large internuclear distance, by exchange of the two electrons of the two atoms a state results that is indistinguishable from the original state. As a result, when the two atoms approach, a periodic exchange of the electrons takes place between the two atoms, which leads to a splitting into two states of different energy (Fig. 143). For this reason, the homopolar forces between two neutral atoms are sometimes also called *"exchange" forces.*[9] The exchange forces are attractive for antiparallel spin orientation and repulsive for parallel spin orientation of the electrons. However, the strong attraction (or repulsion) has nothing to do with the mutual interaction of the spins, just as the energy difference between singlets and triplets is not due to this interaction (see p. 359). The spin comes in only through its effect on the Pauli principle (see A.A., p. 224).[9a]

Calculation shows that the strong attraction or repulsion brought about by the exchange forces decreases very rapidly with increasing internuclear distance; in fact, it *decreases*

---

[9] It should be noted, however, that these forces are not a new type of force. They arise from substituting the ordinary Coulomb forces between the individual particles into the wave equation and solving for the resultant attraction of the two atoms.

[9a] A somewhat different explanation of homopolar attraction has been given by Hellmann (49): In consequence of the Heisenberg uncertainty relation the electron in the H atom has a certain momentum distribution and therefore a certain zero-point energy given by the energy of the ground state of the H atom. If two H atoms are brought together, the space available for each of the electrons (if they satisfy the Pauli principle—that is, have antiparallel spins) is almost doubled. Consequently the minimum uncertainty of the momentum—that is, the zero-point energy—is reduced, or, in other words, the two atoms attract each other. Similar considerations may be applied to other atoms.

exponentially. Thus, with increasing r, the potential energy curve in Fig. 143 approaches the asymptote very rapidly. This fact has proved to be typical for homopolar binding.

The *probability density distribution of the electrons in the* H_2 *molecule*, calculated for the $^1\Sigma$ and $^3\Sigma$ states (for the same internuclear distance), according to London, is illustrated graphically in Fig. 144. It can be seen that in the case of attraction the electron clouds of the two atoms blend into each other, whereas for repulsion they remain almost completely separated.

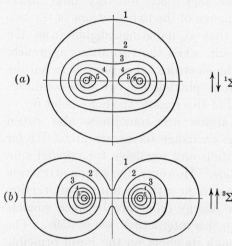

The excited states of the H_2 molecule resulting from a normal and an excited H atom have also been treated on the basis of the Heitler-London theory, although not to such a high approximation as the ground state [see Heitler (293)].

Fig. 144. Probability Density Distribution of the Electrons in the $^1\Sigma$ Ground State and the $^3\Sigma$ Repulsive State of the H_2 Molecule, Approximate [after London (452)]. In both cases the probability distribution is drawn for the nuclear separation in the ground state of H_2 (0.74 Å). The curves are curves of equal probability density in a section going through the internuclear axis. The numbers give the relative values of the probability density.

Generalization of the Heitler-London theory for more complicated atoms. The next simplest case is the case of the interaction of a normal He *atom* with a normal H *atom*. According to the Wigner-Witmer rules, only a single molecular state—namely, $^2\Sigma$—results from He(^1S) + H(^2S). According to Heitler-London, this is a repulsive state, as we can see qualitatively from the fact that the electron of the H atom, as a result of the Pauli principle, is exchangeable only with that electron of He whose spin orientation is parallel to its own:

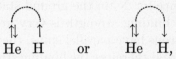

which gives a repulsive exchange force.[10]   In a similar way, repulsion of an H_2 molecule and an H atom, as well as repulsion of two normal He atoms, follows from the theory. These results are in agreement with experiment and with the usual elementary chemical idea of valence.

As we proceed to more complicated atoms, the calculations can only be carried out less and less rigorously.   Nevertheless, Heitler and London were able to show, after neglecting certain things, that of the molecular states of different multiplicities resulting from two atoms in S states *always those with the lowest total spin S lie lowest* and the others lie in the order of their multiplicities.   For example, two

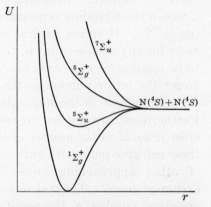

Fig. 145. Potential Curves of the Electronic States of the N_2 Molecule Arising from Normal Atoms, According to Heitler and London (Schematic).

normal N atoms in ^4S states give, according to Wigner and Witmer (see Table 27), the molecular states $^1\Sigma_g{}^+$, $^3\Sigma_u{}^+$, $^5\Sigma_g{}^+$, and $^7\Sigma_u{}^+$.   According to Heitler and London, they lie in this order.   Fig. 145 shows qualitatively the corresponding potential curves.   The states $^1\Sigma_g{}^+$ and $^3\Sigma_u{}^+$ are stable, and the states $^5\Sigma_g{}^+$ and $^7\Sigma_u{}^+$ are unstable. $^1\Sigma_g{}^+$ is the ground state of the N_2 molecule, in agreement with experiment.

---

[10] In contrast to HeH, the ion HeH$^+$ is stable, as one would expect on the basis of its similarity to H_2 [see Glockler and Fuller (261), Beach (82a), and Coulson and Duncanson (169a)].

Here again it is the exchange between each newly formed pair of electrons with antiparallel spins that causes the attraction. Since for N_2 in the ground state there are three such pairs, the binding strength is very great. As soon as two of the electrons have parallel spins, they give a repulsive exchange force, and therefore the binding strength of the $^3\Sigma_u{}^+$ state of N_2 is very much less than that of the ground state.

Thus a molecular state is the more stable the greater the number of electron pairs formed from the unpaired electrons of the separate atoms. In the $^1\Sigma$ ground state of H_2, one new electron pair is formed, and, in the $^1\Sigma$ ground state of N_2, three are formed. According to elementary chemical ideas, a monovalent binding is assumed in H_2 and a trivalent binding in N_2. It seems natural to generalize these considerations for any atoms—that is, to assume the *valency of a bond* to be *equal to the number of newly formed electron pairs.* The larger the latter number is, the stronger is the binding and the more stable is the molecular state under consideration. Furthermore, we are led to assume that the *valency of an atom is equal to the number of unpaired electrons,* since only these can give pairs with antiparallel spins with the electrons of other approaching atoms and thereby an attractive exchange force. The valency is therefore $2S$, if S is the quantum number of the resultant spin of the atom. It is thus one less than the multiplicity. An N atom can, for example, bind three H atoms and is trivalent, since each one of the three unpaired electrons of the N atom can form, with an electron belonging to an H atom, a pair with anti-parallel spin orientations. A fourth H atom will not be attracted, because its electron cannot form an additional pair with antiparallel spins with one of the electrons already present, and consequently there is no further gain in energy— that is, no bonding action.

We see therefore that the *saturation of homopolar valencies* follows naturally from this representation as a *saturation of the spins*—a pairing off in antiparallel pairs.

The valencies obtained in the above-described way for

the atoms in the different columns of the periodic system are
given in Table 34. The numbers given refer to the ground
state and the low-lying excited states. The valencies in the
ground state are printed in heavy type. The normal
chemical valencies of the alkaline earths, the earths, and the
elements of the carbon group must be traced back to *excited*
atomic states in which an electron is transferred from the $2s$
shell to the $2p$ shell. For the C atom, for example, the
ground state $1s^2 2s^2 2p^2$ ^3P has only two unpaired electrons

TABLE 34

HOMOPOLAR VALENCY
(After Heitler and London)

Group in Periodic System	I Alkalis	II Alkaline Earths	III Earths	IV Carbon Group	V Nitrogen Group	VI Oxygen Group	VII Halogens	VIII Inert Gases
Multiplicity..	2	1 3	2 4	1 3 5	2 4 6	1 3 5 7	2 4 6 8	1
Valency.....	**1**	**0** 2	**1** 3	**0** 2 4	**1** **3** **5**	**0** 2 4 6	**1** 3 5 7	**0**

and is, therefore, according to this mode of representation,
divalent. However, the excited state $1s^2 2s 2p^3$ ^5S has four
unpaired electrons and can, with the assumptions mentioned,
explain the *tetravalency of carbon.*

It should be noted that, whereas the first elements in the
oxygen group and the fluorine group—that is, O and F
themselves—have only one valency—namely, 2 and 1,
respectively—the other elements exhibit other valencies in
addition (4, 6, and 3, 5, 7, respectively). This is explained
by the fact that in order to raise the multiplicities of O and F
a very high excitation would be required, whereas this is not
necessary for the other elements of these groups.

The valence theory described here is also called the *spin
valence theory.* While it is attractively simple, we should not
forget that in obtaining it we made implicitly a number of
rather serious reservations. Above all, in the generalization
we have completely neglected the circumstance that the

calculation has been carried out only for atoms in S states. Furthermore, the theory holds only if the separations of neighboring atomic terms are large compared to the binding energies, a condition which is fulfilled for the H atoms and the inert-gas atoms but seldom for other atoms. Therefore, while the Heitler-London theory represents the essentials of chemical valence in broad outline, we must be prepared for deviations in the matter of detail.

Examples of such *deviations*, which are obviously to be traced back to the nonfulfillment of the above two conditions, are the following: According to the elementary Heitler-London theory, one would expect $^1\Sigma_g{}^+$ as the ground state of the molecule C_2, whereas $^3\Pi_u$ is observed. Similarly, $^1\Sigma_g{}^+$ would be expected as the ground state of O_2 (all electrons paired off), whereas $^3\Sigma_g{}^-$ is observed (O_2 gas is paramagnetic; see p. 502). Furthermore, according to the elementary Heitler-London theory, atoms such as Be, Mg, Ca, and so forth, in the ground state should not be able to bind another atom, since they contain only closed shells (^1S state), whereas experimentally relatively stable diatomic hydrides and halides of these elements are known whose ground states lead to normal atoms.

These deviations between theory and experiment can, according to Heitler (293) and Nordheim-Pöschl (533), be removed if we take account of the interaction of states of the same species (p. 324 f.)— that is to say, when we work out *higher approximations*.

Let us consider the BeH molecule as a simple example. For the Be atom, the excited $1s^2 2s 2p\ ^3P$ state lies not very far from the ground state $1s^2 2s^2\ ^1S$. From $^1S + {}^2S$ only one $^2\Sigma^+$ state results; from $^3P + {}^2S$ the states $^2\Sigma^+$, $^2\Pi$, $^4\Sigma^+$, and $^4\Pi$ result (see Fig. 135). The potential curves for these states, as they would be given according to the elementary Heitler-London theory, are drawn quite roughly in Fig. 146 (broken-line curves). According to this figure, only the states $^2\Sigma^+$ and $^2\Pi$, resulting from the excited Be atom (^3P) and the normal H atom, would be stable.

However, if we take account of the interaction of states of the same species, the intersection of the two $^2\Sigma^+$ states (from $^1S + {}^2S$ and from $^3P + {}^2S$) "originally" present is avoided (see Chapter V, section 4). They repel each other quite considerably, and the full-line potential curves are obtained.   In this higher approximation, the $^2\Sigma^+$ state resulting from normal atoms has a potential minimum—that is, it is a stable state, in agreement with experiment—while the $^2\Sigma^+$ state resulting from $^3P + {}^2S$ has a much flatter minimum than originally.   The remaining states given are only slightly affected by taking into account the interaction of states of the same species, since no similar states lie in their neighborhood.   The corresponding broken-line and full-line potential curves therefore almost coincide.   It should be noted that, as a result of mixing of the eigenfunctions (see p. 318), the $^2\Sigma^+$ ground state has to a considerable degree the properties of the $^2\Sigma^+$ state resulting from $^3P + {}^2S$.   In consequence of that, we should expect, for example, that the vibrational quanta in the ground state for small v would rather correspond to a dissociation into $^3P + {}^2S$, although in reality a dissociation into normal atoms takes place.   This has actually been observed for some other hydrides of the elements of the

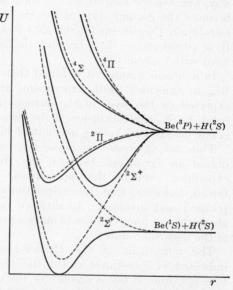

Fig. 146.   Potential Curves of the BeH Molecule; Broken-Line Curves, According to the Elementary Heitler-London Theory; Full-Line Curves, Allowing for the Mutual Interaction of the States.   The curves are drawn only quite schematically, since accurate experimental data are not known.

second column of the periodic system, although not for BeH, where up to the present time sufficient data are not available.[11]

For O_2 we obtain from two normal O atoms (^3P) the 18 different states given in Table 27.   Of these we expect, according to the elementary theory, the singlet states to be the lowest and, in particular, a $^1\Sigma_g^+$ state as the ground state.   However, not very far above $^3P + {}^3P$ there is the combination $^3P + {}^1D$ of the sepa-

---

[11] For a more detailed discussion of the diatomic hydride molecules according to the Heitler-London theory see Stehn (650) and King (400a).

rated atoms, giving rise to the states $^3\Sigma^+$ $^3\Sigma^-(2)$ $^3\Pi(3)$ $^3\Delta(2)$ $^3\Phi$ (see Table 26), occurring both as u and as g states. In first approximation, since ^1D has no unpaired electrons, all these states should be unstable. Now, a number of states arising from $^3P + {}^1D$ are of the same species as some triplet states arising from $^3P + {}^3P$. Therefore in higher approximation these latter triplet states ($^3\Sigma_u{}^+$, $^3\Sigma_g{}^-$, $^3\Pi_g$, $^3\Pi_u$, and $^3\Delta_u$) will be shifted downward. In this way, one can see that at least it *may* happen that a triplet state becomes the ground state of the O_2 molecule. A more detailed calculation [Nordheim-Pöschl (533)] shows indeed that one of these triplet states, $^3\Sigma_g{}^-$, becomes the lowest-lying state, in agreement with experiment.

In a similar manner it is found that the ground state of C_2 is $^3\Pi_u$, in agreement with experiment, and not $^1\Sigma_g{}^+$, as would be expected on the basis of the elementary theory. On the other hand, for N_2 the conclusion of the elementary theory (see above) is not changed by taking account of higher approximations.

Thus, *taking account of higher approximations*, we can actually obtain an agreement between the Heitler-London theory and experiment even for the apparent exceptions. It must be mentioned, however, that the calculations often become very complicated and involved. Qualitative considerations such as the above then no longer suffice to make a prediction about the stability of the molecular states.

The refinement of the Heitler-London theory here briefly indicated is sometimes called the *theory of orbital valence*, or *l-valence*, since it takes account of the orbital angular momentum L of the two atoms as well as the spins [see Heitler (293), Bartlett (81), and Hellmann (49)].

Pauling (553) and Slater (638) have extended the Heitler-London theory in a somewhat different manner. Instead of using as zero approximation certain states of the separated atoms, they start out *from certain electronic configurations* of these atoms and thus at first neglect the finer interaction of the electrons that leads to a splitting of the terms of a given electronic configuration in the atom (for example, to the energy difference between p^2 ^3P, ^1D, and ^1S). For diatomic molecules this approach does not lead to essentially new results, but it does prove very fruitful for polyatomic molecules. A more detailed discussion of it will therefore be postponed until Volume II [see also Hellmann (49)].

Theory of bonding and antibonding electrons for equal nuclear charges. The second method of treating the question of the stability of molecular states does not start out as zero approximation from the states of the separate atoms but from the *motion of the individual electrons in the field of the two centers for various distances between the centers* (Mulliken, Hund, Herzberg, and Lennard-Jones). In this way some experimental facts, given by the Heitler-London theory only when higher approximations are taken into account, can be understood even in first approximation. Conversely, however, other facts are better understood (that is, in lower approximation) on the basis of the Heitler-London theory.

While the starting point for the Heitler-London theory is the H_2 molecule, the starting point for the theory of bonding and antibonding electrons is the H_2^+ *molecule.* The systems H_2 and H_2^+ are the only ones which have up to the present time been exactly worked out on the basis of wave mechanics. For H_2^+, the dependence of the pure electronic energy on internuclear dis-

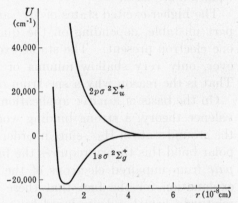

Fig. 147. Potential Curves of the Two Lowest States of H_2^+ [after Teller (663)] (Theoretical).

tance has been calculated on the basis of the wave equation for a number of electronic states, including the ground state [Teller (663), Hylleraas (350), Jaffé (360), Sandeman (614), and Hellmig (296)]. If the potential energy e^2/r of the two nuclei is added to the pure electronic energy, the potential curves of the molecule in the various electronic states are obtained. Fig. 147 shows the curves obtained for the two lowest states (both from normal $H + H^+$). The lowest state (ground state), $1s\sigma$, has a fairly deep potential minimum, whereas the other state, $2p\sigma$, has a purely repulsive potential curve. The heat of dissociation of the ground state obtained theoretically is $D_0(H_2^+) = 21,363 \pm 5$ cm^{-1}, while experimentally an indirect method [from $D_0(H_2)$ and the ionization potentials of H_2 and H (see Chapter VII)] gives the value $21,366 \pm 15$ cm^{-1} [see Beutler and Jünger (96)]. The excellent agreement between theory and experiment, for H_2^+ as well as for H_2 (see p. 376 f.), shows without any doubt that wave mechanics is quite adequate to deal theoretically with electronic motions in molecules. That deviations between theory and experiment appear for heavier molecules is due only to the fact that inadequate approximations for the solutions of the wave equation are used.

The higher excited states of H_2^+ are in part stable and in part unstable, depending on the quantum numbers of the one electron present. The stable excited states have, however, only very shallow minima of their potential curves. That is the reason why a spectrum of H_2^+ is not observed.

On the basis of a naïve application of the Heitler-London valence theory, a strong binding would not be expected in the ground state of H_2^+, since in order to form a strong homopolar bond this theory requires the formation of an electron *pair* from unpaired electrons of the separated atoms. An explanation for the fact that there is, in spite of that, a relatively firm bond produced by one electron only can be given in two different ways, depending on which zero approximation is used to treat the H_2^+ molecule.

If we start from a large internuclear distance as zero approximation, there is a *resonance degeneracy*, because the state "electron with the one nucleus" has the same energy as the state "electron with the other nucleus." At smaller internuclear distances this degeneracy is removed in such a way that of the two resulting components, σ_g and σ_u, the one is shifted upward and the other downward from the position for large internuclear distance. A stable state $(1s\sigma)$ and an unstable state $(2p\sigma)$ result.

However, in the case of H_2^+ we can also start out from small and intermediate internuclear distances and regard the relatively large binding strength of the ground state as due to the fact that the orbital $1s\sigma$ for small internuclear distance transforms into the ground state of the united atom (ion) He^+, whereas the orbital $2p\sigma$, on the other hand, transforms into an excited state of this ion.   Fig. 148 shows schematically the variation of the purely electronic energy (that is, ignoring nuclear repulsion) for the two lowest states of H_2^+.   The ground state of He^+ lies 40 volts lower than the ground state of H, while the 2-quantum state of He^+ lies at about the same height as the ground state of the H atom.   If now, in addition, we take account of the nuclear repulsion, it is understandable that (as the accurate calculation proves) the $2p\sigma$ state gives only repulsion and the $1s\sigma$ state gives a strong attraction.

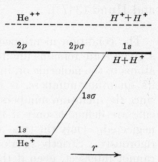

Fig. 148.   Correlation of the Two Lowest States of H_2^+ with Those of the United Atom. To the left the nuclear separation is 0, and to the right it is ∞.   The broken line gives the energy when the one electron is completely removed.   The corresponding states $H^+ + H^+$ and He^{++} lie at the same height, since the nuclear repulsion is neglected in the figure.

On the basis of the above considerations it is natural to assume that, also if a number of electrons are present, *each individual electron, when the nuclei are brought together, gives either a positive or a negative contribution to the binding*—is either *bonding* or *antibonding*.   Whether an electron in a given orbital is bonding or antibonding is not necessarily determined by the same conditions as for H_2^+, since in the more general case the electron does not move in the field of two point charges but in the field of the nuclei plus that of the other electrons.   A condition that this method of bonding and antibonding electrons shall lead to usable results is that, in the transition from the separated atoms to the molecule, each electron, in a way, shall retain its individuality; that is (for equal nuclear charges), a σ_u electron shall remain a σ_u electron, and so on.   Thus we assume that in the earlier scheme, Fig. 139 or 138, *a given state has the same electronic configuration for large and medium internuclear distances.* If we then know which electrons are bonding and which are antibonding, we can find out which of the electronic states of the molecule are stable and which are unstable, since at least roughly we should expect that a *stable* molecular state would result *if the number of bonding electrons is greater than the number of antibonding electrons* [Herzberg (304) and (308), and Hund (347)].

The condition mentioned, that the electronic configuration for a given state remains unaltered in a transition from the separated atoms to the molecule or, in other words, that each electron retains its quantum numbers, is certainly only approximately fulfilled, since the quantum numbers of the individual electrons in the molecule are definable only if the finer interaction of the electrons is neglected. Only the type of the total term (the species) is defined rigorously. Strictly speaking, terms of the same total term type cannot intersect, even if they have different electronic configurations (see p. 324). However, when we make the above assumption, we must allow such points of intersection of states of different electronic configurations, even if they have the same term type. Thus the whole procedure is admittedly only a very rough approximation.

The question is now: When is an electron bonding and when is it antibonding? We should expect that *orbitals that move downward* relative to the others in Fig. 139 in going over from the separated atoms to the united atom are *bonding*, whereas the *orbitals moving upward* are *antibonding*. In agreement with these expectations, calculation shows [Hund (347)] that, at least for large internuclear distances, the orbitals σ_g and π_u lie lower than the corresponding orbitals σ_u and π_g (that is, for example, $\sigma_g 1s$ lies lower than $\sigma_u 1s$, $\sigma_g 2p$ lies lower than $\sigma_u 2p$, and so on. See right-hand part of Fig. 139).

The bonding orbitals are those whose eigenfunctions are, in the previously mentioned approximation (p. 354), a sum of the atomic orbitals, whereas for the antibonding orbitals the eigenfunctions are the differences of the atomic orbitals [Mulliken (519)][12] [that is, the latter eigenfunctions have at least one or in general an odd number of nodal surfaces between the nuclei (see Fig. 137)].

The manner in which the rules mentioned lead to an understanding of molecule formation is best made clear by some examples.

In the formation of the H_2 *molecule* from two H atoms, both electrons can go into the $\sigma_g 1s$ orbital, and, since for H_2^+ this orbital gives an appreciable attraction (bonding electron), we should expect, on the basis of the supposition that each electron contributes a certain amount to the binding, that with two electrons in this bonding orbital the attraction would be considerably strengthened, as is actually observed $[D_0(H_2) = 4.478$ volts, compared to $D_0(H_2^+)$ $= 2.649$ volts].[13]   According to the Pauli principle, both electrons can be $\sigma_g 1s$ electrons only if their spins are antiparallel.   Thus a $^1\Sigma_g^+$ state results.   If the two electrons have parallel spins, they must be in different orbitals.   The only possibility for this, when both electrons in the separated atoms are $1s$ electrons, is $(\sigma_g 1s)(\sigma_u 1s)\ ^3\Sigma_u^+$ (see Fig. 139). In this case we have one bonding and one antibonding electron, and we should therefore not expect a binding. Thus for the molecular states resulting from two normal H atoms we obtain the same results (which agree with experiment) here as from the Heitler-London theory.

Since at infinitely large internuclear distances the two orbitals $\sigma_u 1s$ and $\sigma_g 1s$ have equal energies, the H_2 states $(\sigma_u 1s)^2\ ^1\Sigma_g^+$ and $(\sigma_g 1s)(\sigma_u 1s)^1\Sigma_u^+$ would have the same energy for $r \to \infty$ as the aforementioned states $(\sigma_g 1s)^2\ ^1\Sigma_g^+$ and $(\sigma_g 1s)(\sigma_u 1s)\ ^3\Sigma_u^+$ if the finer interaction of the electrons is neglected.   They correspond, as Hund (347) has shown in detail, to the *ionic states* $H^- + H^+$

---

[12] Mulliken originally (509a) assumed that all those electrons were antibonding that had higher quantum numbers in the united atom than in the separated atoms.   He called them *promoted electrons*.   This assumption does not coincide with that given in the text.

[13] If the two electrons were completely independent of each other, we should expect a doubling of the bond energy.   That the true value is smaller by about 1 volt is due to the interaction (repulsion) of the electrons.   This influence may also quantitatively be taken into account.

and $H^+ + H^-$, in which both electrons are also in $1s$ orbits, as for $H + H$. In reality, for large internuclear distance these ionic states lie about 13 volts above the state $H + H$. Thus neglecting the finer interaction of the electrons leads here to a very considerable error. This applies, however, only for quite large internuclear distances, for which, in any case, the Heitler-London method is the better approximation, while for smaller internuclear distance these ionic states move rapidly upward according to Fig. 139. In most practical cases of molecules with like atoms we reach conclusions in agreement with experiment if we neglect the ionic states completely and if we always, at large internuclear distances, first fill the bonding electron shells, since, even when the separation of the two atoms is still fairly large, these bonding orbitals lie lower than the corresponding antibonding orbitals.

Two normal He *atoms* give, at large internuclear distances, the electronic configuration $(\sigma_g 1s)^2 (\sigma_u 1s)^2$—that is, a bonding and an antibonding electron pair. Therefore, according to the above rule, no stable molecular state results when the atoms approach, in agreement with experiment. On the other hand, when we bring a normal and an excited He atom together [for example, He $(1s^2) +$ He $(1s\,2s)$], we obtain a stable molecular state if the excited electron is bonding— for example, in the configuration $(\sigma_g 1s)^2(\sigma_u 1s)(\sigma_g 2s)$—since then three bonding electrons and one antibonding electron are present. The experiments show indeed that the observed He_2 bands are to be ascribed to a molecule resulting from a normal and an excited He atom. The limiting case, $He + He^+$, also gives a stable molecule, as may easily be seen.

The state $(\sigma_g 1s)^2 (\sigma_u 1s)^2\,{}^1\Sigma_g{}^+$, formed from two normal He atoms, goes into the state $1s\sigma^2\,2p\sigma^2\,{}^1\Sigma_g{}^+$ for close nuclei (according to Fig. 139) if we correlate terms of the same electronic configuration with one another in accordance with the aforementioned correlation rule (p. 388). However, in the transition to close nuclei, an intersection with the state $1s\sigma^2\,2s\sigma^2\,{}^1\Sigma_g{}^+$ occurs which for small internuclear distance lies lower and for large internuclear distance lies considerably higher than $1s\sigma^2\,2p\sigma^2\,{}^1\Sigma_g{}^+$. This is shown in Fig. 149 (solid-line correlation). However, this intersection can occur only in the approximation in which the finer interaction of the electrons is neglected.   In the actual molecule, since the two states are of the same species, this intersection is avoided (broken-line correlation in Fig. 149); that is, the state $(\sigma_g 1s)^2 (\sigma_u 1s)^2\ {}^1\Sigma_g{}^+$ of the separated atoms in actuality goes over into $1s\sigma^2\ 2s\sigma^2\ {}^1\Sigma_g{}^+$ for very close nuclei in spite of the fact that $\sigma_u 1s$ if considered alone

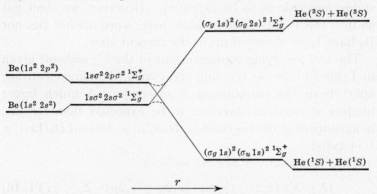

Fig. 149.   Correlation with the United Atom for He + He.

would go over into $2p\sigma$.   However, it can be seen from Fig. 149 that the strong repulsion between He atoms holds in any approxi-mation, since the terms of the united atom lie considerably higher than those of the separated atoms if, as in Fig. 149, the nuclear repulsion is neglected, and therefore a fortiori if it is taken into account.

According to Fig. 139, *two* Li *atoms* have as their lowest electron configuration $(K)(K)(\sigma_g 2s)^2$ for large as well as medium internuclear distances.   For the K electrons, no molecular symbol is given in Table 33, p. 368, since the K electrons remain practically uninfluenced in the molecule formation.   They are neither bonding nor antibonding electrons and may be called *nonbonding* (inactive) *electrons*. Since the $\sigma_g 2s$ orbital is bonding, we should thus expect a stable $^1\Sigma_g{}^+$ ground state of Li_2, which is in agreement with experiment.   If the two outer electrons of the Li atoms have parallel spins as the atoms approach, they can form only the configuration $(K)(K)\ \sigma_g 2s\ \sigma_u 2s\ {}^3\Sigma_u{}^+$, with one bonding and one antibonding electron.   This state is repulsive, as for H_2.

For *two normal* Be *atoms* the behavior is quite similar to that for two normal He atoms. We have as many bonding as antibonding electrons and therefore do not expect a stable molecule. For *two normal* B *atoms*, on the other hand, a stable molecule is to be expected. However, we shall not go into this in any greater detail here, since neither Be_2 nor B_2 have been observed up to the present time.

The two low-lying configurations of the C_2 *molecule* given in Table 33 have six bonding and two antibonding electrons, apart from the nonbonding K electrons. A much larger binding strength is therefore to be expected than for Li_2, in agreement with observation [$D_0(C_2) = 3.6$ and $D_0(Li_2) = 1.14$ volts].

The lowest state of the N_2 *molecule*,

$$(K)\ (K)\ (\sigma_g 2s)^2\ (\sigma_u 2s)^2\ (\pi_u 2p)^4\ (\sigma_g 2p)^2\ {}^1\Sigma_g{}^+, \quad \text{(VI, 16)}$$

has two antibonding and eight bonding electrons, apart from the K electrons. We expect as a result a strong binding, in agreement with experiment. It is characteristic of N_2 and a further reason for its stability that in going over to very small internuclear distances (different from C_2, He_2, and others) the configuration (VI, 16) always remains the ground state. The next orbital, $\pi_g 2p$, above those filled in the ground state is an antibonding orbital. Its separation from the bonding orbital, $\sigma_g 2p$, is therefore large for medium internuclear distances and consequently the first excitation energy of N_2 is very large (inert-gas character). In the excited states having a $\pi_g 2p$ electron, the binding strength would be expected to be considerably smaller, since an antibonding electron has taken the place of a bonding electron. This is also in agreement with experiment.

The two electrons that are added in going from the N_2 to the O_2 *molecule* must go into the antibonding $\pi_g 2p$ shell. We have thus to expect that the binding in the ground state of the O_2 molecule will be weaker than that for the N_2 molecule, since we have now four antibonding electrons and eight bonding electrons. This conclusion is confirmed by experiment: $D_0(N_2) = 7.38$ volts, and $D_0(O_2) = 5.08$ volts. As we have seen, it follows immediately from the lowest electronic configuration $[\cdots (\sigma_g 2p)^2 (\pi_g 2p)^2]$ that the ground state of the O_2 molecule is a $^3\Sigma_g{}^-$ state and therefore that O_2 is paramagnetic (see Chapter VIII, section 2), in agreement with observation. The Heitler-London theory leads to this result only when higher approximations and exact quantitative calculations are used (see p. 383 f.).

That the $\pi_g 2p$ orbital is antibonding may also be shown by the following observations. The binding strength of the $O_2{}^+$ molecule, for which in the ground state only one electron is in the $\pi_g 2p$ orbital, is found to be greater than that of O_2 $[D_0(O_2{}^+) = 6.48$ volts], and the internuclear distance in the equilibrium position is appreciably smaller (1.12 Å, compared to 1.21 Å). Furthermore, when in $O_2{}^+$ an electron is brought from the bonding $\pi_u 2p$ orbital into the antibonding $\pi_g 2p$ orbital, the internuclear distance is appreciably raised and the heat of dissociation is considerably lowered.

For the F_2 *molecule*, two more electrons come into the antibonding $\pi_g 2p$ shell, and correspondingly, in agreement with experiment, the binding strength in the ground state is further decreased (see Table 33). When finally *two* Ne *atoms* are brought together, the two additional electrons come into the antibonding $\sigma_u 2p$ shell. The number of antibonding electrons is then equal to the number of bonding electrons. Therefore we do not obtain a stable molecule.

The considerations for the binding strengths of the molecules Na_2, P_2, S_2, and Cl_2, according to the method of bonding and antibonding electrons, correspond exactly to those for Li_2, N_2, O_2, and F_2. Only the principal quantum numbers are raised by 1, and as a result the energy relationships are somewhat different.

When we compare the above results with the elementary chemical conceptions, we are led to the following rule [Herzberg (304) and (308)]: *The valency of a bond is equal to the number of bonding electron pairs minus the number of antibonding electron pairs. This difference can at the same time be regarded as a measure of the strength of the bond.* N_2, for example, has four bonding electron pairs and one anti-bonding electron pair—that is, a trivalent bond, which is very strong. In Table 33 the corresponding numbers for the other molecules treated above are given, together with the observed values for the heats of dissociation. For molecules such as N_2^+ and O_2^+ the valency of the bond is half integral, corresponding to the fact that in the method of bonding and antibonding electrons each electron (that is, half an electron pair) gives a positive or a negative contribution. The above generalization about binding strength can naturally be regarded only as a very rough rule of thumb, since in reality the bonding and antibonding actions of the individual electrons are not always equal in magnitude.

Unlike nuclear charges. As long as the charges on the nuclei are not too different, they may be regarded as equal in the discussion of electron configurations (see p. 370). In this case essentially the same conclusions also hold in regard to binding strength, even though the characterization of bonding and antibonding electrons is no longer possible in such a definite manner, since the symmetry property g–u is now only approximately defined.

For the CO *molecule*, for example, there are eight bonding and two antibonding electrons in the ground state, similar to N_2. According to the above rule, we could with some justification call the bond in CO trivalent, analogous to the bond in N_2. Actually, the bond strength of CO is even greater than that of N_2 [$D_0(CO) = 9.144$ volts, compared to $D_0(N_2) = 7.384$ volts].

The electronic configuration of the NO *molecule* in the ground state is the same as that of O_2^+ (see Table 33). Owing to the addition of an antibonding electron, $\pi_g 2p$, a smaller binding strength is to be expected than for CO, in agreement with experiment [$D_0(NO) = 5.29$ volts].

All the necessary information about the other molecules with not very different nuclei may be obtained from Table 33.

It is worthy of note that for NO the observed first excited state, $^2\Sigma$, has a much greater binding strength than the ground state. The reason is that the emission electron has gone from the anti-bonding $\pi_g 2p$ orbital into the bonding $\sigma_g 3s$ orbital (see Fig. 139). Actually, this excited $^2\Sigma$ state does appear to give a normal atom and an atom in a 3-quantum state when the atoms are separated from each other. However, we must remember that the distinction between σ_u and σ_g loses its strict meaning for unlike nuclei. As a result, the intersection of $\sigma_g 3s$ and $\sigma_u 2p$ occurring for like nuclei (for example, O_2^+) is avoided here, and the excited $^2\Sigma$ state of NO should not give an atom in a 3-quantum state on dissociation. However, the experimental data show that here we have a case like that in Fig. 130(d), where an intersection of the potential curves *almost* takes place.

If the *nuclei* are *very different in charge*—for example, in the hydrides—we cannot use the method of bonding and antibonding electrons in the above form. The procedure then to be used will be explained by the example of the NH *molecule* [see Mulliken (514)]. The potential curves of the different electronic states of this molecule are given in Fig. 150, in which the correlation with the united atom (here, oxygen), to which all the hydrides approach fairly closely, is also indicated. The electronic states corresponding to the two lowest electronic configurations of the molecule (Table 32) have been observed to be stable. We now wish to find a theoretical basis for this, to find the correlation with the terms of the separated atoms, and to obtain some information concerning the stability of other molecular states.

For the low-lying states of NH we can limit ourselves to the consideration of a normal H atom (^2S_g) and an N atom in one of the three low states ^4S_u, ^2D_u, and ^2P_u (all with the configuration $1s^2 2s^2 2p^3$); that is, we shall consider the three combinations $^2S_g + {}^4S_u$, $^2S_g + {}^2D_u$, and $^2S_g + {}^2P_u$, of which the first lies lowest. From $^2S_g + {}^4S_u$ the molecular states $^3\Sigma^-$ and $^5\Sigma^-$ result according to Table 26. Now, on the basis of the electronic configuration, the ground state of the molecule is a $^3\Sigma^-$ state (see Table 32). If we wish to avoid intersections,[14] we must correlate this state with the $^3\Sigma^-$ state resulting from two normal atoms. We can expect

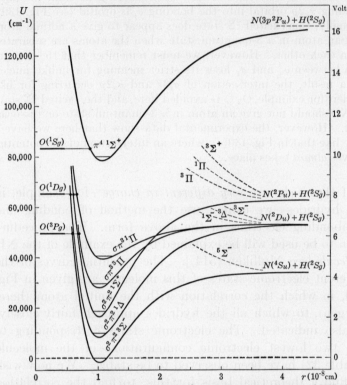

Fig. 150.   Potential Curves of the Observed Electronic States of NH. The figure is similar to a figure of Mulliken's (514). Between the uppermost and the lower curves a number of other curves is to be expected. The relative position of the singlet and triplet states is uncertain. The horizontal lines drawn somewhat above the potential minima are the levels $v = 0$. The energy scales to the left (in cm^{-1}) and to the right (in volts) refer to the state $v = 0$ as zero. The heat of dissociation of the ground state is not accurately known. It is therefore possible that the asymptotes of all the curves are to be shifted a certain amount upward or downward. Recently King (400a), by comparison with other hydrides, has estimated $D_0(NH)$ to be 3.4 e-volts.

that it will be stable, as demanded by experiment, since it corresponds to a low-lying state (^3P) of the united atom (see Fig. 150). Thus the stable ground state of NH dis-

[14] We have to do this in any case for the hydrides, since the symmetry property g–u of the electrons is no longer even approximately defined.

sociates into normal atoms. On the other hand, the $^5\Sigma^-$ state resulting from normal atoms must certainly be unstable, since the lowest state of the united atom that can give rise to such a quintet state lies very high above the ground state.

Since the $^3\Sigma^-$ state is stable, the two states $^1\Delta$ and $^1\Sigma^+$, which have the same electronic configuration ($K2s\sigma^2 2p\sigma^2 2p\pi^2$) in the molecule, must also be stable. However, they have to be correlated in a different manner with the separated atoms and the united atom. The lowest state of the separated atoms which can give rise to $^1\Delta$ is $^2D_u + {}^2S_g$, while $^1\Sigma^+$ can result only from $^2P_u + {}^2S_g$ (see Fig. 150). Both states, $^1\Delta$ and $^1\Sigma^+$, lead in the united atom to ^1D_g. From $^2D_u + {}^2S_g$, in addition to $^1\Delta$, the terms $^3\Delta$, $^1\Pi$, $^3\Pi$, $^1\Sigma^-$, and $^3\Sigma^-$ result. Only two of these, $^1\Pi$ and $^3\Pi$, can be correlated with low-lying states of the united atom (namely, with ^1D_g and ^3P_g). Therefore, they alone are to be expected as stable molecular states. They belong to the configuration $K2s\sigma^2\,2p\sigma\,2p\pi^3$ (see Table 32) and have also been observed. The other states resulting from $^2D_u + {}^2S_g$ can be correlated only with very highly excited states of the united atom and are therefore not stable (broken-line curves in Fig. 150).

From $^2P_u + {}^2S_g$ the states $^3\Sigma^+$, $^1\Pi$, and $^3\Pi$ result, in addition to the $^1\Sigma^+$ state already mentioned. All three states are unstable, since they correspond to very highly excited states of the united atom. Of the molecular states resulting from the low-lying states of the separated atoms or of the united atom, only the $^1\Sigma^+$ state, which results from the ^1S_g term of the united atom, remains to be discussed. It must have the configuration $K2s\sigma^2\,2p\pi^4$, since this is the only configuration left that has four $2p$ electrons, as have the low-lying states of the united atom O. We can see from Fig. 150 that this state cannot arise from any of the three low states of the separated atoms but must result from a highly excited state. It is therefore a stable state; it has also been observed [see (471a)].

Other hydrides or molecules with very different nuclear charges can be treated in a corresponding manner [see

Mulliken (514)]. The above procedure can also be applied to molecules with equal nuclei, but the transition to the united atom leads to unambiguous pronouncements only for the hydrides, as in the example of NH.

On the whole, we can say that the method that uses electron configurations even for estimating the stability (bonding and antibonding electrons for equal and nearly equal nuclei, correlation with the united atom for hydrides, and the like) gives just as good a picture of homopolar chemical binding as the Heitler-London theory. While the results are not perhaps of such a general nature, the method is rather suitable for discussion of special cases. A large number of such special cases have been discussed in detail by Mulliken [(514) and (519–521)].

Recently Lessheim, Hunter, and Samuel [(442), (349), and (613)] have raised objections to the theory of bonding and anti-bonding electrons. They appear to be based on rather uncertain experimental material and in part are directed only against Mulliken's original idea (now given up by him) that electrons whose principal quantum number is raised in the transition to the united atom ("promoted" electrons; see p. 389) are always anti-bonding.

(b) Heteropolar Binding (Ionic Binding)

In heteropolar binding the molecules are held together simply by the classical *electrostatic attraction between oppositely charged ions*. For two pointlike ions of charge ε ($= 4.8029 \cdot 10^{-10}$ e.s.u.) the potential energy, according to Coulomb's law, is

$$V = -\frac{\varepsilon^2}{r} = -\frac{11.613}{r} \cdot 10^4, \qquad \text{(VI, 17)}$$

where the units used for V are cm^{-1} and those used for r are Ångström units. As a result of the finite extent of the actual ions, a deviation from the simple Coulomb potential (VI, 17) takes place at small internuclear distances when the two electron clouds of the two ions start to penetrate each other appreciably.   This deviation is always in the sense of a *repulsion*.   According to Born and Mayer (121), this repulsion can be represented by an exponential term, so that we obtain

$$V = -\frac{\varepsilon^2}{r} + Be^{-r/\rho}, \qquad (VI, 18)$$

where B and ρ are constants. ρ is a measure of the sum of the radii of the ions under consideration.   In Fig. 151(a) and (b) the solid-line curves marked I give the potential energy of two singly charged ions.   The broken-line branch of each of the curves corresponds to the pure Coulomb potential (VI, 17).   It should be noted that the force of

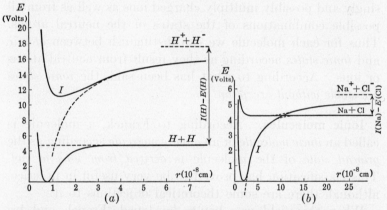

Fig. 151.   Potential Curves of the States Resulting from Normal Atoms and Ions.   (a) For H_2.   (b) For NaCl.   Only the lowest of the states resulting from normal atoms is drawn.   The broken-line branch of the ionic curves corresponds to the pure Coulomb attraction.   For NaCl, the fact that the two curves actually do not cross is indicated by broken connecting lines.   However, in reality the region in which the actual curves differ from the solid-line curves is much smaller than can be drawn.

attraction extends to much greater distances for ions than for neutral atoms, for which it drops off exponentially (see p. 378).   In Fig. 151 this makes itself felt by the fact that the ionic curves do not reach their asymptotes even at the extreme right of the figure (large r), whereas the two other curves, which correspond to atomic binding, do.

Naturally, the Wigner-Witmer correlation rules hold also

for the states that result from ions. If, as is often the case, the ions are in ^1S states [for example, $Na^+(^1S)$ and $Cl^-(^1S)$], only one $^1\Sigma$ molecular state, which has a potential curve of the type described, results from the ions. According to (VI, 18), the right part of the curve is very nearly the same for all singly charged ions. If we have ions that are not in ^1S states [for example, $Be^+(^2S)$ and $O^-(^2P)$], we obtain a number of molecular states (see Table 26) whose potential curves, however, very nearly coincide at least for large r values and which, therefore, are all stable.

If we wish to obtain all the possible states of a diatomic molecule, we have to derive all the states resulting from the singly and possibly multiply charged ions as well as from all possible combinations of the states of the neutral atoms. Thus for each molecule we can distinguish between *atomic* and *ionic states* according as they result from neutral atoms or ions. According to what has been said, the *ionic states are stable without exception.*

Ionic molecules. According to Franck, a molecule is called an *ionic molecule* or an *atomic molecule* according as the *ground state* of the molecule is *derived from ions or not.* This classification has proved to be very useful in practice, although there are some theoretical objections to it.

When this field was being developed, Franck and his co-workers gave some spectroscopic criteria for distinguishing between atomic and ionic molecules. However, although at first these proved to be very fruitful, they were not subsequently confirmed by more detailed wave mechanical considerations [see, for example, Mulliken (520) and (521)]. We can therefore omit their discussion here. However, we can in many cases decide in other ways whether the molecule under consideration is an atomic or an ionic molecule.

If A and B are the two atoms forming a molecule, the *energy difference*, for large internuclear distances, *between the lowest ionic state $A^+ + B^-$ and the lowest atomic state $A + B$* is given by

$$I(A) - E(B),$$

where $I(A)$ is the ionization potential of A and $E(B)$ is the electron affinity of B.   Only when the difference $I(A) - E(B)$ is small can an ionic molecule occur; only then can the ground state dissociate into ions.   In order to see this, let us consider two extreme examples, the molecules H_2 and NaCl, for which the potential curves of the states resulting from normal atoms and normal ions are given in Fig. 151.

For H_2 the state $H^+ + H^-$ lies above the state $H + H$ by an amount $13.60 - 0.72 = 12.88$ volts.   The point of intersection of the pure Coulomb curve (dashed) with the asymptote of the $H + H$ potential curve lies at 1.1 Å—that is, in the region in which the attractive $H + H$ potential curve already lies considerably below the asymptote.   At this distance, the ions can certainly no longer be regarded as pointlike, but we must take into account the repulsion between the ions.   The ionic curve therefore has its minimum above the asymptote of the $H + H$ curve (actually very much above), and therefore the ionic state cannot be the ground state.   Like all other elementary molecules, H_2 is a *typical atomic molecule*.   However, there are two stable excited states of H_2 that are known to be ionic states.

The relations for NaCl are quite different.   Here, at large internuclear distances, the state $Na^+ + Cl^-$ lies only $5.14 - 3.75 = 1.39$ volts above the state $Na + Cl$, and the ionic curve already intersects the asymptote of the atomic curve at 10.5 Å.   At this internuclear distance, the atomic curve is still completely horizontal, whereas the ionic curve does not yet deviate from the pure Coulomb curve (VI, 17).   Therefore at smaller distances, which correspond to the stable molecule, the ionic curve lies below the atomic curve (see Fig. 151).   The molecule is therefore an *ionic molecule*. A corresponding state of affairs exists for all the alkali halides.

It is clear that everything depends on the *difference* $I(A) - E(B)$.   If it is *small*, we have an *ionic molecule*; if it is *large*, we have an *atomic molecule*.   This purely qualitative rule can be expressed somewhat more quantitatively if we assume a knowledge of the ionic radii or if we know the internuclear distance for the molecule in the ground state: We can say that, if the intersection of the pure Coulomb curve (VI, 17) with the asymptote of the atomic curve (normal atoms) lies at an internuclear distance that is not greater than the sum of the ionic radii or is not greater than about 1.5 times the internuclear distance in the normal molecule, we can be certain that we have an atomic molecule (see the above example). On the other hand, if this point of intersection lies at an internuclear distance which is greater than roughly 1.5 times the sum of the ionic radii or twice the internuclear distance in the ground state, we can be certain that we have an ionic molecule. For, since the potential curve of the atomic state approaches its asymptote exponentially, at $2r_0$ it already lies fairly close to the asymptote. Therefore, when the intersection with the ionic curve takes place at an internuclear distance $> 2r_0$, the ionic curve is the lower one at smaller r and thus forms the ground state.

It is clear, of course, that, according to the above rough rule, if the point of intersection lies between $1.5r_0$ and $2r_0$, no definite decision is possible. This uncertainty has also a theoretical basis (see below). However, in most of the cases occurring in practice the point of intersection lies at such an r value that an unambiguous decision according to the rule is possible.

Let us consider the further example of the molecule HCl, which from a chemical standpoint might plausibly be assumed to have an ionic binding in the ground state, since HCl dissociates into ions in solution. For HCl the difference $I(A) - E(B)$ is 9.83 volts. From this we might already conclude qualitatively that it is highly probable that we are dealing with an atomic molecule. A determination of the intersection of the Coulomb curve with the asymptote of the potential curve of the normal atoms according to (VI, 17) gives $r = 1.45$ Å. The ionic radius of Cl^- is 1.8 Å, and the internuclear distance in HCl is 1.27 Å. From this it follows that HCl in the gaseous state is certainly an atomic molecule. The same holds for the remaining halogen hydrides.

Transition cases. With one exception (CsF), for all the diatomic molecules thus far known the electron affinity of the one atom is less than the ionization potential of the other. As a result (apart from CsF), *only if the ionic curve crosses the atomic curve* can the ionic state be the ground state of the molecule under consideration and thus the molecule be an ionic molecule. We know, however (see p. 324), that, strictly speaking, such intersections can occur only when the intersecting terms are of unlike species. But actually the ionic states are in general of the same species (usually $^1\Sigma$) as one of the states resulting from normal atoms, or, if that is not the case, as one of the molecular states resulting from an excited state of the atoms that still lies below the ionic state for large r. As a result, the intersection of the atomic with the ionic curve is always avoided [see the dotted connecting curves in Fig. 151(b)]. Therefore, strictly speaking, the ground state of the molecule always leads to neutral atoms, and thus, in the exact sense of the word, there are only atomic molecules (apart from CsF).

When, however, as is the case for NaCl (see Fig. 151) and many other molecules, the point of intersection lies at an internuclear distance at which the atomic curve scarcely deviates at all from the asymptote, the interaction of the states is so small that a deviation from the "original" course occurs only in the immediate neighborhood of the point of intersection [see London (456)], since at these large separations the two atoms or ions can still be regarded approximately as separate systems. If a transition from the atomic to the ionic state is to take place, an electron must go from one atom to the other, and this exchange, for large internuclear distances, can occur only for extremely sharp resonance between the two states—that is, only in the immediate neighborhood of the point of intersection. Therefore, even at a very small distance from the point of intersection the potential curves run as if they actually had crossed, and consequently at smaller internuclear distances the properties of the lower state (eigenfunctions, behavior of vibrational quanta, and so on) are exactly what they would be for the ionic state. Thus in such cases we are doubtless justified in designating the molecule under consideration as an ionic molecule.

The more the point of intersection shifts towards smaller r values, the stronger will be the interaction of the two states and the more will the two curves draw away from each other. Finally, a point is reached at which there is scarcely any sense in saying that "originally"—that is, in zero approximation—an intersection of the ionic and atomic curves has been present and that therefore the molecule is an ionic molecule. Rather, it is much more appropriate to speak of an atomic molecule (that is, in other words, to choose another zero approximation).

From the foregoing considerations it is seen that the *dividing line between atomic and ionic molecules is not at all rigid*. However, the border-line cases in which we can speak with equal justification of the molecule as an ionic or an atomic molecule are relatively rare.

In transition cases and also in the case of atomic molecules, the *ionic state*, when it does not lie too high, *influences the ground state*. It forces the ground state downward and at the same time makes a contribution to its eigenfunction (see p. 317f.). There is, therefore, some point in saying that a molecule may be regarded as being to a certain fraction an ionic molecule. These relationships were first recognized by Pauling (554) [see also (49a)].

Mulliken (520) has introduced the concept of *ionicness* for the fractional contribution of the ionic states to the eigenfunction of a given electronic state. The ionicness of the ground states of the alkali halides is practically 100 per cent, whereas for H_2, HCl, and similar molecules it is very small. All polar molecules (that is, molecules with a dipole moment different from zero) have an ionicness different from zero in the ground state; however, a molecule in a state with great ionicness has not necessarily a dipole moment. In the ionic states of molecules such as H_2, for example, there is no polarity (no dipole moment), owing to the continual interchange between $H^+ H^-$ and $H^- H^+$.

(c) Van der Waals' Binding

When there is no valence force either of homopolar or of heteropolar kind acting between two atoms, as, for example, between two inert-gas atoms, a very small attraction between them still remains which is responsible for the deviations of the behavior of the gas from the ideal gas laws and their liquefaction at sufficiently low temperatures. These deviations from the ideal gas laws are taken care of in the well-known van der Waals' equation, and therefore the residual attraction is called a *van der Waals' force*. Correspondingly, we speak of *van der Waals' binding* (or sometimes of polarization binding) and of *van der Waals' molecules* (or polarization molecules).

London [(454) and (455)] has treated these forces on the basis of quantum mechanics and has shown that they are due (for example, for He + He) to the perturbation of the repulsive ground state by the higher electronic states of the system consisting of the two atoms. He found that this perturbation at large internuclear distances gives a *potential energy decreasing as* $-1/r^6$ *toward smaller r values.*[15] Naturally, at smaller distances the strong repulsion of the zerovalent atoms sets in (see above), so that only a very shallow minimum at a relatively large internuclear distance results [compare the potential curves in Fig. 152(*b*) and (*c*)]. London has called these attractive forces *dispersion forces*, because they are to be ascribed to the same influences as the dispersion of light by gases (influence of the higher states).[16]

The London dispersion forces exist for every molecular state. However, in general they are overshadowed by the valence forces. They are noticeable only when the valence forces are very weak or zero—that is, in general, at large internuclear distances. As a result of these dispersion forces, for example, two H atoms with parallel spins or two He atoms, which in consequence of valence forces repel one another very strongly for small internuclear distances, attract one another very weakly at large internuclear distances. However, in the case of He + He the potential minimum corresponding to this attraction is only $1.9 \cdot 10^{-5}$ volt below the asymptote [Page (549a)].

One might be tempted to regard also the binding between a normal alkaline-earth atom and an H atom or halogen atom as van der Waals' binding. We have seen above that for this case the elementary Heitler-London theory gives no binding and that the binding actually observed may be explained as due to the influence of higher electronic states—that is, to the same influences that give rise to the dispersion effect. However, London's calculations actually hold only if the distance of the higher electronic states from the ground state is large, and the dispersion forces are then due to the more or less equal influence of a large number of higher

---

[15] For an experimental verification of this relation see p. 419 f.

[16] In the interaction of saturated *molecules* with one another the orientation effect and the induction effect are added to the dispersion effect (the first only for dipole molecules), both causing an additional van der Waals' attraction.

states, whereas the relatively large binding strength of molecules such as BeH, MgF, and so on, is produced by the interaction of the ground state with *one* relatively low-lying excited state. The $1/r^6$ law does *not* hold in this case. It is therefore useful to limit the designation "van der Waals' binding" to those cases for which the excited states of the participating atoms either lie very high or, if they do not lie very high, are unable to give valence binding. They are thus those molecules or molecular states for which we cannot speak of valence binding, even in higher approximation, as, for example, He + He in the ground state; H + H and Na + Na in the $^3\Sigma$ repulsive state; A + Hg; and others. For A + Hg, there is, for example, a relatively low-lying state of the separated atoms $[A(^1S) + Hg(^3P)]$. However, it does not give any strong binding and therefore influences the ground state only slightly, different from, say, Be + H (see p. 382 f.).

CHAPTER VII

Continuous and Diffuse Molecular Spectra; Dissociation and Predissociation

1. CONTINUOUS SPECTRA AND BAND CONVERGENCE LIMITS; DISSOCIATION OF MOLECULES

Sometimes, in absorption as well as in emission, continuous molecular spectra appear in addition to discrete molecular spectra (see Chapter II). Quite generally, such continuous spectra result from transitions between two states, one of which at least can take a *continuous range of energy values*.

For any atomic system, continuous ranges of terms always correspond to *aperiodic motions* for which parts of the system approach one another or separate from one another with a relative kinetic energy which is not zero even at infinity (see Chapter I, p. 10). For atoms, a continuous term spectrum joins onto each series of electronic states and corresponds to the removal of an electron (*ionization*) with more or less relative kinetic energy or, conversely, to the capture of an electron by the corresponding ion (*recombination*). According to the old Bohr theory, the corresponding orbits are hyperbolic orbits. According to wave mechanics, the corresponding wave functions are outgoing and incoming spherical waves.

For molecules, such continuous term spectra, corresponding to ionization, are also possible. However, we have here in addition continuous term spectra that correspond to a *splitting of the molecule into atomic components* (normal or excited atoms, or positive and negative ions)—that is, correspond to a *dissociation*. As we have already seen (Chapter III), they join onto the series of vibrational levels

407

of every electronic state and are also present if the electronic state under consideration has no discrete vibrational levels at all (unstable state).

As Franck first realized, the investigations of continuous spectra lead to important conclusions about *dissociation processes* and *heats of dissociation* of molecules.

(a) Absorption

Up to the present time, only in two cases, that of O_2 [Price and Collins (571)] and that of N_2 [Worley and Jenkins (722)], has the continuous spectrum that joins onto a Rydberg series of bands (or band systems) and that corresponds to ionization (*ionization continuum*) been identified with certainty. In the cases mentioned it corresponds to the formation of $O_2{}^+$ and $N_2{}^+$, respectively. The long-wave-length limit of the continuum—that is, the convergence limit of the Rydberg series—gives an exact value for one of the *ionization potentials* of the molecule. We say *one* of the ionization potentials, since the observed limit does not necessarily correspond to the transition to the ground state of the ion but may also correspond to an ionization leaving the ion in an excited state. Owing to the magnitude of the ionization potential of most molecules, these absorption spectra lie in the far ultraviolet (below 1000 Å).

Continuous absorption spectra corresponding to a *dissociation* are much more frequently observed than the ionization continua, since, like the discrete band systems, they result from transitions between two electronic states and can therefore lie in the visible and near ultraviolet regions.

Three cases of dissociation continua are possible: those for which the upper state is continuous, those for which the lower state is continuous, and those for which the upper as well as the lower state is continuous.

Upper state continuous. The most important of the above-mentioned cases is that in which a transition takes place from a stable lower state to a continuous upper state.

Absorption of a light quantum in the resulting continuous spectrum then leads to a dissociation of the molecule under consideration (*photodissociation*).

If the upper electronic state has discrete vibrational levels, the continuous spectrum may join onto a series of converging bands (*band convergence*). On the other hand, the continuous spectrum may also appear without these accompanying bands. The latter is the case when the potential curve of the excited state has no minimum [Fig. 152(*a*)] or when this minimum lies at a much greater internuclear distance than that of the ground state (see below).

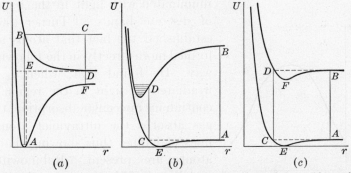

Fig. 152. **Potential Curves for the Explanation of Continuous Absorption Spectra.** The lower curve in (*b*) and both curves in (*c*), which correspond to van der Waals' attraction, are actually much shallower than drawn.

The I_2 absorption spectrum in the visible, reproduced in Fig. 15, p. 37, is an example of the first case (*band convergence with adjoining continuum*). It is the one that was first studied in this connection by Franck and his co-workers (229). Further spectra of this type have been found for Br_2 (426), O_2 (440), and some other molecules. The *convergence limit of the bands* (the beginning of the continuum), which can be observed in these cases with great accuracy, gives the exact position of the asymptote of the potential curve of the upper state. This asymptote is also called *dissociation limit*. In the case of I_2 (and similarly of the other halogen molecules) it can be shown (see section 3) that at the convergence limit dissociation takes place into one normal atom in the $^2P_{\frac{3}{2}}$ state and one in the slightly excited metastable $^2P_{\frac{1}{2}}$ state; that is, the asymptote of the potential curve of the upper state does not coincide with that of the ground state [compare Fig. 83(c), p. 214].

That the absorption in the continuous region actually corresponds to a *dissociation into atoms* has been verified by a number of experiments which refer principally to the very readily accessible continuous absorption of the I_2 molecule. Dymond (196) has shown that no fluorescence appears on illumination with light in the continuous region, while, on the other hand, an intense fluorescence appears when the gas is illuminated with light in the region of discrete bands.   Turner (669) established the fact that atoms are formed more directly in the following way: He found that, when I_2 is irradiated by light in the region of continuous molecular absorption, the gas absorbs the ultraviolet atomic lines of iodine, thus showing that I atoms are present.   Rabinowitch and Wood (575), by measuring the intensity of molecular absorption, detected the decrease in the number of molecules due to dissociation of some of the molecules.   Finally, Senftleben and Germer (628) showed that the heat conductivity of the gas is changed in consequence of the dissociation of a certain fraction of the molecules.

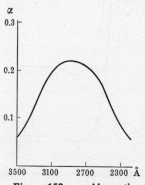

Fig.   153.   Absorption Curve of F_2 [after von Wartenberg, Sprenger, and Taylor (689)].

The absorption spectra of F_2 (689) and the halogen hydrides [(263) and (264)] are examples of the case where *only the continuum*, without the adjoining band series, is observed.   In Fig. 153 the absorption coefficient of F_2 is plotted against wave length.   It can be seen that, on coming from long wave lengths, the absorption at first increases, then reaches a maximum, and finally decreases.   The extent of the continuum depends on the thickness of the absorbing layer.

The absorption spectrum of Cl_2 may be regarded as a *transition case* insofar as only continuous absorption is observed for thin and medium layers, whereas for thicker layers a series of converging bands appears at the long-wavelength limit of the continuum. This transition case makes it particularly clear that there can be no doubt that a pure continuous spectrum, without an adjoining band series, represents an electronic transition of the same type as discrete absorption spectra, except that the upper state is unstable (continuous). The existence of the continua shows at the same time that the unstable molecular states (without an appreciable potential minimum) are just as real as the stable molecular states.

The *long-wave-length limit of the continuum* is obviously given theoretically by the height of the asymptote of the potential curve of the upper state above the vibrationless ground state [AE in Fig. 152(a)], corresponding to the band convergence limit in the case where discrete bands are also present. However, the observed long-wave-length limit of a continuum is often at considerably shorter wave lengths than the theoretical limit. The explanation for this and also the approximate variation of intensity with wave length are given by the Franck-Condon principle.

According to the *Franck-Condon principle*, the most probable transition in absorption is that going vertically upward from the minimum of the lower potential curve [AB in Fig. 152(a)]. This transition gives the maximum of the intensity, which, in general, if the upper state is a repulsive state, lies at appreciably shorter wave lengths than the theoretical limit; that is, at the maximum of absorption the two atoms generally separate from each other with an appreciable kinetic energy [corresponding to CD in Fig. 152(a)]. The smaller the slope of the repulsive curve is, the more rapidly the intensity falls off to either side of this maximum. For a repulsive curve like that in Fig. 152(a), a transition in the neighborhood of the theoretical long-wave-length limit would correspond to a very large change in internuclear distance $(A-D)$. Consequently, such a transition practically does not occur. The continuum first begins at an appreciably shorter wave length but *without a sharp limit*. The theoretical long-wave-length limit can be observed only when a case such as that in Fig. 83(c), in which the band convergence is also observed, occurs, or when the repulsive curve runs quite flat up to relatively small internuclear distances. In the latter case the continuum is rather narrow and possibly has the appearance of a diffuse band or even of a diffuse line [see also section 2(d)].

Hogness and Franck (324) have proved directly that there is a *large relative velocity* of the two atoms resulting from absorption in a continuous spectrum by investigating the line width of the Na atomic lines emitted after the photo-dissociation of NaI vapor [NaI $\rightarrow$ Na* (^2P) + I]. The yellow sodium lines excited in this way exhibit an anomalously large width, which is due to the *Doppler effect* of the motion of the atoms flying apart with large velocities after the light absorption. The width is found to be the larger the shorter the wave length of the light producing the dissociation, as is to be expected.

In the *quantitative theoretical determination of the intensity distribution* we have to take into account the form of the eigenfunctions in the upper and in the lower state. According to the wave mechanical formulation of the Franck-Condon principle [see Chapter IV, section 4(a), and formula (I, 18)], the intensity of a band of a given electronic transition in absorption is proportional to

$$\nu \left[\int \psi_{v'} \psi_{v''} dr \right]^2, \qquad \text{(VII, 1)}$$

where $\psi_{v'}$ and $\psi_{v''}$ are the vibrational eigenfunctions of the upper and lower states. It may be shown that the same expression holds for the present case of a continuous spectrum if we refer the intensity of the continuum at every point to the same wave-number interval. For an evaluation of the integral, in addition to a knowledge of the vibrational eigenfunction of the stable state (see Figs. 41 and 47, pp. 82 and 101), a knowledge of the "vibrational" eigenfunction of the unstable state is required.

The *eigenfunctions of the nuclear motions* for three different energy values of the upper state of the continuous absorption of

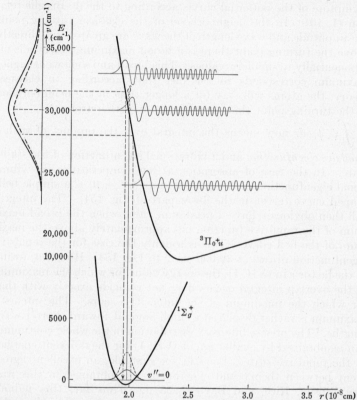

Fig. 154.   Potential Curves and Repulsive Eigenfunctions for Cl_2. Adaptation of a similar figure by Gibson, Rice, and Bayliss (259). The ordinate scale in cm $^{-1}$ holds for the potential curves (heavy lines) as well as for the intensity distribution in the continuous spectrum drawn to the left; however, it has, of course, nothing to do with the eigenfunctions (thin full lines). The abscissae are the same for the potential curves and the eigenfunctions. The dotted curve denoted by δ is to be thought of as infinitely thin and infinitely high, so that the area under it $= 1$. The "reflection" of the curve ψ_v'' for the lower state $v'' = 0$ (lower broken-line curve) at the upper potential curve is indicated by the broken leading lines. The upper potential curve is drawn under the assumption that the discrete absorption bands of Cl_2 in the visible have the same upper electronic state as the continuous spectrum ($^3\Pi_{0u}{}^+$). However, according to a more recent investigation of Aickin and Bayliss (60a) the continuous spectrum is due mainly to another electronic transition ($^1\Pi_{1u} \leftarrow {}^1\Sigma_g{}^+$).

the Cl_2 molecule, as obtained from theory, are reproduced in Fig. 154. At some distance from the classical turning point of the motion, we have a simple sine wave of constant amplitude whose wave length is the smaller the higher the energy lies above the asymptote of the potential curve, according to the de Broglie relation (I, 10). In the neighborhood of the classical turning point the amplitude and wave length of the wave are greater, and directly above the turning point there is a broad maximum which falls off exponentially to smaller r values. This broad and somewhat higher maximum corresponds to the fact that, according to classical theory, the atoms will stay for a longer time in the neighborhood of the turning point than at some distance therefrom.

$\int \psi_{v'}\psi_{v''}dr$ now means the integral over the product of such a *repulsive eigenfunction* and a vibrational eigenfunction of the stable state. In the case of absorption at low temperatures the vibrational eigenfunction of the ground state ($v'' = 0$) is a simple bell-shaped curve (given in the lower part of Fig. 154). The integral will then obviously have a maximum value when the broad maximum of the repulsive function lies approximately above the maximum of the bell curve. This is roughly the case for the repulsive eigenfunction drawn at 30,000 cm^{-1} in Fig. 154. However, owing to the factor ν in (VII, 1), the energy value for which the maximum of the overlap integral occurs does not coincide exactly with that for which the maximum of the intensity occurs. The intensity maximum is rather displaced a small amount toward shorter wave lengths. The precise intensity distribution in the whole continuum can be obtained by evaluation of (VII, 1) for the different energies in the repulsive state. For Cl$_2$, for example, an excellent agreement between theory and experiment was obtained in this way [see Gibson, Rice, and Bayliss (259)]. Thus far, this tedious procedure has been applied in only a very few cases [see also Coolidge, James, and Present (162)].

Usually, an *approximation* first given by Winans and Stueckelberg (717) is used to derive the intensity distribution in continuous spectra: The repulsive eigenfunction is replaced by a so-called δ function, which is different from zero only at the classical turning points (dotted curve denoted by δ in Fig. 154). This would appear to be a very poor approximation for the repulsive eigenfunction. Actually, however, the results obtained therewith deviate only very slightly from those obtained with the accurate repulsive eigenfunctions, as Coolidge, James, and Present (162) have shown in detail.

The construction of the theoretical intensity distribution according to this procedure is illustrated graphically in Fig. 154 for the

case of the Cl_2 absorption spectrum. Owing to the assumed form
of the repulsive eigenfunction, in the integration (VII, 1) now only
the value of $\psi_{v''}$ at the position vertically below the classical turning point for a given energy of the unstable state matters. The
intensity is therefore simply proportional to $\nu\psi_{v''}^2$, where $\psi_{v''}$ is to
be taken for the r value that corresponds to the ν considered.
We have therefore simply to *"reflect" the function* $\psi_{v''}^2$ (that is, the
probability density distribution in the lower state; see Fig. 154)
at the repulsive potential curve (obtaining the broken-line curve
to the left in Fig. 154) and then to multiply by ν in order to obtain
the theoretical intensity distribution (full-line curve left). Conversely, we can obviously use the observed intensity distribution
to derive the course of the repulsive part of the potential curve
[see also Bayliss (82)].

From the above discussion it can be seen immediately that the
continuous spectrum corresponding to transitions *from the lower
vibrational state* $v'' = 1$ must show *two intensity maxima* (instead
of the one for $v'' = 0$), since the probability density distribution
curve has two maxima (see Fig. 41). Correspondingly, three maxima, of which the middle one has no analogue in the elementary
classical description, are to be expected in the continuum corresponding to transitions from $v'' = 2$, and so on. However, in
absorption actually only a single maximum is observed in the
continuous spectrum, since most of the molecules are always in
the state $v'' = 0$ and the maxima corresponding to $v'' = 1, 2, \cdots$
produce at most a broadening of the maximum corresponding to
$v'' = 0$ but do not appear separately.[1] It is, however, clear that
with increasing temperature the height of the central maximum
of an absorption continuum must decrease, while the margins
increase in intensity. This behavior has been quantitatively investigated and confirmed for Cl_2 by Gibson and Bayliss (256).

Lower state or both lower and upper state continuous.
The case in which the lower state or both the lower and the
upper state for an observed continuous absorption spectrum
belong to a continuous region occurs for monatomic gases

---

[1] It should be noted that the theoretical limit of the absorption continuum
corresponding to the state $v'' = 1$ lies $\Delta G_{\frac{1}{2}}''$ farther to long wave lengths than
that corresponding to $v'' = 0$. Therefore it may happen that the absorption
continuum for higher temperatures or for extremely thick layers extends
beyond the theoretical long-wave-length limit corresponding to $v'' = 0$ to
still longer wave lengths. This is a further reason why the long-wave-length
limit of a continuum that does not join onto a band series is not sharp.

(metal vapors and inert gases). The potential curves for the two cases are drawn in Fig. 152(b) and (c).

In these cases, in the ground state, *only van der Waals' forces* act between the two atoms, apart from the repulsive forces which come into play at smaller distances. These van der Waals' forces give a very shallow minimum in the potential curve at rather large internuclear distances [see Chapter VI, section 4(c)].

For not too low temperature ($kT \gtrsim$ heat of dissociation) and for low pressure, most of the molecules are dissociated, since thermal collisions are sufficient to throw the molecules out of the shallow minimum; that is, the gas is monatomic. The absorption spectrum then consists solely of atomic lines ($A \rightarrow B$ and transitions to higher levels) which correspond to the differences between the asymptotes of the potential curves.

However, when the pressure is sufficiently high, the atoms are relatively often in the *state of collision* (sometimes called the state of the *quasi molecule*). This means that the potential energy is different from that of the separated atoms. If absorption takes place during a collision, frequencies other than those for the widely separated atoms will be absorbed, as we can see immediately from Fig. 152(b) and (c) if we consider that, according to the Franck-Condon principle, mainly transitions vertically upward occur. Since the kinetic and potential energies of the colliding atoms can take any value within a certain range, a continuous absorption spectrum results.

We shall consider first of all the case where the *collision of the atoms* takes place *centrally or nearly centrally*. The turning point of the motion is then given by the point of intersection of the horizontal line corresponding to the total energy of the system with the potential curve [for example, C in Fig. 152(b) and (c)]. Since the atoms stay relatively the longest time in the neighborhood of the turning point, the transition (absorption) takes place mainly at this position and does so preferentially vertically upward.

In the case where the *upper state* is *stable* [Fig. 153(*b*)], a transition into one of the discrete vibrational states of the upper state takes place. Since, however, the collision can take place with more or less kinetic energy [that is, different heights of the point *C* in Fig. 152(*b*) and (*c*)], we obtain a continuous absorption spectrum for each given upper state. The different continua overlap one another and give an extended continuum—possibly with intensity fluctuations [see section 2(d)]. This continuum lies on the long-wavelength side of the atomic line under consideration. It may join directly onto the atomic line or lie at some distance from it, depending on the shape of the upper potential curve. The longest-wave-length region of the continuum will be absorbed by those atoms in the state of collision that collide with the greatest kinetic energy. The higher the temperature, the greater is this kinetic energy. We should therefore expect the extent and the intensity of the long-wave-length part of the continuum to be very sensitive to temperature.

When the *upper state* is a *repulsive state*, a continuum results in a corresponding manner [transitions *C–D* in Fig. 152(*c*)], but it has in general a much smaller extent than when the upper state is stable, and it usually joins directly onto the atomic line. In this case the continuum extends to longer or shorter wave lengths from the atomic line, depending on the course of the upper potential curve relative to the lower. When, at one position, there is a maximum vertical separation of the two potential curves, a short-wave-length limit to the continuum results.

Such continua, for stable as well as unstable upper states, have been observed and investigated in detail, particularly for the vapors of Cd, Zn, and Hg [Winans (716); see also Sponer (649) and Finkelnburg (218) and (42)]. In absorption, at high pressures fairly extended continua join onto the resonance lines $^3P - {}^1S$ and $^1P - {}^1S$ of these atoms, to longer wave lengths. They correspond to transitions from the unstable ground state (two normal ^1S atoms in the state of collision) to a stable molecular state resulting from an excited ^3P or ^1P atom and a normal ^1S atom.   As Kuhn and Freudenberg (434) have shown for Hg, the intensity of these continua increases quadratically with the pressure, as it must on the basis of the above explanation, since the number of atoms in the state of collision increases quadratically with the pressure.   A temperature dependence of the long-wavelength part has also been observed by them.   Furthermore, narrow continuous extensions are found which join onto some atomic lines at higher pressure, as would be expected when the upper as well as the lower state is unstable.   The case of a short-wave-length limit has also been observed.

Such continua have also been observed in mixtures of Hg at low pressure with inert gases at high pressure, in the neighborhood of the Hg lines [Oldenberg (537)].   They correspond to collisions between Hg and inert-gas atoms.

Since in many cases *several* molecular states result from a given combination of the excited states of the separate atoms (see Chapter VI, section 1), a number of different continua can sometimes join onto or correspond to one and the same atomic line [see Finkelnburg (42)].   For example, for the resonance line $^1P - ^1S$ (and similarly $^3P - ^1S$) of Hg, two continua (one with fluctuations of intensity; see above) have been observed, corresponding to the excited states $^1\Pi_u$ and $^1\Sigma_u^+$ [the states $^1\Pi_g$ and $^1\Sigma_g^+$, which likewise result from $^1P + ^1S$ (see p. 342), cannot combine with the ground state].

In many cases we have, furthermore, to take account of the fact that the Franck-Condon principle in its wave mechanical formulation holds only under the condition that the probability for the electronic transition [that is, R_e in (IV, 57 and 58)] is constant, independent of the internuclear distance.   Actually, this condition is usually quite well fulfilled for discrete electronic transitions, since for them only a small range of internuclear distances is concerned.   However, for collisions of atoms, such a large range of internuclear distances is covered that the condition mentioned is often no longer fulfilled, and therefore the derivation of the intensity distribution can no longer be carried out in the manner previously discussed.   In particular, it may happen that a transition is forbidden in the separated atoms but is allowed as the atoms approach each other, since then the selection rules for molecules apply.   We then observe a continuum without the atomic line belonging to it [see also Finkelnburg (222) and Coolidge, James, and Present (162)].

We shall now consider the case where the *collision* of the atoms is *noncentral*. During noncentral collisions the atoms do not approach each other so closely, and at no point in their path is their relative velocity zero. With an accuracy sufficient for many purposes we may simply consider the atoms as flying past each other. Thus in the application of the Franck-Condon principle the turning point is no longer favored. For each nuclear separation traversed, a transition to the upper state can take place with about the same probability. The *frequencies absorbed correspond to the separation of the two potential curves for the r value at which the quantum jump occurs*, since, according to the Franck-Condon principle, the kinetic energy is practically unaltered by the electron jump. Therefore a continuous spectrum results, corresponding to transitions vertically upward from every point between A and E in Fig. 152(c), and joining directly onto the atomic line. It extends to longer or shorter wave lengths according to whether the potential curve has a deeper or a shallower minimum in the upper state than in the lower state. An extension toward longer wave lengths is much more frequent, since excited states usually give a stronger van der Waals' binding than does the ground state.

The intensity distribution in the continuum corresponding to the noncentral collisions can be easily derived, since the frequency of occurrence of the different values of the internuclear distance is proportional to r^2 and the wave number corresponding to each r can be taken from the potential curve diagram. According to the London theory of van der Waals' binding, for large r the potential energy, apart from an additive constant, is proportional to $-1/r^6$. If this holds for the upper as well as the lower state, it can be easily shown that the *intensity of the continuum* should vary *inversely proportional to* $(\Delta\nu)^{\frac{3}{2}}$ if $\Delta\nu$ is the separation from the atomic line [Kuhn (430)]. The continuum usually extends from the atomic line toward longer wave lengths (see above) with decreasing intensity. When two or more molecular states result from the upper state of the atomic line, a continuum may join onto either side of the line.

The variation of intensity with $1/(\Delta\nu)^{\frac{3}{2}}$ demanded by theory has been quantitatively confirmed in experimental investigations of the broadening of the Na resonance lines when argon is added to the sodium [Minkowski (497)] and of the Hg line 2537 Å when argon is added to the mercury, or at high Hg pressures [Kuhn (431); see also Rühmkorf (604b)]. It holds up to a distance of several hundred cm^{-1} from the atomic line. In this way the correctness of the London formula for van der Waals' forces is proved at the same time. The proportionality factor is also of the correct order of magnitude.

It can be seen that the above considerations give at the same time a very satisfactory theoretical explanation of the *broadening of spectral lines by a high pressure* of a foreign gas or of the gas itself, as well as of the dissymmetries that appear.[2] However, small broadenings of less than 10 to 20 cm^{-1} and small shifts of the maxima of the lines are not explained by these statistical considerations [see Kuhn and London (435) and Margenau (480)]. For these small broadenings (shifts)—that is, small deviations of the potential energy from the asymptotes (large r values)—the fact becomes noticeable that the Franck-Condon principle does not hold rigorously—that small alterations of the kinetic energy can take place during light absorption. A combination of the statistical theory with the usual theory of collision damping has to be used here [Weisskopff (702), Kuhn and London (435), Margenau and Watson (481), and Hughes and Lloyd (341a)].

Naturally, *both central and noncentral collisions* take place. However, the former are the rarer, and it is therefore not surprising that the continua not too far distant from the atomic lines can in many cases be explained quantitatively by the noncentral collisions. The central collisions are responsible only for continua lying at a larger distance from the atomic line under consideration and in some cases also for the narrow short-wave-length extensions.

At sufficiently low temperatures, the *discrete vibrational levels in the shallow minimum of the potential curve* of the ground state are also occupied [E in Fig. 152(b) and (c)]. The transition from these levels to the discrete levels of the

---

[2] The relation between line broadening and the potential curve diagrams was first realized by Jabłoński (359).

upper state is a transition between two stable states and therefore, strictly speaking, does not belong here.   However, owing to the shallowness of the potential curve for the lower state, the vibrational levels lie so close together that the individual bands of the resulting band system are frequently not resolved and only one or a few maxima of an apparently continuous spectrum are observed in the neighborhood of the corresponding atomic line. Thus for Hg we find a maximum at 2540 Å, corresponding to the Hg line 2537 and representing the transition between the two corresponding potential minima [E–F in Fig. 152(c)].   The intensity of this band is a measure of the concentration of Hg_2 molecules. Correspondingly, its intensity decreases with increasing temperature.   By accurate measurements of the intensity of this band at different temperatures, the *heat of dissociation* of the Hg_2 van der Waals' molecule in the ground state has been estimated to be about 1.8 kcal. [see Kuhn (431)].   The occurrence of such bands in the neighborhood of the absorption lines of the alkalis is also noteworthy [Kuhn (429)]. They correspond to transitions between the repulsive states resulting from the atomic states considered (alkali atoms with parallel spin; see p. 406).   Furthermore, such bands also appear in the neighborhood of the atomic lines in Hg for high pressures of the added inert gas, whereby it is shown that Hg atoms and inert-gas atoms can form a weakly bound van der Waals' molecule [Oldenberg (537), Kuhn (431), and Rühmkorf (604b)].

It is clear from what has been said that the investigation of these continuous spectra is of great importance in arriving at a deeper and quantitative *understanding of van der Waals' binding* and thus of the forces producing solidification and liquefaction of gases. The investigation of this field has only just begun.

(b) Emission

The emission continua of molecules result from the converse process to that producing absorption continua.   To the ionization continua there correspond emission continua resulting from the recombination of molecular ions and electrons. Thus far, however, they have not been observed for molecules. But the emission continua corresponding to the other absorption continua have been observed.

Upper state continuous (molecule formation in a two-body collision). The converse of the direct dissociation of a stable molecule by light absorption is the *recombination* of the two atoms *in a two-body collision* with emission of radiation.

Let us consider two atoms approaching each other in such a way that their potential energy in its dependence on the internuclear distance is given by the upper potential curve

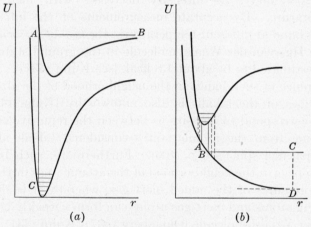

(a)　　　　　　　　　　　(b)

Fig. 155. Potential Curves for the Explanation of Continuous Emission Spectra. In (b), CD gives the relative kinetic energy of the two atoms after the transition of the molecule from the upper state ($v = 0$) to the lower (B).

in Fig. 155(a). The total energy of the two atoms is represented by the horizontal line AB. At every point the relative kinetic energy is given by the distance of this line from the potential curve. At the point A, the kinetic energy is completely converted into potential energy. Classically, it is the turning point for the motion. After reaching it, the potential curve is traversed in the opposite direction, and the two atoms fly apart from each other again.[3]

---

[3] Compare the mechanical analogy, p. 216.

A permanent recombination of the two atoms will take place only *when energy is removed* during the short time of the collision (about 10^{-13} sec.). This may happen in one of two ways: either by collision with a third particle during the collision time (*recombination by three-body collision*) or by radiation of the energy (*recombination by a two-body collision*). In the latter case a transition takes place mainly at the classical turning point A [Fig. 155(a)] to one of the vibrational levels in the ground state, whose turning point lies nearly vertically below A. Since the kinetic energy of the colliding atoms can take all possible values within a certain range, a continuous spectrum results—the *recombination continuum*, corresponding to the dissociation continuum (see above). This recombination in a two-body collision is, however, a *very rare process*, since the time that elapses on the average before an excited molecule radiates (about 10^{-8} sec.) is very large compared to the duration of the collision (10^{-13} sec.), during which the electron jump must take place in order to lead to a recombination. As a result, recombination by a two-body collision takes place only for an extremely small fraction of the collisions (about 10^{-5}).

Furthermore, in order that such a recombination with radiation may take place, it is necessary that the two atoms approach each other on a potential curve of an *excited* molecular state that combines with the ground state. In many cases this is possible only if one of the atoms is excited, as, for example, for the case in Fig. 155(a), and this leads to a further reduction of the frequency of occurrence of the recombination in a two-body collision. Moreover, it has to be considered that, of the various molecular states arising from the particular combination of the separated atoms, only one or a few are of such a nature that a transition to the discrete part of the ground state can occur. The probability that these particular molecular states are formed in the collision is proportional to their statistical weights and is, of course, smaller than unity.

If the two atoms approach on the potential curve of the ground state, molecule formation by a two-body collision is practically impossible, since the transition probability for the infrared transition, which would lead to a removal of energy, is very much smaller than that for electronic transitions. For two like nuclei, this possibility disappears altogether (see Chapter III, p. 85 f.).[4]

On the other hand, *recombination by three-body collision* without radiation of light is a much more frequent process, particularly at high pressures, since the number of three-body collisions increases more rapidly than the number of two-body collisions with increasing pressure.[5] Therefore, when molecule formation from free atoms plays a part in chemical elementary reactions or other collision processes, mostly only the three-body collision recombinations occur.

However, in spite of their rareness, *two-body recombinations* can be observed spectroscopically by the *continuous spectrum* emitted.   Thus far, this has been done only for the halogens and Te_2.   Kondratjew and Leipunsky (410) found that, for example, I_2 vapor at high temperatures emitted a continuum as well as discrete bands.   This continuum is to be explained as a recombination continuum (converse of the dissociation continuum).   In consequence of the high temperature employed, atoms, some of which are in the excited state required, are continuously produced by dissociation of the molecules.   In a small fraction of the cases, the atoms recombine by a two-body collision with radiation instead of by a three-body collision and this gives rise to the continuum. For Te_2 in an intense discharge, in which a strong dissociation of the vapor takes place, Rompe (596) found a continuum that is in all probability to be explained in a corresponding manner.

Lower state continuous.   Those emission continua for which the *lower* state belongs to a continuous range while the

---

[4] Strictly speaking, for like nuclei a quadrupole rotation-vibration spectrum is possible (see p. 305), but it is 10^8 times weaker than ordinary infrared spectra and therefore need not be taken into account here.

[5] At atmospheric pressure roughly one in every 10^3 collisions is a three-body collision, whereas even in favorable cases only one in every 10^5 collisions leads to a two-body recombination.

upper state is a discrete state are of much greater intensity and thus of greater importance. The potential curve diagram for this case is given in Fig. 155(b). According to the Franck-Condon principle, the transitions from the vibrationless state ($v' = 0$) of the excited electronic state take place to points on the lower potential curve that lie above the asymptote—that is, in the continuous range [roughly between A and B in Fig. 155(b)]. The resulting spectrum is therefore continuous. At the same time, when the system has once gone over to the lower state, a *dissociation* takes place (not recombination, as in the emission continua previously considered). The atoms fly apart with kinetic energies that depend on the magnitude of the emitted quantum—that is, on the height above the asymptote of the point reached after the quantum jump. When the lower potential curve is steep, the kinetic energy may be rather large. In such cases the extent of the continuous spectrum is considerable. If different vibrational states in the upper state are excited, the extent of the continuum is still further increased [see Fig. 155(b)].

The most important example of such a continuum is the well-known *continuous spectrum of the* H_2 *molecule*, which appears intensely in almost any electrical discharge in H_2.[6] As was first recognized by Winans and Stueckelberg (717), this spectrum corresponds to the transition from the lowest stable triplet state of the H_2 molecule ($1s\sigma 2s\sigma\ ^3\Sigma_g{}^+$) to the repulsive state ($1s\sigma 2p\sigma\ ^3\Sigma_u{}^+$) resulting from two normal atoms (see p. 376). The great extent of the continuum (1600 to 5000 Å) is to be explained in the above-mentioned way. The large intensity of the continuum has its cause in the fact that the upper state is a stable molecular state, and therefore the molecule will stay in it until the transition to the repulsive state takes place. The intensity is therefore of the same order of magnitude as that of an intense band system.

---

[6] It is very often employed as a continuous background for absorption spectra in the ultraviolet.

The theoretical *intensity distribution* can, in principle, be calculated by the method given above for absorption continua. This method has recently been applied to H_2 by Coolidge, James, and Present (162), who derived the course of the repulsive potential curve theoretically. A satisfactory comparison between the theoretical and the observed intensity distributions cannot yet be made, since the relative numbers of molecules occupying the vibrational states in the excited electronic state are not known in the experiments. In addition, it appears that the dependence of the electronic transition probability on internuclear distance has to be taken into account [James and Coolidge (363)].

The intense He_2 *continuum* between 500 and 1000 Å discovered by Hopfield (330) is to be explained in a manner quite similar to that for the H_2 continuum. For He_2, only a repulsive state $[(\sigma_g 1s)^2(\sigma_u 1s)^2 \; {}^1\Sigma_g{}^+]$ results from normal atoms (see p. 390). The continuum corresponds to the transition from the lowest stable excited singlet state $[(\sigma_g 1s)^2(\sigma_u 1s)(\sigma_g 2s) \; {}^1\Sigma_u{}^+]$ to this repulsive state.

Similar continua have been observed for various metallic vapors—for example, for Hg, excited by an electrical discharge or by light. They represent exactly the converse of the absorption continua with stable upper states discussed above (p. 417 f.). In emission they result if the excited metal atoms form, with normal atoms, stable excited molecules which, in going over to the ground state, decompose again with emission of the continuum. The intensity distribution in emission is in general different from that in absorption, since in emission (in contrast to absorption) also the left-hand turning points of the vibrational motion in the upper state [Fig. 152(b)] lead to intensity maxima which in general lie at much greater wave lengths. The continuum at 3300 Å, which is observed in every mercury lamp, is to be explained in this way. The upper state is the stable molecular state resulting from Hg $({}^3P_1)$ + Hg $({}^1S)$. This state is the same one that produces the absorption continuum joining onto the long-wave-length side of the line 2537 Å.

Another emission continuum of Hg_2, at 4800 Å, is interesting, since no corresponding absorption continuum is observed. It has as upper state the stable molecular state resulting from $Hg(^3P_0)$ + Hg (^1S), which does not combine with the ground state at large internuclear distances (absorption) but does do so at small internuclear distances (emission), since then the molecular selection rules have to be used. This is a particularly characteristic example of a case in which the electronic transition probability is not constant (see p. 418).

Both upper and lower state continuous. Continuous emission spectra corresponding to a transition between an unstable upper and an unstable lower state [see Fig. 152(c)] can occur when excited atoms collide with normal atoms, and then *in the collision state* a transition takes place to the lower unstable state. We have thus the exact converse of the earlier case of absorption in Fig. 152(c). We have once more to distinguish between *central and noncentral collisions*, the latter being the more important. A continuous spectrum results, which joins onto the long- or the short-wave-length side of the emission line. These continua were first investigated in detail by Oldenberg (537) in the fluorescence spectrum of Hg vapor to which inert gases at high pressure had been added [see also Kuhn and Oldenberg (436) and Preston (569a)]. Corresponding to what has been said, the emission spectrum is rather similar to the absorption spectrum under these conditions. There is an unsymmetrical *broadening*, usually toward longer wave lengths, *of the fluorescence lines* under consideration. In certain cases, if the unsymmetry of the broadening is strong, this may lead to a shift of the maximum of the particular atomic line. Thus at least some cases of the well-known pressure shift of spectral lines may be explained [see Kuhn (432)].

It is clear that, when a metal vapor, such as Hg, Zn, or Cd, is excited by light or an electrical discharge, all the kinds of continuous emission spectra described above can appear simultaneously, and this may give rise to a rather complicated spectrum [for details see Finkelnburg (218), (221), and (42)].

2. DIFFUSE MOLECULAR SPECTRA, PREDISSOCIATION, AND RELATED TOPICS

In this section we shall deal mainly with two characteristic phenomena in band spectra that have already been briefly described in Chapter II—namely, the *diffuse band spectra* and the phenomenon of the *breaking off* in the rotational structure of emission bands.   It will appear that these two phenomena have in many cases the same origin—namely, the so-called *predissociation*, or sometimes *preionization*. Some cases of diffuse band spectra, however, are to be explained differently.   The study of predissociation has led to many valuable conclusions concerning molecular structure, to an explanation of some photochemical processes, and to a determination of important heats of dissociation (see section 3).

(a) General Discussion of Spontaneous Radiationless Decomposition Processes

The Auger process.   As we have seen in Chapter V, when two different states in an atomic system have approximately equal energies, an interaction (perturbation) generally takes place.   This interaction manifests itself first of all in a shift of each of the two levels (repulsion) and secondly in a mixing of the eigenfunctions of the two states, each of the actual levels being, so to speak, a hybrid of the two original (in zero approximation) nearly coinciding levels. Semiclassically, we may consider this hybrid formation as a continual oscillation of the system between the two states, similar to the case of two coupled pendulums in resonance.

In general, only one or a few terms of a term series are influenced by such a perturbation (see Chapter V, section 4). If, however, one term in a discrete series has the same energy as a term of a *continuous* term spectrum, all the higher terms of the series have the same energy as correspondingly higher terms of the continuous range, and therefore all the higher terms of this series may be perturbed (see Fig. 156).   In such a perturbation by a continuous term the shift of the originally discrete level can assume a continuous series of values. That is, the level becomes *diffuse*; the system can assume all energy values in a more or less narrow region (depending on the strength of the perturbation). To the left in Fig. 156 the probability distribution of these energy values is indicated schematically. A spectral line corresponding to a transition to or from such a diffuse level is not sharp but more or less strongly broadened (diffuse).

A *mixing of the eigenfunctions* also takes place here; that is, a periodic interchange occurs between the two states, the discrete and the continuous. However, a continuous state means a fission of the system and a flying apart of the parts with more or less kinetic energy (the eigenfunction is an outgoing spherical wave). Therefore, when, as a result of the mutual perturbation, the system has once gone from the discrete into the

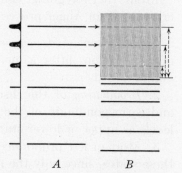

Fig. 156. Explanation of the Auger Process. The three uppermost levels of the series *A* are overlapped by the continuum of the series *B*. To the extreme left the width of the levels is indicated schematically. The radiationless transitions from the discrete to the continuous state are indicated by horizontal arrows.

continuous state, it cannot return to the discrete state, since the parts are soon widely separated from each other. Therefore, *if an atomic system is transferred to such a diffuse state*—for example, by light absorption—*it undergoes a radiationless decomposition after a certain lifetime.* This process was first observed by Auger for X rays and is therefore usually called the *Auger process*. It has to be carefully distinguished from the decomposition (ionization or dissociation) of the system by direct transition into a continuous state, since, in the case of the diffuse state, instead of a decomposition a transition with emission of light into a lower-lying discrete state may also take place during the lifetime, which is not possible for a direct transition into the continuum.

In a somewhat less accurate but more descriptive way, we may also consider this Auger process as a *radiationless transition* (quantum jump) from a discrete into a continuous state [see Kuhn and Martin (437)]. In the following we shall mostly use this mode of expression.

From the foregoing considerations there appear three criteria for an Auger process:

1. *Radiationless decomposition* of the system (ionization or dissociation) after a mean life τ_l—that is, with a probability $\gamma = 1/\tau_l$.

2. *Broadening* of the discrete levels under consideration and correspondingly of the spectral lines which have these levels as upper or lower states.

3. More or less pronounced *weakening of the emission* from these states, since only the molecules that do not decompose can radiate.

As an example of the Auger process, let us consider an atom with a number of electrons. The terms corresponding to the excitation of the outermost electron form a Rydberg series, onto which a continuous term spectrum joins, as, for example, to the right of Fig. 156. If two outer electrons (or an inner electron) are excited, a Rydberg series of terms lying considerably higher results, which, at least in part, lies above the limit of the first-mentioned series (see Fig. 156, left). Thus, in these states an Auger process—that is, a radiationless transition into the continuous state—and thereby an ionization of the atom can take place. Actually, for the spectral lines under consideration, a broadening in emission and in absorption and an abnormally small intensity in emission have been observed for a number of atoms. In this case the Auger process is also called *preionization*, in analogy to the longer-known process for molecules, or also *autoionization* (see A.A., p. 171).

The greater the probability of decomposition γ, the greater

is the broadening of the discrete levels.　Quite generally we
have the relation $b = (h/2\pi)\gamma$, where b is the half width of
a level, or, since $\gamma = 1/\tau_l$ (see above),

$$b\tau_l = \frac{h}{2\pi}. \tag{VII, 2}$$

This means that *the greater the mean life of a state, the smaller
is its width—that is, the sharper it is.*　This relation still holds
even when no decomposition is possible and the mean life
refers only to transitions with radiation into lower states.
The width which then results is extremely small—namely,
of the order of 0.001 cm^{-1}.　It is the *"natural" line width* of
spectral lines.　Incidentally, the relation (VII, 2) is none
other than the Heisenberg uncertainty relation (I, 15)
without the $>$ sign.

　　The *magnitude γ of the probability of a radiationless transition* depends on the strength of the mutual interaction of the
two states, which can be calculated on the basis of their eigenfunctions.[7]　This calculation is similar to that of the transition probability for transitions with radiation from the
eigenfunctions of the two participating states.

　　It is to be expected that a radiationless decomposition will
be observable only if the transition probability γ for the
radiationless quantum jump is not appreciably smaller than
the transition probability β for the transition with radiation
into lower states.　This is due to the fact that, if $\gamma \ll \beta$,
the system will generally have returned to a stable state long
before the radiationless decomposition would have taken
place.　Conversely, if $\gamma \gg \beta$, practically no emission is to
be expected.

　　The ratio of the number of light quanta emitted to the total number of atoms (molecules) in the diffuse state—that is, the yield of
light emission—is obviously given by $\beta/(\beta + \gamma) = 1/[1 + (\gamma/\beta)]$,
whereas the yield of the decomposition is given by $\gamma/(\beta + \gamma) =$

---

[7] The calculation shows that the transition probability is given by the
square of the matrix element of the perturbation function (see p. 310).

$1/[1 + (\beta/\gamma)]$.   It is seen that the former ≈ 1 if $\gamma \ll \beta$, whereas the latter ≈ 1 if $\beta \ll \gamma$.

Passage through potential barriers.   When the potential energy curve for an oscillator has the shape indicated in Fig. 157(a), a typical quantum mechanical phenomenon occurs if the energy of the oscillator (denoted by E in the figure) is smaller than the height of the potential hill but greater than the height of the two minima.   According to quantum mechanics, there is then always a finite probability that the mass point, when it is initially in the neighborhood of the left minimum, will be, after a time, in the neighborhood of

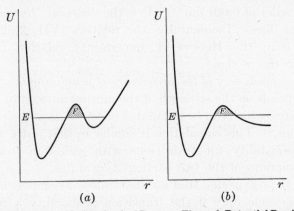

(a)   (b)

Fig. 157.   Quantum Mechanical Passage Through Potential Barriers.

the right minimum, and vice versa.   This is due to the fact that the eigenfunction for this oscillator is different from zero in the region to the left as well as in the region to the right. Thus, quantum mechanically, a *passage through the potential hill* takes place, whereas classically the mass point can go from the left into the right trough (and vice versa) only if the energy is greater than that of the maximum.

If the potential curve has a shape as in Fig. 157(b), the same phenomenon occurs, except that now a passage through the potential barrier means that the mass point flies off to infinity; that is, a *radiationless decomposition of the system* results.   This process is in many respects analogous to the

Auger effect; when the particle is in the left trough and if we ignore the right-hand part, we have a series of discrete energy levels which are in part overlapped by the continuum corresponding to the right-hand part of the potential curve if we ignore the left-hand part. Here, also, a transition from the discrete into the continuous state causes a *broadening* of the discrete state which is inversely proportional to the mean life. In this case, it is found that *the smaller the area of the slice F of the potential hill cut off by the line representing the energy level and the greater the frequency of the vibration, the shorter is the mean life* and therefore the greater is the diffuseness.

This phenomenon of going through a potential hill has proved to be of great importance in the explanation of many physical processes (for example, radioactivity, emission of electrons from metals, and so forth) and will also be important in the following discussion.

(b) Radiationless Decomposition Processes in the Molecule

Bonhoeffer and Farkas (116) and Kronig (421), following certain considerations put forward by Born and Franck (120) and by Polyani and Wigner (566), first realized that in a large number of diffuse molecular spectra the *Auger effect is responsible for the diffuseness.*

In a molecule the overlapping of a discrete term spectrum by a continuous term spectrum, necessary for the occurrence of this process, is very often present. First of all, a *preionization* is possible, exactly as for atoms (see p. 430), when discrete electronic states are overlapped by a continuous term spectrum that corresponds to the separation of an electron (ionization). However, for molecules, we have in addition the much more frequent case of overlapping by one of the continuous term spectra that correspond to a *dissociation into atoms* (or ions) and that occur for every electronic state (compare Fig. 158) whether it has in addition other discrete vibrational levels or not. The *possibility of going over without radiation from a discrete state into such a dissociated state* is, according to Bonhoeffer, Farkas, and Kronig, the reason for the diffuseness of the bands. In Fig. 158, for example, the vibrational levels of the upper state *B* from $v = 4$ on

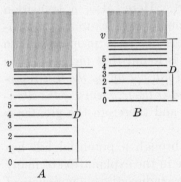

are overlapped by the continuum of the lower state. As in Fig. 156, the system can go over from the discrete state, without radiating, into the continuous state lying at the same height, except that here the continuous state corresponds to a dissociation; that is, the molecule dissociates after the radiationless transition. This process is called *predissociation*.

Fig. 158. Two Electronic States of a Molecule (with Their Continuous Term Spectra) for Which Predissociation Is Possible.

In the following paragraphs the correctness of this explanation of many cases of diffuse spectra will be proved with the help of the criteria previously given for the occurrence of an Auger process (p. 430).

Diffuseness of the bands. The second criterion given on p. 430—namely, the broadening of the lines—was the one by which the diffuse bands were first noticed [V. Henri (299)]. Kronig has, in fact, shown by a quantum mechanical calculation that under certain conditions (see below) the mean lifetime τ_l, until radiationless decomposition takes place, of a discrete state overlapped by a dissociation continuum may be less than the period of rotation of the molecule ($\sim 10^{-11}$ sec.). The line width of the spectral lines under consideration is then of the order of magnitude of the separation of successive lines in the fine structure. Thus in this case the band should have just the diffuse appearance observed experimentally (see Fig. 16, p. 38). However, the vibrational structure generally remains, as is also observed, since the vibrational frequency is ten to a hundred times greater than the rotational frequency (see p. 87).

The diffuseness of the bands is itself a sufficient proof of the presence of predissociation if the bands belong to a series in which sharp bands also appear at the beginning of the series. Such a case was first observed for S_2 by Henri and Teves (301) (see Fig. 16).

Naturally, the radiationless transition probability need not always be so great that the bands are completely diffuse. It may happen that only the *individual lines* are *somewhat broadened*. Both cases have been observed in the S_2 absorption spectrum—at first a lack of sharpness of the individual rotational lines and then a complete washing out of the rotational structure (see Fig. 16).

It may also happen that, although the transition probability for the radiationless decomposition is not zero, it is yet so small that the line broadening cannot be detected *directly* because of insuffi-

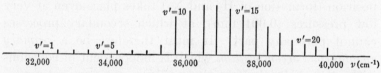

Fig. 159. **Anomalous Intensity Distribution in a Series of Absorption Bands, Due to Predissociation, for Small Resolving Power of the Spectrograph.** The figure refers to the case of the S_2 spectrum. The height of the vertical lines gives the estimated intensities of the bands. The jump in intensity occurs at $v' = 10$.

cient resolving power of the spectral apparatus used. In spite of this, the presence of a broadening and thereby of predissociation in this case can be proved *indirectly* if the line width caused by the radiationless transition is greater than that due to the Doppler effect caused by the thermal motion of the molecules. In a spectral apparatus of not too great resolving power, the sharper an absorption line is, the weaker it appears, since the parts of the continuous background to either side of the absorption line are less and less well separated. Therefore, if at one place in a series of lines or bands such a small "broadening" appears, it is detected by the fact that the *broadened lines apparently have a greater intensity than the nonbroadened lines*. The intensity distribution in a band progression ($v'' = 0$) then has the appearance indicated schematically in Fig. 159. This phenomenon has actually been used for the detection of predissociation in H_2 [Beutler, Deubner, and Jünger

(92)] and in S_2 and NO [Herzberg and Mundie (317)].   In Fig. 16 it can be seen that, for S_2, the bands before the 10–0 band are all very weak, whereas the 10–0 band itself and the following bands have a very great intensity (see also Fig. 159), although the 10–0 band does not appear to be broadened.   However, from this intensity distribution we must conclude that there is already a small broadening present for it.   Recent investigations with large dispersion [Olsson (547)] have indeed shown that the lines of the 10–0 band are slightly broadened, although they had always been considered as sharp before Olsson's investigation.

Photochemical decomposition.   That a decomposition really does take place (first criterion on p. 430) when the molecule is brought by light absorption into the upper state of the diffuse bands was first shown by Bonhoeffer and Farkas (116).   They found that a photochemical decomposition of NH_3 takes place on illumination with light of the wave length of the diffuse absorption bands.   This decomposition (formation of H_2 and N_2) takes place even at very low pressures (0.001 mm), at which secondary processes cannot play any part.   It must therefore be a *primary spontaneous decomposition* which is independent of collisions with other molecules (see also p. 518).

Breaking off of bands.   If the explanation of the diffuse absorption bands by the process of predissociation (Auger process) is correct, the corresponding bands in emission must either be very weak or be completely missing (third criterion on p. 430).   Actually, for S_2 [van Iddekinge (352)], only those bands appear in emission that correspond to the *sharp* absorption bands, whereas the diffuse bands of the same band system (or other bands with the same upper levels) are in no way to be obtained in emission (in electric discharges or in fluorescence).   Thus *in emission the band system breaks off at a definite value of the vibrational quantum number v'.*

Conversely, we are led to conclude that also those cases of breaking off for which an observation in absorption is not feasible are to be explained as predissociation.   This explanation holds particularly for the characteristic cases in which the bands in emission *break off sharply at a certain value of the rotational quantum number* (see p. 54 f.). In one of these cases, that of AlH (see Fig. 28), it has actually been observed that the higher rotational lines that do not appear in emission do appear in absorption but are diffuse [Farkas (212)]. The correctness of this explanation of the breaking off is further confirmed by the fact that for isotopic molecules—for example, CaH and CaD—the breaking off occurs at different J values or even different v values but at very nearly equal energies above the minimum of the potential curve of the ground state, corresponding to the fact that the dissociation limits for isotopic molecules are the same.

Thus in general we can regard a predissociation as proved either by the absorption bands becoming diffuse, or by the emission bands breaking off at a certain point in a series.

A diffuseness of the individual rotational lines is of course noticeable only when the line width is greater than the width produced by the Doppler effect due to the motion of the individual molecules—that is, greater than 0.01 to 0.1 Å. On the other hand, the natural line width, if no decomposition is possible, is of the order of 0.001 to 0.01 Å, corresponding to a mean life of 10^{-8} sec. (see p. 431). Therefore, in order that the line width shall be greater than the Doppler width, the decomposition probability γ must be at least 10 to 100 times greater than the transition probability β with radiation. This means that, if the lines of the bands *in absorption* appear to be diffuse, the intensity of the corresponding transitions *in emission* is vanishingly small compared to the intensity of the transitions from the nonpredissociated levels.

On the other hand, a weakening of the intensity in a series of lines or bands is easily detectable when the intensity falls off suddenly to only, shall we say, one half. In this case, even with very high resolution, no diffuseness would be discoverable in absorption, since it would be hidden by the Doppler width. The *breaking off of emission bands* is thus a *much more sensitive criterion for the presence of a predissociation*. A still more sensitive criterion is the occurrence of a photochemical decomposition, since under suitable conditions this can be established even when only a small fraction of the molecules brought into the excited state decomposes and when, therefore, there is no noticeable weakening in the intensity of the bands under consideration. In no case can we conclude with certainty from the absence of a diffuseness in the absorption bands that there is no predissociation. This point is often overlooked.

The above-mentioned indirect method of detecting the line broadening by the strengthening of the absorption is not as sensitive a test for predissociation as the breaking off of emission bands or as photochemical decomposition, although it is more sensitive than the direct visible broadening.

Different types of predissociation. Corresponding to the three forms of energy of the molecule (electronic, vibrational, and rotational energy), theoretically three kinds of overlapping of molecular energy levels by a dissociation continuum—that is, three possible cases of predissociation—might be thought possible:

I. Overlapping of an *excited electronic state* (that is, of its vibrational or rotational levels) by a dissociation continuum belonging to another electronic state—*radiationless transition into this other dissociated electronic state* (compare Fig. 158).

II. Overlapping of the higher *vibrational levels* of an electronic state of a polyatomic molecule by the dissociation continuum of a definite vibration of the same electronic state—radiationless splitting off of the particular atom or group of atoms (*predissociation by vibration*).

III. Overlapping of the higher *rotational levels* of a given vibrational state of a molecule by the dissociation continuum belonging to the same vibration and to the same electronic state—radiationless decomposition of the molecule with no change of electronic state (*predissociation by rotation*).

For diatomic molecules, case I is the most important. It always applies if the bands become diffuse or break off at a large distance from the point of convergence of the band system, as, for example, for the diffuse S_2 bands in Fig. 16 and the CaH band showing a breaking off in Fig. 27 [Grundström (268)]. Case II applies for polyatomic molecules only. We shall therefore leave it completely out of consideration here (see Volume II). Case III can occur for the vibrational levels of an electronic state that lie in the neighborhood of the dissociation limit, since, as we shall see later, the higher discrete rotational levels of such vibrational levels can lie higher than the dissociation limit. This case is observed when the heat of dissociation of the electronic state is small, as, for example, for AlH (see Fig. 28) and HgH. Sometimes it is not possible to distinguish unambiguously between cases I and III.

In all cases the place in the energy level diagram of a molecule at which a predissociation begins (*predissociation limit*) [8] gives at least an *upper limiting value for the corresponding dissociation limit*. However, we shall see that under some circumstances the predissociation limit can lie appreciably higher than the dissociation limit belonging to it.

Preionization. The same phenomena that are produced by predissociation—that is, diffuseness of the absorption bands and breaking off of the emission bands—can also be brought about by *preionization* of the molecule. As a condition for this, the upper state of the bands must, of course, lie higher than an ionization limit. In *absorption*, Henning (298) found diffuse bands of CO in the far ultraviolet at 785 to 750 Å whose diffuseness is very probably due to such a preionization. Furthermore, Beutler and Jünger (94) have found diffuse bands in the far ultraviolet absorption spectrum of H_2 which they could ascribe with certainty to such a preionization process and from whose long-wavelength limit they were able to determine a very reliable and accurate value for the ionization potential of the H_2 molecule. Breaking-off points in *emission* that are to be ascribed to preionization have been found for the higher electronic states of H_2 by Beutler and Jünger (95).

---

[8] Obviously it is not the position of a breaking-off point in the spectrum which matters but the energy of the point above the ground state.

Accidental predissociation. Ittmann (358) has pointed out that a certain type of *perturbations* in band spectra can be explained by a process closely related to predissociation which he calls *accidental predissociation.* If a stable electronic state is *perturbed by a diffuse* (predissociating) *state* (compare Fig. 124 (*a*), in which we have to assume in the present case that the term series to the right is diffuse), one or more of the rotational levels of the perturbed state assume the properties of the corresponding predissociating levels; that is, they also predissociate. Therefore, in emission, the corresponding lines of the bands under consideration should be *missing* or have *abnormally small intensities.* At the same time their position may not differ noticeably from the normal position. Perturbations of this type have been observed, for example, in the second positive nitrogen group—an abnormally small intensity of one or two lines with certain J values in all the bands with the same v' [Coster, Brons, and van der Ziel (167)]. In absorption the lines considered should be broadened or, when the broadening is too small, should have an abnormally high intensity (see p. 435); but thus far in no such case has an observation in absorption been possible.

The essential *experimental* difference between accidental and normal predissociation is that for the former only one or a few lines have abnormally low intensity, while for the latter a complete breaking off usually takes place or at least a large number of successive lines have abnormally small intensity. The essential *theoretical* difference is that for normal predissociation a radiationless transition takes place from a discrete level directly into the dissociated state, whereas for accidental predissociation this happens only after a detour through a third state. It is clear that the accidental predissociation can be observed only when, on the basis of the selection rules (see the following subsection), a direct radiationless transition into the dissociated state is not possible.

(c) Selection Rules for Predissociation

Energetically, the possibility of predissociation exists for all the discrete states of a molecule that lie *above the lowest dissociation limit of the molecule* (corresponding to dissociation into normal atoms). That, in spite of this, at least for diatomic molecules, a predissociation is relatively seldom observed is due to the fact that the probability of the transition into the dissociating state, the decomposition probability (γ), is usually so small that long before the decomposition would have taken place the molecule has already gone over into a lower-lying stable state with emission of radiation ($\gamma \ll \beta$). In order for the transition probability to be so large that the bands can be observed to become diffuse or to break off, still further conditions—*selection rules*—must be fulfilled in addition to the condition of equal energy.

Kronig's selection rules.   Since predissociation is nothing else but a special case of the perturbations treated earlier, exactly the same selection rules hold for them as for perturbations [Kronig (421); see Chapter V, section 4].   For the two participating states we must have [9]

$$\Delta J = 0, \quad \Delta S = 0, \quad \Delta \Lambda = 0, \pm 1, \quad + \leftrightarrow -, \quad s \leftrightarrow a.$$

It should be particularly noted that the selection rules $\Delta J = 0$, $+ \leftrightarrow -$, and $s \leftrightarrow a$ remain valid for predissociation, since the *angular momentum J and the symmetry properties are also defined in a continuous term spectrum.* The two atoms can rotate about each other even in the continuous term region; that is, they can separate from each other while rotating or collide noncentrally.   This rotation is quantized just as in stable molecular states.   For a large separation of the atoms, states with different J have practically the same energy (moment of inertia practically ∞), or, conversely, all J values are possible for each energy value in the continuum.   Therefore, if the energy condition is fulfilled, the selection rule $\Delta J = 0$ is always realizable.   It is, however, not always compatible with the other selection rules (see below).

For Σ states, in the continuous as well as in the discrete region, the rotational levels are alternately positive and negative and, for identical nuclei, alternately symmetric and antisymmetric in the nuclei.   For Π, Δ, $\cdots$ states there is a positive and a negative level for each J, which for

---

[9] The adaptation of these selection rules to Hund's case (c) is given immediately by replacing Λ by Ω and taking no account of the selection rule $\Delta S = 0$. The adaptation to preionization (autoionization) has been given in detail by Beutler and Jünger (94).

identical nuclei are symmetric and antisymmetric, or vice versa [see Chapter V, section 2(c)].

The fact that the possibilities for predissociation are very considerably restricted by the Kronig selection rules is best illustrated by a few examples.

If, for unlike nuclei, we have a stable Σ^+ state overlapped by an unstable, continuous Σ^- state, predissociation cannot take place, owing to the rule $+ \leftrightarrow -$, even if all the other selection rules are fulfilled, since for rotational levels with equal J (necessary because of $\Delta J = 0$) the symmetries are always opposite (see Fig. 107, p. 261).

If a discrete Π state is overlapped by the continuum of a Σ state, always only the molecules in the one Λ component of the Π state can decompose, since, at the same time, only for the one component are $\Delta J = 0$ and the symmetries the same (see Figs. 107 and 108). It follows that, when, for example, the discrete Π state combines with a lower Σ state and at the same time is overlapped by a continuous Σ state, a breaking off in the bands under consideration can appear either only in the P and R branches or only in the Q branch [Kronig (422)]. Such a case has been found for MgH by Pearse (556). In the 0–0 band $\lambda 2430$ of the $B^2\Pi - X^2\Sigma$ system, the P and R branches break off at $K' = 11$ (that is, $J' = 10\frac{1}{2}$ and $11\frac{1}{2}$), while the Q branch does not break off. This case is represented schematically in Fig. 160, using K

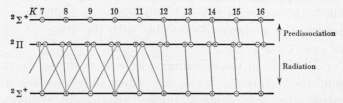

Fig. 160. Predissociation of MgH. The figure shows only the symmetry properties and K values. [All three states belong to case (b)]. The level $K=12$ of the $^2\Pi$ state lies just above the dissociation limit of the upper $^2\Sigma^+$ state.

in place of J, since Hund's case (b) applies. Bands with higher v' have also been found (673a), but these have only Q branches.

Conversely, from the observation that in a Π state pre-dissociation takes place for only one Λ doublet component, we can conclude with certainty that the state causing the predissociation is a Σ state, whereas, if both Λ components break off, the state causing the predissociation must be a Π or Δ state. Such conclusions are often of great importance in the interpretation of dissociation processes (see section 3).

Owing to the selection rule $s \leftrightarrow\!\!\!\!/ \; a$, the possibilities for predissociation are still further restricted *for identical nuclei.* It can easily be seen (compare Figs. 107 and 108) that, according to this rule, a $\Sigma_g{}^+$ state, for example, can pre-dissociate only into a $\Sigma_g{}^+$ or Π_g state but not into $\Sigma_u{}^+$, $\Sigma_g{}^-$, $\Sigma_u{}^-$, or Π_u; a Π_g state only into Σ_g, Π_g, or Δ_g; a Π_u state only into Σ_u, Π_u, or Δ_u; and so on. In addition, of course, the multiplicities of the two combining states must be the same.

If we compare these selection rules for radiationless transitions with the selection rules for transitions with radia-tion [(see Chapter V, section 3(a)], we easily find the follow-ing rule [Herzberg (309)]: *For molecules with identical nuclei, states that can combine with one another with emission or absorp-tion of radiation cannot predissociate into one another, and vice versa.* From this rule we can immediately see why, for example, the upper state of the visible I_2 bands (and corre-spondingly for Br_2) does not predissociate into the continuum joining onto the ground state, although it has an energy that is greater than that of the separated normal atoms.

A more detailed calculation shows that, if $\Delta\Lambda = 0$, the radiation-less transition probability (strength of the mutual interaction) is approximately independent of J, whereas for $\Delta\Lambda = \pm 1$ it is approximately proportional to J and vanishes for $J = 0$ (compare the analogous situation for perturbations). In the first case we have therefore to expect in absorption a fairly uniform broadening of all the lines, and in the second case a broadening increasing with increasing J. This expectation is borne out by the observations, as far as they permit conclusions about the probability of the radiationless transitions. A particularly clear case of a uniform increase of broadening with increasing J ($\Delta\Lambda = \pm 1$) has been observed for TlH [(273) and (317)].

Franck-Condon principle in case I of predissociation. Although the Kronig selection rules restrict the possibilities of predissociation very considerably, they are not sufficient to exclude the theoretical possibility of its occurrence in all cases in which predissociation is not observed.   For NO, for

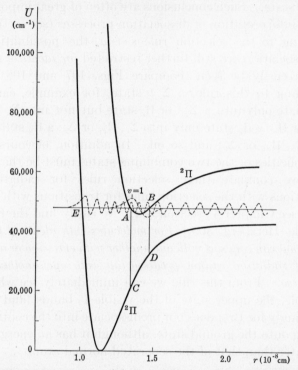

Fig. 161. **Potential Curves of the $^2\Pi$ Ground State and the First Excited $^2\Pi$ State of NO.**   The level AB is the vibrational state $v = 1$ of the upper $^2\Pi$ state.   The broken-line curves are the eigenfunctions for the vibrational state mentioned, as well as for the continuous level of the lower $^2\Pi$ state having the same energy (only qualitatively drawn).

example, an excited $^2\Pi$ state lying 45,500 cm^{-1} above the $^2\Pi$ ground state is known.   The potential curves for the two states are drawn in Fig. 161.   Since the heat of dissociation for the ground state amounts to only 42,700 cm^{-1}, a predissociation of the upper $^2\Pi$ state into the lower is energetically possible for all vibrational and rotational levels of the upper state. In addition, the predissociation is allowed by the Kronig selection rules (see above). However, in this, as in many other similar cases, no predissociation is observed. The reason for this is that, apart from the Kronig selection rules, the *Franck-Condon principle* has to be taken into account *for radiationless transitions* as well as for those with radiation [Franck and Sponer (231) and Herzberg (307)]. It appears quite understandable and may also be proved quantum mechanically (see below) that, for a radiationless transition also, the position and velocity of the nuclei cannot alter appreciably at the instant of the transition.

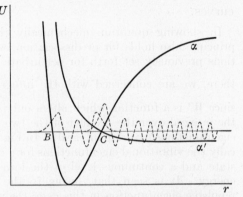

If, in the example of NO (Fig. 161), a radiationless transition to the lower state were to take place during the vibrational motion AB in the upper state, the amount of energy AC or BD or some intermediate amount would have to be instantaneously

Fig. 162. Potential Curves for Which the Franck-Condon Principle Is Fulfilled for the Predissociation. The broken-line curves represent the eigenfunctions (see Fig. 161 and further below in the text).

converted into kinetic energy, or the internuclear distance would have to alter instantaneously by the amount AE or BE or some intermediate amount. According to the Franck-Condon principle, this is impossible (see p. 213 f.). Therefore, in this case, the radiationless transition cannot take place—in agreement with observation.

On the other hand, a radiationless transition is possible, even taking the Franck-Condon principle into account, *if the potential curves of the participating states intersect*, as in Fig. 162, or at least come very close to each other. If the molecule is in the neighborhood of the point of intersection C, obviously a transition from the one curve to the other is possible without an appreciable alteration of position and momentum, and thus a decomposition of the molecule may take place. Naturally, the transition does not take place immediately the molecule is in the neighborhood of the point of intersection, but only with a certain probability, which depends on the types of the electronic states. The molecule will in general carry out a number of vibrations in the stable state BC before it jumps over to the unstable state while traversing the point of intersection of the two potential curves.

In showing quantum mechanically that the Franck-Condon principle also holds for predissociation, we can use the considerations previously set forth for perturbations (see p. 320). Just as there, we are concerned with the integral $\int \psi_n^v W^v \psi_i^v dr$—that is, since W^v is a function which alters only slowly with r, essentially the integral over the product of the two participating vibrational eigenfunctions (overlap integral). In Fig. 161 are drawn schematically the vibrational eigenfunctions for a discrete level of the upper state and a continuous level of the lower state having the same energy. It is seen that, owing to the rapid oscillation of the repulsive eigenfunction in this case, the integral over the product will be vanishingly small, and therefore a predissociation is not to be expected. On the other hand, if the potential curves intersect (Fig. 162), the eigenfunctions for levels in the neighborhood of the point of intersection lie in such a way with respect to each other that the integral mentioned has a considerable magnitude. The validity of the Franck-Condon principle for predissociation is thus shown.

Three subdivisions of case I *of predissociation* may be distinguished according to whether the point of intersection of the two potential curves lies at about the height of the asymptote of the state giving rise to the predissociation or whether it lies below or above this asymptote. These subcases are represented by Fig. 163(*a*), (*b*), and (*c*). The potential curve n corresponds in each case to the normal state of the molecule, from which, for example, a transition to the excited state α is observed in absorption. α' is the potential curve of a third electronic state with a lower dissociation limit than α.

Let us consider first of all the absorption spectrum in the case of the potential curves, Fig. 163(a) and (b). On the basis of the Franck-Condon principle, as a result of light absorption, transitions take place from the vibrationless ground state n to the region A–B of the potential curve α and to the region F–H of the potential curve α'. Thus for the relative position of the potential curves drawn, in absorp-

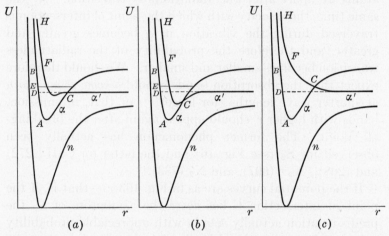

Fig. 163.   **Three Sub-Cases of Case I of Predissociation.**   In each case, the broken line gives the position of the asymptote of the potential curve α'.

tion the transition to α', if it is allowed at all, will be at much shorter wave lengths than that to α. The transition to the region F-H of α' gives a continuous spectrum, while the transition to α gives discrete bands which have quite a normal appearance as long as the upper vibrational level lies below the asymptote of α'—that is, below D. If a state somewhat above D is reached by light absorption, a *radiationless* transition into the state α' is energetically possible (into which, it should be noted, a direct transition from the ground state, in the same wave-length region, is not possible). In addition, owing to the intersection of the two potential curves, the predissociation is possible here without violating the Franck-Condon principle, so that, if the Kronig selection rules are also fulfilled, the bands will be observed to become diffuse in absorption and to break off in emission. The beginning of the diffuseness or, alternatively, the breaking-off point—that is, the *predissociation limit—corresponds exactly to the dissociation limit*—the height of the asymptote of α'.

The higher the level E, reached by absorption, lies above the limit D, the greater is the kinetic energy with which the atoms fly apart after the radiationless transition. At the same time, the velocity with which the point of intersection is traversed during the vibration in α becomes greater and greater, and therefore the probability of the radiationless transition becomes smaller and smaller. We should therefore expect that the absorption bands should *become sharp again* at shorter wave lengths (for larger v') or that, in emission, bands with higher v' should appear again after the breaking-off point. The former phenomenon has actually been observed for S_2 (see Fig. 16) and the latter for CaH [(272) and (268)], $N_2{}^+$ (697), and N_2 (733).[10]

If the potential curves are as in Fig. 163(c)—that is, if the point of intersection C lies *above* the asymptote of α', the predissociation actually sets in with appreciable probability only for those vibrational levels of α that lie *above the point of intersection C*, although energetically it would of course be possible immediately above the asymptote. Thus, here the *predissociation limit does not coincide with the asymptote of α'—that is, the dissociation limit—but lies higher*. Below the point of intersection, but above the asymptote, the internuclear distance would have to alter quite appreciably in order for a radiationless transition to take place, and this is not possible according to the Franck-Condon principle.

---

[10] For S_2 the direct transition from the ground state n to α' has also been observed through the continuous spectrum at shorter wave lengths (see above). In a superficial observation, this continuum appears to join onto the series of bands and to belong to them. However, it begins long before the convergence point of the bands is reached, which shows that it is not the continuum belonging to these bands.

The three cases (a), (b), and (c) also include the cases in which the point of intersection lies on the left limb of α—that is, in cases (a) and (b), when α' has a deep minimum, and, in case (c), when the asymptote of α' lies considerably lower than the minimum of α.

According to quantum mechanics, we have also to allow for the *passage through the potential hill* in case I(c). Consequently, a transition can take place even somewhat below the point of intersection, since then the eigenfunctions of the two states already overlap to some extent (see Fig. 162). In general, this correction does not make very much difference, since for the motion of the heavy nuclei classical mechanics still holds to a good approximation. However, if the potential hill is very thin, as a result of the passage through the potential hill, predissociation may take place appreciably below the point of intersection, although with a smaller probability than above the point of intersection. It is therefore to be expected that in such a case the *diffuseness in the absorption spectrum or the weakening in emission will not set in with maximum strength* but will be strongest at a small distance from the predissociation limit. Such a case seems to apply to the first predissociation limit of S_2 (Fig. 16) [Herzberg and Mundie (317)]. Here the diffuseness of the rotational lines of the 10–0 band is detectable with medium dispersion only by the strengthening of absorption (see p. 435), whereas the lines of the next band, 11–0, do exhibit a broadening easily noticeable with the same dispersion (see Fig. 16). Apart from such rather rare cases, however, the predissociation sets in with maximum probability, even in case I(c), and, as in cases I(a) and (b), the transition probability decreases with increasing separation from the limit.

According to the earlier discussion (p. 324), if a crossing of the potential curves of two states of the same species takes place in a certain approximation, it will always be avoided if we go over to the exact solution of the wave equation (that is, in higher approximation), owing to the mutual repulsion of the two "original" states. In the discussion of case I of predissociation the intersection of potential curves is always meant (at least for $\Delta\Lambda = 0$) in the approximate sense—that is, *intersection in a certain low approximation*. Predissociation in case I is always brought about by the same mutual interaction of the states that also produces the repulsion of the states and that is due to the originally neglected terms in the wave equation.

As we have seen before (see p. 323), the vibrational levels in the neighborhood of the point of intersection cannot be ascribed to a particular one of the two "original" potential curves (electronic states) but they belong partly to the one and partly to the other. Nor can they in general be ascribed to a particular one of the resultant (adiabatic) potential curves, even though the latter for $\Delta\Lambda = 0$ do not cross. That is why the energy levels of the system above the lower of the two asymptotes and in the neighborhood of the point of intersection of the original curves are diffuse (that is, partly continuous and partly discrete). However, if the interaction between the two "original" states is so strong that the resultant potential curves are widely separated (that is, if the "original" curves represented a poor approximation), the vibrational levels can be ascribed unambiguously to either the one or the other resultant electronic state, and above the lower of the two asymptotes there are no diffuse levels. Thus only if the interaction between the original states is comparatively small or, in other words, if the resultant potential curves *almost cross* (Fig. 130), will case I of predissociation occur. The simplified manner of expression used in the above is therefore justified.

Though case I predissociation does not occur if the interaction between the two original states is strong, case III predissociation may still take place for each of the resultant levels. On the basis of the present discussion, it will be clear, however, that there is *not a sharp limit between case* I *and case* III. Which case we have in a specific example depends to a certain extent on the choice of the "original" states. Fortunately, in most cases thus far observed a decision seems to be possible [compare, for example, Büttenbender and Herzberg (147)].

An interesting example of case I(c) [see Fig. 163(c)] was found by Brown and Gibson (137) for ICl. Here the interaction is strong enough to produce, in effect, two resulting states such as given in Fig. 130(d). But there is still a considerable mixing of the states, which produces diffuse levels (for details see the paper cited).

Case III (predissociation by rotation); effective potential curves.

For predissociation by rotation the Kronig selection rules can obviously always be fulfilled, since the molecule remains in the same electronic state. This means that always $\Delta\Lambda = 0$ and $\Delta S = 0$ and also the symmetry conditions are fulfilled for equal J. Accordingly, a predissociation could appear as soon as the dissociation limit is reached. In spite of that, in many cases *sharp rotational levels* have been observed *considerably above the dissociation limit*. Fig. 164 gives as an illustration the observed rotational levels of HgH. They do break off, but only somewhat above the dissociation limit, at a height differing for the different vibrational levels. The explanation for this is

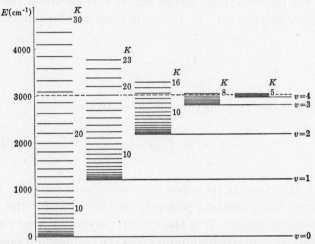

Fig. 164. Observed (Stable) Rotational Levels of HgH for the Different Vibrational Levels of the Ground State $^2\Sigma$ [after Hulthén (**342**)]. The doublet splitting is not shown. The broken line gives the position of the dissociation limit.

again to be sought in the Franck-Condon principle [Oldenberg (**538**)].

Let us consider, on the basis of classical mechanics, the molecule in the vibrationless state for different rotations. The internuclear distance r takes a value r_c such that the centrifugal force equals the restoring force; that is, since the

$$\text{centrifugal force} = \mu r \left(\frac{d\varphi}{dt}\right)^2 = \frac{\left[\mu r^2 \left(\frac{d\varphi}{dt}\right)\right]^2}{\mu r^3} = \frac{P^2}{\mu r^3},$$

$$\frac{P^2}{\mu r_c{}^3} = U_0{}'(r_c), \qquad \text{(VII, 3)}$$

where P is the angular momentum, μ is the reduced mass, and

$U_0'(r_c)$ is the derivative of the potential energy $U_0(r)$—that is, the restoring force in the nonrotating molecule for a distance r_c. From this relation we can determine the equilibrium distance r_c of the rotating molecule, which naturally is greater than r_e.[11]

If the molecule now carries out vibrations about the new equilibrium position, the restoring force will be (apart from sign)

$$U_0'(r) - \frac{P^2}{\mu r^3}.$$

This quantity is, however, the derivative of

$$U(r) = U_0(r) + \frac{P^2}{2\mu r^2}, \qquad (VII, 4)$$

which therefore, in its dependence on r, must have the same meaning for a rotating molecule as $U_0(r)$ has for the nonrotating molecule.   It is the *effective potential energy* for the rotating system; its minimum gives the equilibrium position r_c, and its derivative gives the restoring force for the vibration.

The expression $P^2/2\mu r^2 = P^2/2I$ is, according to (III, 1), the kinetic energy of rotation, which is, according to quantum mechanics, $(h/8\pi^2 c\mu r^2)J(J+1)$ (in cm^{-1}).   Therein J is constant for a given state.   Thus, when the angular momentum is J, we obtain for the effective potential energy (in cm^{-1})

$$U_J(r) = U_0(r) + \frac{h}{8\pi^2 c\mu r^2} J(J+1). \qquad (VII, 5)$$

In Hund's case (b) J is of course replaced by K, since the rotational energy depends in first approximation only on K (see p. 246).   Fig. 165 gives the effective potential curves for different K values for the ground state ($^2\Sigma$) of HgH

---

[11] This difference between r_c and r_e was mentioned before in the discussion of the nonrigid rotator (p. 110).   It is the basis for the introduction of the rotational constant D.

according to this formula. For large r, all the curves
approach asymptotically the same value, the dissociation
limit of the state $[U_0(\infty)]$. However, unlike $U_0(r)$, the
$U_J(r)$ [or $U_K(r)$] curves for J (or K) > 0, in coming from large

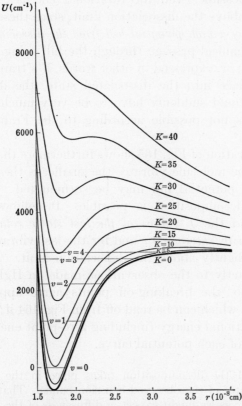

Fig. 165. Effective Potential Curves of HgH in the Ground State [after
Villars and Condon (686)]. The vibrational levels indicated refer to the lowest
curve with $K = 0$. For the remaining curves they are displaced upward by
an amount equal to the difference in heights of the minima.

r values, usually first go through a *maximum* and then
through the minimum corresponding to the equilibrium
position. With increasing J (or K), the minimum becomes
shallower and finally coincides with the maximum at a
point of inflection. Higher rotational states no longer have

a maximum and a minimum. Thus for these states the molecule is *mechanically unstable*, just as it is in unstable electronic states.

It can be seen from Fig. 165 that stable molecular states are still possible even for rotational energies lying considerably above the dissociation limit, since these states are *separated by a high potential hill from the dissociated state*, a wave mechanical passage through the hill being practically impossible; or, expressed in other words, if a transition were to take place into the dissociated state, the internuclear distance would suddenly have to be very much increased, and this is not possible according to the Franck-Condon principle.

Consideration of Fig. 165 shows furthermore that the more strongly the molecule vibrates the smaller is the J value at which the potential hill may be surmounted—that is, at which a decomposition is possible. It follows that the *energy* (and the J value) *of the last stable rotational level decreases with increasing v* and for the last vibrational level lies only slightly above the dissociation limit. This corresponds exactly to the observations made on HgH (see Fig. 164). Also, the breaking-off points agree approximately with those which can be read off from Fig. 164 if we add the pure vibrational energy (including zero-point energy) to the minimum of each potential curve.

For HgH the decomposition takes place in the lower state (ground state) of the observed emission bands. That a breaking off, and not, as we might expect, a diffuseness of the lines, occurs is due to the fact that the higher rotational states are completely unstable. A transition to one of them from a discrete rotational state of a higher electronic state therefore gives only a continuous spectrum whose total intensity is equal to that of only one rotational line and is therefore not observed.

In Fig. 166 the energy of the maxima of the effective potential curves is plotted as a function of $K(K + 1)$. The curve obtained intersects the ordinate axis at the point $U_0(\infty)$. If all the maxima were at the same r value, the curve would be a straight line, as can be seen immediately from (VII, 5). The fact that it is not a straight line shows that the maximum shifts to increasing r values with decreasing K. For $K = 0$ the curve in Fig. 166 has a horizontal tangent. As long as the quantum mechanical passage through potential barriers is neglected (see below), the breaking-off points observed should evidently lie on this curve. They are indicated in Fig. 166 by small circles. Conversely, from the observed breaking-off points plotted in this way, the energy of the asymptote $U_0(\infty)$ may be obtained by a short extrapolation to $K(K + 1) = 0$ such that the curve has a horizontal tangent [see Büttenbender and Herzberg (147) and Schmid and Gerö (622)].

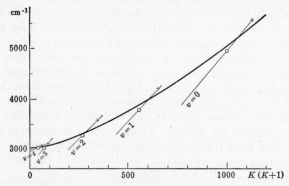

Fig. 166.   Limiting Curve of Dissociation for the Ground State $^2\Sigma$ of HgH.
The oblique straight lines give the rotational levels of the particular vibrational level (average of the two doublet components F_1 and F_2).

Curves such as that in Fig. 166 have been designated *limiting curves of dissociation* by Schmid and Gerö (622).

In the rare cases that the *potential curve without rotation has a maximum* (see p. 325), at least for small K (or J), all the maxima of the corresponding effective potential curves are at the same r value, and the limiting curve of dissociation is a straight line intersecting the ordinate axis at a non-zero angle. Thus it may be decided whether a given state has a potential curve with or without a maximum if it is possible to determine the course of the limiting curve of dissociation [see Herzberg (313)]. For example, for AlH (AlD) a straight line is obtained as limiting curve if the breaking-off points in the upper $^1\Pi$ state of the violet bands are plotted against $J(J + 1)$, proving that this state has a potential curve with maximum even for no rotation (317). The r value of the maximum can be obtained from the slope of the straight line. In this case the point of intersection with the ordinate axis does not give the energy of the asymptote of the potential curve $[U_0(\infty)]$ but that of the maximum.[12]

In predissociation according to case III, for sufficiently increased rotation, the molecule is to a zero approximation (that is, classically) unstable (exactly like an unstable electronic state), even without the mutual interaction of the states necessary for predissociation according to case I. The decomposition thus results without any "transition" from one state to another.[13] However, we still have to take account of the quantum mechanical passage through potential barriers. As a result of this "tunnel effect," a "transition" into the dissociated state can take place even when the vibrational level is *somewhat below the maximum* of the effective potential curve under consideration (for example, $v = 1$ for $K = 20$ in Fig. 165). This transition makes itself manifest in a broadening of the level. Therefore, if the predissociation takes place in the upper state of a band system, in emission the breaking off occurs at a somewhat smaller J value than would be expected on the basis of the effective potential curves, while in absorption all the possible rotational lines appear, but the last rotational lines that fail to appear in emission are diffuse. Their width increases very rapidly from the last lines present in emission with increasing J (or K), since the mean life is an exponential function of the area cut off from the potential hill (see p. 433).

This phenomenon has been investigated in detail, for example, for AlH [Farkas and Levy (215)]. In emission (at low pressure), the violet AlH bands with $v' = 1$ break off suddenly at $J' = 7$ (see Fig. 28, p. 55), while they have been observed in absorption up to $J' = 16$, an increasing width being noticeable from $J' = 12$ up. Thus for the hydride molecules the influence of the tunnel effect gives a relatively large difference between absorption and emission. On the other hand, it is much less noticeable for heavier molecules, such as N_2, P_2, and S_2. In practice, it is often sufficient to use simply the effective potential curves without considering the passage through the potential hill.

---

[12] Case III of predissociation for a potential curve with maximum is of course equivalent to case I(c) (see also below), since a maximum may always be considered as arising from the intersection of two zero approximation potential curves [see Fig. 130(d) and accompanying discussion].

[13] This process is therefore often called *"dissociation by rotation"* in the literature. The name *predissociation by rotation* is chosen here in order to indicate the close connection with predissociation and also because, as will be shown presently, a decomposition can take place somewhat below the classical instability limit as a result of a "transition" into the dissociated state. In addition, cases are also possible and have been observed in which a distinction between cases I and III is very difficult and sometimes impossible.

It may be remarked that the effective potential curves are also to be used when dealing with *noncentral collisions of two atoms* (see p. 419), since, of course, an angular momentum is present for noncentral collisions. It can be seen from the curves in Fig. 165 that in a noncentral collision the colliding atoms may possibly not come within the region of mutual attraction (that is, of positive slope of the effective potential curve) if the velocity of the atoms is small.

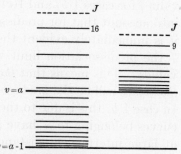

Fig. 167. Breaking Off in Two Successive Vibrational Levels in Case I of Predissociation. The first level that does not occur in emission is drawn with a broken line.

Influence of rotation in case I. In a number of cases undoubtedly belonging to case I of predissociation (as, for example, the ultraviolet P_2 bands) a breaking off of the rotational structure has not only been observed in one but also in two or more successive vibrational levels, of course at a correspondingly higher J value for the lower vibrational

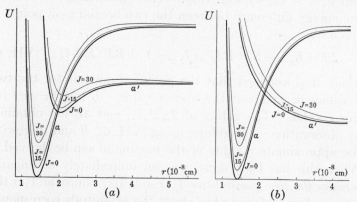

Fig. 168. Effective Potential Curves for Case I(b) and I(c) of Predissociation.

levels. An exact determination of the energy values shows that the breaking-off points in the lower vibrational levels lie at somewhat higher energy values, as indicated schematically in Fig. 167. The explanation for this is to be sought in the fact that *also in case* I *we must use the effective potential curves* instead of the ordinary potential curves.

Fig. 168 shows the effective potential curves for some J values for cases I(b) and I(c) (see Fig. 163).   When we take into account that for predissociation ΔJ must be equal to 0, it is immediately evident that in both cases with increasing J the predissociation limit will be shifted to higher energy values.   This means that *the smaller the vibrational energy is the higher* will be the *predissociation limit* (compare Fig. 167). In case I(b) this is due to the fact that the effective potential curves belonging to α' have a maximum of increasing height at large internuclear distances, while in case I(c) the intersection of corresponding α and α' curves lies higher and higher as J increases.

Let $v = a$ be the last observed vibrational level before a breaking-off point, J_a be the J value of the last observed rotational level, and E_a be its energy value; furthermore, let J_{a-1} be the J value and E_{a-1} be the energy value of the last rotational level in the vibrational state $v = a - 1$ ($J_{a-1} > J_a$ and $E_{a-1} > E_a$; see Fig. 167).   Then, according to (VII, 5), the energy difference between the two breaking-off points is given by

$$\Delta E = E_{a-1} - E_a = BJ_{a-1}(J_{a-1}+1) - BJ_a(J_a+1), \quad \text{(VII, 6)}$$

where it is assumed that the potential maxima for the two J values lie at about the same r value. B is $h/8\pi^2 c\mu r^2$ for this r value.   The values of J_a, J_{a-1}, and ΔE are obtained by observation.   Therefore, using (VII, 6), B and therewith the approximate r value of the maximum can be derived.[14] When this has been done, we can immediately *distinguish between the two possibilities* I(b) *and* I(c), since in I(c) the internuclear distance r has about the magnitude correspond-

---

[14] Since the "true" breaking-off point may be anywhere between the last observed and the first unobserved level, the best procedure is to substitute first of all the J values of the last observed levels in (VII, 6) and then those of the first missing levels. The mean of the B (or r) values so obtained is then taken.

ing to the right limb of the potential curve of the discrete state, whereas in case I(b) the potential maximum lies at an appreciably greater r value (see Fig. 168). In case I(a) the situation would be similar to that in case I(c).

In case I(c) the predissociation limit lies above the dissociation limit by an unknown amount, which may sometimes be rather large; in case I(b), on the other hand, it is only a very small amount, for which even an upper limit can be given [Herzberg (311)]. According to (VII, 5), the maximum of the effective potential curve for J_a—that is, E_a—lies above the potential curve $U_0(r)$ by an amount $BJ_a(J_a+1)$, where B is the rotational constant evaluated above, and where $U_0(r)$, for case I(b), is smaller than the energy of the dissociation limit $U_0(\infty)$. The energy $E_a - BJ_a(J_a+1) = U_0(r)$ therefore represents a lower limiting value for the dissociation limit under consideration, whereas E_a is an upper limiting value. Since the r value of the maximum is usually large, $BJ_a(J_a + 1)$ is very small. The *dissociation limit* is therefore obtained *within very narrow limits* in this way. Similarly, also in case III an upper and a lower limiting value may be obtained for the dissociation limit.

The two or more breaking-off points in case I(b) must lie on the limiting curve of dissociation (see p. 454 and Fig. 166) for the state α' that produces the predissociation. The above procedure for determining a lower limit for the dissociation limit corresponds to approximating the limiting curve by a straight line. If more than two breaking-off points are observed, an even better approximation can be obtained by using a curve having a horizontal tangent at $J = 0$ instead of a straight line. In case I(c) the breaking-off points, plotted as a function of $J(J + 1)$, do not lie on such a limiting curve but on a straight line, just as in the case of a maximum of a potential curve (see above).

Most of the cases in which a breaking-off point has been observed in two or more successive vibrational levels have been shown to belong to case I(b) or III. This is understandable, since, in case I(c), ΔE in (VII, 6) and thereby J_{a-1} are very large, so large that the rotational levels in question would not generally be observed even without predissociation.

Violation of Kronig's selection rules; induced predissociation.
For radiationless transitions, the selection rule $\Delta S = 0$ holds only
to the same degree as it does for transitions with radiation. Radiationless transitions, forbidden according to this rule, will therefore
be observed with a slight probability, particularly for heavy molecules. Since a completely allowed predissociation leads to a mean
life of about 10^{-11} sec. of the state under consideration (see p.
434), a transition with $\Delta S \neq 0$ (*intercombination*) can still reduce
the lifetime sufficiently to bring about a breaking off or at least a
drop in intensity in emission. Actually, the predissociations in
the ultraviolet P_2 bands and in the Ångström bands of CO can be
explained only by assuming an intercombination [Herzberg (311)
and Coster and Brons (165)].

It has been shown by Turner (670) that the observed quenching
of I_2 fluorescence by a magnetic field is due to an otherwise *forbidden predissociation induced by the magnetic field*. The theory of
this phenomenon has been given by Van Vleck (680). He showed
that the selection rule $\Delta J = 0$ no longer holds strictly in a magnetic
field, and that, as a result, the upper state of the I_2 bands can go
over into one of the states leading to normal atoms, into which it
could not go in the absence of a field when the rule $\Delta J = 0$ holds
strictly [see also (247), (248), (625), (639), and (604a)].

Turner (672) has furthermore shown that the forbidden predissociation of I_2 can also be brought about (induced) by the
addition of argon at high pressure. Under these conditions, in
fluorescence a quenching of those I_2 bands whose upper state lies
above the predissociation limit is observed. Turner (673) has, in
fact, directly detected the appearance of free atoms resulting from
this induced predissociation by absorption of the iodine atomic
lines.

In recent years this *predissociation induced by collisions* (that is,
by high pressure of a foreign gas or of the gas itself) has been found
and investigated in detail in a number of cases both in emission
and in absorption. The small line broadenings brought about by
induced predissociation are usually recognized in absorption by
the effect mentioned earlier (p. 435) that broad lines under small or
medium dispersion appear more intense than sharp ones. In consequence of that, the intensity of the bands under consideration
increases abnormally with increasing pressure—that is, more
strongly than corresponds to the Lambert-Beer law [Loomis and
Fuller (461)]. Predissociation induced by pressure has been observed for I_2 [(672), (673), (461), and (413)], N_2 (395), Br_2 [(412)
and (73)], NO [(723) and (414)], S_2 [(411), (448), and (597)], Te_2
[(409) and (597)], and Se_2 (597).

It must be remarked that a line broadening increasing with pressure and similarly a breaking off in emission setting in at high pressure may also have causes other than induced predissociation [see, for example, Franck, Sponer, and Teller (232)]. It is not always easy to decide whether or not there is actually an induced predissociation.

Influence of the conditions of excitation on the breaking off. Mörikofer (503a) first found that the AlH bands that break off under certain conditions of excitation in consequence of predissociation do not break off under other conditions of excitation. Bengtsson and Rydberg (87), who first studied this effect in more detail, ascribed it to a *pressure effect*, because they found that the breaking off occurs in an arc between Al electrodes at low pressure of H_2, whereas it does not at high pressure. However, no breaking off of the AlH bands occurs in the aureole of an arc even at fairly low pressure [Mörikofer (503a)], whereas they do break off in the core of the arc at the same pressure.

According to Farkas (212) the explanation for this phenomenon is that in the case of the arc at high pressure, and in the aureole even at comparatively low pressure, *thermal equilibrium* is approached. In ordinary excitation by electron collisions at low pressure, in general every molecule that has been excited will either radiate or predissociate, and thus, if the radiationless transition probability is large, the intensity of radiation from the predissociating levels will be very slight compared to that from the nonpredissociating levels, since the probability of excitation to both groups of levels is roughly the same. However, in thermal equilibrium only a small fraction of the excited molecules radiate or predissociate. Most of them lose their excitation energy by collisions before radiation or predissociation could have taken place. In consequence of that, the number of molecules that actually radiate depends only on the probability of radiation and not on the radiationless transition probability. Thus the intensity of the lines from the predissociating rotational levels is of the same order (corresponding to the thermal distribution curve) as the intensity of the lines from the nonpredissociating levels. However, the lines exhibit an increasing width just as in absorption (see p. 456).

Thus indirectly this phenomenon depends on the pressure, since the rate at which thermal equilibrium is set up increases with increasing pressure. But for different means of excitation at the same pressure there are great variations of the phenomenon.

A "pressure effect" similar to that for AlH has been observed for the CaH band, reproduced in Fig. 27, by Grundström and Hulthén (272) and for the corresponding SrH band by Humphreys

and Fredrickson (345a). In fact, this effect is to be expected for all
cases of breaking off if they can be studied under conditions
approaching thermal equilibrium. Olsson (546) showed that even
at comparatively low pressure the CaH band mentioned does not
break off when excited strictly thermally.

A more detailed discussion of this effect is given by Herzberg
(309) and more recently by Olsson (548).

In a very recent paper Schüler, Gollnow, and Haber (626a) suggest a somewhat different explanation of the "pressure effect" in
AlH. However, their implication that the breaking off at low
pressure is not due to predissociation does not seem to be
acceptable.

(d) Other Diffuse Molecular Spectra

As already mentioned, apart from the predissociation
spectra treated in the foregoing, there is another type of
diffuse band spectra for which, also, the bands are in the
strict sense diffuse and do not simply have an unresolved
fine structure. The Hg_2 spectrum reproduced in Fig. 17
affords an example of this type.   In general, here, in contrast
to predissociation spectra, there are *symmetrical* fluctuations
of intensity, which appear in emission as well as in absorption, and which do not form the continuation of a series of
discrete bands but appear independently of them.   There
is also no breaking off in emission here.

It has been found that this type of diffuse band spectra
is merely a *special case of continuous spectra* resulting from
the combination of an unstable with a stable state [Winans
(716), Sommermeyer (644), and Kuhn (428)].

If, for example, in absorption from a stable ground state
to an unstable state the potential curve for the latter is
nearly horizontal down to comparatively small r values, as
shown in Fig. 169(a), the continuous spectrum corresponding to the transition from the vibrationless state will be very
narrow, as a result of the Franck-Condon principle; that is,
it will have the appearance of a diffuse band (see p. 412).
If, at higher temperatures, the higher vibrational states of
the ground state are excited to an appreciable extent, for
each turning point of these vibrational states there will be a

narrow continuous absorption spectrum. If the upper potential curve is sufficiently flat, the narrow continua (AA', BB', $\cdots$ in the figure) corresponding to the turning points to the right will be separate from one another. We thus observe a *series of diffuse bands* whose separations decrease toward longer wave lengths and correspond to the vibrational quanta in the ground state of the molecule. At the same time, of course, the intensity in this series decreases

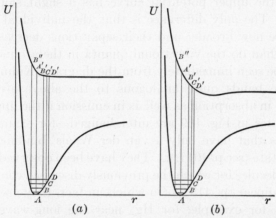

Fig. 169. Potential Curves for the Explanation of Diffuse Bands.

rapidly because of the Boltzmann factor, unless the vibrational quanta are very small.

Owing to the rising of the potential curve of the upper state at smaller internuclear distances, the continua corresponding to the left turning points of the vibrational motion in the lower state will be very much broader and will overlap one another so that they usually will appear as one extended continuum, lying to the short-wave-length side of the diffuse bands. Such cases have been observed, for example, for the alkali halides by Sommermeyer (644). The upper state in this case corresponds to dissociation into normal atoms [see p. 401 and Fig. 151(b)]. The wave number of the shortest-wave-length band, corresponding to the transition from the vibrationless ground state, gives directly the *heat of dissociation* of the halide into normal atoms [see Fig. 169(*a*)]. The same bands have also been observed in emission in alkali halide flames by Beutler and Josephy (93). They correspond here to a recombination of the two atoms (alkali and halogen) to form the molecule (see p. 422 f.).

Naturally, only in very rare cases will the upper potential curve run exactly horizontally in the region in question. However, the above considerations remain practically unaltered if the upper potential curve has a slight slope [Fig. 169(*b*)]. The only difference is that the individual diffuse bands are now broader and their separations decrease more rapidly than do the vibrational quanta in the ground state, as may be seen immediately from the diagram [Kuhn (428)].

Diffuse bands quite analogous to the above are to be expected in absorption as well as in emission if the upper and lower states in Fig. 169 are interchanged—for example, for molecules that have only a van der Waals' binding in the ground state (see p. 404 f.). They have been observed for the same molecules for which the previously discussed continuous spectra appear (p. 415 f.) (to which, in fact, they are closely related)—for example, for Hg_2 near the long-wave-length end of the continuum joining onto the resonance line 2537 Å (see Fig. 17). Such diffuse bands correspond in absorption to the central or nearly central collisions of the normal atoms (see p. 416) and in emission to transitions from the different vibrational states of an excited stable molecular state to an unstable ground state. For a detailed discussion see (218), (428), (537), and (42).

3. DETERMINATION OF HEATS OF DISSOCIATION

On the basis of the considerations in sections 1 and 2, it is clear that the investigation of continuous and diffuse spectra, the convergence of bands, and the breaking off in band systems can lead to important conclusions concerning the dissociation processes in diatomic molecules and in particular to the determination of heats of dissociation.

In agreement with chemical usage we consider *the heat of dissociation D_0 of a diatomic molecule* to be the work that is needed to *dissociate the molecule from the lowest level* ($v = 0$, $J = \Omega$) *of the electronic ground state into normal atoms.*[15] (This corresponds in thermal measurements to giving the results for the temperature $T = 0°$ K.) The molecule has also a certain heat of dissociation in each of its excited electronic states, which corresponds to a dissociation from the lowest level of the electronic state considered by increasing the vibrational energy (without altering the electronic state). The products of dissociation may be normal or excited atoms.[16] Every combination of states of the two atoms corresponds to a definite *dissociation limit*, to which, in general, several molecular states belong (see Chapter VI, section 1).

The spectroscopic determination of the heat of dissociation of a molecule always involves two steps: (1) determination of the energy of a dissociation limit (or possibly several limits) above the ground state, and (2) determination of the products of dissociation at this limit. As soon as the position E_d of a dissociation limit and the dissociation products at this limit (excitation energy A) are known, the heat of dissociation of the molecule is immediately obtained. We have only to subtract the excitation energy of the dissociation products from the energy of the dissociation limit [see, for example, Fig. 83(c)]; that is,

$$D_0 = E_d - A. \qquad \text{(VII, 7)}$$

In what follows we shall consider the two steps separately.

---

[15] From this we have to distinguish the dissociation energy D_e, which refers to the minimum of the potential curve (see p. 107) but which is only of theoretical interest.

[16] It is possible that the electronic ground state, when the vibrational energy is increased (without alteration of the electronic state), does not lead to normal atoms. The dissociation energy of the ground state is then not the dissociation energy of the molecule in the above sense. Such cases are, however, very rare. One case is the BeO molecule, whose ground state is $^1\Sigma$, which according to the Wigner-Witmer rules cannot result from normal atoms Be(^1S) + O(^3P).

(a) Determination of Dissociation Limits

Most of the methods for the determination of dissociation limits have already been dealt with. In the following they are summarized, and some further methods are added to them.

1. Band convergences. A very accurate and reliable value for a dissociation limit is obtained when a convergence limit of bands, with its adjoining continuum, is observed in absorption.[17] The position of the *convergence limit*—that is, the beginning of the continuum—corresponds to the *dissociation limit of the excited molecular state under consideration*.[18] Such convergence limits have been observed, for example, for the halogen molecules (see Fig. 15, p. 37) and for O_2 and H_2.

2. Extrapolation to convergence limits. For the numerous cases in which an investigation of the absorption spectrum is impossible or in which no band convergence is observed, Birge and Sponer (113) have suggested an *extrapolation* to the position of the convergence limit from the observed bands. From cases in which a convergence is observed, we know approximately how the vibrational quanta ΔG (that is, the separation of successive bands in a progression) depend on the vibrational quantum number. Fig. 170 shows, for example, the behavior for the upper state of the ultraviolet O_2 bands (see also Fig. 49, p. 108, for the ground state of H_2). If, for example, we had observed only the first five vibrational quanta, we could have extrapolated the further vibrational quanta—say, linearly—as indicated by the broken line. It can be seen that all the extrapolated

---

[17] In principle, a convergence limit with adjoining continuum is also possible in emission, but such a case has not yet been observed.

[18] We must, however, keep in mind the remote possibility that the upper state may have a potential curve with a maximum [see Fig. 130(d)]. In this case abnormalities in the course of the vibrational quanta and also the aforementioned (p. 455) peculiarities of the rotational structure, which would indicate the presence of such a maximum, are to be expected. We shall not discuss this possibility in detail [see Mulliken (522) and Herzberg (313)].

vibrational quanta are too high but that at least approximate values are obtained.

According to the relation (III, 69), the heat of dissociation is equal to the sum of all the vibrational quanta—that is, very nearly equal to the area under the ΔG curve. From Fig. 170 it can be seen that the area under the linearly extrapolated ΔG curve is not very much greater than that under the true ΔG curve. We can therefore expect that, even in those cases in which only the first few vibrational quanta are observed, extrapolation will lead to an *approxi-*

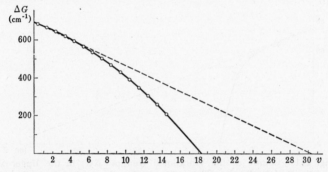

Fig. 170. Course of the Vibrational Quanta (ΔG) in the Upper State ($^3\Sigma_u^-$) of the Ultraviolet O_2 Bands. The data are taken from Curry, Herzberg, and Herzberg (176) and Knauss and Ballard (406).

mate D_0 value for the state under consideration. Analytically, we obtain the heat of dissociation by linear extrapolation according to (III, 73). The extrapolation method can naturally be improved if we extrapolate, say, according to a parabolic formula instead of linearly—that is, if we take account of higher terms in the formula for the observed vibrational levels.[19] We obtain in this way the heat of dissociation of the electronic state whose vibrational quanta are used. In order to obtain the energy of the dissociation limit under consideration we have to add the excitation energy of the electronic state.

[19] Birge (104) and Rydberg (608) have suggested two further extrapolation methods, which, however, have thus far not found general application.

The advantage of this procedure is that it can be applied to each electronic state of any diatomic molecule if only a number of vibrational levels (at least three) are known. The values so obtained are the more accurate and reliable the smaller is the number of extrapolated vibrational quanta in comparison to the total number. In the limiting case, in which almost all the vibrational levels are observed, a completely reliable and very accurate value for D is obtained even when the adjoining continuum is not observed. This is, for example, the case for H_2 in the ground state (see the

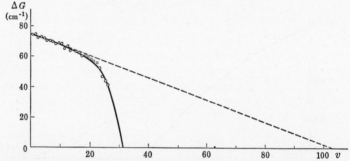

Fig. 171. Course of the Vibrational Quanta (ΔG) in the Upper State ($^1\Pi$) of the Red K_2 Bands. The data are taken from Loomis and Nusbaum (464). It should be noted that the vibrational quanta are much smaller than for O_2.

ΔG curve in Fig. 49), where the value thus obtained has been confirmed in several other ways [see Beutler and Jünger (96)].

Since the variation of the vibrational quanta is not necessarily always like that for O_2, the D_0 values calculated from only a few vibrational quanta are always subject to a considerable *uncertainty*, as is seen particularly well in the ΔG curve for the $^1\Pi$ state of K_2 in Fig. 171. Here the curvature of the ΔG curve for large v values is much stronger than that of the ΔG curve for O_2 (Fig. 170). Therefore, if in this case we had observed only, say, 10 vibrational quanta, we should have obtained by linear extrapolation (broken line) a D_0 value that was much too high (namely, $D_0 = 3860$, compared to the true value, $D_0 = 1790$ cm^{-1}). In a similar way is to be explained the fact that in the case of the nitrogen molecule, $D_0(N_2) = 11.5$ volts was obtained by linear extrapolation of the vibrational quanta in the ground state [Sponer (647) and (648)], whereas the actual value derived later amounted to only 7.38 volts (see below). Thus the extrapolation method is to be used with great caution when only a few vibrational levels are observed. Lack of such caution has led in the past to contradictions and false conclusions in many places in the literature.

In general, as may be seen from the above examples (but not always), the *linear extrapolation* leads to too high a value for D_0, the heat of dissociation of the electronic state considered, and thus gives an *upper limiting value* for it, while naturally the *height of the last observed vibrational level* gives a *lower limiting value* for D_0.

3. Long-wave-length limit of an absorption continuum. According to the previous discussion, when a continuous absorption is observed, its long-wave-length limit is an *upper limiting value for the dissociation limit under consideration.* It should, however, be noted that the true value may lie considerably below this upper limiting value [see also Franck and Kuhn (230)]. We have seen before that, if the potential curve of an upper unstable state is steep, the continuum first begins at an appreciable distance beyond the theoretical long-wave-length limit, in consequence of the Franck-Condon principle [see Fig. 152(a)]. At the same time, the continuum is then very extensive, as is observed, for example, for the halogen hydrides [Goodeve and Taylor (263) and (264)]. When, on the other hand, the continuum is of very small extent (that is, when it is a diffuse band; see p. 462), we can conversely conclude that the repulsive potential curve of the upper state is very flat and therefore that the dissociation limit is very close to the long-wavelength limit of the continuum, as, for example, for the alkali halides [Sommermeyer (644)].

4. Predissociation limits. The energy of a predissociation limit gives immediately an *upper limiting value for the* *dissociation limit of the state bringing about the predissocia-tion.*[20] As we have seen, the dissociation limit may lie appreciably lower [case I(c)].   Only in cases I(a) and (b) and in case III does the predissociation limit (in the "last" vibrational level below the limit) very nearly coincide with the dissociation limit.   Thus only in these cases is it possible to determine a dissociation limit from a predissociation limit; in case I(c), on the other hand, only an upper limiting value can be obtained for it.   Which case applies can be decided *if a breaking off in the rotational structure is observed not only in the last but also in the second last* (and possibly the third last, and so on) *vibrational level* (see p. 457 f.).   If, in this way, it is found that case I(a) or (b) or case III apply, also a *lower limiting value* for the dissociation limit can be given and thereby the latter can be fixed within very narrow bounds.   This method of determining dissociation limits is very accurate.   It has been applied, for example, to P_2 (311), N_2 [(147) and (319)], SO (482), H_2 (91), and CO (619).

When a breaking off is observed in only one vibrational level, a distinction between case I(b) and case III on the one hand and case I(c) on the other cannot be made.   The possibility that the dissociation limit lies considerably below the breaking-off point (predissociation limit) cannot then be excluded.

According to what has been said previously, in case I(c) we should expect a sharp breaking-off point only when the potential hill is not too narrow. Conversely, it follows from this that, when a sharp breaking-off point is observed in a single vibrational level, the dissociation limit cannot in general lie very much below the breaking-off point. In the upper state of the first positive group of N_2, for example, a breaking-off point has been observed [van der Ziel (732)] which has been shown to lie 0.08 volt above the cor-responding dissociation limit (319). This is the order of magnitude of the differences to be expected.

When, however, no breaking-off point in the rotational structure but only a breaking off of the vibrational structure for a given v' is

---

[20] This holds also for the case of accidental predissociation (see p. 440) and for induced predissociation (see p. 460).

observed, the corresponding dissociation limit may possibly lie very considerably below this breaking-off point. The same holds when, in absorption, the diffuseness sets in at a certain band but not at a certain line in the rotational structure, and in particular when the diffuseness does not start with the maximum strength but reaches its maximum strength only some distance beyond the limit [see Turner (671) and p. 449]. An example for the latter case is the first predissociation of S_2 [see Fig. 16 and Herzberg and Mundie (317)].

5. Excitation of atomic fluorescence. When a continuous or diffuse absorption spectrum corresponds to dissociation into a normal and an excited atom, on illumination with light in the absorption region in question we have to expect the corresponding atomic line in fluorescence, provided the excited atomic state is not metastable. The *long-wave-length limit for the appearance of the atomic fluorescence* obviously gives an *upper limiting value for a dissociation limit* [Terenin (665)]. The advantage of this method is that it yields at the same time the kind of dissociation products produced at the limit and thus, according to (VII, 7), an upper limiting value for the heat of dissociation of the molecule. Terenin has applied this method particularly to the alkali halides. By irradiation of the alkali halides (in vapor form) with light of sufficiently short wave length, the resonance lines of the alkali atoms are observed in fluorescence.

6. Chemiluminescence. As we have previously seen, recombination of atoms to form molecules usually takes place by means of a three-body collision. The energy of dissociation set free in the formation of the molecule may be divided in different ways between the collision partners. It may be converted either into energy of excitation of the third collision partner or of the newly formed molecule or into excitation energy of both systems. Part of the energy set free may also be converted into translational energy of the products of the collision. However, according to the principle of resonance for collisions of the second kind, this part is always very small (see A.A., p. 231). If suitable excited states of the newly formed molecule are present, a discrete band spectrum may be emitted concomitant with this recombination. This spectrum will generally have an intensity distribution differing widely from the normal. It is to be expected that the *highest level excited* in such a recombination process will *correspond to the heat of dissociation of the molecule*, which can therefore be determined in this way.

Such a process was first assumed by Sponer (646) for the recombination of atomic nitrogen in order to explain the afterglow of active nitrogen. But, in this case, since the heat of dissociation of N_2 is very large, complications appear, owing to the formation of metastable atomic and molecular states. However, such a simple chemiluminescence process does apparently occur in the recombination of C atoms to a C_2 molecule [Herzberg (316)]. It is found that in the electrical excitation of CO at high pressures a selective excitation of the Swan bands of C_2 with $v' = 6$ occurs outside the direct path of the discharge. This phenomenon is most simply explained by assuming that C atoms, set free by the dissociation of CO, form C_2 molecules in the above-described manner with excitation of the state $^3\Pi_g$ ($v = 6$). The only difficulty in this explanation is the great selectivity of the excitation, only one vibrational level being excited. In order to account for it one has to assume (Beutler, private discussion) that we have here an inverse induced predissociation; that is, the two atoms recombine only when they approach each other on a potential curve from which a radiationless transition into the upper state of the Swan bands is possible under the action of a third particle. Once formed, the molecule will not predissociate again except in collisions (induced predissociation). At any rate the energy of the level $v = 6$ of the $^3\Pi_g$ state should correspond to the heat of dissociation of C_2. The latter is found in this way to be 3.6 volts.

(b) Determination of the Dissociation Products

The dissociation limits obtained in one of the ways described correspond in general to dissociation into atoms which may be more or less highly excited. In order to derive the heat of dissociation D_0 of the ground state into normal atoms, we have to know the *type and excitation energies of the products of dissociation* [see equation (VII, 7)]. If it is not possible to determine the dissociation products, the dissociation limit represents only an upper limit for the heat of dissociation of the molecule into normal atoms.

The type of the atomic states corresponding to a given dissociation limit can be determined in three different ways, as follows:

1. Energy differences of dissociation limits. If two or more different dissociation limits of a molecule have been determined, their differences must be equal to *possible energy* *differences of the separate atoms.* The number of possibilities for the dissociation products can thereby at least be reduced considerably.

In general, in deriving the possible energy differences we need take into account only the low-lying states of the atoms considered, provided we are not dealing with highly excited molecular states.

Sometimes we can distinguish between the possible dissociation products if only one dissociation limit is accurately known and another is approximately known. In particular, if an approximate value for the heat of dissociation is known from thermal measurements, it is possible to decide which products of dissociation are formed at a spectroscopically observed dissociation limit, and, once that has been done, a more accurate value for D_0 is obtained from the spectroscopic data. It was in this way that in the case of the halogens it was found that at the convergence limit of the strong absorption system in the visible region one normal $^2P_{\frac{3}{2}}$ and one excited $^2P_{\frac{1}{2}}$ atom are formed (see p. 410). In the case of I_2 and Br_2 this conclusion was later confirmed by the observation in a weak red band system of a second convergence limit whose distance from the other convergence limit is exactly equal to the excitation energy of the $^2P_{\frac{1}{2}}$ state.

2. Application of the Wigner-Witmer correlation rules. In determining the dissociation products, the Wigner-Witmer correlation rules have to be taken into account (see p. 336 f.). We have to find out whether the molecular state under consideration, whose dissociation limit is to be determined, can actually result from the assumed atomic states. Such considerations have been very important, for example, in the determination of the heat of dissociation of O_2 (see below).

3. Observation of atomic fluorescence. This method of determining the dissociation products has already been dealt with in the foregoing subsection (p. 471). It will not be discussed further, since it can be applied only in few cases.

Examples. For a better understanding of the method of determining the dissociation products and thus determining the heat of dissociation we shall consider two particularly important examples—the determinations of the heats of dissociation of molecular oxygen and nitrogen.

The energy level diagram of the *oxygen molecule*, including the potential curves, is given in Fig. 172. In it the well-known ultraviolet O_2 absorption bands (Schumann-Runge bands) correspond to the transition from the ground state

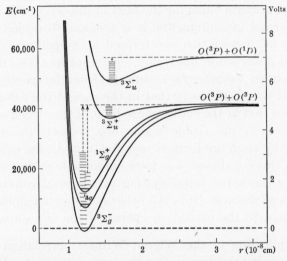

Fig. 172. Potential Curves of the Observed States of the O_2 Molecule.
A number of states lying above 100,000 cm^{-1} [Price and Collins (571)] are not drawn, since sufficiently accurate data are not available for them. In each of the electronic states drawn, all the observed vibrational levels have been indicated by short horizontal lines.

$^3\Sigma_g^-$ to the highest state shown, $^3\Sigma_u^-$. They show a well-developed convergence, onto which a continuous spectrum joins. The convergence limit lies at 1759 Å, corresponding to 7.049 volts. It represents a dissociation limit of the O_2 molecule (see Fig. 172).

The oxygen atom has three low-lying states: the ^3P ground state and the metastable states ^1D and ^1S, which lie 1.967

and 4.190 volts, respectively, above the ground state. Higher excited states do not need to be considered in the discussion of dissociation products, since the next excited state lies 9.1 volts above the ground state. If one of the atoms were in this state at the limit 7.049 volts, a negative value for $D_0(O_2)$ would be obtained.

The following combinations might be possible as dissociation products at the convergence limit of 7.049 volts: $^3P + {}^3P$, $^3P + {}^1D$, $^3P + {}^1S$, $^1D + {}^1D$, $^1D + {}^1S$, and $^1S + {}^1S$. The last three possibilities can be eliminated immediately, since, according to Wigner and Witmer (see p. 339 f.), they cannot give a triplet state, and the upper state of the ultraviolet O_2 bands, as is shown by the rotational structure [(509a) and (449)], is certainly a triplet state ($^3\Sigma_u{}^-$). It can be seen further from Table 27, p. 342, that a $^3\Sigma_u{}^-$ state cannot result from $^3P + {}^3P$ [Herzberg (305)]. Thus there remain only the two possibilities $^3P + {}^1D$ and $^3P + {}^1S$ for the dissociation products. From these, according to (VII, 7), we obtain for the heat of dissociation of O_2 either $7.049 - 1.967 = 5.082$ or $7.049 - 4.190 = 2.859$ volts. The latter value is smaller than the energy of the highest observed vibrational level in the ground state, which lies 3.4 volts above the vibrationless state. Thus there remains only the value $D_0(O_2) = 5.082$ volts $= 117.2$ kcal./mol, corresponding to a dissociation at the convergence limit 7.049 volts into $^3P + {}^1D$. In this way the heat of dissociation of O_2 is unambiguously determined, and, in fact, from a single accurately known dissociation limit.

As a matter of fact, later a further convergence limit was found in the forbidden bands $^3\Sigma_u{}^+ \leftarrow {}^3\Sigma_g{}^-$ (see Fig. 172) [Herzberg (310)]. This limit lies at 5.110 volts and therefore obviously corresponds to a dissociation into two normal atoms $^3P + {}^3P$ (in agreement with the Wigner-Witmer rules). The small difference between the two values, 5.110 and 5.082 volts, is due to the fact that at the dissociation limits different components of the ^3P term result whose total splitting amounts to 0.08 volt. With the finding of this second convergence limit, the reliability of the method is shown. The spectroscopic value for $D_0(O_2)$ is today quite

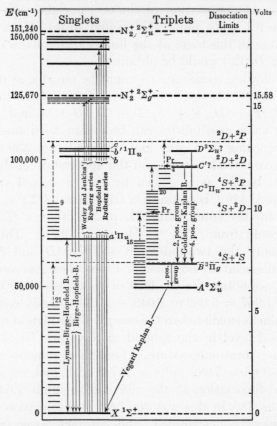

Fig. 173.   Energy Level Diagram of the N_2 Molecule. The heavy full horizontal lines give the electronic states; the short, thinner lines give the vibrational levels in each of them. The small, heavy arrows designated Pr give the positions of observed predissociation limits. Two ionization limits are given (heavy broken horizontal lines across whole figure), corresponding to the two states $^2\Sigma_g^+$ and $^2\Sigma_u^+$ of N_2^+. Recently Takamine, Suga, and Tanaka (660a) have measured further members in Hopfield's Rydberg series. They have also found a new Rydberg series in emission close to the former. These new data have not been included in the diagram. Also several higher members of Worley and Jenkins' Rydberg series could not be drawn because they are too close together.

certain and much more accurate than any value for $D_0(O_2)$ obtained by thermal or chemical means.

Once the second convergence limit of O_2 is known, the heat of dissociation of O_2 may also be determined without the help of the vibrational quanta in the ground state.[21] From the difference between the two convergence limits it follows immediately that at the upper convergence limit one atom must be in a ^1D state. Since the upper molecular electronic state is a triplet state, according to the correlation rules the other atom must be in the ^3P state.

Whereas for O_2 only convergence limits were used to determine the heat of dissociation, for the *nitrogen molecule* mainly predissociation limits have been used. The energy level diagram of N_2 is given in Fig. 173. In the $C\ ^3\Pi$ state, a breaking off was observed by Büttenbender and Herzberg (147) in three successive vibrational levels, $v' = 2, 3,$ and $4,$ which has led to the exact determination of a dissociation limit [case I(b)]. It lies at 12.145 volts above the ground state.

The nitrogen atom has three low-lying states which alone need be considered as dissociation products: the ^4S ground state and the metastable states ^2D and ^2P, lying at 2.381 and 3.572 volts, respectively, above ^4S. Consequently, we have to discuss as possible dissociation products at the limit those given in the first column of Table 35. Depending on which pair we assume, we get one of the heats of dissociation given in the second column. The possibility $^4S + {}^4S$ is immediately eliminated by the consideration that it can give only Σ states, whereas it follows from the spectrum that the state causing the predissociation is a Π or a Δ term. (If this were not the case, only one of the Λ components of each level of the $C\ ^3\Pi$ state could predissociate; see p. 442.) The possibility $^2P + {}^2P$ drops out, since the $D_0(N_2)$ value corresponding to it is smaller than the sum of the observed vibrational quanta in the ground state (5.5 volts). A further elimination, solely on the basis of the predissociation limit at 12.145 volts, is not possible.

---

[21] It might have been conceivable, although it is extremely improbable, that the ground state resulted from excited atoms. Then the last observed vibrational level could lie above the lowest dissociation limit.

TABLE 35

DETERMINATION OF THE HEAT OF DISSOCIATION OF N_2

Possible Dissociation Products at 12.145 v	Heat of Dissociation	
$^4S + {}^4S$	12.145	Not compatible with the type of pre-dissociation at 12.145 volts
$^4S + {}^2D$	9.764	Not compatible with the type of pre-dissociation at 9.844 volts
$^4S + {}^2P$	8.573	Not compatible with the energy of pre-dissociation at 9.844 volts
$^2D + {}^2D$	7.383	Actual value
$^2D + {}^2P$	6.192	Not compatible with the dissociation limit of $N_2{}^+$ at 6.3 volts
$^2P + {}^2P$	5.001	Not compatible with the vibrational quanta in the ground state

However, van der Ziel (732) has found a further predissociation limit in the $B\ {}^3\Pi$ state (see Fig. 173). It lies 9.844 volts above the ground state. In this case the breaking off is observed in only one vibrational level. The figure given is therefore only an upper limiting value for the corresponding dissociation limit. From what has been said previously, the difference between the upper limiting value and the true value cannot be very great. For the same reason as for the first predissociation limit, the state bringing about this second predissociation cannot result from normal atoms $^4S + {}^4S$. Depending on whether the dissociation products at the second predissociation limit are $^4S + {}^2D$, $^4S + {}^2P$, $^2D + {}^2D$, $^2D + {}^2P$, or $^2P + {}^2P$, we obtain for $D_0(N_2)$ the upper limiting values 7.46, 6.27, 5.08, 3.89, or 2.70 volts, respectively. However, since the last observed vibrational state of the ground state lies at 5.5 volts, only the first two (7.46 and 6.27), corresponding to a dissociation at the limit 9.844 volts into $^4S + {}^2D$ and $^4S + {}^2P$, respectively, come into consideration. The two upper limiting values, 7.46 and

6.27 volts, correspond to the heats of dissociation, 7.383 and 6.192 volts, derived from the predissociation limit at 12.145 volts (see Table 35). The former value, 7.383 volts, is by far the more probable, since the value 6.192 volts lies too near the last observed vibrational level in the ground state.

The value 6.192 volts can also be excluded with the help of a dissociation limit of N_2^+ that lies between 6.18 and 6.46 volts above the ground state of N_2^+ and consequently, since the ionization potential of N_2 is 15.58 volts, lies 21.76 to 22.04 volts above the ground state of N_2. The atomic excitation energy A in (VII, 7) is in this case the work of ionization of the atom plus a possible excitation energy. If we assume a dissociation into normal N plus normal N^+, it follows [with $I(N) = 14.55$ volts] that $D_0(N_2)$ lies between 7.21 and 7.49 volts, which agrees very well with the more accurate value, 7.383 volts, given above. No agreement with the value 6.192 volts can be obtained, even assuming excited dissociation products [see van der Ziel (733)].

A number of other heats of dissociation have been determined in a manner similar to that used for O_2 and N_2 (see Table 36). Unfortunately, not in all other cases are the experimental data so complete. There is still a great deal of work to be done in this field [see also Mulliken (522)].

CHAPTER VIII

Examples, Results, and Applications

1. ENERGY LEVEL DIAGRAMS; MOLECULAR CONSTANTS

In the foregoing chapters the complete *energy level diagrams* of H_2 (Fig. 142), Li_2 (Fig. 65), N_2 (Fig. 173), O_2 (Fig. 172), and NH (Fig. 150) have been reproduced in accordance with the latest data. In addition, in order to have an example of each of the most important types of diatomic molecules, the energy level diagrams of the molecules CO, NO, C_2, CN, Br_2, and CaH are reproduced in Figs. 174–179. In the energy level diagrams, with the exception of that of Br_2, all the observed vibrational levels of each of the different electronic states are given. In some of the figures the potential energy curves of the electronic states are drawn, and in the remaining figures at least the dissociation limits, so far as they appear to be known with certainty, are indicated by broken horizontal lines.

The spectroscopically determined constants ω_e, $\omega_e x_e$, D_0 (heat of dissociation), B_e, α_e, and r_e for the *ground states* of all diatomic molecules thus far investigated are given in Table 36 (in alphabetical order). The values of the force constants are not given but can be derived in a simple manner from the ω_e values by use of formula (III, 68). For the constants of the excited electronic states, the extensive tables by Sponer (36) should be consulted. In the last column of the table are given the references from which the constants were taken.

From the data given in Table 36, the *position of the rotational and vibrational levels for the ground state* can be derived by use of formulae (III, 83 and 88). Furthermore from

480

these data the *potential curves* can be calculated easily by use of the Morse function (III, 74).

In a few cases it has been possible to determine the internuclear distances by an entirely different method—namely, by *electron or* X-*ray diffraction* in gases (or in the solid sub-

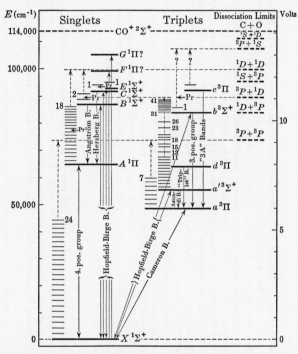

Fig. 174. Energy Level Diagram of the CO Molecule. Compare the remarks for Fig. 173. The dissociation limits are drawn under the assumption $D_0(CO) = 9.144$ volts. However, the value 6.921 volts is not as yet excluded with certainty [see Schmid and Gerö (624) and Herzberg (314)]. Therefore the dissociation limits might possibly have to be shifted downward by 2.2 volts. Henning's absorption bands (298) between 113,000 and 138,000 cm^{-1} are not given, since they have not been analyzed in any detail.

stances when they are molecular lattices). These cases are N_2 (244), O_2 (244), S_2 (484a), Cl_2 [(589) and (555)], Br_2 [(711), (555), and (687)] [see also Brockway (128)]. The results have always been (within the limits of accuracy of the diffraction method) in agreement with the band-spectro-

TABLE 36

VIBRATIONAL AND ROTATIONAL CONSTANTS FOR THE ELECTRONIC GROUND STATES
OF ALL KNOWN DIATOMIC MOLECULES

The molecules are given in alphabetic order. In general only the constants for the most abundant isotope are given except for the hydrides, for which also the constants for the corresponding deuterides are given. The mass numbers of the atoms are in general added to the symbols. If they are not given, the data refer to the isotopic mixture.

The molecular constants are taken from those original papers (see last column) that the author considered most reliable. From the values ω_e and $\omega_e x_e$ given, the vibrational levels in the ground state may be calculated according to (III, 56) and the force constants according to (III, 68). From the constants B_e and α_e given, the rotational levels in the different vibrational states can be calculated according to (III, 83 and 87), and the moments of inertia and the rotational frequencies according to (IV, 36) and (III, 20), respectively. Although the internuclear distances r_e may be obtained from B_e according to (IV, 37), they have been given explicitly, since they are of particular interest.

All of the internuclear distances have been recalculated by the author from the B_e values given, since in the original papers the r_e values are not always based on the same physical constants (e, h, N_A) and since the latter have been changed appreciably in recent years (see Table 1, p. 3). The precise masses of the atoms (Aston's scale) necessary for the calculation of the r_e have been taken from a table of Hahn (279). All of the heats of dissociation (D_0, corresponding to a dissociation into normal atoms) have been recalculated by the author from the data in the original papers, using the new conversion factor of cm^{-1} into electron-volts.—In order to obtain the values in kcal. or cm^{-1} the conversion factors in Table 2, p. 4, should be used.

Abbreviations:

( ) Constants and symbols in parentheses are uncertain. In the case of mass numbers it indicates that it is not stated in the original paper whether the data refer to the isotopic mixture or the most abundant isotope. The r_e values in these cases have been calculated with the masses of the isotopes given. Heats of dissociation obtained by long extrapolations are also put in parentheses.

[ ] If for a molecule only B_0 (and r_0) and not B_e (and r_e) or only $\Delta G_{1/2}$ and not ω_e is known, these values are given in square brackets in the column for B_e, r_e and ω_e, respectively.

H after ω_e means that the vibrational constants have been obtained from measurements of band heads.

Z after ω_e indicates that the vibrational constants have been obtained from the zero lines of the bands (band origins).

* after $\omega_e x_e$ or α_e indicates that terms with higher powers of $(v + \frac{1}{2})$ are known in the expressions (III, 56 and 83).

A in the last column means that some of the constants of the particular molecule have been recalculated by the author.

Molecule	Ground State	ω_e (cm^{-1})	$\omega_e x_e$ (cm^{-1})	D_0 (e-volt)	B_e (cm^{-1})	α_e (cm^{-1})	r_e (Å)	References
$Ag^{109}Br^{81}$	$(^2\Sigma)$	247.72 H	0.6795	2.6[1]				126
$Ag^{107}Cl^{35}$	$(^2\Sigma)$	343.2 H	1.65	3.1[1]				125, 376
AgH^1	$^1\Sigma^+$	1760.0 Z	34.05*	(2.3)	6.453	0.203	1.618	86
AgH^2	$^1\Sigma^+$				3.2595	0.0732	1.6174	415
$Ag^{107}I^{127}$	$(^2\Sigma)$	206.18 H	0.4327	2.0[1]				126
AgO^{16}	$(^2\Sigma^-)$	493.2 H	4.10	(1.8)				466
$AlBr$	$^1\Sigma$	379.21 H	1.560	(4.3)	0.242	0.002	2.14	336, 492
$Al^{27}Cl^{35}$	$^1\Sigma^+$	481.3 H	1.95	$\leqq 4.72$				327, 100, A
$Al^{27}H^1$	$^1\Sigma^+$	1682.57 Z	29.145*	<3.07	6.3962	0.188	1.6461[2]	328, A
$Al^{27}H^2$	$^1\Sigma^+$	1212.02 Z	15.200*	<3.10	3.3185	0.069	1.6458[2]	328
$(Al^{27}H^1)^+$	$^2\Sigma^+$	(1610)			6.763	0.398	1.602	67
$Al^{27}I^{127}$	$^1\Sigma$	316.1 H	1.0	(3.1)				492
$Al^{27}O^{16}$	$^2\Sigma^+$	977 H	7.0	(4.2)	0.6415	0.00575	1.618	567
As_2^{75}	$^1\Sigma_g^+$	429.44 H	1.120*	3.96				401
$(As_2^{75})^+$?		314.8 H	1.25	(2.4)				401
$As^{75}N^{14}$	$^1\Sigma^+$	1067.96 H	5.36	(6.5)				645
$As^{75}O^{16}$	$^2\Pi$ [3]	966.6 H	4.92	(4.9)				378
$Au^{197}Cl^{35}$	$(^1\Sigma)$	382.8 H	1.30	(3.5)				216
$Au^{197}H^1$	$^1\Sigma^+$	2305.01 Z	43.12	(3.6)	7.2401	0.2136	1.5239	353
$Au^{197}H^2$	$^1\Sigma^+$	1634.98 Z	21.66*	(3.7)	3.6415	0.0761	1.5239	353
$BaBr$	$(^2\Sigma)$	[192] H						285
$Ba^{138}Cl^{35}$	$^2\Sigma^+$	279.2 H	0.78	(2.2)				550
BaF^{19}	$^2\Sigma^+$	468.9 H	1.79	(3.8)				371

[1] These values have been obtained from thermochemical data.

[2] These r_e values have been calculated from the true B_e values and not the effective B_e values given in the table [see (328)].

[3] Doublet splitting: 1023.7 cm^{-1}.

TABLE 36 (Cont.)

Molecule	Ground State	ω_e (cm^{-1})	$\omega_e x_e$ (cm^{-1})	D_0 (e-volt)	B_e (cm^{-1})	α_e (cm^{-1})	r_e (Å)	References
BaH[1]	$^2\Sigma^+$	1172 Z	16	<1.82	3.382	0.066	2.232	417, 270, 241, A
BaO[16]	$(^1\Sigma)$ [4]	671.48 H	2.20	(6.3)	0.3644	0.0016	1.797	476
B[11]Br[79]	$^1\Sigma$	686.3 H	3.8	(4.4)				492
B[11]Cl[35]	$^1\Sigma$	830.0 H	5.26	(5.1)				492
Be[9]Cl[35]	$^2\Sigma^+$ [4]	846.58 H	5.11	(4.3)				233a
Be[9]F[19]	$^2\Sigma^+$	1265.62 H	9.12	(5.4)	1.4877	0.01685	1.3616	367
Be[9]H[1]	$^2\Sigma^+$	2058.5 Z	35.5*	(2.2)	10.308	0.300	1.343	541
Be[9]H[2]	$^2\Sigma^+$				5.6807	0.1218	1.3427	416
(Be[9]H[1])$^+$	$^1\Sigma^+$	2221.7 Z	39.79*	(3.6)	10.7996	0.2935*	1.3123	696
(Be[9]H[2])$^+$	$^1\Sigma^+$	1647.6 Z	21.9*	(3.6)	5.9546	0.1233	1.3114	416
Be[9]O[16]	$^1\Sigma^+$	1486.87 Z	11.70	(5.7)	1.6514	0.0186	1.3308	602, 320
B[11]F[19]	$^3\Pi$ [5]	1323.64 H	9.40	(5.7)	1.4120	0.0179	1.3088	656, 552a
B[11]H[1]	$^1\Sigma^+$	(2366)	(49)	<3.49	12.018	0.413	1.2326	667, 63, A
B[11]H[2]	$^2\Sigma^+$	(1780)		<3.53	6.532	0.166	1.231	667, A
(B[11]H[1])$^+$	$(^1\Sigma)$	(2435)			[12.374]		[1.2148]	63
Bi$_2$[209]		173.7 H	0.41	3.34[6]				526
Bi[209]Br[79]		209.34 H	0.468	2.9				501
Bi[209]Cl[35]		307.66 H	0.954	(3.0)				501
Bi[209]F[19]		510.7 H	2.05	(3.9)				338
Bi[209]H[1]	$^1\Sigma$ [4]	1698.9 Z	31.6	(2.7)	5.137	0.148	1.809	287, 288
Bi[209]H[2]	$^1\Sigma$ [4]	1205.5 Z	16.05	(2.7)	2.592	0.054	1.806	287, 288
Bi[209]I[127]		163.9 H	0.31	(2.7)				501
Bi[209]O[16]	$^2\Sigma^+$ [4]	493.39 H	1.32	(5.7)				266
B[11]O[16]	$^2\Sigma^+$	1885.44 Z	11.769	(9.1)	1.7803	0.01648	1.2050	373
Br[79]Br[81]	$^1\Sigma_g^+$	323.2 Z	1.07	1.971	0.08091	0.00027	2.284	134, 179
BrCl	$(^1\Sigma^+)$	[430] H		2.26[7]				163

C_2^{12}	$^3\Pi_u$	1641.70 Z	11.71	3.6	1.6320	0.01659	1.3121	227, 316
CaBr	$(^2\Sigma)$	[280.2] H						285
$CaCl^{35}$	$(^2\Sigma)$	364.5 H	0.80	≦2.76	[0.26]		[1.9]	551, 297
$Ca^{(40)}F^{19}$	$^1\Sigma$	857.3 H	(2.5)	≧3.15	[0.3215]		[2.018]	391, 281, 297
$Ca^{(40)}H^1$	$^2\Sigma^+$	1299 Z	19.5	≧1.70	4.278	0.096	2.002	691, 269
$Ca^{(40)}H^2$	$^2\Sigma^+$				2.196	0.035	2.001	691
CaI^{127}	$(^2\Sigma)$	242.0 H	0.64	(2.1)				490a
$Ca^{(40)}O^{16}$	$^1\Sigma$ [4]	843 H	6.0	(3.6)	[0.480]		[1.75]	129
$C^{12}Cl$	$^2\Pi$ [8]	[843.6] H						70
Cd_2	$^1\Sigma_g^+$ [4]			0.087				433
CdBr	$^2\Sigma$	230.0 H	0.50	(2.5)				708
$CdCl^{35}$	$^2\Sigma^+$	330.5 H	1.2					164
CdH^1	$^2\Sigma^+$	1430.7 Z	46.3*	0.678	5.437	0.218*	1.762	658
CdH^2	$^2\Sigma^+$			0.704	2.788	0.168	1.75	658, A
$(CdH^1)^+$	$^1\Sigma^+$	1775 H	37.3	(2.0)	6.070	0.187	1.668	659
$(CdH^2)^+$	$^1\Sigma^+$	1262.5 Z	19.01	(2.0)	3.075	0.0682	1.665	734
CdI^{127}	$(^2\Sigma)$	178.5 H	0.625	(1.6)				708
CeO^{16}	[4]	865.0 H	2.99	(7.7)				693
$C^{12}H^1$	$^2\Pi_r$ [9]	2824 Z	46	3.47	14.453	0.528	1.1201	636, A
$C^{12}H^2$	$^2\Pi_r$ [9]	2073 Z	25	3.52	7.805	0.204	1.119	636, A
Cl_2^{35}	$^1\Sigma_g^+$	564.9 Z	4.0	2.481	0.2438	0.0017	1.989	200, 426
$(Cl_2^{35})^+$	$(^2\Pi)$ [4]	645.3 H	2.90	(4.4)	0.270	0.002	1.89	201
$C^{12}N^{14}$	$^2\Sigma^+$	2068.705 Z	13.144	(5.96)[10]	1.8991	0.01735	1.1721	377, 379

[4] It is not certain whether this is the ground state.

[5] This is the lowest known state; however, in all probability, it is not the ground state.

[6] From thermal data [Ko (408)].

[7] From $D_0(Br_2)$, $D_0(Cl_2)$, and the heat of formation of BrCl obtained thermochemically [Bichowsky and Rossini (44a)].

[8] Doublet splitting: 136 cm^{-1}.

[9] Coupling constant $A = 28.4$ ($\approx$ doublet splitting).

[10] Calculated with the aid of thermal data from $D(CO)$ (see footnote 11). A different value has been given by Schmid, Gerö, and Zemplén (624a).

TABLE 36 (Cont.)

Molecule	Ground State	ω_e (cm^{-1})	$\omega_e x_e$ (cm^{-1})	D_0 (e-volt)	B_e (cm^{-1})	α_e (cm^{-1})	r_e (Å)	References
$C^{12}O^{16}$	$^1\Sigma^+$	2168.2 Z	13.04*	(9.144)[11]	1.9310	0.01744	1.1284	252, 250, 314
$(C^{12}O^{16})^+$	$^2\Sigma^+$	2211.1 H	15.12	(6.5)[12]	1.978	0.0214	1.115	114, 143, A
CoBr	[4]	(310) H						490
CoCl	[4]	420.8 H	0.69	(7.9)				498
CoH^1	$^3\Phi_4$	(1890)		(6.9)	[7.151]		[1.543]	288, 289
$C^{12}P^{31}$	$^2\Sigma^+$	1239.67 H	6.86		0.79863	0.00597	1.5622	77
CrH^1								245a
CrO^{16}		898.8 H	6.5	(3.8)				265
Cs_2^{133}	$^1\Sigma_g^+$ [13]	41.990 H	0.08005*	0.45				462
$C^{12}S^{32}$	$^1\Sigma^+$	1285.1 H	6.5	(7.8)	0.8190	0.005	1.536	174
$C^{12}Se$	$^1\Sigma^+$	1053 H	8	(4)	2.709	0.057	2.494	599
$Cs^{133}H^1$	$^1\Sigma^+$	890.7 Z	12.6	(1.9)				65
$Cu^{63}Br^{79}$		314.13 H	0.865	(3.5)				591
$Cu^{63}Cl^{35}$		417.02 H	1.64	(3.3)				591
$Cu^{63}F^{19}$		619.5 H	3.79	(3.1)				591
$Cu^{63}H^1$	$^1\Sigma^+$	1940.4 Z	37.2*	(3.0)	7.938	0.249	1.463	291, 292
$Cu^{63}H^2$	$^1\Sigma^+$	1384.38 Z	19.14	(3.0)	4.0375	0.0914	1.4627	382
$Cu^{63}I^{127}$		264.83 H	0.71	(3.0)				591
CuO^{16}	$(^2\Sigma)$	([620])						474
F_2^{19}	$^1\Sigma_g^+$ [4]	406.6 H		2.8[14]			1.45[15]	689
FeCl			1.2	(4.3)				494
FeH^1					[7.8155]		[1.4761]	286
$Ga^{69}Br^{81}$	$^1\Sigma$	263.0 H	0.8	(2.7)				495
$Ga^{69}Cl^{35}$	$^1\Sigma$	365.0 H	1.1	(3.7)				495
$Ga^{69}I^{127}$	$^1\Sigma$	216.4 H	0.5	2.9				495, 561

GaO^{16}	$(^2\Sigma)$[4]	767.69 H	6.34			(2.9)		278
GdO^{16}	[16]	836 H	3.0					564
GeBr	$^2\Pi$[16]	296.6 H	0.9			(3)		386
Ge^{74}Cl^{35}	$^2\Pi$[17]	408.4 H	1.6			(3.2)		386
Ge^{74}O^{16}	$^1\Sigma$	985.7 H	4.3	0.4704	0.0029	(6.9)	1.651	387, 631a
Ge^{74}S^{32}	$(^1\Sigma)$	575.8 H	1.80			(5.6)		632
H$_2^1$	$^1\Sigma_g^+$	4405.3 Z[18]	125.325*[18]	60.872	3.0671*	4.4776	0.7414	380, 91, 662
H^{1}H^2	$^1\Sigma_g^+$	3817.1 Z[18]	94.958*[18]	45.668[19]	1.9931*[19]	4.5133	0.7413	662, 238, 91
H$_2^2$	$^1\Sigma_g^+$	3118.8 Z	64.15*	30.429	1.0492*	4.5557	0.7417	381, 91
(H$_2^1$)$^+$	$^2\Sigma_g^+$	2297	62	29.8	1.4	2.6490	1.06	96, 585
H^{1}Br	$^1\Sigma^+$	2649.67 Z	45.21	8.471	0.226	3.60[20]	1.414	563, A
(H^{1}Br)$^+$	$^2\Pi_i$[21]			[7.955]		3.3[22]	[1.459]	534, A

[11] A $D_0(CO)$ value of 6.921 e-volts [see (624)] is not yet definitely excluded but appears much less likely to be the correct one than the value given above [see (314)].

[12] From the cycle $D_0(CO^+) = D_0(CO) + I(C) - I(CO)$, taking the ionization potential I of CO to be 13.9 e-volts and $D_0(CO) = 9.144$ e-volts (see, however, footnote 11).

[13] According to Finkelnburg and Hahn (223), the analysis of the Cs$_2$ bands by Loomis and Kusch (462) used above is not correct. But they do not advance a new interpretation of the bands.

[14] This value has been obtained by a comparison of the purely continuous absorption spectrum of F$_2$ with the continuous absorption of the other halogens.

[15] From electron diffraction experiments of Brockway (127).

[16] Doublet splitting: 1150 cm^{-1}.

[17] Doublet splitting: 975 cm^{-1}.

[18] These are the data of Teal and MacWood (662), who have corrected the constants given by Jeppesen (380) by the aid of Raman data.

[19] These data have not been observed directly but have been calculated from the constants of H$_2^1$ according to the formulae for the isotope effect.

[20] From D_0(H$_2$), D_0(Br$_2$), and the heat of formation of HBr obtained thermochemically [Bichowsky and Rossini (44a)].

[21] Doublet splitting: 2653 cm^{-1}.

[22] From D_0(HBr), I(HBr) = 12.1 e-volts [Price (570)] and I(Br) = 11.8 e-volts.

TABLE 36 (Cont.)

Molecule	Ground State	ω_e (cm⁻¹)	$\omega_e x_e$ (cm⁻¹)	D_0 (e-volt)	B_e (cm⁻¹)	α_e (cm⁻¹)	r_e (Å)	References
H¹Cl³⁵	¹Σ⁺	2988.95 Z	51.65	4.431²³	10.5909	0.3019	1.2747	318, A
H²Cl³⁵	¹Σ⁺	[2090.78] Z		4.48	5.445	0.1118	1.275	280, A
(H¹Cl³⁵)+	²Πi ²⁴	2675.4 Z	53.5	4.5²⁵	9.9463	0.3183	1.3154	535, A
(H²Cl³⁵)+	²Πi ²⁴	[1863.96] Z		4.6²⁵	5.1108	0.1170	1.3161	535, A
He⁴	³Σu⁺	[1732] Z		(2.5)²⁶ᵃ	7.695	0.21	1.046	33
(He₂⁴)+	²Σu⁺ ²⁶	[1628]		(3)²⁶ᵃ	[7.09]	(0.25)	[1.09]	33, 707
H¹F¹⁹	¹Σ⁺	4141.305 Z	90.866*	6.4²⁷	20.967	0.879*	0.9166	403, A
Hg₂	¹Σg⁺	(36)		0.08			3.3²⁸	431, 198
HgBr	(²Σ)	186.25 H	0.975	(1.1)				708
HgCl³⁵	(²Σ)	292.63 H	1.62*	1.1				710
HgH¹	²Σ⁺	1387.09 Z	82.75*	0.372	5.549	0.312*	1.741	237
HgH²	²Σ⁺	995.15 Z	49.93*	0.395	2.799	0.113*	1.738	237
(HgH¹)+	¹Σ⁺	2033.87 Z	46.16*	(2.5)	6.613	0.206	1.594	335, 506
(HgH²)+	¹Σ⁺	1442.15 Z	23.24*	(2.5)	3.328	0.0736	1.594	335, 506
HgI¹²⁷	(²Σ)	125.0 H	1.0	(0.5)				709
H¹I¹²⁷	¹Σ⁺	2309.53 Z	39.73	2.75²⁹	6.551	0.183	1.604	531, A
H¹S³²	²Πi ³⁰				[9.47]		[1.35]	445a
I₂¹²⁷	¹Σg⁺	214.36 H	0.593*	1.5422	0.03736	0.00012	2.667	457, 132
I¹²⁷Br⁷⁹	¹Σ⁺	268.4 H	0.78	1.818				135
I¹²⁷Cl³⁵	¹Σ⁺	384.18 Z	1.465	2.153	0.11414	0.000502*	2.321	137, 177
In¹¹⁵Br⁸¹	¹Σ⁺	221.0 H	0.6	≦3.3				701, 627
In¹¹⁵Cl³⁵	¹Σ⁺	316.8 H	1.0	(3.1)				701
InH¹	¹Σ⁺ ⁴				[4.921]		[1.852]	271
In¹¹⁵I¹²⁷	¹Σ	177.1 H	0.4	≦2.7				701, 627
InO¹⁶	²Σ ⁴	703.09 H	3.71*	(1.3)				699

488

K_2^{39}	$^1\Sigma_g^+$	92.64 H	0.354	0.514	0.05622	0.000219	3.923	458, 464
KBr	$^1\Sigma^+$	231 H	0.75	3.96			2.94[31]	443
KCl	$^1\Sigma^+$	280 H	0.9	4.53		0.0673*	2.79[31]	443
$K^{(39)}H^1$	$^1\Sigma^+$	983.3 Z	14.40	(1.9)	3.407		2.244	334, 62
$K^{(39)}H^2$	$^1\Sigma^+$				[1.641]		[2.32]	353a
KI^{127}	$^1\Sigma^+$	212 H	0.7	3.33			3.23[31]	443
$La^{139}O^{16}$	$^2\Sigma$	811.6 H	2.23	(9)				34
Li_2^7	$^1\Sigma_g^+$	351.346 Z	2.557*	1.14	0.67293	0.00719	2.6723	463, 64
Li^7Cs^{133}	$^1\Sigma^+$	[167] H						706
Li^7H^1	$^1\Sigma^+$	1405.65 Z	23.20*	(2.5)	7.5131	0.2132*	1.5956[2]	173
Li^7H^2	$^1\Sigma^+$	1055.12 Z	13.228*	(2.5)	4.2338	0.09198*	1.5951[2]	172
LiI^{127}	$^1\Sigma^+$	450 H	1.5	3.58				443
LiK	$^1\Sigma^+$	[207] H						706
LiRb	$^1\Sigma^+$	[185] H						706
LuO^{16}	$^1\Sigma^+$	841.66 H	4.07	(5.3)				698
$Mg^{24}Br$	$(^2\Sigma)$	373.2 H	1.34	(3.2)				503
$Mg^{24}Cl^{35}$	$(^2\Sigma)$	466.0 H	2.10	(3.2)				503
$Mg^{(24)}F^{19}$	$^2\Sigma$	690.75 H	3.95	(3.7)	[0.518]	0.1668*	[1.75]	370, 392
$Mg^{(24)}H^1$	$^2\Sigma^+$	1494.9 Z	31.5	<2.50	5.818		1.731	277, 309
$Mg^{(24)}H^2$	$^2\Sigma^+$	1077.76 Z	16.09	<2.52	3.0307	0.0654	1.7302	235, A

23 From $D_0(H_2)$, $D_0(Cl_2)$, and the heat of formation of HCl obtained thermochemically [Bichowsky and Rossini (44a)].

24 Coupling constant $A = 643.3$ cm⁻¹ (≈ doublet splitting).

25 From $D_0(HCl)$, $I(HCl) = 12.9$ e-volts [Price (570)] and $I(Cl) = 13.0$ e-volts.

26 This is the lowest stable state which is not the ground state.

26a Recently Arnot and M'Ewen (68a), from electron collision experiments, have derived $D_0(He_2) \geqq 4.23$ and $D_0(He_2^+) \geqq 4.70$ e-volts.

27 From $D_0(H_2)$, $D_0(F_2)$, and the heat of formation of HF obtained thermochemically [Bichowsky and Rossini (44a)].

28 From data concerning liquid Hg.

29 From $D_0(H_2)$, $D_0(I_2)$, and the heat of formation of HI obtained thermochemically [Bichowsky and Rossini (44a)].

30 Coupling constant $A = 378.6$ cm⁻¹ (≈ doublet splitting).

31 From electron diffraction experiments of Maxwell, Hendricks, and Mosley (483).

TABLE 36 (Cont.)

Molecule	Ground State	ω_e (cm^{-1})	$\omega_e x_e$ (cm^{-1})	D_0 (e-volt)	B_e (cm^{-1})	α_e (cm^{-1})	r_e (Å)	References
$(Mg^{(24)}H^1)^+$	$^1\Sigma^+$	1695.3 Z	30.2*	(2.1)	6.390	0.190	1.652	275
$(Mg^{(24)}H^2)^+$	$^1\Sigma^+$	1226.6 Z	16.30*	(2.1)	3.321	0.064*	1.653	394
MgI^{127}	$(^2\Sigma)$ [4]	[312] H						503
MgO^{16}	$(^2\Sigma)$	665.74 H	4.41	(3.1)				475
MnH^1		[1580] H						559
MnO^{16}	[4]	840.70 H	4.89	(4.4)				630
N_2^{14}	$^1\Sigma_g^+$	2359.61 H	14.445	7.384	2.007	0.018	1.095	111, 697, 147
$(N_2^{14})^+$	$^2\Sigma_g^+$	2207.19 Z	16.136*	6.351[32]	1.931	0.020	1.117	169, 130, A
Na_2^{23}	$^1\Sigma_g^+$	159.23 H	0.726*	0.763	0.15471	0.00079*	3.079	465, 467
$Na^{23}Br$	$^1\Sigma^+$	315 H	1.15	3.85			2.64[31]	443
$Na^{23}Cl$	$^1\Sigma^+$	380 H	1.0	4.25			2.51[31]	443
$Na^{23}Cs^{133}$	$^1\Sigma^+$	([97]) H						706
$Na^{23}H^1$	$^1\Sigma^+$	1170.8 Z	18.9	(2.2)	4.9012	0.1353	1.8875	333, 543
$Na^{23}H^2$	$^1\Sigma^+$	[826.10] Z		(2.2)	2.5575	0.0520	1.8867	543
$Na^{23}I^{127}$	$^1\Sigma^+$	286 H	0.75	3.16			2.90[31]	443
$Na^{23}K$	$^1\Sigma^+$	123.29 H	0.400	0.63				459
$Na^{23}Rb$	$^1\Sigma^+$	106.64 H	0.455	(0.8)				438
$N^{14}Br^{81}$	[4]	693 H	5.0					200a
$N^{14}H^1$	$^3\Sigma^-$	(3300)		(3.4)	16.65	0.64	1.038	240, 400a
NiBr	$^2\Pi$ [33] [4]	(350) H		(7.3)				490
NiCl	$^2\Delta_{3/2}$	418.1 H	0.74					498
NiH^1	[34]	[1926.6] Z			7.823	0.248	1.475	288
$N^{14}O^{16}$	$^2\Pi_r$ [36]	1906.52 Z	14.504	5.29[35]	1.709	0.0183	1.150	369, 618, 518, A
$(N^{14}O^{16})^+$					[1.961]		[1.073]	192, 365, A
$N^{14}S^{32}$	$^2\Pi_r$ [37]	1220.0 H	7.75	(5.9)				226

490

Molecule	State	ω_e	$\omega_e x_e$	D_0 (e-volts)	B_e	α_e	r_e	References
O_2^{16}	$^3\Sigma_g^-$ [38]	1580.36 Z	12.073*	5.082	1.4456	0.0158	1.2076	175, 406
$(O_2^{16})^+$	$^2\Pi_g$ [39]	1876.4 H	16.53	6.48	1.6722	0.01984	1.1228	204, 524, 123
$O^{16}H^1$	$^2\Pi_i$ [39]	3727.95 Z	78.15*	4.3[40]	18.862	0.693	0.9710	661, A
$O^{16}H^2$	$^2\Pi_i$	[2955] Z		4.3[40]	10.028	0.325	0.969	355
$(O^{16}H^1)^+$	$^3\Sigma^-$				16.793	0.732	1.0290	460
P_2^{31}	$^1\Sigma_g^+$	780.43 H	2.804*	5.033[41]	0.3046	0.00165*	1.890	69, 311, A
Pb_2		256.5 H	2.96	(0.7)				634
$PbBr^{79}$		207.5 H	0.50	(2.7)				502
$PbCl^{35}$		303.9 H	0.88	(3.2)				502, 592
PbF^{19}		507.2 H	2.31	(3.4)				502, 592
PbH^1	$^2\Pi$ [42]	1565.2 Z	30.3	$\leqq 2.57$	4.972	0.145	1.839	694
$Pb^{206}O^{16}$	$^2\Sigma$	721.8 H	3.70	(4.3)	0.3073	0.0019	1.923	337, 156
$Pb^{208}S^{32}$	$^1\Sigma$	428.14 H	1.201	(5)	0.10605	0.00087	2.395	595, 83
PbSe	$(^1\Sigma)$	277.78 H	0.452	(5)				688
PbTe	$(^1\Sigma)$	211.79 H	0.119	(12)				688
$P^{31}H^1$	$^3\Sigma^-$	(2380)			[8.411]		[1.433]	557
$P^{31}H^2$	$^3\Sigma^-$							356

32 From $D_0(N_2)$, $I(N)$, and $I(N_2)$ (see Table 37).

33 Doublet splitting: 484 cm⁻¹.

34 Doublet splitting: 120.5 cm⁻¹.

35 From $D_0(N_2)$, $D_0(O_2)$, and the heat of formation of NO obtained thermochemically [Bichowsky and Rossini (44a)].

36 This is probably not the ground state.

37 Doublet splitting: 223 cm⁻¹.

38 Doublet splitting: 198 cm⁻¹.

39 Coupling constant $A = 140$ cm⁻¹ ($\approx$ doublet splitting).

40 Mean of the value obtained by extrapolation of the vibrational quanta and the value obtained from the separation energy of an H atom from H_2O [see (590)] combined with the atomic heat of formation of H_2O (see p. 520).

41 On the basis of the data at present available the alternative value 4.120 e-volts is not entirely excluded.

42 Doublet splitting: 8266 cm⁻¹. The constants given refer to the lower doublet component.

TABLE 36 (Cont.)

Molecule	Ground State	ω_e (cm⁻¹)	$\omega_e x_e$ (cm⁻¹)	D_0 (e-volt)	B_e (cm⁻¹)	α_e (cm⁻¹)	r_e (Å)	References
$P^{31}N^{14}$	$^1\Sigma^+$	1337.24 Z	6.983	(6.3)	0.7862	0.00557	1.491	176
$P^{31}O^{16}$	$^2\Pi_r$ 43	1230.64 H	6.52	(6.2)	0.7629	0.0055	1.447	631, 605, 267
$Pr^{141}O^{16}$	4	818.9 H	1.20					693
Rb_2^{85}	$^1\Sigma_g^+$	56.78 H	0.0785*	0.49				668
$RbCs^{133}$	$^1\Sigma^+$	49.41 H						438
RbH^1	$^1\Sigma^+$	936	14		3.019	0.07	2.368	246
S_2^{32}	$^3\Sigma_g^-$	725.8 H	2.85	≤3.6	0.296	0.0016	1.89	548, 545, A
Sb_2	$(^1\Sigma)$	269.85 H	0.567	(3.7)				66, 528a
$SbBi^{209}$	$(^1\Sigma)$	220.0 H	0.50	(3.0)				526
$SbCl$		488 H	2.9					341
SbF^{19}	$(^3\Pi)$	614.0 H	2.67	(4.0)				594, 340a
SbN^{14}	$(^1\Sigma)$	[925] H						170
SbO^{16}		824.3 H	5.9	(3.5)				507
$Sc^{45}O^{16}$	$^2\Sigma$	971.55 H	3.95	(7)				34
Se_2^{80}	$(^1\Sigma_g^+)$	391.77 H	1.06	2.7	0.0907	0.00027	2.16	542, 71, 548, 598
SeO^{16}		908.9 H	4.8	(5)				115
$SiBr$	$^2\Pi$ 44	425.4 H	1.5	(3.7)				385
$Si^{28}Cl^{35}$	$^2\Pi$ 45	535.4 H	2.20	(4.2)				384
$Si^{(28)}F^{19}$	$^2\Pi$ 46	856.7 H	4.7	(4.8)	[0.5795]		[1.603]	72, 210
$Si^{(28)}H^1$	$^2\Pi_r$ 47	(2080)			7.496	0.213	1.521	593
$Si^{(28)}H^2$	$^2\Pi_r$ 47				[3.842]		[1.528]	593
$Si^{28}N^{14}$	$^2\Sigma^+$	1151.680 Z	6.5600	(6.2)	0.7310	0.00567	1.572	372
$Si^{28}O^{16}$	$^1\Sigma^+$	1242.03 Z	6.047*	(7.4)	0.7263	0.00494	1.510	615

Molecule	State	ω_e	$\omega_e x_e$	D (e-volts)	B_e	α_e	r_e	References
$Si^{28}S^{32}$	$^1\Sigma^+$	749.5 H	2.56	(6.2)				80
SiSe	$(^1\Sigma)$	580.0 H	1.78*	(5.8)				79
$Si^{28}Te$	$(^1\Sigma)$	480.4 H	1.16*	(5.5)				79
SnBr	$^2\Pi$ [48]	247.7 H	0.62	(3.0)				385
$SnCl^{35}$	$^2\Pi$ [49]	352.4 H	1.1	(3.5)				217, 383
SnF^{19}	$^2\Pi$ [50]	585.3 H	2.67	(3.9)				375
SnH	$^2\Pi$ [51]				[5.31]			699a
SnO^{16}	$^1\Sigma$	822.4 H	3.73	(5.7)	0.3540	0.00450	1.838	384a, 478
SnS^{32}	$(^1\Sigma)$	488.25 H	1.47	(5.0)	[0.157]		[2.06]	633
SnSe	$(^1\Sigma)$	333.16 H	1.247	(2.7)				688
$S^{32}O^{16}$	$^3\Sigma^-$	1123.73 Z	6.116	4.002 [52]	0.70894	0.00562	1.4935	482, A
SrBr	$^2\Sigma$	[212] H	0.71	(3.9)				285
$SrCl^{35}$	$(^2\Sigma)$	301.1 H	(2.2)	(1.2)				551, 499
SrF^{19}	$^2\Sigma^+$	500.1 H		(1.2)				391, 371
SrH^1	$^2\Sigma^+$	1206.2 Z	17.0	(2.2)	3.6751	0.0814	2.1457	695, 499
SrH^2					1.8609	0.0292	2.1451	695
SrI^{127}		173.9 H	0.42					490a
SrO^{16}	$^1\Sigma$ [4]	633.14 H	2.35	(5.2)	0.3738	0.00085	1.826	479

43 Doublet splitting: 221.0 cm⁻¹.
44 Doublet splitting: 418 cm⁻¹.
45 Doublet splitting: 207.9 cm⁻¹.
46 Doublet splitting: 160.83 cm⁻¹.
47 Coupling constant $A = 141.9$ cm⁻¹ (≈ doublet splitting).
48 Doublet splitting: 2467 cm⁻¹.
49 Doublet splitting: 2360 cm⁻¹.
50 Doublet splitting: 2317.3 cm⁻¹.
51 Coupling constant $A = 2182.7$ cm⁻¹ (≈ doublet splitting).
52 The value $D(SO) = 5.148$ is also compatible with the spectroscopic data [Martin (482)]. But the value given above seems more likely to be correct. It is based on the assumption that at the predissociation limit at 5.148 e-volts a dissociation into $S(^1D) + O(^3P)$ takes place.

TABLE 36 (*Cont.*)

Molecule	Ground State	ω_e (cm^{-1})	$\omega_e x_e$ (cm^{-1})	D_0 (e-volt)	B_e (cm^{-1})	α_e (cm^{-1})	r_e (Å)	References
Te$_2$	($^3\Sigma$)	251.5 H	1.0	2.3			2.59[53]	544, 262, 484
TeO^{16}		796.1 H	3.40	(5.7)				637
Ti^{48}Cl^{35}	^{4}	456.4 H	6.3	(1.0)				500
Ti$^{(48)}$O^{16}	$^3\Pi_n$ [54]	1008.12 H	4.519	(6.9)	0.5355	0.0031	1.620	155, 139
TlBr^{81}	($^1\Sigma$)	192.5 H	0.32	3.189				146
TlCl^{35}	$^1\Sigma$	287.47 H	1.24	3.797				146, 340
TlF^{19}	$^1\Sigma$	475.00 H	1.89	<4.72				339
TlH^1	($^1\Sigma+$)	1390.7 Z	22.7	(2.6)	4.806	0.154*	1.870	273
TlI^{127}	($^1\Sigma$)	[150]		$\leqq$2.6				146
V^{51}O^{16}	($^2\Delta$) ^{4}	1012.7 H	4.9	(6.4)	0.3876	0.0024	1.890	477
Y^{89}O^{16}	($^2\Sigma$)	855.1 H	2.49	(9)				389
ZnCl^{35}	$^2\Sigma$	390.5 H	1.55	(3.0)	6.6794	0.2500*	1.5947	164
ZnH^1	$^2\Sigma+$	1607.60 Z	55.135*	0.85	[3.3497]		[1.605]	652
ZnH^2	$^2\Sigma+$							236
(ZnH^1)+	$^1\Sigma+$	1916 Z	39*	(2.5)	7.41	0.25	1.51	84
(ZnH^2)+	$^1\Sigma+$	1364.8 Z	19.8	(2.5)	3.767	0.107	1.513	242, A
ZnI^{127}	^{4}	223.4 H	0.75	(2.0)				708
Zr^{90}O^{16}	$^3\Pi$ [55]	936.6 H	3.45	(7.8)	(0.619)[56]	(0.007)	(1.416)	470, 471

[53] From electron diffraction experiments by Maxwell and Mosley (484).

[54] Coupling constant $A = 100$ cm^{-1}.

[55] The three triplet components have the energies 0, 292.1, 605.5 cm^{-1}.

[56] This B_e value taken from (471) is very probably incorrect, since the r_e value derived from it is much too small, for example, compared to that of TiO.

494

scopic values.[1]   However, where complete measurements are
available, the accuracy of the latter values is generally very
much greater.

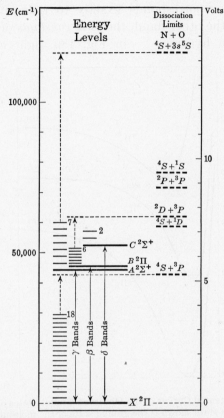

Fig. 175.   Energy Level Diagram of the NO Molecule. See the remarks
for Fig. 173.   A further state $D\,^2\Sigma^+$ is given by earlier authors.   It is assumed
here that it is really a continuation of the $A\,^2\Sigma^+$ state [see Herzberg and
Mundie (317)].

An interesting regularity is found for the *internuclear
distances of the hydrides* in the ground state when they are
plotted, as was first done by Mecke (488), against the atomic

[1] There is one case, that of Te$_2$, in which a considerable deviation occurred
[see Maxwell and Mosley (484)].   This is, however, undoubtedly due to the
fact that the spectroscopic analysis was based on insufficient data.

number (∘ in Fig. 180, heavy curve).   We can see that the r_e values in every period of the periodic system fall off regularly and then rise suddenly in going over to the next period. This behavior corresponds exactly to that of the atomic radius.   On the other hand, the *force constants* of the ground states of the hydrides (× in Fig. 180, light curve) show

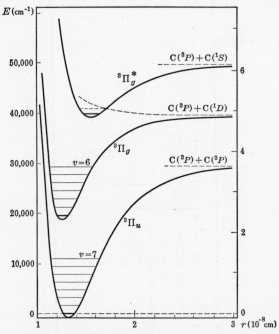

Fig. 176.   Potential Curves of the Observed Triplet States of the C₂ Mole-cule.   The lowest state shown is the ground state of the molecule. In addition to the triplet states shown, two ¹Σ states and two ¹Π states have been observed [see (189 and (514)]; but their relative positions are not known. Therefore they have not been included in the diagram.

the opposite behavior, a regular increase in a period.   The internuclear distances and force constants of the oxides and halides of the elements, so far as they are known, exhibit a similar behavior.

On the basis of our earlier discussions, it is clear that, the stronger the binding, the smaller is the internuclear distance in a molecular state and the greater is the force constant.

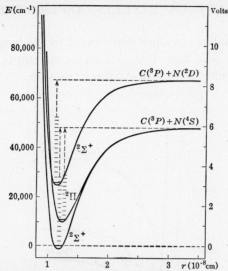

Fig. 177. Potential Curves of the Observed Electronic States of the CN Molecule. The magnitude of the heat of dissociation is not yet completely certain. If Schmid and Gerö's (624) low value for $D_0(CO)$ should turn out to be correct, a $D_0(CN)$ value of 3.74 volts would follow and the asymptotes in the figure would have to be altered correspondingly.

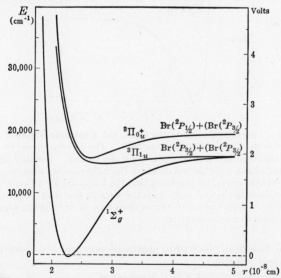

Fig. 178. Potential Curves of the Observed Electronic States of the Br$_2$ Molecule. The vibrational levels lie so close together that they cannot be drawn separately to the scale of the figure. In addition to the states shown, the unstable part of a $^1\Pi_u$ state has been observed by means of a continuous absorption [Bayliss (82); see also Mulliken (519b)].

497

Thus the smaller r_e values correspond to the larger k_e and ω_e values (see also Fig. 180). Various attempts have been made to develop a quantitative relationship.

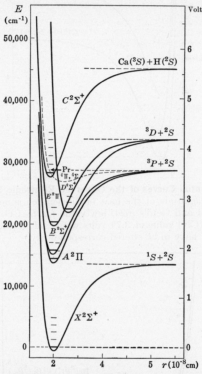

Fig. 179. Potential Curves of the Observed Electronic States of the CaH Molecule after the Data of Grundström (269). The correlation of the observed states with the dissociation products is not quite certain. Possibly all the dissociation limits have to be shifted down by the difference between ^3D and ^3P of Ca. It should, however, be remarked that the two pairs of $^2\Sigma^+$ and $^2\Pi$ terms, according to Table 26, cannot come from the same atomic states, as Grundström assumes. The broken-line curve corresponds to a $^4\Pi$ or $^4\Sigma$ term, which brings about the observed predissociation.

For the different electronic states of *one and the same molecule* the empirical relation

$$r_e{}^2\omega_e = \text{constant} \qquad (\text{VIII, 1})$$

holds fairly well [Birge (102) and Mecke (487)], and from it, if r_e is known for one state of a molecule, the r_e values for the other states can be derived approximately if only their ω_e values are known.

The r_e and ω_e values of the electronic states of *different molecules* are represented approximately by a formula first given by Morse (504) and later improved by Clark (157):

$$r_e{}^3\omega_e\sqrt{n} = C. \qquad\qquad \text{(VIII, 2)}$$

Here n is the number of electrons outside the closed atomic shells, and C is a constant that is the same for molecules with the same closed atomic shells (for example, for molecules having only closed K shells, $C = 9550$; if the K shell is closed in one atom and the

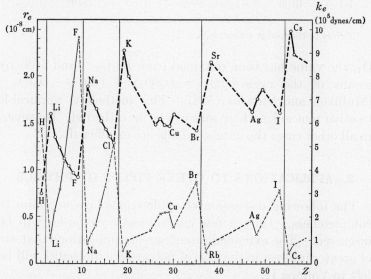

Fig. 180.   **Internuclear Distances and Force Constants of the Hydrides as Functions of the Atomic Number.**   The heavy curve gives the internuclear distances (left scale of ordinates), and the thin curve gives the force constants (right ordinate scale).   The parts of the curves for which points are lacking are given by broken lines.   The vertical lines indicate the periods in the periodic system.   The few hydrides observed above $Z = 60$ have been omitted.

L shell in the other, $C = 12,850$, if ω_e is in cm^{-1} and r_e is in Ångström units).   Other formulae have been given by Badger (76) and Allen and Longair (61).   It should be remarked that up to the present time there is no theoretical basis for these formulae and that they are by no means exactly fulfilled.

The *ionization potentials* of diatomic molecules thus far derived spectroscopically are given in Table 37.   The method of determination is indicated in each case in the table.   For

TABLE 37

SPECTROSCOPICALLY DETERMINED IONIZATION POTENTIALS
OF DIATOMIC MOLECULES

Molecule	I (volts)	Determined from	References
H_2	15.427	Preionization (Rydberg series)	(94), (47)
He_2*	4.253	Rydberg series	(33)
N_2	15.581	Rydberg series	(518), (733), (722)
O_2	12.2	Cycle	(524)
HI	10.38	Rydberg series	(570)

* Refers to the lowest stable state $2\,^3\Sigma_g{}^+$.

O_2, the value has been obtained from $D_0(O_2{}^+)$ and $I(O)$ by means of the cycle $I(O_2) = D_0(O_2) + I(O) - D_0(O_2{}^+)$ [Mulliken and Stevens (524)]. This method is applicable to other molecules whose ions can be investigated. However, in all other cases the data available are insufficient.

2. APPLICATIONS TO OTHER FIELDS OF PHYSICS

The following discussion of applications lays no claim to completeness. Only a few characteristic examples will be discussed. The extended discussion of applications that are of greater interest in the case of polyatomic molecules will be left to Volume II.

Nuclear physics. In Chapters III and V the relation between *nuclear spin* as well as *nuclear statistics* and the observed intensity alternation in band spectra has been treated in detail. The nuclear spin values and statistics determined by band spectra are collected in Table 38. The nuclear spin can also be obtained by the investigation of hyperfine structure in atomic spectra (see A.A., Chapter V). It should, however, be noted that the unambiguous establishment of a spin $I = 0$ by hyperfine-structure investigations (other than by band spectra) is practically impossible, since the apparent absence of a hyperfine-structure splitting may also be due to a very small magnetic moment of the

TABLE 38

NUCLEAR SPIN VALUES AND NUCLEAR STATISTICS OBTAINED
FROM BAND SPECTRA

Nucleus	I	Statistics	References
H^1	$\frac{1}{2}$ (S)	Fermi	(346), (397), (578)
D^2	1 (S)	Bose	(525)
He^4	0	Bose	(703), (33)
Li^7	$\frac{3}{2}$ (H)	Fermi	(282)
C^{12}	0	Bose	(511)
N^{14}	1	Bose	(549), (294), (579)
N^{15}	$\frac{1}{2}$	Fermi	(424), (720a)
O^{16}	0	Bose	(510), (511)
F^{19}	$\frac{1}{2}$	?	(243), (51)
Na^{23}	$\frac{3}{2}$ (S)(H)	Fermi	(388)
P^{31}	$\frac{1}{2}$	Fermi	(368), (311)
S^{32}	0	Bose ?	(545)
Cl^{35}	$\frac{5}{2}$ (H)	Fermi	(199), (511)
K^{39}	$> \frac{1}{2}$ (S)(H)	Fermi	(468), (458)
Se^{80}	0	Bose ?	(725), (542)
$Br^{79, 81}$	>0 (H)	Fermi	(134)
I^{127}	$\frac{5}{2}$ (H)	Fermi	(655)

(S) means confirmed by Stern-Gerlach experiment.
(H) means confirmed by hyperfine-structure investigations.

atomic nucleus. For example, the atomic spectrum of
nitrogen shows no noticeable hyperfine structure, whereas
band spectra show definitely that the nuclear spin I is equal
to 1 (see p. 229).   However, in other cases, in which both
methods yield a nuclear spin $I \neq 0$, there is a good agreement (see Table 38).   The nuclear statistics cannot be
deduced at all from hyperfine-structure investigations.
Apart from band spectra, nuclear statistics can be derived
only by means of difficult scattering measurements, which
have thus far been performed only for H and He.

Table 38 shows, as a result of the band-spectroscopic investigations of intensity alternation, that nuclei with even mass numbers,
such as D^2, He^4, C^{12}, N^{14}, O^{16}, and so on, follow Bose statistics,
while, on the other hand, nuclei with odd mass numbers, such as
H^1, Li^7, Na^{23}, and so on, follow Fermi statistics.   To this is related
the rule that the nuclear spin is integral for even mass number and

half integral for odd mass number (see Table 38). The fact that these two rules hold not only for nuclei with even atomic numbers but also for those with odd (D^2 and N^{14}) has become one of the essential reasons for rejecting the picture of the atomic nucleus consisting of electrons and protons and accepting the model of the *nucleus consisting of protons and neutrons* [see, for example, Rasetti (28) and Bethe and Bacher (88)].

Paramagnetism. Those gases whose molecules have a permanent magnetic moment in the ground state show a paramagnetism that depends on the temperature T according to Curie's law

$$\kappa = \frac{N\bar{\mu}^2}{3kT}. \qquad \text{(VIII, 3)}$$

Here κ is the *paramagnetic susceptibility*, N is the number of molecules per cubic centimeter, and $\bar{\mu}$ is the average magnetic moment of the atom or molecule in question (see also A.A., p. 205). For diatomic molecules, as we have already seen (Chapter V, section 5), the average magnetic moment of the molecule is different for different J values, and therefore, strictly speaking, we should average over the different states. However, it may be shown [see Van Vleck (45)] that, if the multiplet splitting is large compared to kT, we obtain a very good approximation if we simply substitute for $\bar{\mu}$ in (VIII, 3) the magnetic moment along the line joining the nuclei (see p. 327):

$$\bar{\mu} = (\Lambda + 2\Sigma)\mu_0. \qquad \text{(VIII, 4)}$$

If, on the other hand, the multiplet splitting is small compared to kT, which is always the case in Hund's case (b), for example, we have simply to sum the contributions of the magnetic moment caused by the spin and the orbital motion [see also Nordheim (532)]; that is, we have to put

$$\bar{\mu}^2 = [\Lambda^2 + 4S(S + 1)]\mu_0^2. \qquad \text{(VIII, 5)}$$

Most chemically stable diatomic molecules have a $^1\Sigma$ state as ground state (see Table 36) and as a result have no magnetic moment; they are diamagnetic. Only the molecules O_2 and NO (and possibly S_2 and Se_2) have a ground state different from $^1\Sigma$ and are therefore paramagnetic.

The ground state of O_2 is $^3\Sigma$; that is, $S = 1$, and therefore, according to (VIII, 5), $\bar{\mu}^2 = 8\mu_0^2$ has to be substituted in (VIII, 3), which gives a susceptibility agreeing very well with the observed value.

The ground state of NO is a $^2\Pi$ state, whose splitting is 120.5 cm^{-1} and for which the $^2\Pi_{\frac{1}{2}}$ component lies lowest. Since at room temperature the doublet splitting is of the order of magnitude of kT, neither of the above approximate formulae (VIII, 4 and 5) holds. On the other hand, at low temperatures, when practically all the molecules are in the $^2\Pi_{\frac{1}{2}}$ state, the magnetic moment and therefore also the paramagnetic susceptibility are zero, since $\Lambda + 2\Sigma = 0$ (see p. 327). At higher temperatures, when the multiplet splitting is small compared to kT, the $^2\Pi_{\frac{3}{2}}$ term, whose magnetic moment is not zero, is also fully excited, and, according to (VIII, 5), $\bar{\mu}^2 = 4\mu_0^2$ has to be substituted in (VIII, 3)—that is, $\kappa = N \cdot 4\mu_0^2/3kT$. The variation of the susceptibility between the two limiting values 0 and $N \cdot 4\mu_0^2/3kT$ for intermediate temperatures has been calculated in detail by Van Vleck (45). The agreement with experiment is very satisfactory [Scherrer and Stössel (616) and (654)].

Collision processes. In the *excitation of atoms by collisions with other atoms or ions* a diatomic molecule (quasi molecule) is momentarily formed. It is therefore clear that the application of our knowledge of diatomic molecules can lead to a deeper understanding of these collision processes.

Let us consider the collision of two atoms in the ground state (Fig. 181). In general, the atoms remain on the same potential curve α while they approach each other and then separate again. However, if this potential curve crosses a potential curve α', leading to one normal and one excited atom, a transition (similar to predissociation; see Chapter VII, section 2) can take place such that after the collision one of the atoms is excited.

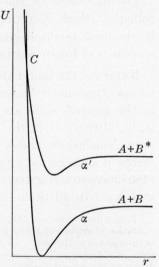

Fig. 181. Potential Curves for the Excitation of Atoms by Collision with Other Atoms.

But it can be seen that in the example shown in the figure the point of intersection can be reached and therefore a transition can take place only when the kinetic energy with which the two atoms (A and B) collide is considerably greater than the excitation energy of the atom B. As a result of the interaction of the two potential curves (see p. 319 f.) and the overlapping of the eigenfunctions (tunnel effect), a transition may take place somewhat below the point of intersection of the two potential curves. The collision yield depends on the radiationless transition probability.

On the basis of such considerations, Weizel and Beeck (705) have discussed the experimental observations on the excitation and ionization of the inert gases by alkali ions [see also Rice (584), Jabłoński (359), and Stueckelberg (657)].[2] Other collision processes have already been dealt with in the discussion of continuous spectra (see p. 416 f.) and of induced predissociation (see p. 460).

The discussion of the exchange of vibrational energy by collision, which is of importance in sound propagation and in chemical reaction kinetics, will be left until Volume II, since it is of importance mainly for polyatomic molecules.

Nature of the liquid and the solid state.   When molecules whose structure is known from spectroscopic investigations in the gaseous state are investigated in the liquid or solid state, alterations in the spectra appear from which we can draw conclusions about the nature and properties of these states of aggregation. For example, McLennan and McLeod (485) have investigated the Raman spectra of liquid H_2, O_2, and N_2. In all three cases the vibrational bands observed

---

[2] It may be pointed out that recent findings of Hanle (279a) concerning the excitation of argon and He by hydrogen and deuterium positive rays may also be interpreted in this way. He found that excitation by D positive rays takes place at a higher kinetic energy but lower velocity than by H positive rays. Although the potential curves and thus the energy of the point of intersection in Fig. 181 are essentially the same for H and D the penetration of the narrow potential hill takes place at a lower energy for H than for D because of the smaller mass. For equal kinetic energy the velocity of D is, of course, to the velocity of H as 1 is to $\sqrt{2}$. Since the necessary kinetic energy of D is larger than that of H, the velocities have a ratio closer to one, but the velocity of D is still the smaller.

for the corresponding gas appear in the liquid with only a slight shift, in agreement with the assumption that in these liquids different molecules are bound to one another only very weakly, so that the binding within a molecule is not appreciably altered.   In H_2, the rotational lines also appear unaltered, showing that in the liquid the H_2 molecule can carry out *quantized rotations*.   Indications of quantized rotations have also been found for solid HCl [(320a) and (635a)].   However, for most other molecules the intermolecular forces appear to be sufficiently great so that the rotation is no longer quantized independently of the other motions.   By investigating the gas under consideration at different pressures, the transition from sharp quantization to irregular motion can be followed.

It is worthy of note that for O_2 even the electronic band spectra in the liquid and solid states are only very slightly shifted compared to those in the gaseous state.   However, the rotational structure of the bands is completely washed out, and deviations from the relative intensities of the bands in the gaseous state appear.   In addition, some new bands have been observed, but we cannot go into their interpretation here [see, for example, Ellis and Kneser (202), Salow and Steiner (612), and Prikhotko (572)].

Recently, the infrared and Raman spectra of molecules such as HCl have been widely investigated in different solutions.   There appears to be a relation between the shift of the bands and the polarity of the solvent [see, for example, (563a), (707a), and (439b)].

Determination of high temperatures.   As already mentioned in Chapter IV, the intensity distribution in a band can be used for determining the temperature.   The maximum of the intensity in a branch shifts toward higher J values with increasing temperature.   Thus from the position of the maximum the temperature of the light source or of the absorption vessel can be determined.   More accurate and reliable values are obtained when the whole intensity distribution is measured and the values of $\log I/(J' + J'' + 1)$ plotted against $J(J + 1)$ (see Fig. 87). According to (IV, 59) an accurate value for the temperature can be obtained from the slope of the straight line obtained. Another method has recently been used by Knauss and McCay (407). They determine for which value of J (or K) the intensity in two overlapping branches of a band (for instance, a P and an R branch) is the same for equal or nearly equal wave number. This position shifts to larger J (or K) values with increasing temperature. This method has the advantage of not requiring precise intensity measurements but is limited to bands for which the head is not too far from the zero line.

The band-spectroscopic methods for the determination of temperature are naturally of particular importance when the usual methods cannot be used—for example, in the determination of the *temperature of the electric arc*. Lochte-Holtgreven and Maecker (450) have recently determined the temperature of the free-burning carbon arc in this way, using the CN band 3883 Å and allowing for all sources of error, such as self-absorption, self-reversal, and so on. They found that the temperature in the axis of the arc is 7600° K. This method is, of course, applicable to many other cases, such as flames, explosions, and the like. It is also of great importance in astrophysics (see below).

Calculation of quantities important in thermodynamics. The heat content of a gas is composed of the energies of translation, rotation, and vibration of the molecules. While, in classical theory, the heat content of a perfect gas is strictly proportional to the absolute temperature, according to quantum theory this is the case only for sufficiently high temperatures.

The translational part of the internal energy of a gas can always be calculated separately and is given by the familiar expression

$$E_t = \tfrac{3}{2}NkT, \tag{VIII, 6}$$

where N is the Avogadro number and k is the Boltzmann constant. This formula holds to an extremely good approximation even if wave mechanics is applied to the translational motion of the molecules.

For the *contribution of the inner degrees of freedom* (rotation and vibration) we have quite generally

$$E_i = N_1\varepsilon_1 + N_2\varepsilon_2 + N_3\varepsilon_3 + \cdots, \qquad \text{(VIII, 7)}$$

where ε_1, ε_2, $\cdots$ are the energies of the various molecular states above the lowest state and N_1, N_2, $\cdots$ are the corresponding numbers of molecules in them. The summation is to extend over all molecular states for which $N_n \neq 0$. As in the previous equation (III, 112), the numbers N_n are given by

$$N_n = N \frac{g_n e^{-\varepsilon_n/kT}}{1 + g_1 e^{-\varepsilon_1/kT} + g_2 e^{-\varepsilon_2/kT} + g_3 e^{-\varepsilon_3/kT} + \cdots}, \qquad \text{(VIII, 8)}$$

where g_n is the statistical weight of the state n. The sum in the denominator of (VIII, 8) is the *state sum* (or *partition function*):

$$Q = 1 + g_1 e^{-\varepsilon_1/kT} + g_2 e^{-\varepsilon_2/kT} + g_3 e^{-\varepsilon_3/kT} + \cdots. \quad \text{(VIII, 9)}$$

Using this, (VIII, 7) may also be written

$$E_i = \frac{N \, \Sigma g_n \varepsilon_n e^{-\varepsilon_n/kT}}{Q} = \frac{NkT^2 \dfrac{dQ}{dT}}{Q} = NkT^2 \frac{d}{dT} (\log Q).$$

Thus we have for the *total internal energy of one mol*

$$E = E_t + E_i = \frac{3}{2} NkT + NkT^2 \frac{d(\log Q)}{dT}. \qquad \text{(VIII, 10)}$$

The *molal heat capacity* (for constant volume) is the rate of change of the internal energy with temperature. From (VIII, 10) we obtain

$$C_v = \frac{dE}{dT} = \frac{3}{2} Nk + Nk \frac{d}{dT}\left(T^2 \frac{d \log Q}{dT}\right). \qquad \text{(VIII, 11)}$$

From the formulae (VIII, 10 and 11) it is seen that the internal energy and the heat capacity can be *predicted* for a molecular gas if the state sum Q (for the inner degrees of freedom) is known. This state sum, however, can be calculated according to (VIII, 9) if the energy levels of the molecules and their statistical weights have been derived from the spectrum. The above formulae are of quite general validity. In some cases they may be simplified considerably by the use of certain approximations [see Giauque (252a), Johnston and Davis (392a), Gordon and Barnes (264a), and Kassel (398)].

The values for the heat capacity thus obtained from band-spectroscopic data agree extremely well with those observed by direct thermal measurements, as far as such measurements are available. In fact, it seems that the theory can be trusted to such an extent that further direct measurements, which are very difficult, particularly at high temperatures, are hardly necessary for diatomic molecules [see Eucken and Mücke (207)]. In addition, the spectroscopic data allow one to predict the heat capacity even for chemically unstable molecules, such as OH, CH, and others, for which it cannot be directly measured at all.

It should be noted that in the summation (VIII, 9) *all* the low-lying states of a molecule must be included; that is, if there are low-lying excited *electronic* states, they have also to be included. Thus, in the case of O_2, agreement with experiment was obtained [Lewis and von Elbe (444)] only after allowance was made for the two low-lying states $^1\Delta$ and $^1\Sigma$ (see p. 370). In fact, the $^1\Delta$ state was detected in this way before it was observed spectroscopically.

In the calculation of heat content and heat capacity for *homonuclear molecules with non-zero nuclear spin* the fact has to be taken into consideration, as was first pointed out by Dennison (181), that there are two almost noninterconvertible modifications, of which one has only the even and the other only the odd rotational levels [see Chapter III, section 2(f)]. Because of the extreme slowness of the inter-conversion it is not sufficient simply to substitute the appropriate statistical weights in (VIII, 9) [for H_2, $3(2J + 1)$ for the odd levels], but we have to calculate the heat capacity separately for each modification and then obtain the heat capacity for the *mixture* according to the abundance ratio of the two modifications [for H_2, $C_v = \frac{3}{4}C_v$ (ortho) $+ \frac{1}{4}C_v$ (para)]. The variation of the heat capacity with temperature is quite different for the two modifications and different again for the mixture. This difference supplies a convenient way of distinguishing between the modifications if a separation has been effected (see p. 149). However, the difference in heat capacity of the two modifications as well as the difference between the heat capacity of the mixture and that calculated from (VIII, 9) becomes noticeable only at temperatures that are so low that kT and B are of the same order. In consequence of this the difference has been observed up to now only for H_2 and D_2, for which B is relatively large [see Urey and Teal (677)].

Closely connected with the calculation of heat capacities is the calculation of the *entropy* S and the *free energy* F. According to statistical mechanics, we have (assuming an ideal gas) for the entropy

$$S = S_t + Nk \log Q + NkT \frac{d \log Q}{dT} , \qquad \text{(VIII, 12)}$$

and for the free energy

$$F = \frac{5}{2}NkT - S_t T - NkT \log Q + E_0, \qquad \text{(VIII, 13)}$$

where S_t is the translational part of the entropy and E_0 is the internal energy at absolute zero. Thus the entropy and the free energy (the latter apart from the unknown constant E_0) can be calculated immediately if the state sum Q is known; that is, they also can be predicted very accurately from spectroscopic data [see Kassel (398), Zeise (731), and Jeune-homme (382a)].

3. APPLICATIONS TO CHEMISTRY

In addition to the problem of valence, or, quite generally, the problem of chemical attraction, already treated in detail in Chapter VI, the results of band spectroscopy are of importance in a number of other chemical problems.

Free radicals. Spectroscopic investigation has shown that many band spectra appearing in electric discharges, flames, and so on, are emitted by diatomic molecules that are not chemically stable under ordinary conditions—that is, by *free radicals* [see also Mecke (489)]. Their existence had already been assumed in chemistry to explain many processes; but their actual occurrence was first unambiguously demonstrated by the investigation of band spectra. Thus, for example, when water vapor is present in discharges and flames, bands often appear at 3060 Å whose analysis shows that they belong to the free OH radical. The existence of the radicals CH, C_2, CN, NH, and many others has been demonstrated in a similar manner. In addition to the proof of the existence and physical stability of these radicals, their internuclear distances, vibrational frequencies, heats of dissociation, and electronic structures have also been determined (see Table 36).

Emission spectra cannot serve as a quantitative measure of the concentration of free radicals, since, for the appearance of an emission spectrum, not only the occurrence of free radicals but also their *excitation* is necessary. However, the *absorption spectrum* can be used for such a *quantitative test*. Bonhoeffer and Reichardt (119) first used the absorption of the OH bands for the detection of OH radicals in H_2O vapor heated to high temperatures (in which an emission of OH bands does not appear). Later, Franck and Reichardt (228) showed the existence of free NH (imine) in a similar manner in the thermal decomposition of NH_3. Oldenberg [(540), (234), and (540a)] and his co-workers by means of the absorption spectrum have tested quantitatively for OH in discharges in H_2O and H_2O_2 and have investigated the disappearance of OH after cutting off the discharge [see also Miescher (493) and White (707b)].

Closely connected with the proof of the existence of free radicals is the detection of diatomic molecules in the vapors of the alkali metals, previously regarded as monatomic.

Elementary chemical reactions in gases and chemiluminescence. After it had been pioved that free radicals occur, for example, in flames, the problem of determining the individual steps in a given combustion process could be attacked with much greater success. At the same time an understanding of the chemiluminescence occurring in flames could be obtained.

Let us consider as an example the *burning of* H_2 *to* H_2O,

$$2H_2 + O_2 = 2H_2O(gas) + 114.2 \text{ kcal.} \quad \text{(VIII, 14)}$$

It seems probable that this reaction does not occur simply by the collision of two hydrogen molecules and an oxygen molecule. However, only quite indefinite conjectures could be made concerning the individual steps in this process until it was shown that the bands appearing in the spectrum of the oxy-hydrogen flame (as chemiluminescence) were emitted by free OH radicals. After it had been shown in this way that these radicals do appear in the flame, Bonhoeffer and Haber (117) were led to assume the following two elementary reactions in the formation of H_2O:

$$H + O_2 + H_2 = H_2O + OH + 97.9 \text{ kcal.,} \quad \text{(VIII, 15)}$$

$$OH + H_2 = H_2O + H + 16.3 \text{ kcal.} \quad \text{(VIII, 16)}$$

This means that, when once some H atoms have been formed —for example, by ignition—each of these produces an OH radical and an H_2O molecule according to (VIII, 15). Each OH radical in its turn, in addition to forming another H_2O molecule, reproduces an H atom according to (VIII, 16), and with the latter the process can begin again. We have a *chain reaction*. The correctness of this mechanism has been supported further by Haber and his co-workers by experiments in which definite amounts of H atoms were added [see also Kassel (399)].

It is of particular importance that the *heats of the elementary reactions*, which obviously are not susceptible to direct measurement, can be calculated accurately from the heats of dissociation of the molecules involved (see Table 36). For example, in equation (VIII, 15) the energy required to dissociate all molecules on the left-hand side into atoms is $D(O_2) + D(H_2) = 220.4$ kcal., whereas on the right-hand side it is $D(H_2O) + D(OH) = 318.3$ kcal. [for $D(H_2O)$ see below]. The difference of the two figures, 97.9 kcal., is evidently the heat of reaction. The heats of reaction for (VIII, 16) and for the reactions further below have been calculated in a similar way and are given in the equations.

It is seen that both reaction (VIII, 15) and reaction (VIII, 16) are strongly exothermic. Actually, in (VIII, 15) the liberated energy is sufficient to excite OH to the upper state of the ultraviolet bands. The experiments actually seem to show that the observed excitation of these bands in the flame (as chemiluminescence) follows directly from the elementary process (VIII, 15); that is, in this process, excited and not normal OH radicals result [see L. Farkas (213)]. The *excited* OH can either go over with emission of radiation to the ground state and then react further according to (VIII, 16), or else, while it is still excited, react with H_2. Since the energy that is carried by the excited OH is 92.8 kcal., at high temperatures the processes

$$OH^* + H_2 = OH + H + H - 10.4 \text{ kcal.} \qquad \text{(VIII, 17)}$$

$$\text{or} \quad OH^* + H_2 = O + H + H_2 - 6.6 \text{ kcal.} \qquad \text{(VIII, 18)}$$

can also take place as well as reaction (VIII, 16). In addition to normal OH, (VIII, 17) gives two H atoms, both of which can begin a new chain (*chain branching*), so that with rising temperature the reaction goes faster and faster (*explosion*). Also, reaction (VIII, 18) gives rise to a chain branching, since the O atoms (which may also be produced artificially) can react further according to

$$O + H_2 = OH + H - 3.8\,kcal. \qquad (VIII, 19)$$

In practice, however, this reaction has a comparatively small probability.

The knowledge of the spectroscopically derived heats of reaction is of particular value in establishing *whether a postulated reaction actually can occur*. For example, using the dissociation energies of H_2, O_2, and OH, the reactions

$$H + O_2 + H_2 = 2OH + H - 21.6\,kcal. \qquad (VIII, 20)$$

and $\qquad H + O_2 = OH + O - 17.8\,kcal. \qquad (VIII, 21)$

are found to have the heats of reaction given. They are strongly endothermic and therefore do not occur at low temperatures. However, when once the temperature is raised by starting the reaction in the aforementioned manner, they may take place and then lead to chain branching.

Considerations similar to those for the burning of hydrogen have been applied to several other combustion processes and to other chemical reactions [see, for example, Kassel (44)].

It can be seen from (VIII, 17 and 18) that a knowledge of the *excited states* of the radicals is of great importance. It not only gives us an understanding of the appearance or non-appearance of *chemiluminescence* but in addition sometimes supplies the only way to understand the occurrence of certain elementary processes. If a suitable excited state exists, as, for example, for OH, the radicals can carry with them the energy necessary for a reaction. Reactions (VIII, 17 and 18) would be quite impossible with unexcited OH, except at extremely high temperatures.

Atoms or molecules in *metastable states* are particularly effective as *energy carriers* in chemical reactions, since in general their energy cannot be given off as radiation. The action of metastable Hg atoms in the $^3P_0$ state (see A.A.,

p. 229) is, of course, well known. It is probable that the metastable $^1\Delta$ and $^1\Sigma$ states of the O_2 molecule (see Fig. 172) play a similar part in some chemical reactions. According to what has been said earlier, the *higher vibrational states* of a molecule are also to be regarded as metastable, and therefore they too may be of importance in chemical elementary processes. For example, the chemiluminescent emission of the sodium D lines in the combination of chlorine and sodium vapor at low pressures was traced back by Beutler, Polanyi, and co-workers (98) to the strongly vibrating NaCl molecules resulting from the reaction

$$Na_2 + Cl = NaCl + Na + 80.5 \text{ kcal}. \qquad \text{(VIII, 22)}$$

These NaCl molecules, on collision with Na atoms, may excite them to the upper state ^2P of the D lines.

There are *four main reasons why certain elementary reactions do not occur at every collision even if they take place with the liberation of energy.*

1. There may be an *energy of activation*; that is, in order that the reaction may take place, the energy of the system must be raised a certain amount above that of the initial state. This is particularly the case for reactions between saturated molecules (for example, $2H_2 + O_2 = 2H_2O$); however, it also occurs for reactions in which radicals or free atoms take part. Such activation energies were first treated theoretically on the basis of quantum mechanics by London (453). Since in these reactions the interaction of at least three atoms is concerned, the discussion will be postponed to Volume II. We may mention, however, that a knowledge of the potential curves of the participating diatomic molecules is necessary [Eyring and Polanyi (209)].

2. A *steric factor* may be present; that is, a reaction may take place only when the collision partners meet in space in a definite orientation. This also plays a part only in systems with more than two atoms.

3. In the recombination of two atoms (or radicals) the *prohibition of recombinations in a two-body collision* discussed

in Chapter VII, section 1(b), holds. For example, the reaction

$$H + H \rightarrow H_2 + 102.7 \text{ kcal.,} \qquad (VIII, 23)$$

which would lead to a breaking of the chain (VIII, 15 and 16), can take place only when a third atom or molecule is present at the moment of the collision (*three-body collision*). The reaction (VIII, 23) is therefore of very rare occurrence. The chain (VIII, 15 and 16) is broken only after very many links. The association of atoms to form diatomic molecules has been thoroughly investigated both theoretically and experimentally in recent years by Steiner [(651) and (321)], Rabinowitch [(574) and (576)], and co-workers. They have confirmed fully the validity of the prohibition of recombinations in a two-body collision and, in addition, have found interesting differences in the effectiveness of various atoms and molecules as third collision partners.

4. If an electronic transition takes place in the reaction (case I of predissociation; see p. 503), the *transition probability may be small*, and therefore the reaction may not take place at every collision (for example, singlet-triplet transitions; see Volume II).

It might be thought that in suitable cases, for a diatomic molecule, the *converse of a predissociation process* might lead to molecule formation in a two-body collision or at least to a very much increased life of the intermediate state and thereby to a greater yield for the triple collision. According to this idea, the two atoms would approach each other on the potential curve α' in Fig. 163 and then jump with a certain probability onto the potential curve α. They would then stay on this a certain time until they either transferred to α' again and thereby separated from each other or went into a lower stable state by collision or radiation. However, it should be noted that the more stable α is with respect to predissociation the smaller is the probability of formation of the state α from α'. Apart from that, if the probability of predissociation is small, a transition takes place only when the two colliding atoms have by chance exactly the discrete energies corresponding to the quantum states of α. As a result of these two factors, the possibility of an inverse predissociation actually gives no greater probability for recombination of two atoms in a two-body or three-body collision.

Photochemical primary processes. A particularly important special case of chemical elementary processes are the primary processes of photochemical reactions; because of their importance we shall now consider them separately. The elucidation of these photochemical primary processes has been made possible in large measure by the investigation of molecular spectra [see, for example, Bonhoeffer and Harteck (46)].

It is obvious that a photochemical reaction in a gas can be brought about only by light that is absorbed by the gas under consideration. The number of primarily influenced molecules or atoms is equal to the number of absorbed light quanta (Einstein's *law of photochemical equivalence*). The result of a photochemical reaction depends first of all on the primary effect of the light (*primary process*) and, in addition, on the subsequent reactions (*secondary processes*). The latter are of the same type as the chemical elementary processes just dealt with. We shall consider here only the primary process.

The kind of photochemical primary process occurring can usually be deduced with certainty from the absorption spectrum of the gas in question on the basis of our earlier discussions. We have to distinguish three cases:

1. *Absorption in a discrete band spectrum.* By light absorption the molecules are brought into a discrete excited electronic state, from which, in general, they return to the ground state (or another lower state) after a time of the order of 10^{-8} sec. with emission of radiation (fluorescence). The energy of excitation can be used for a chemical reaction only when a collision with another molecule takes place within the life [3] of the excited state. In this case the excited mole-

---

[3] The life of the excited state is not the same for all the molecules of a gas but should be understood in the same way as the mean life of a radio active substance.

cule may itself be dissociated by the collision with the other molecule or it may react with the collision partner or it may simply transfer its energy to the collision partner, which then carries out the actual photochemical reaction (dissociates, for example).   In the latter case, the primarily absorbing molecule acts only as a sensitizer and suffers no lasting alteration in the reaction (*sensitized photochemical reaction*).   In all these cases the yield of the photochemical reaction (referred to the number of absorbed quanta) *depends strongly on the pressure* and falls to zero with decreasing pressure.

The case in which the absorbing molecule is itself dissociated by collision with like molecules or foreign gas molecules is observed for NO (225), I_2 (575), and others (see also induced predissociation, p. 460).   The case in which a reaction with or a dissociation of another molecule takes place has thus far been observed with certainty only when atoms are the absorbing systems.   For example, Hg vapor mixed with O_2, on excitation with light of the Hg resonance line, gives the reaction

$$Hg^* + O_2 \rightarrow HgO + O$$

or, mixed with H_2, causes the dissociation of the H_2 (see A.A., p. 230) according to

$$Hg^* + H_2 \rightarrow HgH + H$$

or $$Hg^* + H_2 \rightarrow Hg + H + H.$$

2. *Absorption in a continuous spectrum.*   The absorbing molecules are raised by light into an unstable state and decompose with more or less kinetic energy (see Chapter VII, section 1).   This decomposition is independent of any secondary processes—that is, *independent of pressure*.   The number of atoms formed is exactly twice as great as the number of absorbed light quanta.   Naturally, the subsequent reactions of the atoms formed may depend on the pressure.   In such cases also the total yield of the whole reaction will depend on the pressure.

The best-known example of this case is the explosion of an H_2–Cl_2 mixture by irradiation. By absorption in the continuous region of the spectrum (see p. 411) the Cl_2 molecules split up into two atoms ($Cl_2 + h\nu \rightarrow Cl + Cl$), which most probably react further according to the Nernst chain,

$$Cl + H_2 \rightarrow HCl + H, \qquad (VIII, 24)$$

$$H + Cl_2 \rightarrow HCl + Cl, \qquad (VIII, 25)$$

and thereby lead to explosion. It may perhaps be of some significance that one of the atoms formed in the primary process is in the excited $^2P_{\frac{1}{2}}$ state (see p. 473); this makes the first reaction more exothermic. Many similar photoreactions (not all explosive) are known, in which the direct dissociation of the halogens, of oxygen, or of other molecules is the primary process.[4]

3. *Absorption in a diffuse (predissociation) spectrum.* By light absorption the molecules are raised to a discrete state which they then leave spontaneously, either by emission of radiation, or by a radiationless transition to an unstable dissociating state. Here also, as in 2, the decomposition is *independent of collisions.* However, not every molecule that has absorbed a light quantum in the diffuse absorption region dissociates, but only a certain fraction of them. All the same, according to what has previously been said (p. 437), this fraction is very close to 1 if the absorption bands in question appear diffuse. Only if the absorption bands appear sharp even under large resolution and the predissociation is only detected, say, by a breaking off (or a weakening of the intensity) in emission is a yield essentially different from 1 to be expected for the primary process. The fact that a predissociation (that is, a pressure-independent yield of the primary process) may be present even in this case (no noticeable diffuseness in absorption) is often overlooked.

Photochemical reactions brought about by predissocia-

---

[4] In addition to a photodissociation into normal or excited atoms, a photodissociation into ions has also been observed [Terenin and Popov (666)].

tion have not been investigated to any great extent for *diatomic* molecules. A photochemical formation of H_2S has been found when a mixture of H_2 and S_2 is irradiated by light in the region of the diffuse S_2 bands [see Henri (300)]. Furthermore, predissociation may possibly play a part in the photochemical ozone formation by irradiation of O_2 with light below 1900 Å [Flory (224)]. Many such cases are known for polyatomic molecules (see Volume II).

Chemical equilibria. Not only is the study of elementary processes in chemical reactions furthered by band spectroscopy, but also the *equilibria* of chemical reactions may be predicted on the basis of spectroscopic data [see, for example, Giauque (252a), Johnston and Davis (392a), Gordon and Barnes (264a), and Jeunehomme (382a)]. The equilibrium constant $K_p = p_{A'} p_{B'} \cdots / p_A p_B \cdots$ of a chemical reaction $A + B + \cdots \rightleftarrows A' + B' + \cdots$ in the gaseous state is given by the relation

$$RT \log K_p = - \Delta E_0{}^0 - (F^0 - E_0{}^0)_{A'} - (F^0 - E_0{}^0)_{B'} - \cdots$$
$$+ (F^0 - E_0{}^0)_A + (F^0 - E_0{}^0)_B + \cdots, \quad \text{(VIII, 26)}$$

where $\Delta E_0{}^0$ is the *zero-point energy change*, F^0 is the free energy, and $E_0{}^0$ is the internal energy at absolute zero (zero-point energy) for the gas in question. $F^0 - E_0{}^0$ can be derived from spectroscopic data for every component of the system according to (VIII, 13). The superscript ^{0} indicates that each of these quantities refers to the standard state. In simple cases also the heat of reaction—that is, $\Delta E_0{}^0$—can be obtained spectroscopically, so that the equilibrium and its dependence on temperature can be completely calculated. In this manner, for example, the dependence of the thermal I_2 dissociation equilibrium on temperature has been calculated [Gibson and Heitler (257)] and is in complete agreement with experiment. Similarly, the *dissociation equilibria* of all other diatomic gases, so far as their heats of dissociation are known, can be predicted with certainty in this way [see the tables of Lewis and von Elbe (445)].

Sometimes, for more complicated equilibria, only the $F^0 - E_0{}^0$ values of the participating gases can be calculated, while the heats of reaction must be taken from thermal measurements. However, it is just the former quantities that are in general not easily obtained from thermal data, whereas the heats of reaction can be relatively easily measured. The band-spectroscopic data are therefore of great value in calculating gas equilibria with great accuracy—for example, in the combustion of CO, the ammonia synthesis, the methanol synthesis, and the preparation of water gas. Naturally, when polyatomic molecules take part in a reaction, the structure of these molecules must also be known in order to calculate the equilibrium constant (see Volume II). An interesting technical application to the calculation of the efficiency of combustion machines has been discussed by Kühl (425).

Atomic heats of formation and related topics. The exact knowledge of the heats of dissociation of diatomic molecules and radicals is of particular importance in determining the so-called *atomic heats of formation of polyatomic molecules*. The atomic heat of formation is the energy necessary to split a polyatomic molecule completely into free atoms. It is obtained in the case of the H_2O molecule, for example, from $D(O_2)$ and $D(H_2)$, together with the accurately known heat of combustion of H_2, by means of the following equations:

$$H_2O = H_2 + \tfrac{1}{2}O_2 - 57.11 \text{ kcal.} \qquad \text{[see Rossini (604)]}$$

$$\tfrac{1}{2}O_2 = O - 58.6 \text{ kcal.} \qquad \text{(see Table 36)}$$

$$\underline{H_2 = 2H - 103.2 \text{ kcal.} \qquad \text{(see Table 36)}}$$

$$H_2O = O + H + H - 218.9 \text{ kcal.} \qquad \text{(VIII, 27)}$$

Thus the energy necessary to split an H_2O molecule into one O atom and two H atoms in the ground state is 218.9 kcal.

The atomic heats of formation of a large number of molecules, particularly of organic molecules, have been determined in a similar manner. However, in calculations involving organic molecules, one fact leads to difficulties— the *heat of sublimation* L_1 *of solid carbon* is thus far not known with certainty [see Herzberg (314)]. This heat of sublimation could be obtained accurately if the heat of dissociation of CO were known with certainty, by using the following equations:

$$CO = C_{gas} + O - D(CO).$$

$$O = \tfrac{1}{2}O_2 + 58.6 \text{ kcal.}$$

$$\underline{C_{solid} + \tfrac{1}{2}O_2 = CO + 27.40 \text{ kcal.}}$$

$$C_{solid} = C_{gas} - D(CO) + 86.0 \text{ kcal.} \qquad \text{(VIII, 28)}$$

In this way we see that $L_1 = D(CO) - 86.0$ kcal. If we assume that $D(CO) = 9.144$ volts $= 210.8$ kcal., a value that is not yet quite certain, we obtain $L_1 = 124.8$ kcal. If L_1 is known, we can calculate, for example, the atomic heat of formation of methane on the basis of the following equations:

$$CH_4 = C_{solid} + 2H_2 - 16.18 \text{ kcal.}$$

$$2H_2 = 4H - 206.4 \text{ kcal.}$$

$$\underline{C_{solid} = C_{gas} - L_1}$$

$$CH_4 = C_{gas} + 4H - (L_1 + 222.6 \text{ kcal.}) \qquad \text{(VIII, 29)}$$

With the above L_1 value we obtain for the *atomic heat of formation of methane* 347.4 kcal.[5]

The assumption is often made that the same kind of bond in different polyatomic molecules has the same separation energy (*bond energy*); that, for example, the energy of an OH bond is half the atomic heat of formation of H_2O [see (VIII, 27)]—that is, 109.5 kcal.—and that it has this value also in other molecules that contain an OH bond. Similarly,

---

[5] In the above discussion all numerical values are based on the new conversion factors given in the introduction. Therefore they differ slightly from those given in the original papers cited.

it is assumed that the CH bond energy is equal to one-fourth the atomic heat of formation of CH_4—that is, with the value of L_1 assumed above, 86.9 kcal. Assuming these values, we can, for example, derive the strength of the CO single bond from the atomic heat of formation of CH_3OH. In a similar manner we may derive the strength of the C—C, C=C and C≡C, C≡N and like bonds from other suitable molecules.

The values obtained in this way have naturally no great claim to high accuracy, since the postulate of equal energy of like bonds in different molecules is certainly only approximately fulfilled. However, the values obtained are useful in giving at least some idea of the energy relations in polyatomic molecules, the more so since the direct determination of the work required to remove individual atoms from polyatomic molecules has up to now been possible only in very few cases. The deviation of the true separation energies from the bond energies obtained from atomic heats of formation is illustrated by the case of H_2O, for which the separation energy of the first H atom is 119.5 kcal. [see (590)] and that of the second is 99.4 kcal. [$= D(OH)$], whereas half the atomic heat of formation is 109.5 kcal. Naturally, it does not follow from this that a dissymmetry exists in the H_2O molecule as a whole.

4. APPLICATIONS TO ASTROPHYSICS

The applications of molecular spectra to astrophysics have increased very greatly in extent and importance in recent years. We are able to give here only a short and in no way complete survey of the various problems. However, we shall include the few cases in which *polyatomic* molecular spectra are of importance in astrophysics.

The earth's atmosphere. On the way through the earth's atmosphere, an *absorption* of stellar light (for example, sunlight) takes place (terrestrial Fraunhofer lines). This absorption is entirely molecular. *Oxygen* gives the strong terrestrial bands in the red and infrared already briefly mentioned (p. 304 f. and Fig. 73) and, in addition, complete absorption below 2400 Å. This complete absorption is due, between 2400 and 2000 Å, to the continuum corresponding to the forbidden transition $^3\Sigma_u{}^+ \leftarrow {}^3\Sigma_g{}^-$ (see p. 475 and Fig. 172), and below 2000 Å to the well-known and extremely intense system of the Schumann-Runge bands and the adjoining continuum (see p. 474). The *water vapor* in the atmosphere gives rise to a large number of intense absorption lines in the yellow, the red, and the near infrared which represent the rotation-vibration spectrum of the H_2O molecule and lines in the far infrared which represent the rotation spectrum. Furthermore, the rotation-vibration spectrum of *carbon dioxide* appears strongly in the infrared. Like the inert gases, molecular nitrogen first absorbs in the vacuum region—that is, where O_2 absorbs everything in any case. In addition to these absorptions, there is still another intense absorption below 3000 Å, which cuts off all the stellar spectra below this wave length and is due to the *ozone* (O_3) *molecule*. While at the earth's surface there is practically no ozone at all, investigations of the sun's spectrum at different altitudes of the sun and during balloon flights have shown that the ozone concentration rises to a maximum at a height of about 20 to 30 km and then falls off again. The total amount of ozone corresponds to a layer of only 3 mm thickness at atmospheric pressure. The formation of ozone is brought about photochemically by the dissociation of O_2 in the ultraviolet region of absorption below 2400 Å (see p. 474 f.). More details about the formation of O_3 from O_2 in the upper atmosphere are given by Ladenburg (439) and Wulf (724). Recently, Adel, Slipher, Barker, and Fouts [(59) and (60)] have also observed ozone bands in the *infrared* solar spectrum.[6]

Emission band spectra are exhibited by the aurora and the light of the night sky. They are produced in the upper

---

[6] In a still more recent paper Adel and Lampland (55b) have found an infrared absorption band (at 7.6 μ) that seems to be due to N_2O_5. This compound might be formed in the ozone layer.

layers of the atmosphere. Apart from the "forbidden" oxygen lines (see A.A., p. 158), these spectra consist almost exclusively of bands of the *nitrogen molecule* [see the review by Déjardin (180)].[6a]   Corresponding to the fact that in the *aurora* the excitation is due to beams of electrons, the relative intensity of the different band systems of N_2 is about the same as in an electric discharge at low pressures. The negative nitrogen bands $(N_2{}^+)$ appear most strongly. In addition, though relatively weakly, the forbidden $^3\Sigma - {}^1\Sigma$ bands of N_2 appear (see Fig. 173). These bands can be observed in a discharge only under very special conditions [Vegard (684) and Kaplan (396)]. Their appearance in the aurora is connected with the fact that, at very low pressure and in the absence of vessel walls, the N_2 molecule remains undisturbed in the $^3\Sigma$ state for a sufficiently long time for it to be able to radiate. The $^3\Sigma - {}^1\Sigma$ bands appear with relatively great intensity in the *light of the night sky*. This difference from the aurora indicates that the excitation process is entirely different. Chapman (153) has explained the light of the night sky as chemiluminescence resulting from the recombination of free O atoms formed during the day by sunlight (see also p. 471). This explanation appears to have a great deal in its favor. However, we cannot go into details here.

The temperature of the atmospheric layers in which the emission takes place can be determined from the intensity distribution in the bands. Vegard and Tønsberg (685), for this purpose, have measured the intensity distribution in the $N_2{}^+$ bands occurring in the northern lights—however, without resolving the bands. For a more accurate determination it would be necessary to resolve the fine structure, and, owing to the small light intensity, this is beset with difficulties.

Planetary atmospheres. In addition to the terrestrial bands of O_2, O_3, and H_2O appearing in the solar spectrum and all stellar spectra, in the spectrum of the sunlight

---

[6a] Recently Bernard (87a) has detected the yellow sodium lines in the spectrum of the night sky, and Cabannes, Dufay, and Gauzit (148b) have tentatively identified some observed bands as CH and CN bands.

reflected from the planets Venus, Jupiter, Saturn, Uranus, and Neptune some further characteristic bands appear, mostly in the red, that obviously result from an absorption in the planetary atmosphere under consideration.

For *Venus*, three strong bands at 8696, 7889, and 7826 Å have been observed which have a very simple structure (simple P and R branches) and which have been identified with certainty as rotation-vibration bands of the (linear) CO_2 *molecule* [Adams and Dunham (52) and Adel and Dennison (55a)]. The same bands were subsequently also produced in the laboratory by Adel and Slipher (57) by use of a 45 m layer of CO_2 at a pressure of 47 atm. From the intensity of the bands in the spectrum of Venus, Adel (54) has concluded that there are 200 m-atm. of CO_2 above the reflecting layer in its atmosphere. Furthermore, from the maximum of the intensity distribution in the bands, Adel (55) has estimated the temperature of the atmosphere of Venus to be somewhat above 50° C. More accurate measurements are not yet available. Thus far, gases other than CO_2 have not been identified in the atmosphere of Venus.

The intense and broad absorption bands appearing in the red and near infrared spectra of the planets *Jupiter, Saturn, Uranus, and Neptune* and extending for the last two into the green have been unambiguously identified by Wildt [(713a) and (714)] and Dunham (195) (by comparison with laboratory measurements) as due to *methane*. For Jupiter a few of the weaker bands were assigned to *ammonia* [see also Adel and Slipher (56)]. The amount of methane on the larger planets, estimated from the intensity of the bands, is enormous [40 km-atm. on Neptune, according to Adel and Slipher (58)]. The absence of other hydrocarbons is due in part to the low temperature and in part also to the fact that they are photochemically decomposed by sunlight [Wildt (715)]. The presence of large amounts of methane makes it very probable that there is also a large amount of *molecular hydrogen* present in the atmospheres of the major planets [see, for example, Russell (607)]. A direct spectroscopic proof of the presence of H_2 is difficult, since H_2 has an electronic absorption spectrum only in the vacuum region and has no normal rotation-vibration spectrum. However, for sufficiently large amounts of H_2 it should be possible to observe its quadrupole rotation-vibration spectrum (see p. 305) [Herzberg (315)]. From a knowledge of the ultraviolet H_2 spectrum (380) the position of the expected lines can be accurately predicted. However, since the lines are very sharp and widely separated from one another, their detection is not easy and has not yet been accomplished.

In spite of the strong O_2 and H_2O absorption in the earth's atmosphere, the detection of relatively small amounts of these gases in planetary atmospheres is possible, since as a result of the Doppler effect the whole spectrum of the planet will be shifted under favorable conditions by a small amount compared to the normal position. In this manner, Adams and Dunham (53) have shown with certainty that the atmosphere of Mars contains less than $\frac{1}{1000}$ of the amount of O_2 in the earth's atmosphere, if indeed any at all. Similarly it has been shown that the concentration of H_2O vapor in the Martian atmosphere is very small if not zero.

Comets. In the spectra of comets, apart from a weak continuum with Fraunhofer lines (reflected sunlight), *intense emission bands* appear, in particular the red and violet CN bands, the Swan bands of C_2 (see Fig. 7), several CH bands, the $^2\Pi - ^2\Sigma$ bands of CO^+ [comet-tail bands; see Fig. 11(a)], and the violet N_2^+ bands.[7] The bands of CN, C_2, and CH appear only in the head of the comet, whereas the CO^+ and N_2^+ bands are observed mainly in the tail. For all band systems the lower state is the ground state of the molecule in question. It therefore seems plausible to assume that the occurrence of these bands in comets is due to *fluorescence* excited by direct sunlight. More detailed investigations have shown [Zanstra (730)] that this assump-

---

[7] Some bands emitted by the nuclei of comets are not yet identified [see Baldet (78) and Cabannes and Dufay (148a)].

tion can explain the brightness of comets and is also in agreement with other facts.   Conversely, on the basis of this assumption, Wurm (728) has obtained from the intensity of the Swan bands in the head (also called *coma*) and nucleus of the comet an estimate of the order of magnitude of the pressure.   He obtained $p < 10^{-10}$ mm in the nucleus and $p < 10^{-13}$ mm in the head.

In the absorption of a light quantum a recoil of the absorbing system takes place in the original direction of motion of the light quantum (light pressure).   In the present case it results in the molecules being strongly accelerated away from the sun.   The *tail* of the comet, which always points away from the sun, is produced in this way.

Wurm (728) has tried to explain the important fact already mentioned that the C_2 *and* CN *bands do not appear at all in the tail*, although they are more intense than those of CO^+ and N_2^+ in the head.   At the extraordinarily low pressures even in the head of the comet (see above) the destruction of CN and C_2 molecules by collision does not come into the question, since the mean free path is of the order of the diameter of the head.   However, we need only to assume that the molecules of CN and C_2 are being photochemically dissociated or ionized in order to explain their absence in the tail.   Actually, in the case of C_2, according to the Franck-Condon principle, transitions in absorption from the ground state to the new excited state recently found by Fox and Herzberg (227) (see Fig. 176) take place to an unstable or predissociated part of the upper potential curve.   It is not yet possible to give the exact process of the decomposition of CN.   However, according to the foregoing, there can be no doubt that the possibility of a dissociation (or ionization) by the sunlight exists and that CO^+ and N_2^+ might be less easily or even not at all dissociated or ionized under the influence of the active region of the sunlight because, for instance, the corresponding absorption spectrum lies too far in the ultraviolet.

In all probability, the formation of the molecules CN, C_2,

CO^+, and N_2^+ is brought about *photochemically* from gases such as CO_2, CO, $(CN)_2$, N_2, and others given off by the solid parts of the comet. That no fluorescence is observed from these gases themselves is due to the fact that their resonance systems lie in the inaccessible ultraviolet. It is to be expected that frequently the fragments resulting from decomposition of these gases will have a very large kinetic energy (see p. 412), and, according to Wurm (728), in this way is to be explained the fact that the head of the comet extends a considerable distance away from the nucleus and toward the sun (opposite to the light pressure).

The greater the intensity of the irradiation by the sun, the sooner after their formation in the nucleus will the molecules CN and C_2, which give rise to the light of the head of the comet, decompose. Therefore we should observe *a shrinking of the head as the comet approaches the sun*, which actually is the case. This fact must be regarded as a striking confirmation of Wurm's views [for a recent summary see Wurm (729a)].

Fixed stars. Molecular spectra have also been found in the spectra of fixed stars of not too high temperature [see, for example, the reviews by Swings (660) and Bobrovnikoff (115a)]. The spectrum of the *sun* shows, though rather weakly, the bands of C_2, CN, MgH, CH, NH, OH, SiH, SiN, SiF, PH, and CP in absorption. In the sunspots the intensity of absorption of these bands is increased, and, in addition, the bands of AlH, CaH, AlO, BO, TiO, and ZrO appear [see Russell (606)]. Some others are doubtful. All these molecules must be present in the reversing layer of the sun. Some other molecules that are certainly present, such as H_2, O_2, and N_2, cannot be identified, since they have no resonance systems in the accessible spectral region.

In going over from the sun to *stars of lower temperature*, the intensity of the band absorption increases considerably and is finally so great for the stars of types M, N, and R that the bands form the characteristic part of the spectrum. The bands appearing with greatest intensity are those of TiO, ZrO, C_2, and CN.   TiO and ZrO appear chiefly in the main branch K–S–M, while C_2 and CN (usually without TiO and ZrO) appear chiefly in the branch R–N.

Wildt (713), Russell (606), and Rosenfeld and Cambresier [(600) and (149)] have successfully calculated the *dissociation equilibrium in stars*, using the relative abundance of the various elements known approximately from the line spectrum of the sun.   Naturally, for these calculations, an accurate knowledge of the heats of dissociation and other constants of the molecules in question was required (see Table 36).   The above-named authors thus obtained the variation of the concentration of the different molecules in its dependence on the spectral class and also on the mass of the star (giant or dwarf stars).   The agreement with observation is good throughout the main branch K–S–M.   For example, the fact is readily explained that the intensity of the CN, CH, and C_2 bands decreases again for the cooler stars after going through a maximum, whereas the intensity of the TiO bands approaches a very large, nearly constant, value.   The observed relatively large intensity of the hydride and oxide bands is due to the high concentration of hydrogen and oxygen in the stars.

For the stars in the branch R–N a different relative abundance of the elements has to be assumed.   It appears to be sufficient to exchange the abundances of carbon and oxygen in the equations—that is, to assume that carbon is particularly abundant.   In this way one can immediately explain the fact that the TiO bands and other oxide bands do not occur in these stars.   On the other hand, the C_2, CN, and CH bands are intense, since the C atoms are no longer used up in forming the much more stable CO.[8]

Conversely, from the observed great intensity of the Swan

---

[8] For the stars with intense Swan bands, the bands of the isotopic molecule $C^{12}C^{13}$ and even C_2^{13} are also observed.   The intensity ratio seems to indicate a greater abundance of C^{13} than on the earth.   But this point is not yet settled.

bands and the calculations of the dissociation equilibrium we may conclude with certainty that the concentration of carbon in the stars of the branch R–N is very large, and that of oxygen is small. Similarly, from the strength of other molecular absorptions (for example, of BO and SiF) estimates can be made of the concentration of atoms (B and Si) that are detectable only with difficulty by the atomic spectrum. Furthermore, the presence of molecules such as H_2, CO, O_2, and others, which are not directly detectable spectroscopically, can be demonstrated with great certainty with the help of these equilibrium calculations.

The equilibrium calculations are rather sensitive to the values of the heats of dissociation. It is to be expected that a still better agreement between theory and experiment would be obtained if, in addition to the known heats of dissociation of H_2, O_2, and N_2, those of CO, C_2, and other molecules were known with greater accuracy than at present. Another factor of uncertainty is the absolute intensity of the bands, which in addition to the concentration of the molecules, determines the observable intensity of absorption and for which in many cases only very rough estimates can be made.

On the basis of the dependence of dissociation equilibria on temperature, we should expect that for *variable stars of low temperature* the intensity of band absorption should follow the variation of brightness. This is actually the case. There are variable stars for which, for example, the TiO bands are almost completely absent at maximum of light, whereas they are very intense at minimum of light. Of particular interest is the appearance of *bright emission lines* in some long-period variable stars (for example, Mira Ceti) in spite of their comparatively low temperatures. According to Wurm (729) these emission lines are in all probability due to *chemiluminescence* (p. 471), the energy set free by the recombination of two atoms being used to excite the third collision partner. If metastable atoms or molecules take part in this process, we can understand the excitation of lines having a high excitation energy—for example, the atomic lines of hydrogen. However, the details of this phenomenon require further investigation. It is also conceivable that a simple photodissociation into excited atoms is responsible for some of the emission lines.

Owing to the strong dependence of the dissociation equilibrium on temperature, we may conversely draw *conclusions about the temperature* from the observed relative intensities of the bands of different molecules. Another more accurate method for determining the temperature from band spectra uses the measurement of the intensity distribution in the vibrational or rotational structure of the bands. This intensity distribution corresponds, of course, to a pure thermal excitation (at least in general). In this way, Wurm (727) has used the occurrence of C_2 and CN bands with higher v'' values and their intensities relative to the bands with $v'' = 0$ for estimating the temperature [allowing, of course, for the difference in transition probability in consequence of the Franck-Condon principle (see also p. 223 f.)].[9]

For the sun, for which large dispersion can be employed, the fine structure can be used to determine the temperature in the manner previously described (p. 505). At the same time, according to Richardson (588), it is possible to determine not only the temperature itself but also the *temperature gradient* in the reversing layer of the sun: The intensity distribution of the higher rotational lines corresponds to the higher temperature, while the intensity distribution of the lower rotational lines corresponds to the lower temperature of the reversing layer. In this way, using the CH band 4315 Å, Richardson found a temperature of 6080° K. for the lowest part of the reversing layer and 4430° K. for the uppermost part. This corresponds to a temperature gradient of 13°/km.

---

[9] According to more recent investigations of the rotational structure [Wurm (729b)], it seems that in the outer atmospheres of the N stars an extreme deviation from thermal equilibrium occurs. Temperatures derived in the way described above are therefore "vibrational temperatures" (see p. 224) and not true temperatures.

The few examples presented show the value of molecular spectra investigations in astrophysics. This field of investigation is just beginning to be explored, and it is to be expected that many more important results will be obtained by the study of molecular spectra in cosmic sources.

Bibliography

Bibliography

I. HANDBOOKS, MONOGRAPHS, TEXTBOOKS, TABLES

1. Geiger-Scheel, Handbuch der Physik (Springer, Berlin, 1928–33).
   (a) Vol. **19**: Herstellung und Messung des Lichtes.
   (b) Vol. **21**: Licht und Materie.
   (c) Vol. **24**: Part I (second edition), Quantentheorie.
2. Wien-Harms, Handbuch der Experimentalphysik (Akad. Verlagsges., Leipzig, 1927–31).
   (a) Vol. **21**: Anregung der Spektren, Apparate und Methoden der Spektroskopie, Stark-Effekt.
   (b) Supplement. Vol. **1**: Bandenspektren.
3. E. C. C. Baly, Spectroscopy (Longmans, Green and Co., London, 1924–27).
4. Kayser-Konen, Handbuch der Spektroskopie (Hirzel, Leipzig, 1905–33).
5. Handbuch der Radiologie, Vol. **6**, Quantenmechanik der Materie und Strahlung, Part II, Moleküle (Akad. Verlagsges., Leipzig, 1934).
6. Eucken-Wolf, Hand- und Jahrbuch der chemischen Physik (Akad. Verlagsges., Leipzig, 1932–   ).
   (a) Vol. **1**: Theorien des Aufbaus der Materie.
   (b) Vol. **9**: Die Spektren.
7. F. A. Jenkins and H. E. White, Physical Optics (McGraw-Hill, New York, 1937).
8. A. E. Ruark and H. C. Urey, Atoms, Molecules and Quanta (McGraw-Hill, New York, 1933).
9. L. Pauling and S. Goudsmit, The Structure of Line Spectra (McGraw-Hill, New York, 1930).
10. H. Kuhn, Atomspektren (Akad. Verlagsges., Leipzig, 1934).
11. H. E. White, Introduction to Atomic Spectra (McGraw-Hill, New York, 1934).
12. E. U. Condon and E. H. Shortley, The Theory of Atomic Spectra (Cambridge University Press, 1935).
13. G. Herzberg, Atomic Spectra and Atomic Structure (Prentice-Hall, New York, 1937).
14. K. W. Meissner, Spektroskopie, Sammlung Göschen Nr. 1091 (de Gruyter, Berlin, 1935).
15. E. U. Condon and P. M. Morse, Quantum Mechanics (McGraw-Hill, New York, 1929).
16. A. Sommerfeld, Wave Mechanics (Methuen, London, 1930).
17. W. Heisenberg, Physical Principles of the Quantum Theory (Chicago University Press, 1930).
18. P. A. M. Dirac, Principles of Quantum Mechanics (Oxford University Press, 1930).
19. A. Haas, Wave Mechanics and the Quantum Theory (Constable, London, 1931).
20. J. Frenkel, Wave Mechanics, Elementary Theory (Oxford University Press, 1932).
21. H. A. Kramers, Die Grundlagen der Quantentheorie (Akad. Verlagsges., Leipzig, 1933).

22. E. Fues, Einführung in die Quantenmechanik (Akad. Verlagsges., Leip-
    zig, 1935).
23. L. Pauling and E. B. Wilson, Introduction to Quantum Mechanics
    (McGraw-Hill, New York, 1935).
24. A. Landé, Principles of Quantum Mechanics (Cambridge University
    Press, 1937).
25. S. Dushman, Elements of Quantum Mechanics (Wiley, New York, 1938).
26. E. C. Kemble, Fundamental Principles of Quantum Mechanics (McGraw-
    Hill, New York, 1937).
26a. V. Rojansky, Introductory Quantum Mechanics (Prentice-Hall, New
    York, 1938).
27. B. L. van der Waerden, Die gruppentheoretische Methode in der Quan-
    tenmechanik (Springer, Berlin, 1932).
28. F. Rasetti, Nuclear Physics (Prentice-Hall, New York, 1936).
29. E. C. Kemble, R. T. Birge, W. F. Colby, F. W. Loomis, and L. Page,
    Molecular Spectra in Gases, National Research Council Bulletin 57
    (Washington, 1930).
30. R. Mecke, Bandenspektra und ihre Bedeutung für die Chemie (Born-
    traeger, Berlin, 1929).
31. R. de L. Kronig, Band Spectra and Molecular Structure (Cambridge
    University Press, 1930).
32. ————, The Optical Basis of the Theory of Valency (Cambridge Univer-
    sity Press, 1935).
33. W. Weizel, Bandenspektren (Akad. Verlagsges., Leipzig, 1931).
34. W. Jevons, Band Spectra of Diatomic Molecules (Physical Society,
    London, 1932).
35. W. Finkelnburg, R. Mecke, O. Reinkober, and E. Teller, Molekül- und
    Kristallgitterspektren (Akad. Verlagsges., Leipzig, 1934).
36. H. Sponer, Molekülspektren und ihre Anwendung auf chemische
    Probleme, I. Tabellen, II. Text (Springer, Berlin, 1935–36).
37. P. Pringsheim, Fluoreszenz und Phosphoreszenz (Springer, Berlin, 1928).
38. J. Lecompte, Le Spectre Infrarouge (Paris, 1928).
39. F. J. G. Rawlins and A. M. Taylor, Infrared Analysis of Molecular
    Structure (Cambridge University Press, 1929).
40. C. Schaefer and F. Matossi, Das ultrarote Spektrum (Springer, Berlin,
    1930).
41. K. W. F. Kohlrausch, Der Smekal-Raman-Effekt (Springer, Berlin,
    1931). Supplement (Springer, Berlin, 1938).
42. W. Finkelnburg, Kontinuierliche Spektren (Springer, Berlin, 1938).
43. A. E. van Arkel and J. H. de Boer, Chemische Bindung als elektrostatische
    Erscheinung (Akad. Verlagsges., Leipzig, 1931).
44. L. S. Kassel, The Kinetics of Homogeneous Gas Reactions (Chemical
    Catalog Co., New York, 1932).
44a. F. R. Bichowsky and F. D. Rossini, The Thermochemistry of the
    Chemical Substances (Reinhold, New York, 1936).
45. J. H. Van Vleck, The Theory of Electric and Magnetic Susceptibilities
    (Oxford University Press, 1932).
46. K. F. Bonhoeffer and P. Harteck, Grundlagen der Photochemie (Stein-
    kopff, Dresden, 1933).
47. O. W. Richardson, Molecular Hydrogen and Its Spectrum (Yale Univer-
    sity Press, 1934).
48. A. Farkas, Orthohydrogen, Parahydrogen and Heavy Hydrogen (Cam-
    bridge University Press, 1935).
49. H. Hellmann, Einführung in die Quantenchemie (Deuticke, Leipzig,
    1937).
49a. L. Pauling, The Nature of the Chemical Bond (Cornell University
    Press, 1939).
50. R. F. Bacher and S. Goudsmit, Atomic Energy States (McGraw-Hill,
    New York, 1932).

II. References to Individual Papers

51. J. Aars, Z. Physik **79**, 122 (1932).
52. W. S. Adams and Th. Dunham, Publ. Astron. Soc. Pac. **44**, 423 (1932).
53. ———— ————, Astrophys. J. **79**, 308 (1934).
54. A. Adel, Astrophys. J. **85**, 345 (1937).
55. ————, Astrophys. J. **86**, 337 (1937).
55a.———— and D. M. Dennison, Physic. Rev. **43**, 716, **44**, 99 (1933).
55b.———— and C. O. Lampland, Astrophys. J. **87**, 198 (1938).
56. ———— and V. M. Slipher, Physic. Rev. **46**, 902 (1934); **47**, 651 (1935).
57. ———— ————, Physic. Rev. **46**, 240 (1934).
58. ———— ————, Physic. Rev. **47**, 787 (1935).
59. ———— ———— and E. F. Barker, Physic. Rev. **47**, 580 (1935).
60. ———— ———— and O. Fouts, Physic. Rev. **49**, 288 (1936).
60a. R. G. Aickin and N. S. Bayliss, Trans. Faraday Soc. **33**, 1333 (1937).
61. H. S. Allen and A. K. Longair, Phil. Mag. **19**, 1032 (1935).
62. G. M. Almy and C. D. Hause, Physic. Rev. **42**, 242 (1932).
63. ———— and R. B. Horsfall, Physic. Rev. **51**, 491 (1937).
64. ———— and G. R. Irwin, Physic. Rev. **49**, 72 (1936).
65. ———— and M. P. Rassweiler, Physic. Rev. **53**, 890 (1937).
66. ———— and H. A. Schultz, Physic. Rev. **51**, 62 (1937).
67. ———— and M. C. Watson, Physic. Rev. **45**, 871 (1934).
68. E. Amaldi, Z. Physik **79**, 492 (1932).
68a. F. L. Arnot and M. B. M'Ewen, Proc. Roy. Soc. London **171**, 120 (1939).
69. M. F. Ashley, Physic. Rev. **44**, 919 (1933).
70. R. K. Asundi and S. M. Karim, Proc. Ind. Acad. **6A**, 328 (1937).
71. ———— and Y. P. Parti, Proc. Ind. Acad. **6A**, 207 (1937).
72. ———— and R. Samuel, Proc. Ind. Acad. **3A**, 346 (1936).
73. L. Avramenko and V. Kondratjew, Physik. Z. d. Sowjetunion **10**, 741 (1936).
74. H. D. Babcock, Proc. Nat. Acad. Amer. **15**, 471 (1929).
75. ———— and W. P. Hoge, Physic. Rev. **37**, 227 (1931).
76. R. M. Badger, J. Chem. Phys. **2**, 128 (1934); **3**, 710 (1935).
77. H. Baerwald, G. Herzberg, and L. Herzberg, Ann. Physik **20**, 569 (1934).
78. F. Baldet, Ann. Observ. Astronomie physique de Meudon **7**, 53 (1926).
79. R. F. Barrow, Proc. Phys. Soc. London **51**, 267 (1939).
80. ———— and W. Jevons, Proc. Roy. Soc. London **169**, 45 (1938).
80a. E. Bartholomé, Z. physik. Chem. B **23**, 131 (1933).
81. J. H. Bartlett, Physic. Rev. **37**, 507 (1931).
82. N. S. Bayliss, Proc. Roy. Soc. London **158**, 551 (1937).
82a. J. Y. Beach, J. Chem. Phys. **4**, 353 (1936).
83. H. Bell and A. Harvey, Proc. Phys. Soc. London **50**, 427 (1938).
84. E. Bengtsson-Knave, Nova Acta Reg. Soc. Scient. Ups. **8**, No. 4 (1932).
85. ———— and E. Hulthén, Z. Physik **52**, 275 (1928).
86. ———— and E. Olsson, Z. Physik **72**, 163 (1931).
87. ———— and R. Rydberg, Z. Physik **59**, 540 (1930).
87a. R. Bernard, Z. Physik **110**, 291 (1938).
88. H. A. Bethe and R. F. Bacher, Rev. Mod. Phys. **8**, 82 (1936).
89. H. Beutler, Z. Physik **50**, 581 (1928).
90. ————, Z. physik. Chem. B **27**, 287 (1934).
91. ————, Z. physik. Chem. B **29**, 315 (1935).
92. ————, A. Deubner, and H. O. Jünger, Z. Physik **98**, 181 (1935).
93. ———— and B. Josephy, Z. Physik **53**, 747 (1929).
94. ———— and H. O. Jünger, Z. Physik **100**, 80 (1936).
95. ———— ————, Z. Physik **101**, 285 (1936).
96. ———— ————, Z. Physik **101**, 304 (1936).
97. ———— and H. Levi, Z. physik. Chem. B **24**, 263 (1934).
98. ———— and M. Polanyi, Z. physik. Chem. B **1**, 3 (1928).
99. O. Bewersdorff, Z. Physik **103**, 598 (1936).
100. B. N. Bhaduri and A. Fowler, Proc. Roy. Soc. London **145**, 321 (1934).

101. S. Bhagavantam, Physic. Rev. **42**, 437 (1932):
102. R. T. Birge, Physic. Rev. **25**, 240 (1925).
103. ———, Physic. Rev. **28**, 1157 (1926).
104. ———, Trans. Faraday Soc. **25**, 707 (1929).
105. ———, Trans. Faraday Soc. **25**, 718 (1929).
106. ———, Physic. Rev. **37**, 841 (1931).
107. ———, Rev. Mod. Phys. **1**, 1 (1929).
108. ———, Physic. Rev. **40**, 319 (1932).
109. ———, Nature (London) **134**, 771 (1934).
110. ———, Physic. Rev. **52**, 241 (1937).
111. ——— and J. J. Hopfield, Astrophys. J. **68**, 257 (1928).
112. ——— and J. D. Shea, Univ. Cal. Publ. Math. **2**, 67 (1927).
113. ——— and H. Sponer, Physic. Rev. **28**, 259 (1926).
114. H. Biskamp, Z. Physik **86**, 33 (1933).
115. L. and E. Bloch and Ch. Shin-Piaw, C. R. Paris **201**, 824 (1935).
115a. N. T. Bobrovnikoff, Astrophys. J. **89**, 301 (1939).
116. K. F. Bonhoeffer and L. Farkas, Z. physik. Chem. A **134**, 337 (1927).
117. ——— and F. Haber, Z. physik. Chem. A **137**, 263 (1928).
118. ——— and P. Harteck, Z. physik. Chem. B **4**, 113 (1929).
119. ——— and H. Reichardt, Z. physik. Chem. A **139**, 75 (1928).
120. M. Born and J. Franck, Z. Physik **31**, 411 (1925).
121. ——— and J. E. Mayer, Z. Physik **75**, 1 (1932).
122. ——— and R. Oppenheimer, Ann. Physik **84**, 457 (1927).
123. L. v. Bozóky, Z. Physik **104**, 275 (1937).
124. W. H. Brandt, Physic. Rev. **50**, 778 (1936).
125. B. A. Brice, Physic. Rev. **35**, 960 (1930).
126. ———, Physic. Rev. **38**, 658 (1931).
127. L. O. Brockway, J. Amer. Chem. Soc. **60**, 1348 (1938).
128. ———, Rev. Mod. Phys. **8**, 231 (1936).
129. P. H. Brodersen, Z. Physik **104**, 135 (1936).
130. H. H. Brons, Dissertation (Groningen, 1934).
131. ———, Proc. Amst. **38**, 271 (1935).
132. W. G. Brown, Physic. Rev. **38**, 709 (1931).
133. ———, Physic. Rev. **38**, 1179 (1931).
134. ———, Physic. Rev. **39**, 777 (1932).
135. ———, Physic. Rev. **42**, 355 (1932).
136. ———, Z. Physik **82**, 768 (1933).
137. ——— and G. E. Gibson, Physic. Rev. **40**, 529 (1932).
138. A. Budó, Zeeman Verh. (1935), 166.
139. ———, Z. Physik **96**, 219 (1935); **98**, 437 (1936).
140. ———, Z. Physik **105**, 73 (1937).
141. ———, Z. Physik **105**, 579 (1937).
142. ——— and I. Kovács, Z. Physik **109**, 393 (1938); **111**, 633 (1939).
143. H. Bulthuis, Dissertation (Groningen, 1935).
144. ———, Physica **1**, 873 (1934).
145. ——— and D. Coster, Zeeman Verh. (1935), 135.
146. K. Butkow, Z. Physik **58**, 232 (1929).
147. G. Büttenbender and G. Herzberg, Ann. Physik **21**, 577 (1935).
148. W. Burmeister, Ber. deutsch. phys. Ges. **15**, 595 (1913).
148a. J. Cabannes and J. Dufay, C. R. Paris **203**, 903 (1936).
148b. ——— ——— and J. Gauzit, Nature **142**, 718, 755 (1938).
149. Y. Cambresier and L. Rosenfeld, Monthly Notices Roy. Astron. Soc. **93**, 710 (1933).
150. T. Carroll, Physic. Rev. **52**, 822 (1937).
151. H. Casimir, Physica **1**, 1073 (1934).
152. C. N. Challacombe and G. M. Almy, Physic. Rev. **51**, 63, 930 (1937).
153. S. Chapman, Phil. Mag. **23**, 657 (1937).
154. W. H. J. Childs and R. Mecke, Z. Physik **68**, 344 (1931).
155. A. Christy, Physic. Rev. **33**, 701 (1929).
156. ——— and S. Bloomenthal, Physic. Rev. **35**, 46 (1930).

157. C. H. D. Clark, Physic. Rev. **47**, 238 (1935).
158. A. P. Cleaves and C. W. Edwards, Physic. Rev. **48**, 850 (1935).
159. K. Clusius and E. Bartholomé, Z. Elektrochem. **40**, 524 (1934)..
160. E. U. Condon, Physic. Rev. **32**, 858 (1928).
161. ———, Physic. Rev. **41**, 759 (1932).
162. A. S. Coolidge, H. M. James, and R. D. Present, J. Chem. Phys. **4**, 193 (1936).
162a. ——— and E. L. Vernon, Physic. Rev. **54**, 726 (1938).
163. H. Cordes and H. Sponer, Z. Physik **79**, 170 (1932).
164. S. D. Cornell, Physic. Rev. **54**, 341 (1938).
165. D. Coster and F. Brons, Physica **1**, 155 (1934).
166. ——— ———, Physica **1**, 634 (1934).
167. ——— ——— and A. van der Ziel, Z. Physik **84**, 304 (1933).
168. ——— and H. H. Brons, Z. Physik **70**, 492 (1931).
169. ——— ———, Z. Physik **73**, 747 (1932).
169a. C. A. Coulson and W. E. Duncanson, Proc. Roy. Soc. London **165**, 90 (1938).
170. N. H. Coy and H. Sponer, Physic. Rev. **53**, 495 (1938).
171. F. H. Crawford, Rev. Mod. Phys. **6**, 90 (1934).
172. ——— and T. Jorgensen, Physic. Rev. **47**, 358 (1935).
173. ——— ———, Physic. Rev. **47**, 932 (1935); **49**, 745 (1936).
174. ——— and W. A. Shurcliff, Physic. Rev. **45**, 860 (1934).
175. J. Curry and G. Herzberg, Ann. Physik **19**, 800 (1934).
176. ———, L. Herzberg, and G. Herzberg, Z. Physik **86**, 348 (1933).
177. W. E. Curtis and J. Patkowski, Phil. Trans. Roy. Soc. London **232**, 395 (1934).
178. M. Czerny, Z. Physik **34**, 227 (1925).
179. O. Darbyshire, Proc. Roy. Soc. London **159**, 93 (1937).
180. G. Déjardin, Rev. Mod. Phys. **8**, 1 (1936).
181. D. M. Dennison, Proc. Roy. Soc. London **115**, 483 (1927).
182. H. Deslandres, C. R. Paris **103**, 375 (1886).
183. G. H. Dieke, Physic. Rev. **38**, 646 (1931).
184. ———, Physic. Rev. **47**, 661 (1935).
185. ———, Physic. Rev. **47**, 870 (1935).
186. ——— and H. D. Babcock, Proc. Nat. Acad. Amer. **13**, 670 (1927).
187. ——— and R. W. Blue, Physic. Rev. **45**, 395 (1934).
188. ——— and M. N. Lewis, Physic. Rev. **52**, 100 (1937).
189. ——— and W. Lochte-Holtgreven, Z. Physik **62**, 767 (1930).
190. ——— and J. W. Mauchley, Physic. Rev. **43**, 12 (1933).
191. O. S. Duffendack, R. W. Revans, and A. S. Roy, Physic. Rev. **45**, 807 (1934).
192. M. Duffieux and L. Grillet, C. R. Paris **202**, 937 (1936).
193. J. DuMond and V. Bollmann, Physic. Rev. **51**, 400 (1937).
194. J. L. Dunham, Physic. Rev. **41**, 721 (1932).
194a. ———, Physic. Rev. **34**, 438 (1929).
195. Th. Dunham, Publ. Astron. Soc. Pac. **45**, 42 (1933).
196. E. G. Dymond, Z. Physik **34**, 553 (1925).
197. L. T. Earls, Physic. Rev. **48**, 423 (1935).
198. H. Ekstein and M. Magat, C. R. Paris **199**, 264 (1934).
199. A. Elliott, Proc. Roy. Soc. London **123**, 629 (1929).
200. ———, Proc. Roy. Soc. London **127**, 638 (1930).
200a. ———, Proc. Roy. Soc. London **169**, 469 (1939).
201. ——— and W. H. B. Cameron, Proc. Roy. Soc. London **164**, 531 (1938).
202. J. W. Ellis and H. O. Kneser, Z. Physik **86**, 583 (1933).
203. ——— ———, Publ. Astron. Soc. Pac. **46**, 106 (1934).
204. V. M. Ellsworth and J. J. Hopfield, Physic. Rev. **29**, 79 (1927).
205. W. Elsasser, Z. Physik **81**, 332 (1933).
206. A. Eucken and K. Hiller, Z. physik. Chem. B **4**, 142 (1929).
207. ——— and O. Mücke, Z. physik. Chem. B **18**, 167 (1932).
208. R. S. Estey, Physic. Rev. **35**, 309 (1930).

209. H. Eyring and M. Polanyi, Z. physik. Chem. B **11**, 97 (1930).
210. E. H. Eyster, Physic. Rev. **51**, 1078 (1937).
211. A. and L. Farkas and P. Harteck, Proc. Roy. Soc. London **144**, 481 (1934).
212. L. Farkas, Z. Physik **70**, 733 (1931).
213. ———, Von den Kohlen- und Mineralölen, Vol. IV (1931), 35.
214. ———, Erg. d. exakt. Naturwiss. **12**, 163 (1933).
215. ——— and S. Levy, Z. Physik **84**, 195 (1933).
216. W. F. C. Ferguson, Physic. Rev. **31**, 969 (1928).
217. ———, Physic. Rev. **32**, 607 (1928).
218. W. Finkelnburg, Physik. Z. **31**, 1 (1930); **34**, 529 (1933).
219. ———, Z. Physik **90**, 1 (1934).
220. ———, Z. Physik **96**, 699 (1935).
221. ———, Acta Phys. Pol. **5**, 1 (1936).
222. ———, Z. Physik **99**, 798 (1936).
223. ——— and O. T. Hahn, Physik. Z. **39**, 98 (1938).
224. P. J. Flory, J. Chem. Phys. **4**, 23 (1936).
225. ——— and H. L. Johnston, J. Amer. Chem. Soc. **57**, 2641 (1935).
226. A. Fowler and C. J. Bakker, Proc. Roy. Soc. London **136**, 28 (1932).
227. J. G. Fox and G. Herzberg, Physic. Rev. **52**, 638 (1937).
228. H. H. Franck and H. Reichardt, Naturwiss. **24**, 171 (1936).
229. J. Franck, Trans. Faraday Soc. **21**, 536 (1925).
230. ——— and H. Kuhn, Naturwiss. **20**, 923 (1932).
231. ——— and H. Sponer, Gött. Nachr. 1928, p. 241.
232. ——— and E. Teller, Z. physik. Chem. B **18**, 88 (1932).
233. W. R. Fredrickson, Physic. Rev. **34**, 207 (1929).
233a.——— and M. E. Hogan, Physic. Rev. **46**, 454 (1934).
233b.——— and W. W. Watson, Physic. Rev. **39**, 753 (1932).
234. A. A. Frost and O. Oldenberg, J. Chem. Phys. **4**, 642, 781 (1936).
235. Y. Fujioka and Y. Tanaka, Sci. Pap. Inst. Physic. Chem. Res. (Tokyo) **30**, 121 (1936).
236. ——— ———, Sci. Pap. Inst. Physic. Chem. Res. (Tokyo) **32**, 143 (1937).
237. ——— ———, Sci. Pap. Inst. Physic. Chem. Res. (Tokyo) **34**, 713 (1938).
238. ——— and T. Wada, Sci. Pap. Inst. Physic. Chem. Res. (Tokyo) **27**, 210 (1935).
239. G. W. Funke, Z. Physik **84**, 610 (1933).
240. ———, Z. Physik **96**, 787 (1935).
240a.———, Dissertation (Stockholm, 1936).
241. ——— and B. Grundström, Z. Physik **100**, 293 (1936).
242. J. W. Gabel and R. V. Zumstein, Physic. Rev. **52**, 726 (1937).
243. H. G. Gale and G. S. Monk, Astrophys. J. **69**, 77 (1929).
244. H. Gajewski, Physik. Z. **33**, 122 (1932).
245. A. G. Gaydon and R. W. B. Pearse, Proc. Roy. Soc. London **148**, 312 (1935).
245a.——— ———, Nature (London) **140**, 110 (1937).
246. ——— ———, Nature (London) **142**, 291 (1938); Rep. Progress in Physics **5**, 252 (1938).
247. J. Genard, C. R. Paris **197**, 1402 (1933).
248. ———, Physica **1**, 849 (1934).
249. L. Gerö, Z. Physik **99**, 52 (1936).
250. ———, Z. Physik **100**, 374 (1936).
251. ———, Z. Physik **101**, 311 (1936).
252. ———, G. Herzberg, and R. Schmid, Physic. Rev. **52**, 467 (1937).
252a.W. F. Giauque, J. Amer. Chem. Soc. **52**, 4808, 4816 (1930).
253. ——— and H. L. Johnston, Nature (London) **123**, 318 (1929); J. Amer. Chem. Soc. **51**, 1436 (1929).
254. ——— ———, Nature (London) **123**, 831 (1929); J. Amer. Chem. Soc. **51**, 3528 (1929).
255. G. E. Gibson, Z. Physik **50**, 692 (1928).
256. ——— and N. S. Bayliss, Physic. Rev. **44**, 188 (1933).
257. ——— and W. Heitler, Z. Physik **49**, 465 (1928).

258. G. E. Gibson, and R. C. Ramsperger, Physic. Rev. **30**, 598 (1927).
259. ———, O. K. Rice, and N. S. Bayliss, Physic. Rev. **44**, 193 (1933).
260. C. Gilbert, Physic. Rev. **49**, 619 (1936).
261. G. Glockler and D. L. Fuller, J. Chem. Phys. **1**, 886 (1933).
262. P. Goldfinger, W. Jeunehomme, and B. Rosen, Nature (London) **138**, 205 (1936).
263. C. F. Goodeve and A. W. C. Taylor, Proc. Roy. Soc. London **152**, 221 (1935).
264. ——— ———, Proc. Roy. Soc. London **154**, 181 (1936).
264a. A. R. Gordon and C. Barnes, J. Chem. Phys. **1**, 297 (1933).
265. C. Ghosh, Z. Physik **78**, 521 (1932).
266. ———, Z. Physik **86**, 241 (1933).
267. P. N. Ghosh and G. N. Ball, Z. Physik **71**, 362 (1931).
268. B. Grundström, Z. Physik **69**, 235 (1931).
269. ———, Dissertation (Stockholm, 1936).
270. ———, Z. Physik **99**, 595 (1936).
271. ———, Nature (London) **141**, 555 (1938).
272. ——— and E. Hulthén, Nature (London) **125**, 634 (1930).
273. ——— and P. Valberg, Z. Physik **108**, 326 (1938).
274. A. Guntsch, Z. Physik **86**, 262 (1933).
275. ———, Z. Physik **87**, 312 (1934).
276. ———, Z. Physik **93**, 534 (1934).
277. ———, Z. Physik **104**, 584 (1937).
278. M. L. Gurnsey, Physic. Rev. **46**, 114 (1934).
279. O. Hahn, Ber. deutsch. chem. Ges. **71A**, 1 (1938).
279a. W. Hanle, Physik. Z. **38**, 995 (1937).
280. J. D. Hardy, E. F. Barker, and D. M. Dennison, Physic. Rev. **42**, 279 (1932).
281. A. Harvey, Proc. Roy. Soc. London **133**, 336 (1931).
282. ——— and F. A. Jenkins, Physic. Rev. **35**, 789 (1930).
283. L. B. Headrick and G. W. Fox, Physic. Rev. **35**, 1033 (1930).
284. M. H. Hebb, Physic. Rev. **49**, 610 (1936).
285. K. Hedfeld, Z. Physik **68**, 610 (1931).
286. A. Heimer, Naturwiss. **24**, 491 (1936).
286a. ———, Z. Physik **95**, 328 (1935).
287. ———, Z. Physik **103**, 621 (1936).
288. ———, Dissertation (Stockholm, 1937).
289. ———, Z. Physik **104**, 448 (1937).
290. ——— and T. Heimer, Z. Physik **84**, 222 (1933).
291. T. Heimer, Z. Physik **95**, 321 (1935).
292. ———, Dissertation (Stockholm, 1937).
293. W. Heitler, Marx's Handb. d. Radiol. VI, **2**, 485 (1934).
294. ——— and G. Herzberg, Naturwiss. **17**, 673 (1929).
295. ——— and F. London, Z. Physik **44**, 455 (1927).
296. E. Hellmig, Z. Physik **104**, 694 (1937).
297. K. H. Hellwege, Z. Physik **100**, 644 (1936).
298. H. J. Henning, Ann. Physik **13**, 599 (1932).
299. V. Henri, C. R. Paris **177**, 1037 (1923).
300. ———, Leipz. Vortr. **1931**, 131.
301. ——— and M. C. Teves, Nature (London) **114**, 894 (1924).
302. G. Herzberg, Ann. Physik **84**, 565 (1927).
303. ———, Ann. Physik **86**, 189 (1928).
304. ———, Z. Physik **57**, 601 (1929).
305. ———, Z. physik. Chem. B **4**, 223 (1929).
306. ———, Z. physik. Chem. B **9**, 43 (1930).
307. ———, Z. Physik **61**, 604 (1930).
308. ———, Leipz. Vortr. **1931**, 167.
309. ———, Erg. d. exakt. Naturwiss. **10**, 207 (1931).
310. ———, Naturwiss. **20**, 577 (1932).
311. ———, Ann. Physik **15**, 677 (1932).

312. G. Herzberg, Nature (London) **133,** 759 (1934).
313. ———, J. Phys. Chem. **41,** 299 (1937).
314. ———, Chem. Rev. **20,** 145 (1937).
315. ———, Astrophys. J. **87,** 428 (1938).
316. ———, Astrophys. J. **89,** 290 (1939).
317. ——— and L. Mundie (unpublished).
318. ——— and J. W. T. Spinks, Z. Physik **89,** 474 (1934).
319. ——— and H. Sponer, Z. physik. Chem. B **26,** 1 (1934).
320. L. Herzberg, Z. Physik **84,** 571 (1933).
320a. G. Hettner, Z. Physik **89,** 234 (1934).
321. K. Hilferding and W. Steiner, Z. physik. Chem. B **30,** 399 (1935).
322. E. L. Hill, Physic. Rev. **34,** 1507 (1929).
323. ——— and J. H. Van Vleck, Physic. Rev. **32,** 250 (1923).
324. T. R. Hogness and J. Franck, Z. Physik **44,** 26 (1927).
325. W. Holst, Z. Physik **90,** 728 (1934).
326. ———, Z. Physik **90,** 735 (1934).
327. ———, Z. Physik **93,** 55 (1934).
328. ——— and E. Hulthén, Z. Physik **90,** 712 (1934).
329. H. Hönl and F. London, Z. Physik **33,** 803 (1925).
330. J. J. Hopfield, Physic. Rev. **35,** 1130; **36,** 784 (1930).
331. ———, Physic. Rev. **36,** 789 (1930).
332. ——— and R. T. Birge, Physic. Rev. **29,** 922 (1927).
333. T. Hori, Z. Physik **71,** 478 (1931).
334. ———, Mem. Ryojun Coll. Eng. **6,** 1 (1933).
335. ——— and J. Huriuti, Z. Physik **101,** 279 (1936).
336. H. G. Howell, Proc. Roy. Soc. London **148,** 696 (1935).
337. ———, Proc. Roy. Soc. London **153,** 683 (1936).
338. ———, Proc. Roy. Soc. London **155,** 141 (1936).
339. ———, Proc. Roy. Soc. London **160,** 242 (1937).
340. ——— and N. Coulsan, Proc. Roy. Soc. London **166,** 925 (1938).
340a. ——— and G. D. Rochester, Proc. Phys. Soc. London **51,** 329 (1939).
341. I. Hudes, Physic. Rev. **52,** 1256 (1937).
341a. D. S. Hughes and P. E. Lloyd, Physic. Rev. **52,** 1215 (1937).
342. E. Hulthén, Z. Physik **32,** 32 (1925).
342a. ———, Physic. Rev. **29,** 97 (1927).
343. ———, Nature (London) **126,** 56 (1930).
343a. ——— and A. Heimer, Nature (London) **129,** 399 (1932).
344. ——— and G. Johannson, Z. Physik **26,** 308 (1924).
345. ——— and R. Rydberg, Nature (London) **131,** 470 (1933).
345a. R. F. Humphreys and W. R. Fredrickson, Physic. Rev. **50,** 542 (1936).
346. F. Hund, Z. Physik **42,** 93 (1927).
347. ———, Z. Physik **63,** 719 (1930).
348. ———, Handb. d. Phys. **24,** I, 561 (1933).
349. R. F. Hunter and R. Samuel, Nature (London) **138,** 411 (1936).
349a. E. Hutchisson, Physic. Rev. **37,** 45 (1931).
350. E. A. Hylleraas, Z. Physik **71,** 739 (1931).
351. ———, Z. Physik **96,** 643 (1935); Physik. Z. **36,** 599 (1936).
352. H. H. van Iddekinge, Nature (London) **125,** 858 (1930).
353. S. Imanishi, Sci. Pap. Inst. Physic. Chem. Res. (Tokyo) **31,** 247 (1937).
353a. ———, Nature (London **143,** 165 (1939).
354. E. S. Imes, Astrophys. J. **50,** 251 (1919).
355. M. Ishaq, Proc. Roy. Soc. London **159,** 110 (1937).
356. ——— and R. W. B. Pearse, Proc. Roy. Soc. London **156,** 221 (1936).
357. G. P. Ittmann, Z. Physik **61,** 616 (1931).
358. ———, Naturwiss. **22,** 118 (1934).
359. A. Jabłoński, Z. Physik **70,** 723 (1931).
360. G. Jaffé, Z. Physik **87,** 535 (1934).
361. H. M. James and A. S. Coolidge, J. Chem. Phys. **1,** 825 (1933); **3,** 129 (1935).
362. ——— ———, Astrophys. J. **87,** 438 (1938).

363. H. M. James and A. S. Coolidge, Physic. Rev. **55,** 184 (1939).
364. ——— ——— and R. D. Present, J. Chem. Phys. **4,** 187 (1936).
365. C. Jausseran, L. Grillet, and M. Duffieux, C. R. Paris **205,** 39 (1937).
366. F. A. Jenkins, Physic. Rev. **31,** 539 (1928).
367. ———, Physic. Rev. **35,** 315 (1930).
368. ———, Physic. Rev. **47,** 783 (1935).
369. ———, H. A. Barton, and R. S. Mulliken, Physic. Rev. **30,** 150 (1927).
370. ——— and R. Grinfeld, Physic. Rev. **45,** 229 (1934).
371. ——— and A. Harvey, Physic. Rev. **39,** 922 (1932).
372. ——— and H. de Laszlo, Proc. Roy. Soc. London **122,** 103 (1929).
373. ——— and A. McKellar, Physic. Rev. **42,** 464 (1932).
374. ——— and L. S. Ornstein, Proc. Amst. **35,** 1212 (1932).
375. ——— and G. D. Rochester, Physic. Rev. **52,** 1135 (1937).
376. ——— ———, Physic. Rev. **52,** 1141 (1937).
377. ———, Y. K. Roots, and R. S. Mulliken, Physic. Rev. **39,** 16 (1932).
378. ——— and L. A. Strait, Physic. Rev. **47,** 136 (1935).
379. ——— and D. E. Wooldridge, Physic. Rev. **53,** 137 (1938).
380. C. R. Jeppesen, Physic. Rev. **44,** 165 (1933).
381. ———, Physic. Rev. **49,** 797 (1936).
382. M. A. Jeppesen, Physic. Rev. **50,** 445 (1936).
382a. W. Jeunehomme, Actualités scientifiques et industrialles No. 569 (1937).
383. W. Jevons, Proc. Roy. Soc. London **110,** 365 (1926).
384. ———, Proc. Phys. Soc. London **48,** 563 (1936).
384a. ———, Proc. Phys. Soc. London **50,** 910 (1938).
385. ——— and L. A. Bashford, Proc. Phys. Soc. London **49,** 554 (1937).
386. ——— ——— and H. V. A. Briscoe, Proc. Phys. Soc. London **49,** 532 (1937).
387. ——— ——— ———, Proc. Phys. Soc. London **49,** 543 (1937).
388. J. Joffe and H. C. Urey, Physic. Rev. **43,** 761 (1933).
389. L. W. Johnson and R. C. Johnson, Proc. Roy. Soc. London **133,** 207 (1931).
390. R. C. Johnson, Phil. Trans. Roy. Soc. London **226,** 157 (1927).
391. ———, Proc. Roy. Soc. London **122,** 161 (1929).
392. ———, Proc. Roy. Soc. London **122,** 189 (1929).
392a. H. L. Johnston and C. O. Davis, J. Amer. Chem. Soc. **56,** 271 (1934).
393. G. Joos and W. Finkelnburg, Die Physik **4,** 35 (1936).
394. H. Juraszyńska and M. Szulc, Acta Phys. Pol. **7,** 49 (1938).
395. J. Kaplan, Physic. Rev. **38,** 373, 1079 (1931).
396. ———, Physic. Rev. **44,** 947 (1933); **45,** 675 (1934).
397. W. Kapuszinski and J. G. Eymers, Proc. Roy. Soc. London **122,** 58 (1929).
398. L. S. Kassel, Chem. Rev. **18,** 277 (1936).
399. ———, Chem. Rev. **21,** 331 (1937).
400. A. S. King and R. T. Birge, Astrophys. J. **72,** 251 (1930).
400a. G. W. King, J. Chem. Phys. **6,** 378 (1938).
401. G. D. Kinzer and G. M. Almy, Physic. Rev. **52,** 814 (1937).
402. M. Kiuti, Jap. J. Phys. **1,** 29 (1922); **4,** 13 (1925).
402a. ——— and H. Hasunuma, Proc. Phys. Math. Soc. Japan **19,** 821 (1937).
403. D. E. Kirkpatrick and E. O. Salant, Physic. Rev. **48,** 945 (1935).
404. O. Klein, Z. Physik **76,** 226 (1932).
405. A. Klemenc, R. Wechsberg, and G. Wagner, Z. Elektrochem. **40,** 488 (1934).
406. H. P. Knauss and H. S. Ballard, Physic. Rev. **48,** 796 (1935).
407. ——— and M. S. McCay, Physic. Rev. **52,** 1143 (1937).
408. C. C. Ko, Journ. Frankl. Inst. **217,** 173 (1934).
409. V. Kondratjew and A. Lauris, Z. Physik **92,** 741 (1934).
410. ——— and A. Leipunsky, Trans. Faraday Soc. **25,** 736 (1929).
411. ——— and E. Olsson, Z. Physik **99,** 671 (1936).
412. ——— and L. Polak, Z. Physik **76,** 386 (1932).
413. ——— ———, Physik. Z. d. Sowjetunion **4,** 764 (1933).
414. E. Kondratjewa and V. Kondratjew, Acta Phys. Chim. **3,** 1 (1935).

415. P. G. Koontz, Physic. Rev. **48**, 138 (1935).
416. ———, Physic. Rev. **48**, 707 (1935).
417. ——— and W. W. Watson, Physic. Rev. **48**, 937 (1935).
418. H. Kopfermann and H. Schweitzer, Z. Physik **61**, 87 (1930).
419. I. Kovács, Z. Physik **106**, 431 (1937).
420. ———, Z. Physik **109**, 387 (1938); **111**, 640 (1939).
420a. H. A. Kramers, Z. Physik **53**, 422 (1929).
420b. A. Kratzer, Z. Physik **3**, 460 (1920); **4**, 476 (1921).
421. R. de L. Kronig, Z. Physik **50**, 347 (1928).
422. ———, Z. Physik **62**, 300 (1930).
423. ———, Physica **1**, 617 (1934).
424. H. Krüger, Naturwiss. **26**, 445 (1938); Z. Physik **111**, 467 (1939).
425. H. Kühl, VDI.-Forschungsheft 1935, 373.
426. H. Kuhn, Z. Physik **39**, 77 (1926).
427. ———, Naturwiss. **16**, 552 (1928).
428. ———, Z. Physik **63**, 458 (1930).
429. ———, Z. Physik **76**, 782 (1932).
430. ———, Phil. Mag. **18**, 987 (1934).
431. ———, Proc. Roy. Soc. London **158**, 212, 230 (1937).
432. ———, Physic. Rev. **52**, 133 (1937).
433. ——— and S. Arrhenius, Z. Physik **82**, 716 (1933).
434. ——— and K. Freudenberg, Z. Physik **76**, 38 (1932).
435. ——— and F. London, Phil. Mag. **18**, 983 (1934).
436. ——— and O. Oldenberg, Physic. Rev. **41**, 72 (1932).
437. W. Kuhn and H. Martin, Z. Physik **81**, 482 (1933).
438. P. Kusch, Physic. Rev. **49**, 218 (1936).
439. R. W. Ladenburg, J. Opt. Soc. **25**, 259 (1935).
439a. G. O. Langstroth, Proc. Roy. Soc. London **146**, 166 (1934); **150**, 371 (1935).
439b. C. E. Leberknight and J. A. Ord, Physic. Rev. **51**, 430 (1937).
440. S. W. Leifson, Astrophys. J. **63**, 73 (1926).
441. J. E. Lennard-Jones, Trans. Faraday Soc. **25**, 668 (1929).
442. H. Lessheim and R. Samuel, Proc. Ind. Acad. **1**, 623 (1935).
443. H. Levi, Dissertation (Berlin, 1934).
444. B. Lewis and G. v. Elbe, J. Amer. Chem. Soc. **55**, 511 (1933); **57**, 1399 (1935).
445. ——— ———, J. Amer. Chem. Soc. **57**, 612 (1935).
445a. M. N. Lewis and J. V. White, Physic. Rev. **55**, 894 (1939).
446. P. Lindau, Z. Physik **25**, 247; **26**, 343; **30**, 187 (1924).
447. W. Lochte-Holtgreven, Z. Physik **67**, 590 (1931).
448. ———, Z. Physik **103**, 395 (1936).
449. ——— and G. H. Dieke, Ann. Physik **3**, 937 (1929).
450. ——— and H. Maecker, Z. Physik **105**, 1 (1937).
451. ——— and E. S. van der Vleugel, Z. Physik **70**, 188 (1931).
452. F. London, Z. Physik **46**, 455 (1928).
453. ———, Sommerfeld-Festschrift, p. 104 (Leipzig, 1928); Z. Elektrochem. **35**, 552 (1929).
454. ———, Z. Physik **63**, 245 (1930).
455. ———, Z. physik. Chem. B **11**, 222 (1930).
456. ———, Z. Physik **74**, 143 (1932).
456a. F. W. Loomis, Astrophys. J. **52**, 248 (1920).
457. ———, Physic. Rev. **29**, 112 (1927).
458. ———, Physic. Rev. **38**, 2153 (1931).
459. ——— and M. J. Arvin, Physic. Rev. **46**, 286 (1934).
460. ——— and W. H. Brandt, Physic. Rev. **49**, 55 (1936).
461. ——— and H. Q. Fuller, Physic. Rev. **39**, 180 (1932).
462. ——— and P. Kusch, Physic. Rev. **46**, 292 (1934).
463. ——— and R. E. Nusbaum, Physic. Rev. **38**, 1447 (1931).
464. ——— ———, Physic. Rev. **39**, 89 (1932).
465. ——— ———, Physic. Rev. **40**, 380 (1932).

466. F. W. Loomis and T. F. Watson, Physic. Rev. **48**, 280 (1935).
467. —— and R. W. Wood, Physic. Rev. **32**, 223 (1928).
468. —— ——, Physic. Rev. **38**, 854 (1931).
469. W. Lotmar, Z. Physik **93**, 528 (1935).
470. F. Lowater, Proc. Phys. Soc. London **44**, 51 (1932).
471. ——, Phil. Trans. Roy. Soc. London A **234**, 355 (1935).
471a. R. W. Lunt, R. W. B. Pearse, and E. C. W. Smith, Proc. Roy. Soc. London **155**, 173 (1936).
471b. E. R. Lyman, Physic. Rev. **53**, 379 (1938).
472. J. K. L. MacDonald, Proc. Roy. Soc. London **123**, 103 (1929); **131**, 146 (1931).
473. ——, Proc. Roy. Soc. London **138**, 183 (1932).
474. P. C. Mahanti, Nature (London) **125**, 819 (1930).
475. ——, Physic. Rev. **42**, 609 (1932).
476. ——, Proc. Phys. Soc. London **46**, 51 (1934).
477. ——, Proc. Phys. Soc. London **47**, 433 (1935).
478. —— and A. K. Sen Gupta, Z. Physik **109**, 39 (1938).
479. K. Mahla, Z. Physik **81**, 625 (1933).
480. H. Margenau, Physic. Rev. **48**, 755 (1935).
481. —— and W. W. Watson, Rev. Mod. Phys. **8**, 22 (1936).
482. E. V. Martin, Physic. Rev. **41**, 167 (1932).
482a. L. D. Matheson, Physic. Rev. **40**, 813 (1932).
483. L. R. Maxwell, S. B. Hendricks, and V. M. Mosley, Physic. Rev. **52**, 968 (1937).
484. —— and V. M. Mosley, Physic. Rev. **51**, 684 (1937).
484a. —— —— and S. B. Hendricks, Physic. Rev. **50**, 41 (1936).
485. J. C. McLennan and J. H. McLeod, Nature (London) **123**, 160 (1929); Trans. Roy. Soc. Can. III, **22**, 413 (1928); **23**, 19 (1929).
486. R. Mecke, Z. Physik **31**, 709 (1925).
487. ——, Z. Physik **32**, 823 (1925).
488. ——, Z. Physik **42**, 390 (1927).
489. ——, Trans. Faraday Soc. **30**, 200 (1934).
490. P. Mesnage, C. R. Paris **204**, 1929 (1937).
490a. ——, C. R. Paris **206**, 1634 (1938).
491. C. F. Meyer and A. A. Levin, Physic. Rev. **34**, 44 (1929).
492. E. Miescher, Helv. Phys. Acta **8**, 279 (1935).
493. ——, Helv. Phys. Acta **8**, 486 (1935).
494. ——, Helv. Phys. Acta **11**, 463 (1938).
495. —— and M. Wehrli, Helv. Phys. Acta **7**, 331 (1934).
496. R. A. Millikan, Ann. Physik **32**, 34 (1938).
497. R. Minkowski, Z. Physik **93**, 731 (1935).
498. K. R. More, Physic. Rev. **54**, 122 (1938).
499. —— and S. D. Cornell, Physic. Rev. **53**, 806 (1938).
500. —— and A. H. Parker, Physic. Rev. **52**, 1150 (1937).
501. F. Morgan, Physic. Rev. **49**, 41 (1936).
502. ——, Physic. Rev. **49**, 47 (1936).
503. ——, Physic. Rev. **50**, 603 (1936).
503a. W. Mörikofer, Dissertation (Basle, 1925).
504. P. M. Morse, Physic. Rev. **34**, 57 (1929).
505. —— and E. C. G. Stueckelberg, Physic. Rev. **33**, 932 (1929).
505a. S. Mrozowski, Nature (London) **129**, 399 (1932).
506. —— and M. Szulc, Acta Phys. Pol. **6**, 44 (1937).
507. B. C. Mukherji, Z. Physik **70**, 552 (1931).
508. R. S. Mulliken, Physic. Rev. **25**, 259 (1925).
509. ——, Physic. Rev. **25**, 509 (1925).
509a. ——, Physic. Rev. **32**, 186 (1928).
510. ——, Physic. Rev. **32**, 880 (1928).
511. ——, Trans. Faraday Soc. **25**, 634 (1929).
512. ——, Rev. Mod. Phys. **2**, 60 (1930).
513. ——, Rev. Mod. Phys. **3**, 89 (1931).

514. R. S. Mulliken, Rev. Mod. Phys. **4,** 1 (1932).
515. ——, Physic. Rev. **36,** 611 (1930).
516. ——, Physic. Rev. **36,** 699 (1930).
517. ——, Physic. Rev. **41,** 49 (1932).
518. ——, Physic. Rev. **46,** 144 (1934).
519. ——, Physic. Rev. **46,** 549 (1934).
519a.——, J. Chem. Phys. **2,** 400, 712 (1934).
519b.——, J. Chem. Phys. **4,** 620 (1936).
520. ——, Physic. Rev. **50,** 1017, 1028 (1936).
521. ——, Physic. Rev. **51,** 310 (1937).
522. ——, J. Phys. Chem. **41,** 5 (1937).
523. —— and A. Christy, Physic. Rev. **38,** 87 (1931).
524. —— and D. S. Stevens, Physic. Rev. **44,** 720 (1933).
525. G. M. Murphy and H. L. Johnston, Physic. Rev. **46,** 95 (1934).
526. G. Nakamura and T. Shidei, Jap. J. Phys. **10,** 11 (1935).
527. S. M. Naudé, Physic. Rev. **36,** 333 (1930).
528. ——, Proc. Roy. Soc. London **136,** 114 (1932).
528a.——, South African J. Sci. **32,** 103 (1935).
529. J. v. Neumann and E. Wigner, Physik. Z. **30,** 467 (1929).
530. T. E. Nevin, Nature (London) **140,** 1101 (1937); Phil. Trans. Roy. Soc. London **237,** 471 (1938).
531. A. H. Nielsen and H. H. Nielsen, Physic. Rev. **47,** 585 (1935).
532. L. Nordheim, Müller-Pouillet's Lehrb. d. Phys. IV, **4,** 798ff. (1934).
533. G. Nordheim-Pöschl, Ann. Physik **26,** 258 (1936).
534. F. Norling, Z. Physik **95,** 179 (1935).
535. ——, Z. Physik **104,** 638 (1935).
536. ——, Z. Physik **106,** 177 (1937).
537. O. Oldenberg, Z. Physik **47,** 184 (1928); **55,** 1 (1929).
538. ——, Z. Physik **56,** 563 (1929).
539. ——, Physic. Rev. **46,** 210 (1934).
540. ——, J. Phys. Chem. **41,** 293 (1937).
540a.—— and F. F. Rieke, J. Chem. Phys. **6,** 439, 779 (1938).
541. E. Olsson, Z. Physik **73,** 732 (1932).
542. ——, Z. Physik **90,** 138 (1934).
543. ——, Z. Physik **93,** 206 (1935).
544. ——, Z. Physik **95,** 215 (1935).
545. ——, Z. Physik **100,** 656 (1936).
546. ——, Z. Physik **104,** 402 (1937).
547. ——, Z. Physik **108,** 40 (1937).
548. ——, Dissertation (Stockholm, 1938).
549. L. S. Ornstein and W. R. van Wijk, Z. Physik **49,** 315 (1928).
549a. C. H. Page, Physic. Rev. **53,** 426 (1938).
550. A. E. Parker, Physic. Rev. **46,** 301 (1934).
551. ——, Physic. Rev. **47,** 349 (1935).
552. J. Patkowski and W. E. Curtis, Trans. Faraday Soc. **25,** 725 (1929).
552a. F. W. Paul and H. P. Knauss, Physic. Rev. **54,** 1072 (1938).
553. L. Pauling, J. Amer. Chem. Soc. **53,** 1367, 3225 (1931).
554. ——, J. Amer. Chem. Soc. **54,** 988 (1932).
555. —— and L. O. Brockway, J. Chem. Phys. **2,** 867 (1934).
556. R. W. B. Pearse, Proc. Roy. Soc. London **122,** 442 (1929).
557. ——, Proc. Roy. Soc. London **129,** 328 (1930).
558. ——, Proc. Roy. Soc. London **143,** 112 (1934).
559. —— and A. G. Gaydon, Proc. Phys. Soc. London **50,** 201 (1938).
560. W. G. Penney, Phil. Mag. **11,** 602 (1931).
561. A. Petrowa, Acta Physicochim. **4,** 559 (1936).
562. E. Placzek, Marx's Handb. d. Radiol. VI, **2,** 205 (1934).
563. E. K. Plyler and E. F. Barker, Physic. Rev. **44,** 984 (1933).
563a.—— and D. Williams, Physic. Rev. **49,** 215 (1936).
564. G. Piccardi, Gazz. chim. Ital. **63,** 887 (1933).
565. ——, Atti Acad. Lincei **21,** 589 (1935).

566. M. Polanyi and E. Wigner, Z. Physik **33**, 429 (1925).
567. W. C. Pomeroy, Physic. Rev. **29**, 59 (1927).
568. G. Pöschl and E. Teller, Z. Physik **83**, 143 (1933).
569. R. D. Present, Physic. Rev. **48**, 140 (1935).
569a.W. M. Preston, Physic. Rev. **51**, 298 (1937).
570. W. C. Price, Proc. Roy. Soc. London **167**, 216 (1938).
571. ———— and G. Collins, Physic. Rev. **48**, 714 (1935).
572. A. Prikhotko, Physik. Z. d. Sowjetunion **11**, 465 (1937).
573. P. Pringsheim, Handb. d. Phys. **23**, I, 185 (1933).
574. E. Rabinowitch, Trans. Faraday Soc. **33**, 283 (1937).
575. ———— and W. C. Wood, J. Chem. Phys. **4**, 358 (1936).
576. ————————, J. Chem. Phys. **4**, 497 (1936).
577. H. M. Randall, Rev. Mod. Phys. **10**, 72 (1938).
578. F. Rasetti, Physic. Rev. **34**, 367 (1929).
579. ————, Z. Physik **61**, 598 (1930).
580. W. Rave, Z. Physik **94**, 72 (1935).
581. Lord Rayleigh, Proc. Roy. Soc. London **116**, 702 (1927).
582. D. N. Read, Physic. Rev. **46**, 571 (1934).
583. O. Reinkober, Hand- u Jahrb. d. chem. Phys. **9**, II, 1.
584. O. K. Rice, Physic. Rev. **37**, 1187, 1551 (1930).
585. O. W. Richardson, Proc. Roy. Soc. London **152**, 503 (1935).
586. ————, Proc. Roy. Soc. London **160**, 487 (1937); **164**, 316 (1938).
587. ———— and T. B. Rymer, Proc. Roy. Soc. London **147**, 24, 251, 272 (1934).
588. R. S. Richardson, Publ. Astron. Soc. Pac. **44**, 250 (1932).
589. H. Richter, Physik. Z. **33**, 587 (1932); **36**, 85 (1935).
590. O. Riechemeier, H. Senftleben, and H. Pastorff, Ann. Physik **19**, 202 (1934).
591. R. Ritschl, Z. Physik **42**, 172 (1927).
592. G. D. Rochester, Proc. Roy. Soc. London **153**, 407 (1936); **167**, 567 (1938).
593. ————, Z. Physik **101**, 769 (1936).
594. ————, Physic. Rev. **51**, 486 (1937).
595. ———— and H. G. Howell, Proc. Roy. Soc. London **148**, 157 (1935).
596. R. Rompe, Z. Physik **101**, 214 (1936); Physik. Z. **37**, 807 (1936).
597. B. Rosen, Acta Phys. Pol. **5**, 193 (1936).
598. ————, Physica **6**, 205 (1939).
599. ———— and M. Désirant, C. R. Paris **200**, 1659 (1935).
600. L. Rosenfeld, Monthly Notices Roy. Astron. Soc. **93**, 724 (1933).
601. J. E. Rosenthal, Proc. Nat. Acad. Amer. **21**, 281 (1935).
602. ———— and F. A. Jenkins, Physic. Rev. **33**, 163 (1929).
603. ———— ————, Proc. Nat. Acad. Amer. **15**, 381 (1929).
604. F. D. Rossini, Bur. Stand. J. Res. **6**, 1 (1931).
604a.S. Rouppert, Acta Phys. Pol. **6**, 228 (1937).
604b.H. A. Rühmkorf, Ann. Physik. **33**, 21 (1938).
605. K. Rumpf, Z. physik. Chem. B **38**, 469 (1938).
606. H. N. Russell, Astrophys. J. **79**, 317 (1934).
607. ————, Nature (London) **135**, 219 (1935).
608. R. Rydberg, Z. Physik **73**, 376 (1932).
609. ————, Z. Physik **80**, 514 (1933).
610. ————, Dissertation (Stockholm, 1934).
611. E. O. Salant and A. Sandow, Physic. Rev. **37**, 373 (1931).
612. H. Salow and W. Steiner, Z. Physik **99**, 137 (1936).
613. R. Samuel, Current Science **4**, 762 (1936).
614. I. Sandemann, Proc. Roy. Soc. Edinburgh **55**, 72 (1935).
615. P. G. Saper, Physic. Rev. **42**, 498 (1932).
616. P. Scherrer and R. Stössel, Helv. Phys. Acta **3**, 435 (1931).
617. R. Schlapp, Physic. Rev. **51**, 342 (1937).
618. R. Schmid, Z. Physik **49**, 428 (1928); **64**, 84 (1930).
619. ———— and L. Gerö, Z. Physik **93**, 656 (1935).
620. ———— ————, Z. Physik **94**, 386 (1935).
621. ———— ————, Z. Physik **101**, 343 (1936).

622. R. Schmid and L. Gerö, Z. Physik **104**, 724 (1937).
623. ——— ———, Z. Physik **105**, 36 (1937).
624. ——— ———, Z. physik. Chem. B **36**, 105 (1937).
624a.——— ——— and J. Zemplén, Proc. Phys. Soc. London **50**, 283 (1938).
625. E. Scholz, Z. Physik **106**, 230 (1937).
625a. K. Scholz, Z. Physik **78**, 751 (1932).
626. H. Schüler and H. Gollnow, Z. Physik **108**, 714; **109**, 432 (1938).
626a.——— ——— and H. Haber, Z. Physik **111**, 508 (1939).
627. J. Sedov and A. Filippov, C. R. Leningrad **4**, 376 (1934).
628. H. Senftleben and E. Germer, Ann. Physik **2**, 847 (1929).
629. A. K. Sen Gupta, Bull. Acad. Alahabad **2**, 245 (1933).
630. ———, Z. Physik **91**, 471 (1934).
631. ———, Proc. Phys. Soc. London **47**, 247 (1935).
631a.———, Proc. Phys. Soc. London **51**, 62 (1939).
632. C. V. Shapiro, R. C. Gibbs, and A. W. Laubengayer, Physic. Rev. **40**, 354 (1932).
633. E. N. Shawhan, Physic. Rev. **48**, 521 (1935); **49**, 810 (1936).
634. ———, Physic. Rev. **48**, 343 (1935).
635. J. D. Shea, Physic. Rev. **30**, 825 (1927).
635a. P. E. Shearin, Physic. Rev. **48**, 299 (1935).
636. T. Shidei, Jap. J. Phys. **11**, 23 (1936).
637. C. Shin-Piaw, C. R. Paris **201**, 1181 (1935).
638. J. C. Slater, Physic. Rev. **37**, 481; **38**, 1109 (1931).
639. R. Smoluchowski, Z. Physik **85**, 191 (1933).
640. W. R. Smythe, Physic. Rev. **45**, 299 (1934).
641. H. Snell, Phil. Trans. Roy. Soc. London A **234**, 115 (1934).
642. C. P. Snow, J. F. G. Rawlins, and E. K. Rideal, Proc. Roy. Soc. London **124**, 453 (1929).
643. ——— and E. K. Rideal, Proc. Roy. Soc. London **125**, 462 (1929).
644. K. Sommermeyer, Z. Physik **56**, 548 (1929).
645. J. W. T. Spinks, Z. Physik **88**, 511 (1934).
646. H. Sponer, Z. Physik **34**, 622 (1925).
647. ———, Erg. exakt. Naturwiss. **6**, 75 (1927).
648. ———, Z. Physik **41**, 611 (1927).
649. ———, Leipz. Vortr. **1931**, 107.
650. J. R. Stehn, J. Chem. Phys. **5**, 186 (1937).
651. W. Steiner, Z. physik. Chem. B **15**, 249 (1932).
652. G. Stenvinkel, Dissertation (Stockholm, 1936).
653. D. S. Stevens, Physic. Rev. **38**, 1292 (1931).
654. R. Stössel, Ann. Physik **10**, 393 (1931).
655. L. A. Strait and F. A. Jenkins, Physic. Rev. **49**, 635 (1936).
656. H. M. Strong and H. P. Knauss, Physic. Rev. **49**, 740 (1936).
657. E. C. G. Stueckelberg, Helv. Phys. Acta **5**, 369 (1933).
658. E. Svensson, Dissertation (Stockholm, 1935).
659. ——— and F. Tyrén, Z. Physik **85**, 257 (1933).
660. P. Swings, Actualités scientifiques et industrielles Nos. 50 and 162 (1932–34).
660a. T. Takamine, T. Suga, and Y. Tanaka, Sci. Pap. Inst. Physic. Chem. Res. (Tokyo) **34**, 854 (1938).
661. T. Tanaka and Z. Koana, Proc. Phys. Math. Soc. Jap. **16**, 365 (1934).
662. G. K. Teal and G. E. MacWood, J. Chem. Phys. **3**, 760 (1935).
663. E. Teller, Z. Physik **61**, 458 (1930).
664. ———, Hand- u. Jahrb. d. chem. Phys. **9**, II, 43 (1934).
665. A. Terenin, Z. Physik **37**, 98 (1926).
666. ——— and B. Popov, Z. Physik **75**, 338 (1932); Physik. Z. d. Sowjetunion **1**, 307, **2**, 299 (1932).
667. S. F. Thunberg, Z. Physik **100**, 471 (1936).
668. N. Tsi-Ze and T. San-Tsiang, Physic. Rev. **52**, 91 (1937).
669. L. A. Turner, Physic. Rev. **27**, 397 (1926); **31**, 983 (1928); **37**, 1023 (1931).

670. L. A. Turner, Z. Physik **65**, 464 (1930).
671. ———, Z. Physik **68**, 178 (1931).
672. ———, Physic. Rev. **38**, 574 (1931).
673. ———, Physic. Rev. **41**, 627 (1933).
673a.——— and W. T. Harris, Physic. Rev. **52**, 626 (1937).
674. ——— and E. W. Samson, Physic. Rev. **37**, 1023 (1931).
675. H. S. Uhler and R. A. Patterson, Astrophys. J. **42**, 434 (1915).
676. H. C. Urey, F. C. Brickwedde, and G. M. Murphy, Physic. Rev. **39**, 164 (1932).
677. ——— and G. K. Teal, Rev. Mod. Phys. **7**, 34 (1935).
678. J. H. Van Vleck, Physic. Rev. **33**, 467 (1929).
679. ———, Physic. Rev. **37**, 733 (1929).
680. ———, Physic. Rev. **40**, 544 (1932).
681. ———, Astrophys. J. **80**, 161 (1934).
682. ———, J. Chem. Physics **4**, 327 (1936).
683. ——— and A. Sherman, Rev. Mod. Phys. **7**, 167 (1935).
684. L. Vegard, Z. Physik **75**, 30 (1932).
685. ——— and E. Tønsberg, Geophys. Publ. **11**, No. 2 (1935).
686. D. S. Villars and E. U. Condon, Physic. Rev. **35**, 1028 (1930).
687. B. Vonnegut and B. E. Warren, J. Amer. Chem. Soc. **58**, 2459 (1936).
688. J. W. Walker, J. W. Straley, and A. W. Smith, Physic. Rev. **53**, 140 (1938).
689. H. v. Wartenberg, G. Sprenger, and J. Taylor, Z. physik. Chem. Bodenstein-Festb. **1931**, 61.
690. W. W. Watson, Physic. Rev. **32**, 600 (1928).
691. ———, Physic. Rev. **47**, 27 (1935).
692. ———, Physic. Rev. **49**, 70 (1936).
693. ———, Physic. Rev. **53**, 639 (1938).
694. ———, Physic. Rev. **54**, 1068 (1938).
694a.——— and W. R. Fredrickson, Physic. Rev. **39**, 765 (1932).
695. ——— ——— and M. E. Hogan, Physic. Rev. **49**, 150 (1936).
696. ——— and R. F. Humphreys, Physic. Rev. **52**, 318 (1937).
697. ——— and P. G. Koontz, Physic. Rev. **46**, 32 (1934).
698. ——— and W. F. Meggers, Bur. Stand. J. Res. **20**, 125 (1938).
699. ——— and A. Shambon, Physic. Rev. **50**, 607 (1936).
699a.——— and R. Simon, Physic. Rev. **55**, 358 (1939).
700. M. Wehrli, Helv. Phys. Acta **7**, 617, 673 (1934); **9**, 587 (1936).
701. ——— and E. Miescher, Helv. Phys. Acta **7**, 298 (1934).
702. V. Weisskopff, Physik. Z. **34**, 1 (1933).
703. W. Weizel, Z. Physik **54**, 321 (1929).
704. ———, Z. Physik **59**, 320 (1930).
705. ——— and O. Beeck, Z. Physik **76**, 250 (1932).
706. ——— and M. Kulp, Ann. Physik **4**, 971 (1930).
707. ——— and E. Pestel, Z. Physik **56**, 197 (1929).
707a. W. West, P. Arthur, and R. T. Edwards, J. Chem. Phys. **5**, 10, 14 (1937).
707b. J. W. White, J. Chem. Phys. **6**, 294 (1938).
708. K. Wieland, Helv. Phys. Acta **2**, 46 (1929).
709. ———, Z. Physik **76**, 801 (1932).
710. ———, Z. physik. Chem. B **42**, 422 (1939).
711. R. Wierl, Ann. Physik **8**, 521 (1931).
712. E. Wigner and E. E. Witmer, Z. Physik **51**, 859 (1928).
713. R. Wildt, Z. Physik **54**, 856 (1929).
713a.———, Gött. Nachr. **1932**, 87; Naturwiss. **20**, 851 (1932).
714. ———, Veröff. Univ. Sternw. Gött. **1932**, No. 22.
715. ———, Astrophys. J. **86**, 321 (1937).
716. J. G. Winans, Phil. Mag. **7**, 555 (1929).
717. ——— and E. C. G. Stueckelberg, Proc. Nat. Acad. Amer. **14**, 867 (1928).
718. E. E. Witmer, Physic. Rev. **28**, 1223 (1926).
719. R. W. Wood, Phil. Mag. **12**, 329, 499 (1906).
720. ——— and G. H. Dieke, Physic. Rev. **35**, 1355 (1930).
720a.——— ———, J. Chem. Phys. **6**, 734, 908 (1938).

721. R. W. Wood and F. W. Loomis, Physic. Rev. **31**, 705 (1928); Phil. Mag. **6**, 231 (1928).
722. R. E. Worley and F. A. Jenkins, Physic. Rev. **54**, 305 (1938).
723. O. R. Wulf, Physic. Rev. **46**, 316 (1934).
724. ———, J. Opt. Soc. **25**, 231 (1935).
725. K. Wurm, Naturwiss. **20**, 85 (1932).
726. ———, Z. Physik **76**, 309 (1932).
727. ———, Z. Astrophysik **5**, 260 (1932).
728. ———, Z. Astrophysik **8**, 281; **9**, 62 (1934).
729. ———, Z. Astrophysik **10**, 133 (1935).
729a.———, Astrophys. J. **89**, 312 (1939).
729b. ———, unpublished.
730. H. Zanstra, Monthly Notices Roy. Astron. Soc. **89**, 178 (1928).
731. H. Zeise, Z. Elektrochem. **39**, 758, 895 (1933); **40**, 662, 885 (1934).
732. A. van der Ziel, Physica **1**, 353 (1934).
733. ———, Physica **4**, 373 (1937).
734. R. V. Zumstein, J. W. Gabel, and R. E. McKay, Physic. Rev. **51**, 238 (1937).

Indexes

Author Index

A

Aars, J., 501
Adams, W. S., 525, 526
Adel, A., 523, 525
Aickin, R. G., 413
Allen, H. S., 499
Almy, G. M., 256, 271, 281, 290, 291, 483, 484, 486, 489, 492
Amaldi, E., 65
Ångström, A. J., 34, 328, 460, 481
Arnot, F. L., 489
Arrhenius, S., 485
Arthur, P., 505
Arvin, M. J., 333, 490
Ashley, M. F., 271, 491
Aston, F. W., 3, 105, 181, 197, 482
Asundi, R. K., 481, 485, 492
Auger, P., 428–430, 433, 434, 436
Avramenko, L., 460
Azambuja, L. d', 294

B

Babcock, H. D., 180, 181
Bacher, R. F., 502
Back, E., 26, 247, 330, 331
Badger, R. M., 499
Baerwald, H., 273, 486
Bakker, C. J., 490
Baldet, F., 34, 291, 526
Ball, G. N., 492
Ballard, H. S., 467, 491
Balmer, J. J., 8, 29
Baly, E. C. C., 2
Barker, E. F., 65, 153, 487, 488, 523
Barnes, C., 508, 519
Barrow, R. F., 493
Bartholomé, E., 103, 150
Bartlett, J. H., 384
Barton, H. A., 297, 490
Bashford, L. A., 487, 492, 493
Bayliss, N. S., 413–415
Beach, J. Y., 379
Beeck, O., 504
Bell, H., 491

Bengtsson-Knave, E., 46, 55, 278, 279, 283, 323, 324, 461, 483, 494
Bernard, R., 524
Bethe, H. A., 502
Beutler, H., 108, 171, 376, 386, 435, 439, 441, 464, 468, 470, 472, 487, 500, 514
Bewersdorff, O., 102, 223
Bhaduri, B. N., 483
Bhagavantam, S., 65
Bichowsky, F. R., 485, 487, 489, 491
Birge, R. T., 3, 36, 114, 116, 166, 182, 200, 281, 303, 466, 467, 481, 490, 498
Biskamp, H., 486
Bjerrum, N., 56, 57
Bloch, E., 492
Bloch, L., 492
Bloomenthal, S., 491
Blue, R. W., 299
Bobrovnikoff, N. T., 528
Bohr, N., 5–9, 11, 13–15, 17, 160, 327, 346, 363, 407
Bollmann, V., 3
Boltzmann, L., 3, 128, 129, 131, 144, 224, 463, 506
Bonhoeffer, K. F., 149, 433, 434, 436, 510, 511, 516
Born, M., 13, 160, 399, 433
Bose, S. N., 144–147, 271, 276, 501
Bozóky, L. v., 297, 491
Brandt, W. H., 256, 258, 491
Brice, B. A., 36, 177, 483
Brickwedde, F. C., 153
Briscoe, H. V. A., 487
Brockway, L. O., 481, 487
Brodersen, P. H., 485
Broglie, L. de, 11, 414
Brons, F., 316, 440, 460
Brons, H. H., 190, 283, 299, 316, 490
Brown, W. G., 55, 179, 223, 324, 450, 484, 488, 501
Budó, A., 237, 246, 256, 291, 299, 303, 319, 494
Bulthuis, H., 308, 486

Subject Index

This index serves also as an index of the more frequently used letters in the formulae and the symbols. These letters and symbols are listed at the beginning of the section devoted to the corresponding letter. The Greek letters are arranged under the letter with which they begin when they are written in English (for example, π and Ψ are listed under P). Symbols to which a word is joined are arranged under the corresponding symbol (for example, P *branch* is under P, not under Pb).

Italicized page numbers refer to more detailed discussions of the subjects than ordinary page numbers, or to definitions; boldface page numbers refer to figures.

Individual molecules and atoms are listed only under their chemical symbols, and under the symbol is also given all that concerns the molecule or atom it represents (for example, the heat of dissociation of hydrogen is listed as H_2, *heat of dissociation*). Molecules occurring in Table 36 but not in the text are not included, since the table itself is alphabetically arranged.